BRAIN MECHANISMS AND LEARNING

BRAIN MECHANISMS

AND

LEARNING

A SYMPOSIUM

organized by

THE COUNCIL FOR INTERNATIONAL
ORGANIZATIONS OF MEDICAL SCIENCES
Established under the joint auspices of
UNESCO *and* WHO

Consulting Editors

A. FESSARD   R. W. GERARD   J. KONORSKI

Editor for the Council
J. F. DELAFRESNAYE
C.I.O.M.S.
Paris, France

BLACKWELL
SCIENTIFIC PUBLICATIONS
OXFORD

© Blackwell Scientific Publications Ltd., 1961

This book is copyright. It may not be reproduced by any means in whole or in part without permission. Application with regard to copyright should be addressed to the publishers.

Published simultaneously in the United States of America by Charles C Thomas, Publisher, 301-327 East Lawrence Avenue, Springfield, Illinois.

Published simultaneously in Canada by the Ryerson Press, Queen Street West, Toronto 2.

FIRST PUBLISHED 1961

PRINTED IN GREAT BRITAIN IN THE CITY OF OXFORD
AT THE ALDEN PRESS
AND BOUND BY THE KEMP HALL BINDERY, OXFORD

154
C83b
1961

CONTENTS

LIST OF PARTICIPANTS

W. Ross Adey
University of California, Los Angeles (U.S.A.)

P. K. Anokhin
Academy of Medical Sciences, Moscow (U.S.S.R.)

E. Asratyan
Academy of Sciences, Moscow (U.S.S.R.)

P. Buser
Université de Paris (France)

K. L. Chow
University of Chicago (U.S.A.)

M. Covian
Faculdade de Medicina, São Paulo (Brazil)

R. W. Doty
University of Michigan, Ann Arbor (U.S.A.)

J. C. Eccles
The Australian National University, Canberra (Australia)

I. Eibl-Eibesfeldt
Max-Planck-Institut fuer Verhaltensphysiologie, Seewiesen (Germany)

C. Estable
Instituto de Investigación de Ciencias Biológicas, Montevideo (Uruguay)

A. Fessard
Collège de France, Paris (France)

R. Galambos
Walter Reed Army Medical Center, Washington (U.S.A.)

E. García-Austt
Instituto de Neurología, Montevideo (Uruguay)

R. W. Gerard
University of Michigan, Ann Arbor (U.S.A.)

E. Grastyán
University of Pécs (Hungary)

D. O. Hebb
McGill University, Montreal (Canada)

R. Hernández-Peón
Centro Médico del Distrito Federal, México

M. Jouvet
Faculté de Médecine de Lyon (France)

vii

J. KONORSKI
Institute of Experimental Biology, Warsaw (Poland)

K. LISSÁK
University of Pécs (Hungary)

J. LUCO
Universidad Catolica, Santiago (Chile)

H. W. MAGOUN
University of California, Los Angeles (U.S.A.)

F. MORRELL
University of Minnesota, Minneapolis (U.S.A.)

R. E. MYERS
Walter Reed Army Institute of Research, Washington (U.S.A.)

R. NAQUET
Faculté de Médecine de Marseille (France)

J. OLDS
The University of Michigan, Ann Arbor (U.S.A.)

M. PALESTINI
Facultad de Medicina, Santigo (Chile)

T. PINTO HAMUY
Universidad de Chile, Santiago (Chile)

H. E. ROSVOLD
National Institute of Mental Health, Bethesda (U.S.A.)

J. P. SEGUNDO
Instituto de Investigaciòn de Ciencias Biològicas, Montevideo (Uruguay)

W. H. THORPE
University of Cambridge (U.K.)

FOREWORD

Six years after the Laurentian symposium on 'Brain Mechanisms and Consciousness', the Council for International Organizations of Medical Sciences (C.I.O.M.S.) convened a meeting to explore the neurophysiological basis of learning. The meeting was held in Montevideo, from August 2nd to 8th, 1959, and was jointly sponsored by and organized with the Science Co-operation Office of Unesco for Latin America.

Dr A. Fessard was responsible for the scientific planning of the meeting and shared with Dr Ralph Gerard the responsibility of presiding over it. May they both find here an expression of the Council's gratitude for the magnificent way in which they discharged their duties.

Looking back over the years, it is impossible not to draw a parallel between the meeting held in Canada and the one held in Uruguay.

In each case, the meeting was co-ordinated with the International Physiological Congress. Both were 'firsts': the first CIOMS symposium in North America and the first in Latin America. And then, of course, a number of scientists took part in both meetings. But here the parallel must end.

In Montevideo, we were able to cast our net wider and we were pleased to welcome a number of distinguished investigators from Australia, Brazil, Chile, Hungary, Mexico, Poland, Uruguay, and the U.S.S.R., who had not attended the meeting in Canada. An organizing committee composed of Drs R. Arana, D. Bennati, C. Estable, and of Drs E. García-Austt and J. P. Segundo, who acted as joint secretaries, took charge of all technical arrangements and provided much appreciated entertainment for all who took part in the meeting. Credit must go to this committee for having created the right conditions for the development of an atmosphere of understanding and friendliness. May this committee find here an expression of the Council's gratitude.

It is also a pleasant task to put on record the Council's indebtedness to the various agencies which supported directly or indirectly the meeting, and in particular to the European Office, A.R.D.C.[1] whose grant was used to cover the travelling expenses of a number of participants.

I am also pleased to thank Miss Henderson and Dr Christie, who transcribed the discussion, and the secretarial staff, who worked very hard to get everything ready in time.

[1] Contract No. AF61 (052)-207.

This monograph is the record of what happened in Montevideo and has been put together with the help of the consulting editors. May I thank all three but especially Dr Fessard who, being on the spot, has advised me on many points.

It is the hope of all who contributed to this book that it will be of value to all those who study the fundamental processes of learning, wherever they may be.

J. F. DELAFRESNAYE

PREFACIO

El Centro de Cooperación Científica de la UNESCO para América Latina ha contribuído a organizar la reunión que sobre 'Brain Mechanisms and Learning' decidió celebrar en Montevideo el Consejo Internacional de Organizaciones de Ciencias Médicas (C.I.O.M.S.).

Es ya de tradición la organización de Symposia por los Centros de Cooperación Científica de la UNESCO y comienza a ser habitual el que algunos de ellos se monten con la colaboración de la C.I.O.M.S., organización que tan activamente se ocupa de los problemas básicos de la Medicina.

La iniciativa de esta reunión vino de un latinoamericano, el Dr. Raúl Hernández-Peón, y era lógico pensar que el Centro de Montevideo aportase su plena colaboración a esta manifestación.

Hace varios años, igualmente en Montevideo, organizó el Centro de Cooperación Científica un Symposium scerca de otro tema de fisiología, nos referimos al titulado Symposium sobre 'Problemas fundamentales de estructura y fisiología celular' que reunió a investigadores latinoamericanos, norteamericanos y europeos.

Esta insistencia en organizar este tipo de reuniones sobre temas de Biología en Montevideo se justifica por la presencia en el Uruguay del Instituto de Investigaciones de Ciencias Biológicas dirigido por el conocido Profesor Clemente Estable.

El Symposium sobre 'Brain Mechanisms and Learning' es un ejemplo de la cooperación entre organismos internacionales y comités nacionales. La C.I.O.M.S. orientada científicamente en esta reunión por el Dr. A. Fessard, con la incansable tenacidad de su Secretario, el Dr. J. F. Delafresnaye, encontró el apoyo de un Comité local uruguayo que le brindó su plena colaboración. El Centro de Cooperación Científica de la UNESCO para América Latina aportó toda la ayuda que podía prestar. Ha sido una reunión de un alto nivel científico y que ha demostrado plenamente hasta qué punto puede llegarse en la colaboración científica cuando se consigue una perfecta coordinación de esfuerzos.

A. Establier
Director del Centro de Cooperación
Científica para América Latina de la
UNESCO

INTRODUCTION

Les mécanismes du cerveau offrent une matière inépuisable pour des thèmes de symposiums. Après le *Brain Mechanisms and Consciousness* de Ste Marguerite (Canada), en août 1953, bien d'autres réunions scientifiques de même espèce eurent lieu, où l'intérêt se porta tantôt sur les propriétés de la formation réticulée, tantôt sur les rapports des réflexes conditionnés avec l'électroencéphalogramme, ou encore sur les bases nerveuses du comportement, pour ne citer que trois exemples. Le symposium dont il s'agit ici fut consacré aux problèmes de l'Apprentissage, ou *Learning*, l'accent étant mis sur les mécanismes neurophysiologiques dont ces phénomènes dépendent.

L'initiative du choix de ce sujet, ainsi que la conception générale du symposium, reviennent au Dr Raúl Hernández-Peón dont on connaît les importantes contributions expérimentales dans ce domaine. Son projet reçut un excellent accueil. Il eut aussi la bonne fortune de pouvoir être parrainé par le CIOMS, ce qui signifiait que son exécution serait remise aux mains du Dr Delafresnaye, dont les qualités d'organisateur eurent ainsi l'occasion de se manifester une fois de plus. Il vient de nous rappeler tout ce que cette réunion a dû à l'extrême obligeance et à l'activité diligente de nos hôtes uruguayiens et aux institutions qui aidèrent matériellement le projet à se réaliser. Il n'appartient pas aux organisateurs de porter un jugement sur la valeur du résultat: comme il est de règle, leurs buts ne furent que partiellement atteints et ils ne se croient pas à l'abri de toute critique.

Tout d'abord, un thème comme celui-ci pourrait être traité de points de vue bien différents. On nous reprochera probablement certaines lacunes, ou d'avoir donné trop peu de place à certains aspects. Il était impossible en fait de couvrir entièrement un champ aussi vaste que celui qui nous était imposé. On notera cependant que nous nous sommes efforcés de faire appel à des disciplines différentes. Si les neurophysiologistes formèrent, comme il se devait, notre majorité, les points de vue du psychologue et de l'éthologiste purent s'exprimer, et du côté des données de base, une place fut réservée à l'anatomie et aux aspects physicochimiques. Les neurophysiologistes eux-mêmes représentaient des tendances diverses, depuis les électrophysiologistes du cerveau jusqu'aux spécialistes du réflexe conditionné classique.

Le choix des participants a été — est-il besoin de le dire ? — le problème le plus embarrassant pour les organisateurs. Il y a partout dans le monde d'excellents représentants de ce genre de recherches et beaucoup d'entre eux nous ont manqué. Quelques-uns, dont le nom s'imposait, pressentis, déclinèrent l'invitation. Lorsqu'il y eut nécessité de choix, ce furent généralement des raisons contingentes qui décidèrent. L'idée a prévalu qu'il était souhaitable de mettre en présence sur ce thème de l'Apprentissage, des représentants de pays que les circonstances avaient longtemps empêchés de confronter leurs thèses. Que ceux qui sont venus de l'Europe de l'Est aient eu ainsi la possibilité de discuter, sur un sol sud-américain avec les représentants de ce qu'on appelle l'Occident, voilà un signe encourageant pour l'avenir des relations scientifiques internationales.

Le Symposium de Montevideo n'a été comme tout autre, qu'un échantillonnage, dans l'ordre des personnes, comme dans celui des questions traitées, et une grande part de hasard a présidé à cet échantillonnage. Nous espérons cependant que le livre qui en est le reflet apportera à peu près ce qu'ils cherchent à ceux qui désirent prendre une vue d'ensemble sur une question qui représente un aspect majeur de la connaissance de l'Homme et des lois de la nature.

A. FESSARD

DARWIN AND CONCEPTS OF BRAIN FUNCTION

H. W. Magoun

It is appropriate in the Darwin Centennial Year (1959) to recall the impressions made by a visit to South America upon a young graduate of Cambridge whose studies, begun in theology, had turned instead to the sciences. Darwin arrived in South America as a naturalist on the voyage of H.M.S. *Beagle*, circumnavigating the globe. Reaching Buenos Aires, in October of 1832, he found a violent revolution had broken out and wrote, 'I was glad to escape on board a packet bound for Monte Video, the second town of importance on the banks of the Plata' (Darwin, 1839).

His young man's eye was critical, and his opinions mixed: 'The Plata', he wrote, 'looks like a noble estuary on the map; but it is in truth a poor affair. A wide expanse of muddy water, it has neither grandeur nor beauty. At one time of the day the two shores, both of which are extremely low, could just be distinguished from the deck. The land, with the one exception of the Green Mount, 450 feet high, from which it takes its name, is level. Very little of the undulating grassy plain is enclosed, but near the town, there are a few hedgebanks. There is something very delightful in the free expanse, where nothing guides or bounds your walk, yet I am disappointed as regards scenery.'

The short surveying trips of the *Beagle* up and down the coast left Darwin with time ashore. 'In the sporting line, I never enjoyed anything so much as ostrich hunting with the wild soldiers. They catch the birds in a fine, animated chase by throwing two balls which are attached to the ends of a thong so as to entangle their legs.' (One was a new species, later named Rhea Darwinii.) The young man took an interest in gaining dexterity with the bolas: 'One day as I was amusing myself by galloping and whirling the balls around my head, by accident the free one struck a bush and, like magic, caught one hind leg of my horse; the other ball was then jerked out of my hand, and the horse was fairly secured. The gauchos roared with laughter; they cried out that they had seen every sort of an animal caught, but had never before seen a man caught by himself.'

On a trip into the interior, Darwin's party stayed at an estancia belonging to one of the greatest land owners of the country, with whom was a captain in the Army. 'Considering their station, their conversation was rather amusing. Upon finding out we did not catch our horses and cattle in England with the lazo, they cried out, 'Ah, then, you use nothing but the bolas.' The idea of an enclosed country was quite new to them. The Captain at last said he had one question to ask me. I trembled to think how deeply scientific it might be. It was 'whether the ladies of Buenos Ayres were not the handsomest in the world'. I replied like a renegade, 'Charmingly so.' He added, 'Do ladies in the other part of the world wear such large combs?' I solemnly assured him that they did not.

'They were absolutely delighted. The Captain exclaimed, 'Look there! A man who has seen half the world says it is the case; we always thought so but now we know it.' My excellent judgment in combs and beauty procured me a most hospitable reception.' Darwin's remarks may have expressed more than disinterested diplomacy, however, for at this time a letter to his sister read: 'On shore, our chief amusement was riding about and admiring the Spanish ladies. After watching one of these angels gliding down the street, involuntarily we groaned, "How foolish English women are. They can neither walk nor dress." And then, how ugly Miss sounds after Signorita.'

Leaving now the attractive ladies of Buenos Aires, the experiences of Darwin's South American visit led gradually to his formulation of the theory of evolution by natural selection, certainly one of the most outstanding contributions to biology and one with many broad implications. The *Scala naturae*, in which living beings were arranged in a spectrum of increasing complexity, was familiar to earlier naturalists and to the biologists of the eighteenth century, by whom its order was generally conceived as the immutable product of divine creation. Darwin's revolutionary conception, published a century ago, as the *Origin of Species* (1859), proposed instead that natural selection, working on the range of normal variations, led to survival of the fittest and so accounted, in a materialistic way, both for evolution and for the adaptation of existing forms to their environments.

Darwin's later writings, on the *Descent of Man* (1871) and the *Expression of Emotion in Man and Animals* (1872), called more particular attention to the phylogenetic development of the brain. In keeping with his contributions, and related to the interest in evolution created by them, views were subsequently developed by Hughlings Jackson in neurology, by Pavlov in physiology and by Freud in psychiatry, each of whom accounted for the phylogenetic elaboration of the central nervous system in terms of a series of superimposed levels, added successively as the evolutionary scale was ascended.

In each of these conceptual systems (Fig. 1), the management of primitive, innate, stereotyped behaviour, having to do with the preservation of
the individual and the race, was attributed to older, subcortical, neuraxial
portions of the central nervous system, which formed Jackson's lowest
level and subserved the Pavlovian unconditioned reflex and the
Freudian id.

ENGLISH NEUROLOGY Hughlings Jackson	RUSSIAN NEUROPHYSIOLOGY Ivan P. Pavlov	COMPARATIVE NEUROANATOMY Edinger, Kappers, Herrick	PSYCHOANALYTIC PSYCHIATRY Sigmund Freud	SYNTHESIS
HIGHEST LEVEL	SECOND SIGNAL SYSTEM	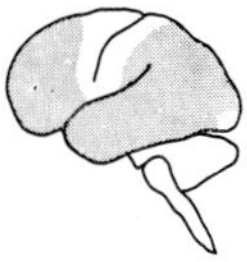	SUPER EGO	ABSTRACTION DISCRIMINATION SYMBOLIZATION COMMUNICATION
MIDDLE LEVEL	CONDITIONED REFLEX	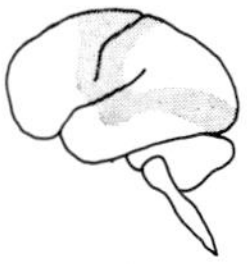	EGO	ACQUIRED ADAPTIVE BEHAVIOR
LOWEST LEVEL	UNCONDITIONED REFLEXES	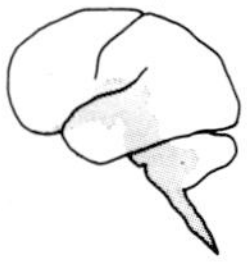	ID	INNATE STEREOTYPED PERFORMANCE

FIG. 1

Chart comparing the evolutionary concepts of the organization and function of the brain
which developed after Darwin and Spencer.
Modified from a chart by Stanley Cobb, Human nature and the understanding of disease,
in: Faxon, N.W. The Hospital in Contemporary Life, Harvard Univ. Press, Cambridge, Mass.,
1949.

Next, the more mutable, adaptive, learned behaviour of Pavlov's
conditioned reflex, together with the capacity of the Freudian ego for
perception and the initiation of movement were ascribed to higher neural
structures, including the sensori-motor cortex of Jackson's middle level,
which developed above or upon the older subjacent parts.

Finally, in the brain of man, hypertrophy of the associational cortices of
the frontal and parieto-occipito-temporal lobes, forming Jackson's highest
level, was correlated with the capacities of Freud's superego and, in the

B

dominant hemisphere, with the capabilities of Pavlov's second signal system for symbolization and communication by means of spoken and written language.

Further testimony for the evolution of neurological function in these terms was provided by Jackson's view of dissolution, or reversal of the phylogenetic process when clinical impairment proceeded from highest through middle to lowest levels during neurological disease in man (Jackson, 1958). Jackson specified that the resulting deficit was usually accompanied by some release of lower activity, normally subjugated to higher control. This latter feature was elaborated also in the Freudian system, in which conflicting interests of the different levels were emphasized as a source of psychic disturbance.

In much the same way that increased complexity and specialization appeared as the ladder of nature was ascended by the earlier classification-ists, more and more elaborate functions came to view as one climbed cephalically up the successive levels of the central nervous system. In its progressive encephalization, the brain came to resemble the earth itself, not simply in its globular form but in consisting as well of a series of strata laid down like those of geology, one upon the other, in evolutionary time. Each neural accretion was associated with a characteristic increment of function and, following Jackson, a dissolutionary school of neurophysiology developed, in which encephalization was reversed by operative transection and evolution traced backward by observing residual capacities diminish in the increasingly truncated, decorticate, decerebrate and spinal preparations.

Probably because such views are still so contemporary, little attention has been given to exploring the role of Darwin, and the interest in evolution excited by his work, in establishing these concepts of neural organization and function. The views of Hughlings Jackson (1958), which might be presumed to be the most directly Darwinian, were, on the contrary, derived chiefly from Thomas Laycock, with whom Jackson began his career in York, and from Herbert Spencer, whom he admired greatly. Both Laycock and Spencer had applied evolutionary principles to concepts of the organization and function of the brain independently of and preceding Darwin. In his *Mind and Brain*, first published in 1859, Laycock wrote: 'As we ascend the scale, the differentiation of tissue takes place and instincts of plants or animals appear. As we ascend still higher in animal life, the instincts gradually lose their unknowing character and the mental faculties emerge with their appropriate organic basis in the encephalon. Finally, with the highest evolution, we find man evincing in art and science the results of the operation of mental powers which in the lower animals are purely instinctive and in the lowest organisms simply vital processes.'

There can also be found in Laycock an expression of the conflicting interests of the different levels with the higher holding the lower in check, to be elaborated later by Jackson and by Freud: 'This entire group of corporeal appetites and animal instincts is characterized by the quality of necessity. They are imperative on the individual; in lower organisms they are performed blindly. In man and higher vertebrates, in whom there is a development of cognitive faculties, they may be made to act as a check upon each other and thus states of consciousness, termed motives, will coincide with a knowing restraint exercised over them. But even with the highest and strongest of human motives, it is often found difficult to curb them effectually. The entire group constitutes "the Flesh" of St Paul. Those classed under the head of primordial instincts or corporeal appetites, most necessary to the well being and maintenance of the organism and the species, are the farthest removed from the will and consciousness.'

His clinical observations in neurology led Laycock to consider disease as 'retrocession', in which changes taking place were the inverse of evolutionary. He proposed a law of '*dis*volution' in certain kinds of brain disease, when there was a decay of the mental powers and return to an earlier, infantile status. Concepts of evolutionary levels of function, conflicting in their interests and exhibiting dissolution in neurological disease, can thus be detected in a germinal stage in Laycock's views.

Jackson's psychological concepts were strongly influenced by Herbert Spencer, from whom Darwin borrowed the term 'survival of the fittest'. After having been an evolutionist for some time, in 1851 Spencer formulated the basic principles that were to be elaborated in most of his later work. He had been asked to write a notice of a new edition of Carpenter's *Principles of Physiology* and 'in the course', he noted (1904), 'of such perusal as was needed to give an account of its contents', came across the theory of von Baer — that the development of all plants and animals was from homogeneity to heterogeneity. This concept of progressive differentiation, added to that of Lamarckian adaptation, became his distinctive evolutionary principle.

Having just turned forty, Spencer determined to devote the remainder of his life to the systematic application of this concept to the whole field of knowledge. Flagging a dilatatory cerebral circulation, with which he was hypochondriacally preoccupied, with bouts of exercise preceding dictation to an amanuensis, Spencer embarked on the exposition of a

System of Synthetic Philosophy, the successive parts of which appeared at intervals through the balance of the nineteenth century.

In the first edition of his *Principles of Psychology*, published in 1855, and thus four years before the *Origin of Species*, Spencer (1899) pointed out that his arguments 'imply a tacit adhesion to the development hypothesis, that Life in its multitudinous and infinitely varied embodiments has risen out of the lowest and simplest beginnings, by steps as gradual as those which evolve a homogenous, microscopic germ into a complex organism, by progressive unbroken evolution, and through the instrumentality of what we call natural causes. Save for those who still adhere to the Hebrew myth or to the doctrine of special creation derived from it, there is no alternative but this hypothesis or no hypothesis'.

Applying his 'development hypothesis' to psychology, Spencer reasoned: 'If the doctrine of Evolution is true, the inevitable implication is that Mind can be understood only by observing how Mind is evolved. If creatures of the most elevated kinds have reached those highly integrated, very definite and extremely heterogeneous organizations they possess, through modification upon modification accumulated during an immeasurable past, if the developed nervous systems of such creatures have gained their complex structure and functions little by little; then, necessarily, the involved forms of consciousness, which are the correlates of these complex structures and functions, must also have arisen by degrees.'

In the study of Mind, 'in its ascending gradations through the various types of sentient beings', Spencer conceived of 'a nascent Mind, possessed by low types in which nerve centres are not yet clearly differentiated from one another', and consisting of 'a confused sentiency formed of recurrent pulses of feeling having but little variety or combination. At a stage above this, while yet the organs of the higher senses are rudimentary, Mind is present probably under the form of a few sensations which, like those yielded by our own viscera, are simple, vague and incoherent. From this upwards, mental evolution exhibits a differentiation of these simple feelings into the more numerous kinds which the special senses yield; an ever increasing integration of such more varied feelings, an ever increasing multiformity in the aggregates of feelings produced, and an ever increasing distinctness of structure in such aggregates; that is to say, there goes on subjectively a change from an indefinite, incoherent homogeneity to a definite, coherent heterogeneity.

Support for his views was marshalled also from pharmacological observations, when Spencer presented, in remarkably vivid detail, the subjective impressions during induction of chloroform anaesthesia for dental extraction, and concluded: 'This degradation of consciousness by chloroform, abolishing first the higher faculties and descending gradually to the lowest, may be considered as reversing that ascending genesis of consciousness which has taken place in the course of evolution; and the stages of descent may be taken as showing in opposite order the stages of ascent.'

'What is the implication of this law as applying to different grades of men?' Spencer asked. And answered, 'It is that those having well developed nervous systems will display a relatively marked premeditation, a greater tendency to suspense of judgment and an earlier modification of judgments that have been formed. Those having nervous systems less developed will be prone to premature conclusions that are difficult to change. Unlikeness of this kind appears when we contrast the larger with the smaller brained races, when, from the comparatively judicial intellect of the civilized man, we pass to that of the uncivilized man, sudden in its inferences, incapable of balancing evidence and adhering obstinately to first impressions.' Though Spencer's association with the female sex was limited, he nevertheless felt qualified 'to observe a difference similar in kind but smaller in degree between the modes of thought of men and women; for women are more quick to draw conclusions and retain more pertinaciously beliefs once formed'.

Returning to the problem 'of how such higher co-ordinations are evolved out of lower ones and how the structure of the nervous system becomes progressively complicated', Spencer proposed the interpolation of new plexuses of fibres and cells between those originally existing. In diagrammatic sketches, apparently of an invertebrate ganglion, Spencer distinguished (Fig. 2,) 'a nervous centre to which afferent fibres bring all order of peripheral feelings, and from which efferent fibres carry to muscle the stimuli producing their appropriately combined contractions'. If a part of the co-ordinating plexus (A) 'takes on a relatively greater development in answer to new adjustments which environing conditions furnish, we may expect one part of this region (a) to become protruberant, as at A''. Because space within the plexus was already pre-empted, 'the interpolated plexus, which effects indirect co-ordination, must be superimposed [Fig. 2, A' above; d, below], and the co-ordinating discharges must take roundabout courses as shown by the arrow. Little by little, there is an enlargement of the superior co-ordinating centre by the interpolation of new co-ordinating plexuses at its periphery' (Fig. 2, e, f, g, below).

With the publication of Darwin's *Origin of Species*, Spencer gave some consideration to the concept of natural selection, but continued to account for the more complex portions of neural evolution primarily in Lamarckian terms: 'Regarding as superimposed, each on the preceding, the structural effects produced generation after generation and species after species, we have formed a general conception of the manner in which the most complex nervous systems have arisen out of the simplest. This

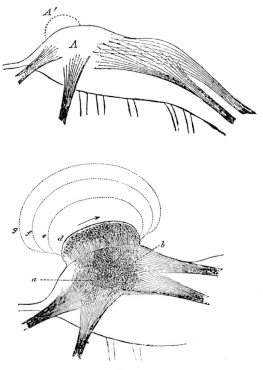

FIG. 2

Diagrams of a ganglion prepared by Spencer (17), showing the development of superimposed levels of neural co-ordination.

general principle can be alleged only on the assumption that changes wrought in nervous structures by nervous functions are inheritable. Throughout the earlier stages of nervous evolution, a leading and perhaps most active cause has been the survival of individuals in which indirect influences have produced favourable variations of nervous structure but, throughout its later stages, the most active cause has been the direct production by functional changes of corresponding changes in nervous structure, and the transmission of these to posterity. Considering how involved are the nervous systems of superior creatures, there apply here with special force reasons for concluding that natural selection is an inadequate cause of evolution where many co-operative parts have to be simultaneously modified; and that in such cases, inheritance of functionally produced modifications becomes the leading agency — survival of the fittest serving as an aid.'

Ivan P. Pavlov. Though Pavlov's work in the physiology of the central nervous system did not commence until his fifties, its conceptualization was influenced strongly by the ideas of Darwin and of Spencer, encountered in his youth through the writings of Pisarev and Sechenov. In his *Autobiography* (1955), Pavlov wrote: 'I was born in the town of Ryazan in 1849 and received my secondary education at the local theological seminary. Influenced by the literature of the 'sixties, and particularly by Pisarev, our intellectual interests turned to natural science and many, myself included, decided to take the subject at the university.'

Pisarev was a writer and critic whose articles in the *Russkoye Slovo* promoted revolutionary-democratic and materialistic ideas among the intelligentsia of the 'sixties. There seems little doubt that Pavlov first became captivated by Darwin and the theory of evolution from reading Pisarev's lengthy, systematic, popular exposition of the *Origin of Species* entitled, *Progress in the Animal and Vegetable Worlds* (1858). The ecstatic attitude towards Darwin, which Pavlov preserved to the end of his days, can easily be identified with Pisarev's lofty expression:

'This brilliant thinker, whose knowledge is enormous,' Pisarev wrote of Darwin, 'took in all the life of nature with such a broad view and penetrated so deeply into all its scattered phenomena that he discovered, not an isolated fact, but a whole series of laws according to which all organic life on our planet is governed and varies; and he told of them so simply, proves them so irrefutably and bases his arguments on such obvious facts, that you, a common human, uninitiated in natural science, are in a state of continual astonishment at not having thought out such conclusions yourself long ago.

'For us ordinary and unenlightened people, Darwin's discoveries are precious and important just because they are so fascinating in their simplicity, so easy to understand; they not only enrich us with new knowledge, they give fresh life to all the system of our ideas and widen our mental horizon in all dimensions. In nearly all branches of natural science, Darwin's ideas bring about a complete revolution. Even experimental psychology finds in his discoveries the guiding principle that will link up the numerous observations already made and put investigators on the way to new fruitful discoveries.

'Every educated man', Pisarev continued, 'must make himself familiar with the ideas of this thinker and, therefore, I think it fitting and useful to give our readers a clear and fairly detailed exposition of the new theory. In it, readers will find the rigorous precision of an exact science, the boundless breadth of philosophical generalization and, finally, the superior and irreplaceable beauty which is the mark of vigorous and healthy human thought. Darwin, Lyell and thinkers like them are the philosophers, the poets, the aestheticians of our time. When human reason, in the person of its most brilliant representatives, has succeeded in rising to a height from which it can survey the basic laws of universal life, we ordinary people, unable to be creative in the realm of thought, owe it to our own human dignity to raise ourselves at least enough to be able to understand the leading brilliant minds, to appreciate their great achievements, to love them as the ornament and pride of our race; to live in thought in the bright and boundless realm that they open for every thinking being. We are wealthy and powerful through the works of these great men.'

A second early influence upon Pavlov was provided by the writings of Sechenov (1935). Later in his career, Pavlov referred (1928) to the beginning study of higher nervous activity with the objective techniques of conditional reflex physiology: 'The most important motive for my decision, even though an unconscious one, arose out of the impression made upon me during my youth by the monograph of I. M. Sechenov, the Father of Russian physiology, entitled *Cerebral Reflexes* and published in 1863. The influence of thoughts which are strong by virtue of their novelty and truth, especially when they act during youth, remains deep and permanent, even though concealed. In this book, a brilliant attempt was made, altogether extraordinary for that time, to represent our subjective world from the standpoint of neurophysiology.'

In a report on objective study of higher nervous activity in 1913, Pavlov (1928) began: 'With full justice, Charles Darwin must be counted as the founder and instigator of the contemporary comparative study of the higher vital phenomena of animals; for, as is known to every educated person, through his highly original support of the idea of evolution, he fertilized the whole mentality of mankind, especially in the field of biology. The hypothesis of the origin of man from animals gave a great impetus to the study of the higher phenomena of animal life. The answer to the question as to how this study should be carried out and the study itself have become the task of the period following Darwin.'

Pavlov concluded: 'I have finished my communication, but I should like to add what seems to me to be of great importance. Exactly half a century ago, in 1863, was published in Russian the article *Reflexes of the Brain*, which presented in clear, precise and charming form the fundamental idea which we have worked out at the present time [see Fig. 3]. What power of creative thought was necessary under the then existing

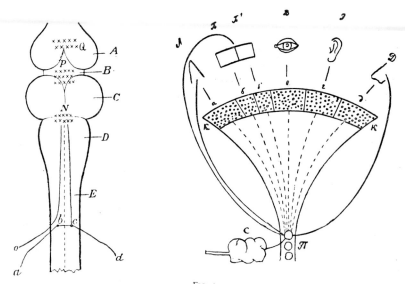

FIG. 3

Diagram of the central nervous system of the frog (left), from Sechenov (16). Stimulation of the sites marked by crosses inhibited spinal reflexes, illustrating the hierarchy of neural levels and the domination of higher over lower.

At the right is a diagram of the mechanism of the Pavlovian conditioned reflex (13). The animal makes adaptive adjustments to its environment by means of new links between the cortical analysers and connections from them to subcortical, unconditioned reflex arcs.

physiological knowledge of nervous activity to give rise to this idea! After the birth of this idea, it grew and ripened until, in our time, it has become an immense force for directing the contemporary investigation of the brain. Allow me at this fiftieth anniversary of the *Reflexes of the Brain* to invite your attention to the author, Ivan M. Sechenov, the pride of Russian thought and the Father of Russian physiology!'

It is interesting to note that Sechenov, like Jackson a contemporary of both Darwin and Spencer, was more directly influenced by Spencer's

writing than by that of Darwin. Though not in time to influence preparation of the *Reflexes of the Brain* (1863), both Darwin's and Spencer's works
were early translated into Russian: the *Origin of Species* in 1864, by Professor S. A. Rashinsky of Moscow University, of whose efforts Pisarev
was highly critical; and a year later in shorter exposition, by K. A.
Timiryazev, the leading Russian Darwinist (Platonov, 1955). Spencer
(1904) learned of a Russian translation of his *First Principles* in 1866 and, a
decade later, heard with surprise, from Professor Sontchitzici, of the
University of Kiev, that all of his works had then been translated into
Russian, excepting the *Sociology*, which was soon to be added to the list.

In his *Elements of Thought*, published in 1883, Sechenov (1935) wrote:
'Darwin's great theory of the evolution of species has placed the idea of
evolution on such a firm basis that it is at present accepted by the vast
majority of naturalists. This logically necessitates the recognition of the
principle of evolution of psychical activities. Spencer's hypothesis may
actually be called the application of Darwinism to the sphere of psychical
phenomena.'

And later: 'Another and no less important success in the study of the
mental development of man in general we owe to the famous English
scientist, Herbert Spencer. It is only on the ground of Spencer's hypothesis,
concerning the sequence of stages of neuropsychical development from
age to age that we can solve the ancient philosophical problem of the
development of mature thought from initial infantile forms. To Spencer
we owe the establishment, on the basis of very wide analogies, of the
general type of mental development in man, as well as the proofs of the
fact that the type of evolution of mental processes remains unchanged
through all stages of the development of thought. The present essay is
based on the theories of Spencer; therefore, our first task will be to
expound the main principles of his theory. It even appeared at the same
time as Darwin's theory and is practically a part of the general theory of
organic evolution.'

Sigmund Freud. Passing now to Freud, his autobiography refers to the
influences leading him to medicine as a career: 'At the time the theories
of Darwin, which were then of topical interest, strongly attracted me, for
they held out hopes of an extraordinary advance in our understanding of
the world; and it was hearing Goethe's beautiful essay on *Nature* read
aloud at a popular lecture, just before I left school, that decided me to
become a medical student.'

There are singularly few other allusions to Darwin in Freud's writings,
and the factors responsible for his visualization of the psychic apparatus

as spatially stratified were, doubtless, unconscious ones. It seems an exaggeration to propose that a continuum can be detected, in any literal sense, in Freud's anatomical, neurological and psychoanalytical works. Instances of a recurring effort to interpret neural organization and function in evolutionary terms can, however, be noted. In his monograph on *Aphasia*, published in 1891, Freud wrote (1953): 'In assessing the functions of the speech apparatus under pathological conditions, we are adopting as a guiding principle Hughlings Jackson's doctrine that all these modes of reaction represent instances of functional retrogression (disinvolution) of a highly organized apparatus, and therefore correspond to earlier stages of its functional development. This means that under all circumstances an arrangement of associations which, having been acquired later, belongs to a higher level of functioning, will be lost, while an earlier and simpler one will be preserved. From this point of view, a great number of aphasic phenomena can be explained.'

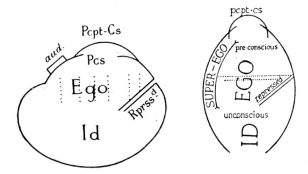

FIG. 4
Two diagrams by Freud (8, 8b), presenting the mental apparatus as though spatially stratified.

In a letter to Fleiss in 1896, Freud (1954) discussed a revision of his Project for a Scientific Psychology and referred to his 'latest bit of specula-tion, the assumption that our psychical mechanism has come about by a process of stratification'. A quarter of a century later, Freud made two attempts to diagram these ideas, with interesting differences in the form of the figures. The first (Fig. 4, left), prepared in 1923, resembled an inverted brain, although reference was made to it as an ovum. The second (Fig. 4, right), prepared a decade later, was on the other hand really egg-shaped. In his lecture on 'The Anatomy of the Mental Personality', Freud (1933) elaborated upon the contents of these figures: 'Superego, ego and id are the three realms, regions or provinces into which we divide the mental apparatus of the individual, and it is their mutual relations with which we shall be concerned.

'The *id* is the obscure, inaccessible part of our personality and can only be described as being all that the ego is not. We can come nearer to the id with images, and call it a chaos, a cauldron of seething excitement. We suppose that it is somewhere in direct contact with somatic processes and takes over from them instinctual needs. These instincts fill it with energy, but it has no organization and no unified will, only an impulsion to obtain satisfaction for the instinctual needs in accordance with the pleasure principle. Contradictory impulses exist side by side in it, without neutralizing each other or drawing apart; at most they combine in compromise formations under the overpowering pressure towards discharging their energy. In the id, there is nothing corresponding to the idea of time. Conative impulses which have never got beyond the id, and even impressions which have been pushed down into it by repression, are virtually immortal and are preserved for whole decades, as though they had only recently occurred. They can only be recognized as belonging to the past, deprived of their significance, and robbed of their charge of energy, after they have been made conscious by the work of analysis, and no small part of the therapeutic effect of analytic treatment rests upon this fact. Naturally the id knows no values, no good and evil, no morality. There is nothing in the id which can be compared to negation. Instinctual cathexes seeking discharge — that, in our view, is all that the id contains.

'The *ego* is directed onto the external world; it mediates perceptions of it and in it are generated, while it is functioning, the phenomena of consciousness. The ego has taken over the task of representing the external world for the id. In the fulfilment of this function, it has to observe the external world and preserve a true picture of it in the memory traces left by its perception. The ego also controls the path of access to motility, but it interpolates between desire and action the procrastinating factor of thought, during which it makes use of the residues of experience stored up in memory. In this way, it dethrones the pleasure principle, which exerts undisputed sway over the processes in the id, and substitutes for it the reality principle, which promises greater security and success. The relation to time, too, is contributed to the ego by the perceptual systems; indeed, it can hardly be doubted that the mode in which this system works is the source of the idea of time. What, however, especially marks the ego out in contradistinction to the id is a tendency to synthesize its contents, to bring together and unify its mental processes, which is entirely absent from the id. In popular language, we may say that the ego stands for reason and circumspection, while the id stands for the untamed passions. One might compare the relation of the ego to the id with that between a rider and his horse: the horse provides the locomotive energy, and the rider has the prerogative of determining the goal and of guiding the movements of his powerful mount.

'The role which the *superego* undertakes later in life is at first played by an external power, by parental authority. It can be traced back to the influence of parents, teachers and so on, and is based upon an overwhelmingly important biological fact, namely, the lengthy dependence of the human child on his parents. We have allocated to the superego the activities of self-observation, conscience and the holding up of ideals. It is the representative of all moral restrictions, the advocate of the impulse towards perfection. In short, it is as much as we have been able to apprehend psychologically of what people call the "higher things in human life". It becomes the vehicle of tradition and of all the age-long values which have been handed down from generation to generation. The ideologies of the superego perpetuate the past, the traditions of the race and the people, which yield but slowly to the influence of the present and to new developments.'

In discussing the interrelations of these parts, Freud, like Spencer, appeared to invoke Lamarckian views: 'The ego has the task of bringing the influence of the external world to bear upon the id. In the ego, perception plays the part which, in the id, develops upon instinct. The experiences undergone by the ego seem at first to be lost to posterity; but, when they have been repeated often enough and with sufficient intensity in the successive individuals of many generations, they transform themselves so to say into experiences of the id, the impress of which is preserved by inheritance. Thus in the id, which is capable of being inherited, are stored up vestiges of the existences led by countless former egos; and, when the ego forms its superego out of the id, it may perhaps only be reviving images of egos that have passed away and be securing them a resurrection.

'The poor ego has, then, to serve three harsh masters and to do its best to reconcile their claims and demands. These demands are always divergent and often seem quite incompatible; no wonder the ego so frequently gives way under its task. The three tyrants are the external world, the superego and the id. It feels itself hemmed in on three sides and threatened by three kinds of danger, towards which it reacts by developing anxiety when too hard pressed.

'Having originated in the experiences of the perceptual system, it is designed to represent the demands of the external world, but it also wishes to be a loyal servant to the id, and to draw the id's libido onto itself. In its attempt to mediate between the id and reality, it is often forced to clothe the unconscious commands of the id with its own preconscious rationalizations, to gloss over the conflicts between the id and reality.

'On the other hand, its every movement is watched by the severe superego, which holds up certain norms of behaviour without regard to any difficulties coming from the id and the external world; and if these norms are not acted up to, it punishes the ego with feelings of tension which manifest themselves as a sense of inferiority or guilt. In this way, goaded on by the id, hemmed in by the superego, and rebuffed by reality, the ego struggles to cope with its task of reducing the forces and influences which work in it and upon it to some kind of harmony. When the ego is forced to acknowledge its weakness, it breaks out into anxiety: reality anxiety in the face of the external world, normal anxiety in the face of the superego, and neurotic anxiety in the face of the strength of the passions of the id.

'It can easily be imagined that certain practices of mystics may succeed in upsetting the normal relations between the different regions of the mind so that, for example, the perceptual system becomes able to grasp relations in the deeper layers of the ego and in the id which would otherwise be inaccessible to it. Whether such a procedure can put one in possession of ultimate truths, from which all good will flow, may be safely doubted. All the same, we must admit that the therapeutic efforts of psychoanalysis have chosen much the same method of approach; for their object is to strengthen the ego, to make it more independent of the superego, to widen its field of vision, and so to extend its organization that it can take over new portions of the id. Where id was, there shall ego be. It is reclamation work, like the draining of the Zuyder Zee.'

Spencer and Darwin. From what has been presented it seems clear that, to their contemporaries, Spencer's ideas of the evolution of the brain and its functions were fully as influential as Darwin's, if not more so. This may be attributable in part to the fact that Spencer applied evolutionary principles to an understanding of the brain earlier than Darwin and, indeed, before the latter's ideas were published at all. Additionally, appeal doubtless attached to the broad sweep of Spencer's interests and to his efforts to account for the whole range of neural function, from instincts to the most complex features of the mind, in keeping with his propensity for global syntheses.

Darwin, by contrast, stuck closer to the observational data then available with emphasis mainly upon instinctive behaviour, supporting the survival of the individual, in feeding, aggression or defence, as well as survival of the species, in behaviour relating to sex. Even in Darwin's *Descent of Man* (1871), for example, greater emphasis was placed upon an exposition of sexual selection than upon development of the associational and communicative functions of the brain, which are easily the most strikingly distinctive features of human evolution.

Darwin and Spencer might be rated equivalently in the impressions they made upon Pisarev and Sechenov and, through these latter, upon Pavlov and Russian neurophysiology. There is no question, however, of the predominant influence of Spencer upon Hughlings Jackson and, through him upon the formation of evolutionary concepts of the organization and function of the brain in Western neurological thought.

Contrasting features of their personalities and outlooks appeared to have led Darwin and Spencer to develop reservations about one another. An early phrenological characterization of Spencer (Spencer, 1904) concluded: 'Such a head as this ought to be in the Church. The self-esteem is very large.' Darwin's tendency to personal deprecation seemed, on the other hand, to have amounted to a real sense of inferiority when comparing himself with Spencer. Each seemed also to have cultivated a possibly wilful difficulty in understanding the other's views. In a letter to Hooker in 1868, Darwin (1925) wrote: 'I feel *Pangenesis* is stillborn. H. Spencer says the view is quite different from his (and this is a great relief to me, as I feared to be accused of plagiarism but utterly failed to be sure what he meant, so thought it safest to give my view as almost the same as his), and he says he is not sure he understands it.'

In other letters, Darwin blew hot and cold. He characteristically acknowledged Spencer's brilliance, but usually expressed some question of the soundness or reliability of his views. In a note thanking Spencer for a present of his *Essays* in 1858, Darwin wrote: 'Your remarks on the general argument of the so-called development theory seem to me admirable. I am at present preparing an Abstract of a larger work on the changes of species; but I treat the subject simply as a naturalist, and not from a general point of view; otherwise, in my opinion, your argument could not have been improved on, and might have been quoted by me with great advantage.'

In a letter to Hooker in 1866, Darwin wrote: 'I have now read the last No. of H. Spencer (*Principles of Biology*). It is wonderfully clever and I daresay mostly true. I feel rather mean when I read him: I could bear and rather enjoy feeling that he was twice as ingenious and clever as myself; but when I feel he is almost a dozen times my superior, even in the master art of wriggling, I feel aggrieved. If he had trained himself to observe more, even at the expense, by the law of balancement, of some loss of thinking power, he would have been a wonderful man.'

In a letter to E. Ray Lankester in 1870, Darwin's regard reached a high point: 'It has pleased me to see how thoroughly you appreciate (and I do not think this is general with men of science) H. Spencer; I suspect that hereafter he will be looked at as by far the greatest living philosopher in England; perhaps equal to any that have lived.' Darwin's regard was also expressed in a note to Spencer himself at this time (1872): 'Dear Spencer — I daresay you will think me a foolish fellow but I cannot resist the wish to express my unbounded admiration for your article. Everyone with eyes to see and ears to hear (the number, I fear, are not many) ought to bow their knee to you, and I for one do.'

In a letter to Fiske, in 1874, reaction had set in: 'With the exception of special points, I did not even understand H. Spencer's general doctrine; for his style is too hard work for me. This may be very narrow minded; but the result is that such parts of H. Spencer as I have read with care impressed my mind with the idea of his inexhaustible wealth of suggestion, but never convinced me.'

In a final judgment, in his *Autobiography* (1958), Darwin commented: 'Herbert Spencer's conversation seemed to me very interesting but I did not like him particularly and did not feel that I could easily become intimate with him. I think he was extremely egotistical. After reading any of Spencer's books, I generally feel enthusiastic admiration for his transcendent talents and have often wondered whether in the distant future he would rank with such great men as Descartes, Leibniz, etc., about whom, however, I know very little. Nevertheless, I am not conscious of having profited in my own work by Spencer's writings. His deductive manner of treating every subject is wholly opposed to my frame of mind. His conclusions never convince me: and over and over again I have said to myself after reading one of his discussions, "Here would be a fine subject for half a dozen year's work." His fundamental generalizations (which have been compared in importance by some persons with Newton's Laws!) — which I daresay may be very valuable under a philosophical point of view — are of such a nature that they do not seem to me to be of any strictly scientific use. They partake more of the nature of definitions than of laws of nature. They do not aid one in predicting what will happen in any particular case. Anyhow, they have not been of any use to me.'

Reciprocal comments on Darwin and his work, by Spencer, were made primarily from the point of view of their relations to Spencer's own ideas and interests. With publication of the *Origin of Species*, Spencer wrote (1904): 'That reading it gave me great satisfaction may be safely inferred. Whether there was any set-off to this, I cannot now say; for I have quite forgotten the ideas and feelings I had. Up to that time, I held that the sole cause of organic evolution is the inheritance of functionally-produced modifications. The *Origin of Species* made it clear to me that I was wrong; and that the larger part of the facts cannot be due to any such cause. Whether proof that what I had supposed to be the sole cause, could be at best but a part cause, gave me any annoyance, I cannot remember; nor can I remember whether I was vexed by the thought that, in 1852, I had failed to carry further the idea then expressed that, among human beings, the survival of those who are the select of their generation is a cause of development. But I doubt not that any such feelings, if they arose, were overwhelmed in the gratification I felt at seeing the theory of organic evolution justified.

'To have the theory of organic evolution justified was, of course, to get further support for that theory of evolution at large, with which, as we have seen, all my conceptions were bound up. Believing as I did, too, that right guidance, individual and social, depends upon acceptance of evolutionary views of mind and of society, I was hopeful that its effects would presently be seen on educational methods, political opinions and men's ideas about human life. Obviously, these hopes that beneficial results would presently be wrought, were too sanguine. My confidence in the rationality of mankind was much greater then than it is now.'

On the revision of his *Principles of Psychology*, in 1870, Spencer wrote, in a similar vein: 'Several feelings united in making me enjoy the resumption of this topic, which I dealt with in 1854-55. At that date, an evolutionary view of Mind was foreign to the ideas of the time, and voted absurd: the result of setting it forth brought pecuniary loss and a good deal of reprobation. Naturally, therefore, after the publication of the *Origin of Species* had caused the current of public opinion to set the other way, a more sympathetic reception was to be counted upon for the doctrine of mental evolution in its elaborated form.'

In 1872, Spencer acknowledged a copy of Darwin's work on *The Expression of the Emotions* as follows: 'Dear Darwin: I have delayed somewhat longer than I intended acknowledging the copy of your new volume which you have been kind enough to send me. I delayed partly in the hope of being able to read more of it before writing to you; but my

C

reading powers are so small, and they are at present so much employed in getting up materials for work in hand, that I have been unable to get on far with it. I have, however, read quite enough to see what an immense mass of evidence you have brought to bear in proof of your propositions.

'I will comment only on one point, on which I see you differ from me ...'

Differing interests in the presentation of observational data and in the derivation from it of speculative syntheses, so apparent in the attitudes of Darwin and Spencer, will doubtless appear in the programme of this present conference as well. To find a topic upon which all may initially agree, let us return to Darwin's South American visit of a century ago. His narrative (1839), under December 6th, 1832, notes:

'The *Beagle* sailed from the Rio Plata never again to enter its muddy stream ... When speaking of these countries, the manner in which they have been brought up by their unnatural parent, Spain, should always be borne in mind. On the whole, perhaps, more credit is due for what has been done, than blame for what may be deficient. It is impossible to doubt but that the extreme liberalism of these countries must ultimately lead to good results. The very general toleration of foreign religions, the regard paid to the means of education, the freedom of the press, the facilities offered to all foreigners, and especially, as I am bound to add, to everyone professing the humblest pretensions to science, should be re-collected with gratitude by all those who have visited Spanish South America.'

The most cordial reception which has been provided the present visitors to Montevideo, in 1959, will, I know, make each of us wish to echo and approve emphatically of Darwin's concluding remarks.

THE FIXATION OF EXPERIENCE[1]

R. W. GERARD

The fixation of experience is a wider topic than is learning, which is a subhead under it. It includes changes in an individual system, at all levels from molecule to taxa or society, that have become irreversible under single or repeated experiences and so have left some material record of a past activity; and it includes racial changes that have cumulated over generations of a self-reproducing system. It underlies one of the three universal attributes of all systems at all levels; 'becoming'. The architecture of any system, its inhomogenities at a given cross section of time which remain reasonably constant over succeeding cross sections, its 'being', is the base of the behaviour or functioning of the system along time. 'Behaving' represents the transient or functional responses of the system to stimuli or stresses imposed by the environment and are reversible, so that the system essentially reverts after the perturbations have passed. When, however, the stimuli are sufficiently intense or repetitive or meaningful to the system as to leave an irreversible change, and therefore a material residue, the system undergoes a secular change along the longitudinal time axis and has fixed experience. 'Becoming' thus encompasses individual development, racial evolution, cultural history, and many other basic phenomena of orgs in general (material systems) and of animorgs in particular (living material systems).

Irreversible changes of individual units at the molecular level include gene mutations and adaptive enzymes and antibodies. At the cellular level, comes the whole process of cellular differentiation, including the formation or lack of formation of particular organelles and particulates. At the organ level, inductions and gradients and mechanical forces mold the particular organs during development, just as their use through life leaves behind hypertrophied soles or muscles, wrinkled and weathered skin, bone shapes to meet functional strains, and the like. Engrams within the nervous system are entirely comparable residues of experience. At the individual level, come the collective processes of ageing, perceptual and motor habits, conscious memories and the like. And at the group or social level, individual cultures create customs, laws, languages, artifacts, libraries and many other concrete entities or functional roles occupied by concrete entities.

[1] Aided by a grant from the National Institute of Mental Health, U.S.P.H.

At the racial dimension, or successive generations in time, there are the typical character changes which come to identify a taxa—morphological, physiological, chemical and, progressively, behavioural attributes that have accumulatively changed, in a more or less directional manner, over many generations. More important, and less universally recognized, has been the evolution, not of adaptations, but of adaptability. Selection pressures from an environment will produce evolutionary changes only when the stock is malleable and can respond to the pressures. Systems must be able to respond to experience and to fix it in some way if they are to be changed by it; and since heredity must supply the initial plasticity which enables the system to respond adaptively to selection pressures — and there is much current evidence that natural selection does not operate quite so blindly as was at one time believed (e.g. Waddington, 1950, 1960; Gerard, 1960b) — the sharp line between Darwin and Lamarck is beginning to blur. One can inherit not only mutated genes, but genes that are more mutable, even genes that induce mutations in others. Adaptive enzymes come into being only when both the genetic potentiality and also the environmental substate are present. An organism not only can learn, it can learn to learn. Learning set, attention level, motivation intensity, past experience, present physiological state, type of stimulus presentation and many other factors can influence the speed and effectiveness of learning. And the contributions of heredity, of individual experience, and of current situation to many, if not all, of these factors have not remotely been disentangled.

It remains true, none the less, that learning to learn, accelerating adaptation, speeding auto- and hetero- catalysis is the great invention of life stuff. This is the epigenetic mode. It allows living organisms to respond ever more rapidly and adaptively to the environmental challenge; it similarly enables mindful organisms to meet their environmental problems with greater skill and speed; and it has brought about that accelerating cultural change in civilizations which seems almost to have reached an explosive point. Epigenesis was enhanced by increased gene mutability, by the development of chromosomes and sex assortment, by adaptive changes in individual characteristics (in themselves or as a richer array for the action of simple natural selection), by the invention of a nervous system and of highly differentiated or coded responses.

Environment operates upon a system at all levels, differentially selecting for survival particular genes or gene arrays, cells and cell aggregates, organs and organ systems, and individuals and groups of various sizes. The environment operates not so much on the finished product as on the formative process. It supplies the physico-chemical milieu determining molecular changes, the electro-chemico-mechanical field guiding cellular changes, the neuro-chemico-mechanical influences modulating organ development, the material and biotic stimuli that guide the maturation of the individual, and the coded and meaning-laden signs and symbols which are added to these in the course of enculturating an individual into his group. The stresses applied by the environment determine the direction of development of the individual and the selection of the individual in the group. It may determine the adaptations of the body, the behaviour of the individual, the norms of the culture, and, in general, the goals or values that guide the course of future change of a system.

Living things are engaged in a continuous tracking operation, attempting to bring their existing state or their anticipated state into congruence with a desired state. At any instant in time, the system faces its universe, from which it is separated by some kind of boundary, with a certain patterned inhomogenity which is by then its enduring property. In the course of interacting with its environment, irreversible changes are produced in the system and it reaches a new state, the new architecture which it then offers for interaction with further environmental stimuli or stresses. Any individual system, and all its sub-systems, thus brings a new self to succeeding chunks of time. What the zygote brings we ordinarily call heredity, the end-product of ancestral learning and selection. What happens to the zygote we call individual experience, often divided further into experiences *in utero*, which we call congenital, and those affecting the separate organism, first the infant and then the adult.

At each stage and at each level, the system or sub-system presents to the environment a structure which has at least some aspects of a template, and so can lead to the production of more or itself; and at least some aspects of a programme or set of operation rules, so that the kinds of responses it will make to certain situations are roughly indicated. The outcomes are never identical and never foreseeably deterministic, because the fine details of the particular template and programme, even in identical twins, are not absolutely identical and, even more, because the environmental conditions to which these are exposed are never even roughly identical. Despite relative constancy in 'beings', therefore, outcomes are always more variable, the exact one in each case depending on the particular, often chance, details of the individual—environment interaction. Clearly, the line between heredity and individual experience becomes vague indeed. A gene array is a template and a programme; so is an engram.

It is a duty of neurobiology to discover the action rules. (If the nervous system knows the equation for π, it can grind out an unlimited number of digits, and yet carry none of this as bits of information.) It is its function, also, to decipher how existing engrams form the scaffolding for new ones. Here is the crux of the problem of learning. It depends upon the evolved structures — the improved units, patterns, and numbers in the more advanced nervous systems, but it depends no less on the improved physiology — lowered thresholds, faster conduction, greater spontaneity, easier fixation, and a host of other attributes, which are just coming to be recognized as important characteristics of the 'higher' animals as compared with the 'lower' ones. But before coming to grips with the problem of the neural mechanisms of learning, a few more general considerations involving the fixation of experience will be helpful.

Several questions must be faced for all systems that fix experience. The first, of course, is: How does a system at a given time, with an enduring architecture, contributed by the past experience of the race or itself, interact with the environment to give a new enduring architecture? As already indicated, this applies at each level and over all time spans. Second, when does a reversible change — a homeostatic response to stress, or a behavioural change in response to a stimulus — become irreversible? What is the limit of homeostatic tolerance, the Rubicon that is crossed, when the transient response becomes either an adaptive change or a non-adaptive (pathic) breakdown? When does a dynamic memory become a structural one, much as the spoken word becomes fixed in writing? At what stage does the totipotent embryonic cell become irreversibly differentiated and specialized for a particular function? When does the individual growing up in his society acquire the set of values, customs, skills that characterize it? When can he no longer learn a new language without an accent, or face a different culture with no sense of xenophobia? Third, what is the mechanism, or the carrier, of the operation? How is the change in the system given an adaptive (or a non-adaptive) direction? Fourth, turning from the individual to the race, how is the adapted individual selected or, to the extent that individual change is passed on, how is this achieved? Last, what is the mechanism of cumulative racial change?

Such questions are not merely disembodied abstractions, even as regards the nervous system and behaviour. Learning must utimately be at the molecular level, as well as at cellular, organ, and individual levels. The material record of experience must be found in some change in the number, kind, or position of particles; in the pattern of ions or molecules in neurones or at their junctions. As acquired racial information is passed on by the molecular array in the nucleus, the gene number, kind and position, so the acquired individual information must be carried somatically, perhaps at synapses. But that experience fixation may go beyond the comfortable level of ordinary neural activity is indicated by such phenomena as result from operative manipulation of organisms. The classical experiments of Weiss and of Sperry, for example, demonstrated that the discharge of impulses along motor nerves depends on the peripheral connections; if a supernumerary sartorius muscle is implanted in the back of a frog and neurotized by any nerve from the back or legs, the muscle will come to contract simultaneously with the normal muscle of the same name. Some kind of micro-specification of the centres connected to the new muscle 'teaches' them to respond to the same central activity. More recently, the work of Thompson (1957, 1958) and McConnell et al. (1955, 1959) has shown that learning occurs in the essentially non-neural tail of a planarian at least as well as in the ganglionated head. If an individual planarian is taught a conditioned response, cut in two, and the pieces allowed to regenerate, the new worm formed from the tail end performs almost perfectly as soon as put to the test.

Turning at last specifically to the nervous system, the same interaction of heredity and environment is seen in full operation. Heredity gives the embryonic cells which will form neurones under their normal environment, but become skin or lens under a different one; which will continue to multiply, or bifurcate, their extensions sufficiently to satisfy fully the physiological field or need (Weiss, 1955); which will grow fibres in a direction guided by micellar structure and by chemical concentration (Cohen et al., 1954), to reach an appropriate end organ (as shown by various regeneration experiments), or the appropriate central neurone, despite operative mixing (Detwiler, 1936). But all these capacities are present only in the very young embryo; at each successive stage of development the potency shrinks further. Totipotent cells can later become only neurones, distorted patterns can no longer be corrected and, in general, new growth and chemical metabolism decrease in rate. Rate falls off with life time, a basic ageing process, roughly as a decaying exponential curve; growth and its special manifestation, learning, shrink in speed and scope with advancing years until plasticity is essentially lost. Then no new material trace is formed and experience is no longer fixed by the individual.

Specifically for the nervous system, the following questions are important: what experience is retained; under what conditions; where does the change occur, is it local or diffuse; what is the nature of the change, chemical, electrical, structural; and how does fixation occur, at the molecular and at the cellular levels? Some attention will be given to the nature and the locus of the material record, but most attention will be given to the mechanism of fixation.

A neurone, at least in tissue culture, is a restless entity. It shows the usual swellings and churnings of other cells and its processes thrust out and retract pseudopodial branches and terminations unceasingly. The neurone has an unusually high rate of metabolism and, judging by the rate of regeneration and of peripheral flow in axons, a neurone may renew its entire mass of protoplasm three times daily. It is hard to see, therefore, how an enduring modification can be left at the cellular level. Experience must presumably alter some macromolecule, DNA or RNA or protein, which can continue to reproduce itself in the altered form, much as a mutated gene. But then other formidable problems arise. How does neural activity, and the particular pattern of electric currents and attendant change in position and concentration of ions and polar molecules which activity engenders, lead to an altered array of nucleotides or amino-acid moieties in a macromolecule? How does such an altered complement of macromolecules in a neurone come, in turn, to modify its future physiological activity so as to give a new and appropriate pattern of discharges? How is the specificity of the molecular change related to the specific functional past and functional future in an adaptive fashion? Is a sort of natural selection process in a neurone population involved; if not, we again face the sort of problem raised by Lamarck.

Whatever the answer at the molecular level, there are certainly morphological changes with neural activity at the levels of organelle and of cell, and some of these endure for a relatively long time. The chromatolysis of fatigue, with diminished Nissl substance, swollen and rounded cytoplasm, and eccentric nucleus, has long been known. More recently, a change in microsome number and locus around the nucleus has been shown to accompany changes in activity of neurones in tissue culture (Geiger, 1957). The apical dendrite of pyramidal neurones becomes thicker and more twisted with continuing activity. Nerve fibres swell when active (Hill, 1950; Tobias, 1952), sprout additional branches, as seen in the spinal cord (McCouch et al., 1958), and presumably increase the size and number of their terminal knobs. New fibre branches and connections, at least, might endure long enough to constitute a morphological engram.

It is highly doubtful, both from the total number of bits remembered and from the survival of memories despite extensive brain lesions, that each remembered item is located at a particular neurone or synapse. Some localization is, of course, present, as shown by the aphasic defects with regional lesions and by particularized recollections induced by local temporal stimulations. But even these are hardly cell by cell; and it is far more probable that large numbers of neurones, in assemblies or masses, in different patterns and other orderings, are involved in each memory. Partial engrams – of percepts, images and acts – are built into larger ones – concepts, imaginings and skills – much as a small assortment of amino-acids is used to build a limitless variety of proteins. In the same way, learning goes from letters to words to sentences, with plateaux of achievement at each larger unit; and bits of information become aggregated into larger 'chunks' so that a greater quantity can be handled in a given time (Miller, 1956). Not only spacial relations, but also temporal ones must be proper, witness the great disturbances to thought and speech produced by delayed auditory feed-back.

Whatever the micro-locus of the memory trace, most learning involves the cortex. Besides the evidence of cortical localization by stimulation and lesion, there is the further evidence of a general parallel between learning and memory capacity on the one hand and general cortical size on the other, and also there are the recent psycho-physiological experiments initiated by Sperry (1959). With the optic chiasm cut, so that incoming messages from each eye reach only the ipsilateral hemisphere, the two hemispheres remain connected primarily through the corpus callosum. If conditioning is carried on with one eye, a correct response can be elicited through either eye so long as the callosum is intact; but after this is also cut, only the eye used in training can elicit the learned response. The engram, while available to both hemispheres when these remain anatomically connected, is as clearly localized in only one. Comparable findings have been made on learning set or learning to learn. Other evidence for a cortical engram, and one which acts as a template for further engram development, comes from the work of Meyer (1958). Removal of both occipital lobes, but with a two-week interval between ablations, leaves a rat with pattern vision essentially intact if ordinary visual experience is possible during the interval; but if the animal experiences no pattern vision between the removal of the first lobe and that of the second, a permanent loss of pattern vision results. The endurance for months of figural after-effects in the Köhler's satiation-illusion (Wertheimer and Leventhal, 1958) further indicates a cortical locus of the engram.

Not all fixation, however, is in the cortex. Although ordinary conditioning of the spinal animal remains highly dubious, there is solid evidence of card changes produced in the intact animal. If one cerebellar hemisphere or peduncle is cut a few hours prior to a high spinal section, an enduring postural asymmetry remains in the hind quarters (de Giorgio, 1943). This is reminiscent of the continued unidirectional circling by a decorticate dog, the direction depending upon which hemisphere was first removed. A comparable postural asymmetry in the spinal cat is seen long after a severe inflammatory lesion is produced in one paw; the previously damaged leg is pulled into sharp flexion, with crossed extension of the other, when a spinal section is made (Sperensky, 1944). Clinical experience with trigger points, and the demonstration that anginal and other pains can develop a permanent referral to another body region which has been irritated at the time the pain occurs, points in the same direction (see Gerard, 1951).

The growing evidence of a relation of deep forebrain structures to learning and recall has not yet crystallized. The amygdala seems to exert an adverse influence on fixation, and the reticular formation and hypothalamus have also been found to be involved. Conversely, recent memory fails with damage to the mammillary body, the fornix, and the amygdala (Morrell, 1956; Bickford *et al.*, 1958; Jasper and Rasmussen, 1958; Samuels, 1959; Doty, 1960; Gerard, 1960a). Recently, the stimulation of the midbrain tegmentum has been reported (Thompson, 1958; Glickman, 1958) to cause forgetting; while stimulation of the caudate impairs fixation. The whole situation is confused by difficulties in distinguishing between fixation on the one hand and retention and recall on the other. The use of hypnosis as a tool to maximize recall has long given unexpected results; and recent reports by responsible workers — such as the hypnotic recall of a conversation which occurred during surgical anaesthesia of the individual doing the recalling; or recall of experiences during a given year of childhood but only when an hypnotic suggestion had brought the individual back to that age (Sheerer and Reiff, 1959) — demonstrates our small understanding of the complex phenomena of fixation and recall.

The mechanism of fixation of experience is not known, but two sets of data give strong clues concerning its nature. First, is a group of well-known changes that attend continued activity of neurones: thresholds go through increased and decreased phases; after-potentials are increased enormously in magnitude and duration; post-tetanic potentiation is associated with greatly increased reflex responses; and the like. The other phenomena relate to the existence of a considerable period, of minutes to hours, between having an experience and fixing it. If neural activity is interfered with during this fixation period, by electroshock, by cold, by heat-block, and the like, fixation is interfered with and permanent memories are feeble or abolished (Duncan, 1948; Gerard, 1953; Ransmeier, 1954; Leukel, 1957; Otis and Cerf, 1959). Thus, hamsters or rats trained in grouped runs on some learning situation — a maze or an avoidance conditioning or the like — show a normal learning curve if a convulsive electroshock is delivered after each set of runs with an interval of 4 hours or more. If the shocks follow the experience by an hour there is some deterioration, at 15 minutes loss is very considerable, and at 5 minutes or less learning is in effect prevented. If a hamster is promptly cooled after the learning experience, a shock given an hour later can be as deleterious as one given a few minutes later at body temperature; the Q_{10} of the fixation process has been thus determined at nearly three (Ransmeier and Gerard, 1954).

Anoxia acts much like electroshock, and the two sum their effects (Ransmeier and Gerard, 1954; Thompson, 1957). A number of drugs has now been tested for influences on the electroshock effect. Reserpine, like anoxia, potentiates the ECS disruption of learning (Weyner and Reimonis, 1959); ether protects against electroshock effects (Seigel et al., 1949; Potter and Stone, 1947); and, in man, meprobamate decreases the confusion produced following electroshock (Thal, 1956). Miss Rabe and I (1959) have just completed studies of the action of phenobarbital and of meprobamate on ECS action in rats on an avoidance conditioning test. In effect, phenobarbital slows and prolongs the fixation time, as judged by the greater disruptive effects of a convulsive stimulus at 1, 2, 5 and 15 minutes in animals under the barbiturate as compared with undrugged ones; while meprobamate, contrary to expectation, seems to have the reverse effect. Interestingly enough, meprobamate, but not phenobarbital, slows the learning process, aside from any ECS. Strychnine, according to an informal communication from Dr Krech, shortens the fixation time; a convulsive shock at a given time interval is less disruptive in the strychnized rat than in one without the drug.

The above facts fit well into a theory of continued activity in the nervous system, following the arrival of sensory impulses, in the course of which a dynamic memory is fixed as a structural one (Gerard, 1960a). Summation, irradiation and reverberation of messages would lead to repeated activity of the same neurones, with progressively greater and greater residual changes from the continued activity. At 50 reverberations per second, 100,000 actions could easily occur during the fixation time; presumably sufficient to leave an indelible trace.

Any change that would enhance the extent or intensity of reverberation should hasten the fixation process; any agent acting in the converse direction, should slow it. A fall in threshold of cortical neurones, or an increase in impulse bombardment, should hasten fixation. Since epinephrine lowers thresholds, and is released in vivid emotional experiences, such an intense adventure should be highly memorable. Perhaps during imprinting periods, the relevant neurones are similarly in a low threshold or 'soft-shell' stage. Strychnine, by enhancing general activity level and lowering thresholds, should also speed up the fixation process. The reticular formation, the amygdala and other components of the limbic system, the hypothalamus, etc., act through one another or directly on cortical neurones to alter their dendrite potentials, their thresholds, and their responsiveness to the discrete impulses which reach the cortex by non-diffuse afferents or by spread within it. By raising or lowering thresholds of cortical neurones, associated with lowered or increased attention and vigilance, these deep regions could easily modify the ease and completeness of experience fixation even if the nuclei were not themselves loci of engrams. Ether and meprobamate, by raising thresholds, should slow reverberation and therefore make electroshock effects more severe; unless they also decrease the effect of the shock itself due to the increased neurone thresholds. This last possibility is being further tested in the case of meprobamate; it does explain the synergy of reserpine and shock, and of anoxia and shock, since both anoxia and reserpine lower convulsive thresholds.

Fixation would also be modified by changing impulse bombardment; in fact it is the interference with such continued bombardment, by shock or cold or concussion – which latter rather nicely parallels clinically the amnesic effects of electroshock in animals or man – that interrupts the fixation process. Early in any learning experience, as the organism's actions fail to solve the problem and eliminate the disturbing input, there is great central irradiation; muscle tension is increased, there is generalized contraction of irrelevant as well as of the desired muscles, autonomic discharges occur, tension and attention are intense, the 'consciousness of necessity' is high, and many neurones in cortex and deep centres show electrical activity on mass or micro-electrode recording. Later, when learned responses have been established, general radiation disappears, muscles relax, there is little tension and maybe not even attention, habituation is evident in performance and experience, and electric activity has disappeared from all neurones except those specifically involved in the response. With errors or other kinds of emergency situations, the electrical activity and other signs of irradiation promptly return (see Gerard, 1960a for references). As an action is learned and certain paths through the nervous system become canalized, irradiation is eliminated. This requires either feed-back inhibitory arcs or a decrease in the general level of facilitation, as interneurones become less active. This latter would follow the diminished irradiation consequent to effective responses.

Although the effect of continuing or recurring activity has been described in terms of simple feed-back loops, the same results can be obtained by improved synchrony of beating neurones or, especially, by repeated waves of activity passing through a sheet of neurones. This last model, developed by Beurle (1957), depends only on more or less random connections of neurones in a mass, activated only fractionally by controlled waves passing through them. Such waves can cross and at the locus of intersection will leave a group of lowered-threshold neurones. From such a locus the original waves can reinitiate without external stimulation; such loci thus offer engrams for memory, recall, planning of action and for the combination of smaller elements of perception and action into larger wholes of conception and of planning. The model and the physiological support for and predictions from it are more fully discussed elsewhere (Gerard, 1960a).

Reverberation, or some form of continuing reactivation, is probably involved in a number of other mental processes, including perception, attention, repression, anxiety, and the like; but this is not the place to develop these points. Certainly attention is necessary for learning and for discrimination. A dog, faced with an impossible oval or circle choice, develops a neurosis only after it has already learned to pay attention to this discrimination as a problem. Presumably the structures feeding diffuse system impulses to the cortex, discussed above in connection with the altering of fixation and recall, are involved in such influence of attention on the learning process.

The nature of the material change in the brain, of its locus, and of the mechanism of fixation that brings it about are not established, but all these questions are clearly on the way to satisfactory solution. The really difficult problem is none of these, however, and it remains as mysterious as ever. This has to do with *specificity* in the selection and discrimination of what is perceived, in the degree of attention given it, in the presence and firmness of fixation of a memory, in its retention and subsequent recall to consciousness. This qualitative aspect is, of course, not limited to the receiving and retention of experience, but is equally present on the behavioural side and is attached to plans, to values and to actual performance. How choices are made, how priorities are assigned, how shifts occur from one set of active neural processes to a different one, remains still a complete mystery.

Certainly this is related to our subjective experience of free will in choosing what we do and what we attend to. But before accepting un-caused causes, let us recall that computers can also learn to develop a set of values and to choose between programmed activities, so that we need not yet despair of finding the neural mechanisms for this ultimate core of higher behaviour. Given a programme or plan, a computer can rapidly scan the existing situation and select that set of actions which will come closest to matching an 'ideal' that has been given it. Behaviour is similarly tracking; as individual or as race, organisms respond to the challenge of their environment. Behaviour, as remarked earlier, is such as to bring the expected future condition of the organism into congruence with the desired condition. This can be done blindly, starting from the existent state, or it can be done with greater or lesser foresight by projecting the existing state into its probable future condition.

The nervous system and learning endow the animals possessing them with this ability to extrapolate the curve of existence and so to act with foresight. The cat jumps not to where the mouse is, but to where it may be expected to be. Man not only can himself run away from the batter in order to catch a flyball; he can also build into computing tracking mechanisms, as anti-aircraft guns, the same ability. Man himself, with his ten billion or more cortical neurones, can out-perform all other projecient machines, so far built by nature or by him, in projecting further and more elaborately into the future. This is possible because of a great repertoire of past memories, or partially organized and interacting programmes, and of complex probability computers that take account of past and present factors and assign value or utile weights to them. The basic molecular, cellular and organismic mechanisms involved, however, are probably not much different from frog to physiologist. It is an intriguing question whether equally effective ones will one day be evolved for man's machines.

GROUP DISCUSSION

HEBB. I would like to raise two points. One is with respect to the work of McConnell on the flatworm which I found extremely puzzling. I do not know whether it can be compared to learning in mammals. If this type of mechanism applied in the mammal, presumably Sperry's work should not have given the result it did by just cutting the corpus callosum. We must be dealing with a different phenomenon, when we talk of learning in the mammals, from the phenomenon that McConnell studied. Secondly, with respect to the effects of anaesthetics on the consolidation period of learning, I would like to cite some work by Muriel Stern, concerning the effect of barbiturates on learning. The effect you observed may be a general disturbance, rather than a specific interference with the retention period. The effect of barbiturates is that of depressing learning capacity for a period of some weeks in the laboratory rat. The effect disappears in 5 or 6 weeks. The effect is not found with other anaesthesia.

GERARD. I am not prepared to go along with the extreme psychiatrists who say that learning is all over the body and not in the brain, nor with the slogan that 'we think with our blood'. We think in the nervous system and in the upper part of it, but there is continuity. The same kind of mechanisms, which are specialized in the nervous system as a basis for recording experience, probably evolved from basic cellular processes, which are seen at the chemical level. In the case of the flatworm this is closer to the level of total behaviour. As to the second point, the action of these drugs on the fixation process and on learning processes is very complicated and depends on many parameters. With increasing doses of meprobamate, one finds an increasing interference with the learning curve. These experiments were on rats with an avoidance conditioning, given massed trials and tested the next day. The drug, when given, was injected 1 hour for meprobamate, or 3 hours for the barbital (depending on maximum time of action), before the learning experience. Rats were given electroconvulsive shocks at 1, 2, 5, or 15 minutes after the mass runs, which were completed usually well within 15 minutes total time. Although meprobamate definitely interfered with learning, it did not interfere with the fixation; it even improved it. In other words, an electric shock at one minute did not interfere so much with retention on second test of a rat with, as for one without, meprobamate. We are checking to be certain that a raised threshold is not a factor, even though all shocks gave typical convulsions. The phenobarbital had a marked effect in prolonging fixation time; as shown by much deterioration with electroshock, and the greatest deterioration with the closest shock. It did not interfere with initial learning. Your findings seem contrary to what happened in our laboratory; we should examine differences in conditions.

CHOW. May I just make a point about this flatworm work, because that work seems to me to be most striking. If it is true it will probably influence our thinking about learning at the cellular level. There are two points I wish to make about this particular piece of work, the results of which I think should be accepted with some caution. First, there are probably nerve cells in the nerve tract, therefore you have a second or caudal half which still remembers the problem, which may not be due to memory in the nerve fibre itself. Secondly, a very important point is that apparently an essential control was not made. This control is: they should have a group of animals which are given a series of shocks without learning, and cut them into two, wait until they regenerate and do the conditioning, and see if this group without previous training, also show a fast learning.

GERARD. These controls have now been done. I talked to McConnell some months ago and, as I recall, results were going in the proper direction. Even without them, however, it seems hard to explain away the fact that, even if there are a few neurones in the tail as compared to the many in the head, the tail did do as well as, or better than, the head. Maybe if one gets too much stuff in the head, ideas get fixed in a certain way and performances are no longer malleable; a sort of ageing phenomenon. The work will certainly have to be examined carefully, because it is a very disturbing finding. However, the appearance of certain phenomena at this primitive level does not necessarily explain those at a more complicated level. It may well be true that this is a perfectly good type of learning, but it is certainly not the whole story of our learning. Let me give one example of this: Many years ago

Dr. Libet and I found that travelling slow waves in the hemisphere of the frog, starting at the olfactory bulb, would cross a complete section through the brain if this was made with a sharp razor blade and if the two halves were accurately placed together. (I do not think neurohumoural agents were involved). Several investigators checking in mammals found the spread of epileptic activity was blocked by cutting. Aside from the fact that they were not able to get anything like an equivalent opposition, there was no necessity that this be the same phenomenon.

ASRATYAN. I would like to ask a question about the same experiment. For how long is it possible to evoke these responses from the head part and the caudal part? How long does this habit remain? Is it possible to elaborate reflexes on the head part and on the caudal part of the animal after cutting the animal in two and what is the difference in the rate of elaboration and of appearance of learning?

GERARD. I do not know the answer to the second question. As to the first, it takes about 3 weeks for regeneration and, as I recall, the test was made a month after cutting. Uncut planaria also retained the learning for such a period.

BUSER. Did the author exclude the possibility of peripheral network as happens in many invertebrates, as being hypodermic and distinct from the C.N.S. It could be a diffuse system.

GERARD. I can only answer that work is now in progress with a zoologist and histological tests are being made more extensively. This is perhaps the widest loophole; whether there are as yet unrecognized neurones in the tail part of the animal.

ROSVOLD. I was interested in your statement that there is no necessary reason why what happened in planaria need concern us with respect to man's brain or monkey's brain ...

GERARD. May I correct that? I would not say it does not concern us; I think it concerns us enormously or I would not have mentioned it. But I do not think it is the whole story. It is part of the story, the substrate on which other mechanisms are built.

ROSVOLD. From a comparative point of view, however, where can one draw the line? How close can one make the analysis? If one takes your statement literally could not one always, so to speak, wriggle out of an inconsistency? Simply stating that the comparison is too remote and, therefore, is hardly appropriate.

GERARD. I am not really clear as to the question. Is this responsive: I have become a behavioural scientist lately and am in an Institute which devotes itself to behavioural science. We are concerned with finding the constants in the properties of systems at all levels from molecules to societies. We are often attacked for dealing with meaningless analogies because the details are different in each. I suggest that it is extremely important to be aware both of the particularities which differentiate the one from the other and of the general likeness. When I say, as I do, that an idea in society is in many ways like a gene in biology, and that this is the new disturbing element which makes social evolution possible as a new gene makes biological evolution possible, I do not mean that male and female ideas mate and that there are mitoses and all the rest of it. This would be arrant nonsense. But it is still useful to see some of the likenesses. If one can in fact get something, assuming that this holds up, which, objectively, we would have to call learning, in non-neural cells, even though they have undergone division to form a new nervous system, this is something which I should expect to apply in any comparable situation that could be found in man. Indeed, the reason I brought up these findings is the high probability that the engram in neurones, which themselves undergo 'regeneration' by changing their material three times a day, might also be something at a molecular level. Whatever the mechanism, in either case, a new kind of template is formed, new molecules are reproduced according to the template, and this is the way fixation of experience or learning is carried on in the nervous system.

THORPE. With regard to this matter of the planaria there have been a number of examples of what have been called pre-imaginal conditioning in insects where the larva was exposed to an influence which produced the corresponding modification of behaviour in the adult. This was first done with regard to exposure to chemical substances, but there was also a series of experiments reported by Borell du Vernay (1942) in which the larvae of the beetle *Tenebrio moliter* were trained to take a certain path in a 'T' maze and the same effect was observed significantly in the adults.

GERARD. To what extent is the nervous system discontinuous?

THORPE: A steady change takes place. Although the locomotory systems of the larva and the adult are very different there would certainly have been organized nervous tissue present throughout. So, though we are not here dealing with a complete replacement of nervous tissue, I think nevertheless that these experiments are interesting to recall in connection with the subject of our present discussion.

Might I ask you about one other point? A very different one. You referred to this matter of fixation and recall and the distinction between it. I was very puzzled some years ago by some work that Dr McCulloch reported, on the ability of some patients to recall, when under hypnosis, extraordinary details of their own early actions and experiences. One particular case I remember concerned a bricklayer who was able to recall minute details of the bricks he had laid at a certain date of his life. I tried to get the exact particulars of this from Dr McCulloch at the time but he was not able to give anything like the detail which I hoped would be forthcoming. I mentioned it in the hope that other people here, such as Dr Hebb, might have some fresh data to give us on this particularly important topic. Only last year Wilder Penfield (*Proc. Nat. Acad. Sci.*, **44**) stated his belief, based on 25 years experience of surgical treatment of brains of epileptics, that the temporal lobes possess a permanent record of the stream of consciousness in amazing detail — as if the brain cells behaved like a tape recorder which may be played back by a suitable electrical stimulus.

GERARD. I have also been intrigued by that report. As I recall, a bricklayer in his sixties or seventies was asked to describe, say, the fifth brick in the seventh tier of a wall that he had laid in his twenties. The bumps on the top and the bottom of the brick he described under hypnosis could be checked and they were there. It is a dramatic statement and I have referred to it in a paper. I do hope McCulloch is correct, for he is also my source.

Another example, given informally, at a symposium in Kansas City along with the statement about recall of events under deep surgical hypnosis, frightened me even more, because it makes me think of Bridie Murphy. An adult was asked to recall some details of a classroom, desks, etc., in which he sat when 6 years old. He was quite unable, even under hypnosis, to recall any of these things until the suggestion had been made: 'You are now 6 years old'. Then he described them. When he was told he was 7 years old, he couldn't do so. I can only say that a thoroughly reputable psychologist told us this with fear and trembling, but he could not find anything wrong with his experiments.

D

DISTINCTIVE FEATURES OF LEARNING IN THE HIGHER ANIMAL

D. O. Hebb[1]

In the study of learning our problem is not only to understand the way in which synaptic function is modified; it also fundamentally involves control of the concurrent activity of the rest of the central nervous system. One question is more 'molecular' and physiological, essentially concerned with the relations between two individual neurones; the other is 'molar' and psychological, involving the operations of the total system. The second part of my thesis is that we must develop means of dealing experimentally with the so-called autonomous central processes whose activity is at the heart of the learning process in the higher animal, and some research is reported which attempts to make a contribution of this kind.

THE PROBLEM OF EXCESS ACTIVITY IN CNS

Learning consists of a modified direction of transmission in the CNS so that, in the clearest example, a sensory excitation is now conducted to effectors to which it was not conducted before. A new S-R or stimulus-response connection has been established (the clearest example, but not the only form of learning). The term learning may be used to refer to other changes of behaviour in primitive animals, but at least in the case of the mammal's acquisition of prompt, efficient responses, dependent on the all-or-none action of neural cells conducting over considerable distances, the direction of transmission must be determined at the synapse (or close to it: Milner, 1959). It might therefore be thought that the problem of learning is simply to discover when and how synaptic function is modified.

The question is indeed fundamental, and must be answered before the problem of learning will be solved; but it is by no means the whole problem, because of complexities introduced by the structure of the CNS in higher animals, and particularly in mammals and in primates. In the learning process we do not have a one-to-one relation between progressive changes of behaviour and changes at the synapse. The simplest

[1] The presentation of this paper, and some of the experimental work reported herein, was made possible by the National Research Council of Canada. The experiments were done by Jean Campbell, Joseph Deitcher and Eric Rennert.

mammalian behaviour involves an enormous number of synapses, the changes that occur simultaneously may be in opposite directions, and there may be little detectable relation between the course of events at any one synapse and changes of overt behaviour — just as there may be little relation between the activity of an individual neurone and the gross record of the EEG.

If we assume that many of the neurones in the brain of a waking mammal are firing at any given time, and especially if we further assume that some of these are inhibitory, there are certain consequences which have sometimes been overlooked in physiological discussions of learning. The possession of a large brain capable of learning a great many different things inevitably means that there are far more neurones present than is necessary for learning some one specific task. Any random activity in these excess neurones (the ones not needed for the task being learned) is 'noise', which must tend to interfere with the learning. (If the activity is organized instead of random it is not noise, technically speaking, but the effect may still tend to be adverse.) It seems obvious that the number of excess neurones must be very much greater — perhaps thousands of times greater in the brain of the higher animal — than those needed for the learning going on at the moment. It therefore seems that the rate of learning, as observed in the behaviour of the whole animal, may be not an index of capacity for adding new synaptic connections so much as an index of the noise level, and that learning will be fast or slow according as one is successful in establishing an environmental control of the excess neural activity, in order to prevent or minimize interference.

Practically, the significance of this point of view is clear in the term 'lack of concentration', in the case of the student whose learning is inefficient even in a quiet environment, because other thoughts obtrude besides the ones he should be concerned with. Experimentally, the point is made by Ricci, Doane and Jasper (1957), in reporting that a significant part of the conditioning process — perhaps the main part — is in the dropping out of irrelevant connections, rather than the acquisition of new ones. It is clearest of all in a classic experiment of Yerkes.

Yerkes (1912) trained an earthworm to choose one arm of a T-maze, using electric shock as punishment for error and the moist burrow as reward for correct choice. The habit was acquired in twenty trials, 2 days at ten trials per day, about what might be necessary for the laboratory rat. No errors were made on the third day, though behaviour was somewhat inconstant in the following week as between good days and bad days (even worms have them). Yerkes then removed the brain, or principal ganglia, by cutting off the head — the anterior four and a half segments. The animal continued to respond correctly, showing that there were sufficient synaptic modifications in the remaining ganglia to mediate the response — until the new head regenerated, at which time the habit was lost. The noise generated by the new ganglia, the irrelevant neural activity of the uneducated brain, was sufficient to disrupt learning completely.

In this 'case we are dealing with the effects of noise on an established habit, and in a lower animal. It seems clear that the potential disrupting effects must be as great or greater while learning is still going on, and in the large brain of the higher animal. If then the rate of learning reflects the noise level in the system, it becomes intelligible that the higher animal does not learn faster than the lower, when each is given a task to which it is constitutionally adapted. The rate of learning *per se* is not an index of intelligence or level in the phyletic scale (Lashley, 1929); we may note, for example, the occurrence of one-trial learning, by inspection only, in the solitary wasp (Baerends, and Tinbergen and Kruyt, cited by Tinbergen, 1951). There is of course no reason why modifications of the individual synapse should be made more quickly in a system with many synapses than in one with few. When receptors, effectors and intervening neural structures are adapted to a small number of acquired responses, and there is little or no irrelevant concurrent activity, the necessary synaptic modification may occur very rapidly. Much that is considered to be innate, because there is little evidence of practice, may in fact depend on immediate learning at first exposure to the stimulating conditions.

The problem of excess activity or noise in the larger brain is characteristic of those regions of divergent (rather than parallel) conduction in which learning is supposed to occur. If the experimental stimulation is to result in a modification of function at the appropriate synapses, the excitation produced by the stimulus must be conducted to those particular synapses. From the sensory surface to the cortical projection area there is no difficulty; here conduction is in parallel and the same population of units can be reliably excited, time after time, since the units which begin together (and thus are simultaneously excited) end together, and reinforce one another's action at the next synaptic level (Hebb, 1958). But this condition does not hold for the further cortical transmission, especially where the mass ratio of association to sensory cortex is large (the A/S ratio: Hebb, 1949). A relatively small sensory projection area cannot dominate a large region of divergent conduction, maintaining on successive trials the same conditions of transmission with respect to single units. This applies to the large thalamo-cortical sectors which comprise the so-called association areas, and also to other rhinencephalic and basal-gangliar regions which seem to be involved in higher mental processes (cf. the recent review by Rosvold, 1959). Whether a given synaptic junction will be activated in such regions of divergent conduction cannot be determined by control of the stimulating environment, the experimental situation in which the learning is to be established. It is fully dependent also on whether the units concerned are ready to be fired, and on the concurrent activity of other units, not controlled by the present sensory stimulation, which impinge on the synapse in question and which may produce either summation or inhibition. Cumulative learning, in which the second trial adds to a synaptic modification begun by the first, thus depends on what activity is already going on in these regions.

Here is a point at which we find a full convergence of the physiological with the psychological evidence. Psychologically, the problem is that of 'set', 'attention', 'motivation', 'attitude', or the like: all terms developed in an earlier day to refer to (1) the puzzling but unmistakable deviation of behaviour from control by environmental stimulation, and (2) deviations of learning from the simple S-R and CR conceptions, implying a direct, through connection which, as we have seen, cannot be expected to occur in regions of divergent conduction, though it was taken for granted by earlier physiologists as well as psychologists.

Even today, the problems involved here have not always been faced, perhaps because of the complications which they entail. The histological structure of the tissue in question appears to mean that transmission is via a series of the closed pathways described by Lorente de Nó (1943), or groups of them functioning as systems capable of self-maintained activity. Such systems are what I have called 'cell-assemblies' (Hebb, 1949), and Lashley (1958) 'trace systems'; the most adequate discussion of their possible mode of development and internal function is that of Milner (1957). Such conceptions certainly introduce complexities into behavioural theory, but on the other hand the behaviour itself is even more complex, and means of experimental analysis are becoming available. Burns (1958) for example has provided us with much information about the conditions in which self-maintained activity is possible in a slab of isolated cortex, from a physiological approach; and such studies of perception as those of Broadbent (1956) with respect to hearing, and Heron (1957), Kimura (1959) and Bryden (1958) with respect to vision, have begun to transform a very speculative class of theory into something more solidly grounded in fact and susceptible of direct experimental attack. The following experimental work attempts to carry this process further.

THE NATURE OF THE TRACE IN SHORT-TERM MEMORY

In principle, we may distinguish two ways in which a memory trace can be established (cf. e.g. Eccles, 1953). One is a kind of after-discharge, a reverberatory activity set up without necessarily depending on any change in the units involved, other than the discharge of impulses; and one consists of some change in the units which outlasts their period of activity. The first can be called for convenience an *activity trace*, the second a *structural trace*.

In discussing this point earlier (Hebb, 1949) I assumed that the repetition of digits in a test of memory span provides a pure example of the activity trace. Here the experimenter presents verbally a series of digits, and the subject is asked to reproduce them in the same order. After the subject has attempted one series, the experimenter presents a second series and the subject seems to forget the preceding series completely. He does not get the two mixed up just as, in a calculating machine, punching a second set of numbers wipes out the preceding set completely. But is this what happens? Is there no lasting after-effect: no structural change produced by hearing and repeating the digits?

With this question in mind, and with the intention of learning more about the nature of the trace, in short-term memories for highly familiar material, the following experiments were carried out.

Method: the subjects were college students, each tested individually. They were informed that the purpose of the experiment was to see whether the memory span for digits would improve with practice. Twenty-four series of digits were presented. On each of these trials, the experimenter read aloud a series of nine digits at the rate of about one per second. The subject was instructed to listen carefully and repeat the digits in exactly the same order.

Each series consisted of the digits from 1 to 9, in varying order, each digit occurring once only. An example is

591437826.

There was, however, one special feature about which the subject was not informed. On every third trial (3rd, 6th, 9th ... 24th) the same series was repeated, and the object of the experiment was to discover what effect this had. Would the repetition result in learning? If immediate memory for digits in these circumstances is mediated solely by an activity trace, with no structural changes, each new stimulus-event would be expected to wipe the slate clean and set up a new pattern of activities. No cumulative learning would occur. If such learning occurs, however, we may conclude that there is some structural modification, in the sense defined above (in addition to whatever activity trace there may be).

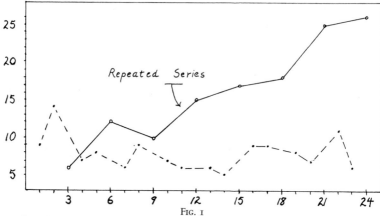

FIG. I

Number of subjects (out of forty) successfully repeating nine digits on each of twenty-four trials, when every third set of digits is the same ('repeated series'); non-correction method.

The results show clearly that cumulative learning occurs. Fig. I illustrates the data for one procedure. Here the subject's errors are not corrected, and the record is made in terms of the number of trials in which the nine digits

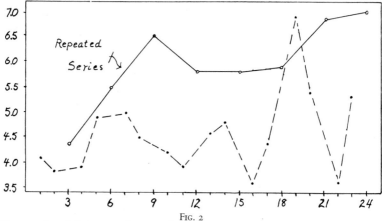

FIG. 2

Mean number of digits correctly repeated on each of twenty-four trials, by twenty-five subjects, when every third set of digits is the same ('repeated series'); correction method.

are repeated without error. Fig. 2 shows the similar result that is obtained when the subject is stopped as soon as he gives one digit out of the proper order (thus providing 'negative reinforcement', or 'punishment' for error); here the record is in terms of the number of digits correctly repeated on each trial. In both cases it is clear that learning occurs.

This can be seen in another way. The forty subjects whose results are diagrammed in Fig. 1 were each asked, following the nineteenth trial, whether they had 'noticed anything unusual' about the procedure. Twenty-two reported that there had been some repetition in the series presented to them, and three of these could give the crucial series without error. If the subject did not volunteer anything, he was asked explicitly about the repetition; three more subjects reported that they had observed it, and one of them could repeat the crucial series correctly. The remaining fifteen subjects had not observed the repetition. (The questioning was done between trials 19 and 20 in order not to direct attention to the crucial series, occurring on trials 18 and 21; none the less, the questions may have affected the subsequent performance on trials 21 and 24, which can be seen in Fig. 1 to show a further sharp improvement.)

The implications of this rather simple-minded experiment are more extensive than may be apparent at first. With such results, I can find no way of avoiding the conclusion that a single repetition of a set of digits, with or without the reinforcement of being told when an error has been made, produces a structural trace which can be cumulative. I assume that an activity trace may also be involved in the actual repetition, but it is the structural change which is of interest here.

It is important to note that we are dealing with highly practised material. Associative connections already exist between any two digits, for the educated subject especially. In addition to the very highly practiced sequence 1-2-3-4 ..., the learning of historical dates, telephone numbers, street addresses, quantitative values such as the speed of light or the number of feet in a mile, and the batting averages of the Boston Red Sox in 1937 — all these varied uses of the nine digits mean that the subject has already learned many sequences, in one or other of which any digit is followed by any other digit. When he is given a specific series to repeat, the memory for that series must depend somehow on a *further* strengthening of the connections already established. This is diagrammed in Fig. 3, where for simplicity the trace systems or cell-assemblies of three numbers only are represented. *1* has a strong connection with *2*, and *2* with *3* (because of the frequency with which the sequence 1-2-3 ... has been repeated in the past); but *2* has connections with *1* as well as with *3*, and *3* with *2* and *1* as well as with *4* (not shown).

Now let us suppose that the subject is given the sequence 3-2-1 ... to repeat. Some change occurs which means that when the experimenter stops speaking, the corresponding trace systems fire, and in the proper order. Undoubtedly there are complexities which this does not take account of; there is certainly not a mere chaining of the systems involved, because — for example — the subject may be able to tell you what the first and last of a group of digits were, though he has lost the intervening ones. Memory for the individual item in the series is not entirely dependent on the preceding item. But the *order* of repetition seems to require a changed synaptic relation between the specific cell-assembly groups, or trace systems, so that in the example of Fig. 3, *3* fires *2*, and not *4* or the

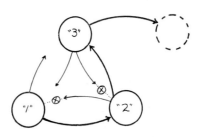

FIG. 3
Diagrammatic representation of the synaptic relations involved in the repetition of the digits 3-2-1. The heavier arrows 1-2 and 2-3 represent more strongly established connections; the encircled *x* indicates the temporary strengthening of less strongly established ones.

central representative of some other number; and *2* fires *1* and not *3*. The synaptic 'strengthening' implied is shown by the encircled *x* in the figure. What can this be?

The difficulty here is that all the synapses concerned must be already asymptotic, in the development of their structural connections. Synapses connecting system *2* with other systems are highly developed; if now when *2* fires it is to fire *1* reliably, and not *4* or *6* or some other system, it must be *significantly* more closely related to *1* for the moment, and it seems most unlikely that this closer relation can consist of a sudden further development of the size of the knobs of the *system-2 — system-1* synapses. Some other mechanism besides growth of the knob, or its closer juxtaposition with the cell body, must be involved.

The mechanism could well be that recently proposed by Milner (1959). He has pointed out that failure of conduction along some axon fibrils may readily occur where they begin to enlarge to form knobs — that is, short of the synapses proper. When there is already some depolarization of cell body or dendrites, the flow of current, it is argued, will make the bottle-neck traversable, and the subsequent depolarization will keep it open for an appreciable period of time. This will be particularly true if there is any considerable activity of the dendrites.

Such a mechanism would clearly help to account for the short-term memories of the present experiment, where we are dealing with associative connections which are already highly practised (i.e. whatever growth process there may be at the synapse is near its maximum), and where a momentary experience is able to make one set of well-developed synaptic connections temporarily dominant over others. The conditions of the experiment demand, of course, that this dominance must be very brief, lasting only for the period in which one set of digits is being held and giving way when the next is presented.

The explanation is of course speculative, but it accounts in principle for phenomena which cannot be plausibly dealt with solely in terms of (1) a reverberatory trace, and (2) growth at the synapse. What I am saying, in short, is that there may be three mechanisms of the memory trace and not two, as suggested earlier. It should be clear, of course, that these are not alternative mechanisms in the actual phenomena of brain function; they occur together, and reinforce one another's actions.

WIDER IMPLICATIONS

It has been urged above that we have no hope of understanding learning in the adult mammal until we know much more about the organized activity (in cell-assembly or trace system) of the regions of divergent conduction in the cerebrum. Lack of such knowledge is the main reason for the great gap between the theory of learning and the practical advice one can give to the student who wants to know how to study more efficiently. The great question always is how to 'concentrate', and how to 'motivate oneself' — that is, to keep on concentrating — and this, clearly, is the theoretical problem of the control of the excess activity, to prevent its interference with the task in hand. If such experiments as the one des-cribed can help us codify the ideas involved, and if further they provide some information about the interaction of cell-assembly groups in learning, we can also see them as a slight contribution to the ultimate understanding of the problem of serial order which, as Lashley (1951) has shown, is the crux of the problem of behaviour in the higher animal.

A more specific implication is with respect to delayed response. If extrinsic reinforcement is not necessary for the establishment of a structural trace — if the subject who only hears and tries to repeat a series of digits none the less has some memory of that specific series which can last despite hearing and repeating other series afterwards — then some revision is called for in my interpretation of the phenomenon of the delayed response (Hebb, 1958). A monkey sees a piece of food being put under a cup at the left, none under a cup at the right; his only response at the time is to look at the left cup, since both are out of reach. Both cups are then hidden by lowering a screen, let us say for 20 seconds. When the monkey is permitted to choose he goes at once to the left cup and gets the food. It seemed to me that this could only be accounted for in terms of a perceptual activity held in reverberatory circuits. In view of the present results, this does not follow. One look may be enough to establish what is, in effect, an S-R connection between the stimulation of the sight of the two cups, and an eye movement to the left. When the monkey is again exposed to the same visual stimulation, he looks left, his hand follows the direction of gaze, and he obtains the food. It is still clear that this 'S-R connection' in the brain of the higher animal can hardly be the kind of direct, one-way route envisaged by earlier theory, and that it must also involve some transmission by re-entrant circuits, but it is still a relatively simple mode of learning. In a lower animal, presumably, the closed-circuit element may not be present, and we can understand better the one-trial learning in the wasp already referred to (Tinbergen, 1951).

GROUP DISCUSSION

ECCLES. I am very grateful to Dr Hebb for putting up some clear ideas to shoot at. I want to shoot at the synaptic knob story he has given which is based on the outmoded theory of electrical synaptic transmission. However, I thought I might leave this synaptic story until tomorrow when I will be talking about the details of what goes on in the synaptic knob during repetitive stimulation and afterwards.

I would like also to comment on one-trial learning. I was listening very carefully when Dr Hebb spoke his series of digits. As soon as he started off the series I repeated this mentally and I went over the first 3 digits quickly when he got to 3, and so on at the 4 and the 5, so as to develop my memory. It wasn't a single trial for me.

HEBB. Did you get it right? That is the question.

ECCLES. I don't suppose I did. (Checking) The first ones were right, and also the last two; there was some muddle in the middle.

HEBB. I think you will find another method is better. Just to listen and then repeat.

ECCLES. While you are even listening to one digit there will be continued activity in the cortex. In 1949 both Dr Gerard and Dr Hebb published the concept that reverberating circuits played the key role at the early stages of learning. I have always thought that it is a very good idea that reverberatory circuit activity gives the basis for formation of memory traces.

HEBB. As Dr Eccles has picked me as a target, I would say that, in my opinion, the notion that transmission is solely chemical is pure dogma. That is to say, I think that Dr Eccles has provided convincing and powerful evidence that the primary transmission is chemical. However I can't see what evidence possibly could rule out an electrical current flow as an ancillary or supporting mechanism of synaptic transmission.

The second point is that I would agree entirely, and I take it that Dr Gerard does also, that one trial means one presentation of the stimulus, but it doesn't mean one burst of impulses. Of course I don't suppose that 'one trial learning' means that only one impulse passes the synapse, and does the trick. But further I would point out that in this experiment of course we are dealing with cumulative effects because we have no direct evidence of learning after one presentation of the digits.

GERARD. First, I think it is unfortunate that Dr Hebb has jumped three levels: from total behaviour, to organ, to cell, organelle or molecule. This is just too far a jump at any one time to be profitable theoretically. I think it unfortunate that he contaminated some very precise and provoking issues by bringing in the synaptic endings, which are irrelevant at this point. I don't think the argument that is brewing, as to whether the synaptic change is electrical or chemical, or whatever, is really relevant to the particular problem raised. It is relevant to all kinds of problems but too diffuse to matter for this one.

Second, I raise the question whether you really are dealing in your experiments with a structural memory, in contrast to a dynamic one. It seems to me you have something very similar to what happens when I look up a telephone number in the phone-book, keep it in my mind for a bit, make the call and immediately forget the number so completely that if something goes wrong, and I must dial again, I must look it up again. This is perhaps related to the point that Dr Eccles was making about keeping the memory going; and the psychologists here are certainly aware of Broadbent's work on the temporary storage of information before passing it into a permanent storage as a lasting memory, whatever the neurological mechanisms there may be.

Third, I completely agree with the point that Dr Hebb makes about what we might call 'imput overload', and the fact that the more elaborate nervous systems often tangle themselves up in their own sophistication. Let me remind you of two experiments. Some of the original work of Bavelas, following Kurt Lewin, involved five people in a certain communication network. Each started with part of the answer to a problem, such as what the colours of certain marbles are; and by communicating in the intervals each had to get the total information. This they did very easily when the marbles were solid colours; but, having worked with a pattern problem, they could not solve the solid colour problem because their attention focused on minute flaws in the colour. This kind of knowing too much was proved at another level, of disease diagnosis. Skilled clinicians diagnosed from a history less correctly than did clerks given certain key items to look for.

So I am not surprised that monkeys may learn certain simple problems with greater difficulty than rats, and perhaps man with even greater difficulty than monkeys. But it is going much too far from that to say that learning has nothing to do with the mass of the brain or the number of neurones. The minute one goes from these simple things to complex ones, there are correlations of performance with the total mass of the brain. Indeed I find myself in most exciting conflict with Dr Hebb on the role of large numbers of neurones. I have used the term 'physiological neurone reserve', distinguishing the potentially activable neurones of the brain, in contradiction to the anatomical population. For various reasons of increased thresholds or previous activation, many neurones may not at a given time be functionally available. The functional neurone reserve does seem to parallel nicely the ability to 'master a situation', a broader and more behaviourally interesting term than simple learning. In other words, while one may not do better on a prescribed simple stimulus response relation, when it is necessary to find the correct concatenation of possible behaviours out of an almost infinite variety, then the larger neurone complement is certainly an advantage and allows greater richness. Such an endowed brain can learn things that the other cannot. Maybe in this last point I am violating what you meant to say, but that is the way it struck me.

HEBB. I don't believe the synapse is irrelevant (what has happened is that I have been restricted to a 15-page document by Dr Delafresnaye and to a 30-minute presentation by Dr Gerard). Behind this statement of mine is an extremely long attempt to see if there was any other way of dealing with the problem. The fact of the matter is that the theory may be bad. I have no doubt that the position suggested by Dr Galambos, by Dr Olds and by others is logically sound. But the fact also is that people do think of a simple theoretical dichotomy — structural modification or a reverberation?

GERARD. It need not be one or the other, but either or both — or neither.

HEBB. I understand that. My only point is that I didn't mean to suggest that it is only structural, and not reverberatory. I had thought before, as you did with the telephone book, that I could look up a telephone number, dial it, and forget it completely. That I could listen to a set of digits, repeat them and forget them completely. I suggest to you that your statement about completely forgetting the telephone number is almost certainly wrong, on the basis of the experimental evidence that I have reported. I would have agreed with you 4 years ago. My idea now is that it is a little more complicated.

One last point on rate of learning in different species. I assumed that we were dealing with simple learning in all cases. Man certainly learns some complex tasks quicker than a monkey does, but the complex task may be regarded as the equivalent of a number of simpler ones. But there is a point that I think needs to be made. It has happened that Baerend's and Tinbergen's data have not been believed because the wasp is too low in the scale to have as fast learning as we have. But I propose that learning for which an organism is suited is likely to be faster, rather than slower, at the lower levels.

KONORSKI. According to my opinion any neurophysiologist concerned with the problems of conditioned reflexes is entitled, and even obliged, to explain the facts he deals with in the terms of synaptic transmission. As a matter of fact our first-hand knowledge about the principles of this transmission comes out from the most simple two-neurone reflex arcs studied by the most refined electrophysiological techniques. We extrapolate these findings to interpret the more complicated spinal reflexes, and we have also a right to utilize them to understand the mechanisms of conditioned reflexes, although they are much more complicated.

As far as Dr Hebb's experimental data are concerned, I find them very interesting and possibly requiring further elucidaton. They show that the dynamic memory trace, produced by presentation of a given series of numbers, is not totally obliterated by the subsequent series. It would be interesting to know what will be the rate of memorizing of the repeated series if it recurs less frequently than in Dr Hebb's experiments, and whether it is possible in this way to prevent memorizing of this series at all.

I realize the difficulty connected with the understanding of transient memory of series of items in terms of reverberating circuits. May be that the place of a given item in the sequence is determined, among other things, by the strength of the retroactive inhibition produced by the following items. I also agree with Dr Hebb that all the series he used in his experiments are in a greater or lesser degree already included in our stable memory repertory and one has only to remember that this and not that sequence was presented at the given moment.

HEBB. I should make clear that Milner did not develop his conception to account for those results. On the contrary, I was still struggling to find some intelligibility in the data when I saw Milner's paper.

If I have given the impression of thinking that Dr Eccles's position was pure dogma I should like to get that corrected right away. It seems to me that it is dogma to maintain the negative proposition that something like electrical facilitation cannot happen. The positive side of chemical transmission has been established well beyond any questioning by me, but there is still the possibility that you might have some ancillary mechanism.

I can find no way, to come to Dr Konorski's second question, of accounting for the ordering in that series. I remind you that the same digits are used trial after trial, and that the essence of the successful response is in the proper ordering. Suppose that each one of these systems is firing and reverberating. What determines the order in which they cause the motor sequence? I would only say that as nearly as I can determine there must be in addition to reverberation, some sort of connection between the separate reverberation systems, so that A fires its motor paths and then causes B to do so — and not vice versa. There is some short-term, essentially structural, modification which with repetition may turn into something more lasting.

GERARD. Dr Konorski, I was not for one moment objecting to going down to the synapse; you will remember I went all the way down to the molecule in the first paper. I simply said that whatever specific mechanism one assumes at the synapse is irrelevant to the problem Dr Hebb is facing. The problem is whether or not a message gets to the synapse, not how it produces a change there. The questions are at different levels.

THORPE. With reference to the one trial learning experiments with the insects *Philanthus* and *Ammophila* by Tinbergen and Baerends I would like to say first that I don't think there is the slightest doubt about the facts. It is quite easy to observe the orientation flights of these insects. Secondly I would like to point out that the task learned on these flights is in itself a very complex one. Moreover it is a kind of serial learning since, because of its very nature, the insect's eye cannot be getting a unitary vision of the whole field; on the contrary it is flying around picking up the various landmarks one after the other — and they may be numerous. So it seems to me to be a decidedly complex piece of learning; not as complex a task perhaps as learning these large numbers that Dr Hebb was discussing, but very complex when one compares it with the kind of learning task the insect normally has to achieve. I think that there is a very real problem here, namely that of explaining the very rapid mastery by the insect brain of a substantial task in serial learning. And then of course one must remember that there are no synaptic knobs, so far described, in the insect's nervous system which could be acting in the way that Milner proposed.

ECCLES. If I understood Dr Hebb correctly, he said he couldn't see how he could explain some of the digital learning processes on the basis of synaptic trace changes.

HEBB. Only when dealing with synapses already so highly developed as must be the case in repeating a sequence as much practised as 1-2-3. Here a single exposure, a single repetition, could hardly make a significant additional change.

ECCLES. Against that concept I would like to say that in the very simplest cerebral actions we are using millions of neurones in the most complicated imaginable patterns. In, say the 1-2-3 sequence, we don't have a group of neurones that are related to 1, another group for 2, and another for 3. I think that in each digital association the most complicated neuronal network is in operation. With a 2-1-3 sequence, we would have a quite different assemblage of neurones in activity. It is not sufficiently realized what an immense number of neurones we have to draw upon for the simplest memory. Lashley says that in the simplest engram there are millions of neurones involved. I would go much further than that myself. There is evidence from EEG record. During mental arithmetic there may be disturbance of the EEG over a wide region of the cerebral cortex. Thus immense assemblage of neurones are used doing some unusual multiplication, say 23×43. Therefore I don't subscribe to Dr Gerard's idea that there is a functional neurone reserve. I like to think that we are using all the neurones in some kind of pattern or other and using them thousands of times over in patterns, but that we can still use them many more thousand times over. It is the pattern that is important, not the neurones.

GERARD. This is not contrary to my notion, except that the more neurones you have the more patterns you can deal with.

ECCLES. I agree entirely. One final point, and that is if there is electrical interaction, and we have seen from Dr Estable's work the complexity of connections, and we now know from the electronmicroscopists that there is no free space, only 200 Å. clefts, everywhere in the central nervous system, then everything should be electrically interacted with everything else. I think this is only electrical background noise and, that when we lift with specific chemical connections above that noise we get a significant operational system. I would say that there is electrical interaction but it is just a noise, a nuisance.

HEBB. I think we are in agreement, at least in part, if I understood this last comment. When you say that the whole cortex is thrown into action when somebody multiplies 23×43 you are suggesting that most of the activity contributes nothing positive. The Jasper, Ricci and Doane experiments at least suggest strongly that the course of learning is throwing out the neurones that are irrelevant, keeping them out of the way while the others do the job. And this may mean that the course of learning involves many more neurones than would be desirable. It may be that though the operation is very complex, it could be done better if there were no other neurones present, for that operation. But the great characteristic of the human brain is the extraordinary variety and complexity of things it can deal wih.

GERARD. I might add, since, the work of Jasper's group has been mentioned so many times in connection with this, that extensive studies have been done by Beck along the same lines, showing the dropping out of neurones.

CHOW. I think that the problem Dr Hebb proposes is a very important one. What kind of mechanism can produce such effects that one exposure will redirect nerve impulses in a certain direction?

I would like to point out Lashley's notion that maybe you are creating some kind of field effect by your repeating the digits. Therefore, in essence you may create a DC potential gradient there, as if you had applied an external DC current. This presumably will modify all your neuronal excitability and will make your impulse flow easily in one direction. I think this may be a possible mechanism.

HEBB. It appears to me that we are dealing very often, not with the activity of all neurones in one topographical area as against the neurones in another topographical area but with selective factors among neurones interlinked with one another. It is very difficult to conceive a functional value from a DC field that is more extensive than a single neurone or 2 or 3 neurones. This is my problem.

E

THE INTERACTIONS OF UNLEARNED BEHAVIOUR
PATTERNS AND LEARNING IN MAMMALS

Irenäus Eibl-Eibesfeldt

I. INTRODUCTION AND OBJECTIVES

The term 'innate' as applied to behaviour patterns has become controversial. Beach, 1954, Hebb, 1953, Lehrmann, 1953, 1956 and Schneirla, 1956 have criticized the ethological approach, which they accuse of performing an artificial dichotomy into innate and acquired patterns. 'I strongly urge that there are not two kinds of factors determining behaviour and that the term "instinct" is completely misleading, as it implies a nervous process or mechanism which is independent of environmental factors and different from the processes into which learning enters '(Hebb, 1953). Lehrmann (1953) accuses ethologists in general and Lorenz in particular of misrepresenting unanalysable part-function in such a way as to give them the specious appearance of natural units, caused by the same physiological mechanism.

The main task of this paper is to show that the two oldest and most important ethological conceptions, that of the fixed motor pattern and that of the Innate Releasing Mechanism (IRM), correspond to very real functional units and that they prove their analytical value in the attempt to analyse the ontogenetic process by which unlearned and learned behaviour becomes integrated into an adaptive functional unit.

2. EXPERIMENTAL EVIDENCE

(a) *The analysis of nest building and retrieving young in the rat.* As is well known, every rat raised in isolation is capable of building a nest. A number of scientists have, therefore, termed this behaviour instinctive. In Munn's (1950) *Handbook of Psychological Research on the Rat*, it is discussed under the heading 'unlearned behaviour', along with retrieving activity; every rat which has given birth retrieves nestlings which were put outside the nest.

Riess (1947) has investigated the problem of the innateness of this behaviour. He raised rats under conditions which gave them no opportunity to manipulate solid objects. From the age of 21 days (some even as

53

young as 14 days) they were kept isolated in wiremesh cages and fed only with powdered food. After they had mated he put them in a wooden box with strips of paper hanging from the walls. Nest building and retrieving were looked for in this testbox, but the animals failed to build nests and to retrieve their babies. They only carried the young around and scattered the paper strips all over the floor. Most of the nestlings died, as they were not sufficiently cared for by their mother. From this failure to build nests and to retrieve, Riess concluded that the nest-building behaviour of the rat must be learned during ontogeny through handling solid objects. One could not apply the term instinct, therefore, to this type of behaviour. The way in which the rat might learn nest building was pointed out by Lehrmann (1954). The rat might collect food and other objects at its sleeping place and thereby observe that some of these collected objects can be used to prevent loss of heat. It would in this way learn to build a nest as soon as it felt cold. No attempt was made to gain detailed observational information concerning either recurring motor patterns or the stimulus situations indispensable to elicit them.

From observing a small number of different rodents (*Mus musculus* L., *Rattus norvegicus* L., *Meriones persicus* Blanf., *Meriones shawi*, *Gerbillus gerbillus* L., *Jaculus jaculus* L., *Cricetus cricetus* L., *Mesocricetus auratus* Waterhouse, *Microtus arvalis* Pall., *Citellus citellus* L., *Glaucomyys volans* Thomas, *Sciurus vulgaris* L., *Glis glis* L., *Muscardinus avellanarius* L., *Dasyprocta aguti*, *Oryctolagus cuniculus* L.) I was familiar with a number of motor patterns recurring in most or all of them (Eibl-Eibesfeldt, 1958).

In all ground-dwelling rodents observed, two phases of nest building can be distinguished: (1) The digging of a burrow (2) the construction of a nest for sleeping and nursing.

The nest-building Norway rat for example starts digging a tunnel, 20 to 30 cm. under the surface, which ends after about 1 metre in a small nesting chamber. Later, additional tunnels are added (Steiniger, 1950). The forelegs scratch the earth with alternating movements from the front under the belly (*scratching*). From there the accumulating earth is pushed backwards by the hindlegs (*kicking backwards*). From time to time the animal turns around pushing the earth by alternating movements of its forelegs out of the tunnel (*pushing*). *Pushing with the snout* is also observed. After digging the animal collects nesting material. This *collection* activity consists in *grasping* the nesting material with the teeth, *pulling* it free and if necessary *biting* it loose from where it is attached, then *carrying* it to the nesting site and *depositing* it there.

The nesting material is pushed into a heap by movements of the forelegs, identical with those performed when pushing earth out of the tunnel and by shoving with the snout. In the centre of the heap the rat starts *scratching*, forming a bowl and, furthermore, turning on its axis and *pushing* the nest material towards the periphery, it forms a ring-shaped mound around itself. Intermittently the rat reaches over the mound, grasping scattered nesting material with its teeth, and deposits it on the rim of the mound or inside the nest. It reminds one of the way geese construct their nests, but whereas the latter are able only to lay the material backwards over their shoulder, the rat shows more plasticity, being capable of depositing nesting material from different positions in relation to the nest. Coarse nesting material, like straw, is split with the teeth longitudinally. The rat holds the material at both ends in its paws and bites along it with the lower incisors. By a sudden lifting of its head it splits the straw (*splitting*). Straw, and even solid wood, are transformed into soft nesting material. Similar movements of nest building are observed in many other rodents and the patterns of splitting, scratching, or pushing, are common to all those species mentioned above. Sometimes additional movements are observed. Tree squirrels, for example, have special movements for bundling the nesting material before transport.

In addition, I was aware of certain environmental situations which were obviously indispensable, for instance, previously explored environment containing known nest locality, or else good cover.[1] At once I suspected that the failure of Riess's rats to build was due to the fact that they did not have a definite nesting place in the unfamiliar testing situation with which they were confronted.

When I took ten virgin rats experienced in nest building, duplicating Riess's test situation, none of them started building. After they had overcome their shyness they first started exploring, in between retreating to one corner where they cleaned themselves and rested. Some pulled out paper strips and scattered them all over the floor, thus behaving like the rats of Riess. But none built a nest within the first hour and only three built within 5 hours.

On the basis of my observations on different species of rodents, Riess's statement of the problem, asking whether 'nest building' as a whole was innate or not, seemed much too simple and consequently his conclusions too strongly generalized. Therefore, I attempted to clarify the following special problems, using experimental procedures as closely as possible similar to those employed by Riess. The question was:

[1] The rats have furthermore to be familiar with the presence of an observer, otherwise they are irritated, showing curiosity or shyness.

(1) Do any motor patterns and taxis components exist which are developed in the individual independently of learning?

(2) Does the assumption made by ethologists hold true that motor patterns which, by the comparison of species can be shown to be phylogenetically homologous, are independent of learning?

(3) What is the role of individual learning, (a) in changing or developing the pattern itself and (b) in integrating such innate elements, if any, into a functional whole?

Albino rats (*Rattus norvegicus* Erxl.) were isolated from the age of 12 to 21 days and raised in cages with a grill floor and given powdered food. Since, in the absence of nest material, rats often carry their own tails, these were amputated in the experimental animals. In contrast to Riess, I tested the rats in their living cages, since it has been shown that in rodents placed in a new room, escape and exploratory behaviour predominate over other activities. For the test, a rack holding 30 g. of crêpe paper strips was fastened on one wall of the cage. The room temperature varied between 17° and 19° C. In this way, the nest-building behaviour of (a) eighty-two virgin rats (2-3 months old), (b) three pregnant rats and the nest building and retrieving of (c) forty-two females, 4 months old, immediately after parturition, were tested.

Of group (a) (subgroup 1) thirty-seven animals had nothing else in their cage than the glass with powdered food, fastened on one wall, and the phial with water hanging from the roof. Eight of these animals started nest building as soon as the paper was presented and four started within an hour. Thirteen of the animals ran around with paper strips in their mouths, and eventually let them fall, thus behaving as Riess described, and six gnawed or played with the strips. They all built nests within 5 hours. The remaining six rats of group (a) (subgroup 1), however, did not build a nest. Observations in the previous days had shown that twelve of these rats had had definite sleeping places. All eight animals that built immediately belonged to this group. I, therefore, conjectured that the structural poverty of the experimental cage might have interfered with the establishment of a definite nesting place. Indeed, this may have hindered many experimental animals and made building in some cases impossible. That some of the experimental animals built in two places is evidence favouring this assumption. To facilitate the choice of a place, I divided one corner of the cages of the other experimental animals (subgroup 2) with a small vertical screen. Of forty-five virgin rats tested in such a cage, thirty-three immediately started nest building behind the screen. Among these were animals who tended to sleep in another corner of the cage. An unlearned preference for the most covered place prevailed in these cases over the effects of previous experience. Three of the experimental animals started behind the screen within 1 hour. Nine decided, within 5 hours, to build in another corner. To sum up: of the eighty-two virgin females, seventy-six built a nest, forty-four of these within the first hour of the test, and only six rats did not build.

In all animals that showed an interest in the nesting material, the above mentioned movements of nest building were observed. Most of the animals explored the rack and the paper at their first encounter by nibbling and sniffing. Then they tore one or a few strips out of the rack and carried them without much hesitation to the prospective nesting site. There they deposited the nesting material, and often nest-building movements like splitting, scratching and pushing appeared, although of no use at this stage. These movements usually lasted for only a few seconds before they started for more paper. From the behaviour of the animal one did not get the impression that they had any idea what the result of their behaviour would be. The behaviour released by the nesting material consisted simply of certain building movements, in disorderly sequence. But, in all cases, a nest was the result of the rat's activity. In five cases the experimental animals were given pieces of straw instead of paper. These, too, started to build, and all started to split the straw, in the characteristic way previously described, thus producing soft nesting material. Here, too, it was evident that the rat did not follow a certain plan by insight. It did not, for example, split one piece of straw after another, but only grasped one piece after another, making the splitting movements and dropping the straw afterwards without looking at the result. Often the blade was only cracked, or a small piece ripped off when it was dropped in order to grasp the next blade of straw. There was only one tendency evident, namely, to let certain movements run off on certain material. But by repetition of this behaviour, all the straw got split eventually. Experienced rats, by the way, seem to follow a plan or scheme, but that still has to be studied in detail.

Although I was interested only in actual nest construction, I let ten of the experimental animals, after testing nest building, dig in earth. They did so with complete co-ordination of all digging movements.

For the purpose of filming, three females (group (*b*)) were tested when pregnant. The reason was that we needed light to film but this produced heat, and as is well known (Kinder, 1927) virgin females do not build a sleeping nest when it is too warm. But in pregnant females, temperature does not influence the behaviour as much. The urge to build a nest is then very strong. As Koller (1955) has shown, this is due to the corpus-luteum hormone, progesterone. All three females built immediately; their behaviour is shown in the film.

Forty-two inexperienced females (group (*c*)) were tested for retrieving and nest building immediately after they had given birth in the experimental cage. Thirty-five of these females retrieved a nestling taken from the corner where they were suckling and deposited in another corner. Only seven of the females did not carry back their babies. In six of these seven cases the nestlings, which were not protected by nesting material, were so cold, that they seemed nearly lifeless, and did not squeak. Squeaking is, however, one of the sign stimuli for the females, releasing search and retrieving in the mother (Zippelius and Schleidt, 1956; Eibl-Eibesfeldt, 1958). Those retrieving behaved like normally raised mothers, with the only difference that they showed some hesitation in grasping the nestlings and often lost them during transport and had to pick them up again. When the nestling squeaked while being grasped, the female changed the grip, a behaviour which is now being studied in more detail.

All forty-two females, including those that did not retrieve, started immediately with the construction of a nest when, after the retrieving test, nesting material was offered. Furthermore they showed the covering of the nestlings typical for the breeding mother. This will be shown in the film.

Our experiments have shown that the handling of solid objects during ontogeny is not a prerequisite for the development of nest-building and retrieving behaviour. Riess did not realize this and he furthermore overlooked that nest building is a complex behaviour, and therefore did not look for the elements which compose it.

The several motor patterns which, on the basis of a comparative study of many species of rodents, had been assumed to be unlearned 'fixed patterns' appeared completely unchanged in the rats reared in the manner employed by Riess. One important difference was, however, found between experienced and inexperienced rats. The sequence in which the above-mentioned motor patterns are used was considerably better adapted to the function in experienced rats, inexperienced rats often employing motor patterns which can develop their function only at an advanced stage of the newly built nest, at a very early stage of building at which the patterns in question did not yet perform their function. The question whether 'nest building' must be learned or not cannot be given a simple answer. Certain essential motor patterns and taxis components are completely independent of learning. The proper sequence in which several patterns are best employed to perform an integrated function is indubitably learned. But no ethologist had ever doubted — as critics of ethology often imply — that learning processes are of the greatest importance in behaviour, Lorenz (1937) has often emphasized that learned and innate elements of behaviour are closely interwoven. His ravens for example had innate nest-building movements, but had to learn which material to use for nest building. Eibl-Eibesfeldt (1956b) has recently shown that red squirrels develop individually different techniques of nut opening on the basis of a few innate patterns, such as gnawing and a certain splitting movement.

In retrieving, learning plays a lesser role than in nest building. The inhibition of biting the nestling seemed even stronger in inexperienced rats. It would seem that the rat has to learn that a baby is not so vulnerable after all.

(b) *The killing technique of the polecat* (Putorius putorius L.). The following deals with the technique of prey killing of inexperienced and experienced polecats. Kuo (1930) has studied the behaviour of cats raised under different conditions towards albino rats, grey Norway rats and mice. Twenty cats were raised in isolation from weaning, twenty-one cats remained with their mother and were allowed to observe how she killed prey, and eighteen cats isolated from other cats were given a rat as companion from an early age on. Of those raised in isolation, nine killed prey (= 25 per cent); of the second group eighteen killed prey (85 per cent); but of those raised with rats, only three killed prey and then only of a type to which they were not accustomed. Towards their rat-companions the latter individuals showed peaceful and positive reactions. They licked and defended them and searched for them persistently if they were taken away. Kuo thus clearly showed that experience influences the behaviour of the cat towards prey, even though the difference in the percentage of killing in the first two groups might be explained as a result of a different state of health due to deprivation. Kuo expresses the opinion that the concept of instinct has been proved useless by his experiments. The bodily structures alone explain why a cat behaves like a cat and not like an ape: one does not need to have recourse to instincts, based on special structures of the central nervous system. What the animal actually does, within the potentiality given by its body, is learned during ontogeny. 'The behaviour of an organism is a passive affair. How an animal or a man will behave in a given situation depends on how it has been brought up and how it is stimulated' (Kuo, p. 37).

It seems, nevertheless, that Kuo did not realize where the problem actually lies. Such a complex behaviour pattern as prey hunting is, of course, not fully innate or learned as a whole, and we agree with Kuo that to pose such an alternative is a mistake. But, like Riess, Kuo did not see that the complex functional unit in any animal's behaviour is formed by a number of smaller behavioural patterns. In his paper, no single, particulate behaviour pattern is described. We investigated the prey-hunting behaviour of the polecat, asking if there were any fixed motor patterns or innate orientation movements involved in the pattern, and if so where and how experience enters.

Every adult polecat kills rodents which are able to defend themselves, by biting them in the neck or occipital region. Prey in flight is often grasped (*grasping*) on another part of the body, but after the polecat has thus stopped the prey's flight, it immediately releases its preliminary hold to grasp the neck. Often it turns the prey on its back and shakes it forcefully (*shaking*), in the way employed by many other carnivorous animals. The polecat furthermore loosens and fastens its grip, in rapid succession, sinking its teeth repeatedly in exactly the same spot, thus gradually perforating the skull (*killing bite*) (Eibl-Eibesfeldt, 1956a).

Studying the ontogeny of this technique in non-deprived animals, one finds that they show little skill in their first attempts to kill a prey, probably partly due to the lack of bodily strength. At the age of 3 months, however, a polecat is a skilful killer.

Twenty polecats were raised under deprivation. They were not confronted with living prey until the test, but were fed with meat and even dead rats to keep them in a good state of health. Eight of the polecats remained with their mother and litter mates. Twelve were isolated at the age of 21 days from members of their own species. Six of the polecats raised in isolation and eight of those raised with their litter mates, but also never being confronted with living prey, were given an adult rat when they were 5 months old. One of those raised in isolation was tested at 10 months, and five raised in isolation were 2 years old when first given a prey. The latter were given chicks.

Those tested at the age of 5 months behaved as follows. If the rat remained motionless on the spot, the polecat approached slowly, sniffing with curiosity at the prey and touching it with the paws. Some licked or carefully tried to bite, but they did not attack. If the rat ran towards the polecat, the latter retreated. But as soon as the rat showed flight reactions by running away, the polecat attacked it vigorously, trying to grasp and bite it. It did not direct its attack towards a special part of the rat's body, as an experienced polecat does, but just bit into what it grasped, the tail, the shoulder or a leg. Then the rat immediately turned in defence, and the polecat, evidently surprised, released its grip, normally attacking again and again. The more anterior the hold on its prey, the more difficult was it for the latter to defend itself. If the polecat was successful in grasping the rat's neck, then it could kill the rat easily. The polecats learned the right grip quite rapidly. One killed its first prey within 20 seconds, with only three attacks. Others needed 1-15 minutes, depending on the behaviour of the rat. After having killed four to six rats, one each day, a polecat was a skilful hunter and its killing bite was always directed towards the neck of the prey. One female that was bitten by the rat showed fear and on the following 3 days, avoided the rat which had been left with her. The rat slept in the polecat's nest, which the polecat avoided. When awake the polecat restlessly ran up and down in the cage. On the fourth day it killed the rat. It became a good hunter from then on.

The one polecat tested at an age of 10 months got bitten too, and it avoided the rat even 1 month later. Unfortunately this polecat escaped.

There were no differences between the behaviour of those seven raised in isolation and that of those left with their litter mates. In both groups, the first attack was released by the fleeing prey, and both had to learn the correct orientation of the killing bite. There are, however, indications that those raised with litter-mates learned this orientation faster, probably as the result of experience while playing. Four succeeded within 1 minute.

The movements described above, such as shaking, killing bite and turning the prey on its back, were observed at the first encounter.

Five polecats, at 2 years of age, were confronted with young chicks of the domestic fowl. They were previously fed with dead chicks. Nevertheless, none of the experimental animals attacked the chicken as long as it did not move. They sniffed at it and only when it ran away did three of the polecats follow and grasp it. Two of them killed it within a few seconds by bites in its back, one that had not got a very good hold released the grip when the chicken started struggling, but killed it with the next bite. All three killed thereafter without hesitation, but they did not aim their bites towards the neck of the prey, very probably because these animals, not capable of self-defence, did not demand the development of a special killing technique. They were equally easily killed by bites in the back, side, chest, or neck.

The other two polecats also showed great interest in the chicken. They sniffed and licked it, meanwhile uttering the low sounds (muttering) that normally express readiness for social contact (Eibl-Eibesfeldt, 1955). After some minutes they turned away, but returned after a while to explore the chick again. When it tried to escape, both chased and caught it, but they showed a very strong inhibition to bite. They just seized the chicks, without causing injury, and carried them into their nesting box. After 5 hours the chicks were still alive there. I took them away. On each of the following 7 days I offered one chick to each of these polecats. During that time they were fed only with very little meat every third day. Until the fourth day, the behaviour of the polecats towards the chick remained nearly the same. After a short investigation they grasped the chick and carried it home, uttering the call of social contact. In one of the polecats a little hostility was observed on the third day; it hissed when it met the chick, but soon started muttering. On the fourth day I left the chicks with the polecats over night. Next morning polecat (*b*) had killed and partly eaten its chick, while the other chick was sitting in the warm nest without showing the slightest damage. A newly offered chick was attacked by the polecat, grasped in the neck but with inhibition to bite, and carried alive to the nest, where it was killed and eaten half an hour later. Polecat (*a*) however, hissed a little, then carried the new chick to its nest, where I found it still alive next morning. After I killed it, the hungry polecat immediately started eating. On the same afternoon, both were given chicks again; both carried them in alive. After 3 hours the chicks were found to be still alive. This time polecat (*a*) killed the chick during the night, whereas polecat (*b*) left it undamaged. The experiments are not finished yet.

The experiments have shown that learning plays an important role in the development of prey-hunting behaviour, but also that there are some important inborn reactions. What is learned is the orientation of the killing bite towards the neck of the prey, a learning process which takes place only if the prey proves difficult to kill otherwise. The polecat has, furthermore, to learn that a quietly sitting rat or chick is prey, even when it has eaten dead rats or chicks before. The first attack is released by a fleeing object, this reaction of chasing and biting fleeing prey is innate, as well as those behaviour patterns, like shaking or killing bite, described above. The inhibition of the two-year-old polecats to kill chicks is secondary and probably due to social frustration. I got the impression that the chicks became substitutes for a social companion.

The different evaluation of the results of the experiments by Kuo, Lehrmann, Riess and the author might first be due to the fact that the former were interested only in the final outcome of the experiments. They noted only: 'prey killed or not killed', 'retrieving or no retrieving', 'nest building or no nest building' but did not care very much about the behaviour of the animal in the test situation. If the author had followed the same line when studying the prey-killing behaviour of the polecat, he, too, would have come to the conclusion that this specific technique is learned, since the animals need several trials before killing efficiently. But the crucial point is that it does not need to learn the shaking movements and it does not need to learn to attack and grasp a fleeing object. If one observes the behaviour one finds that a number of movements are there from the moment the first reaction towards prey is released. Kuo's (1930) experiments on cats do not contradict our experiments, but simply fail to give information on certain important questions. The results of Riess, on the other hand, clearly contradict our observations, due to the fact that Riess made the methodological mistake of testing his animals in a surrounding strange to them. The immediate nest building of our inexperienced animals can hardly be explained by the learning hypothesis. How should our rats have learned that nesting material keeps the animal warm if collected and formed into a nest? And what taught the mother that newborn nestlings need to be covered with nesting material, and that straw has to be split?

3. DISCUSSION OF THE CONCEPTIONS

According to Lorenz (1952) fixed motor patterns are sequences of movements which can appear in an animal without previous exercise and experience. Presumably they are based on specific central nervous mechanisms, which are inherited in the same way as other morphological structures. The characteristics of fixed patterns are:

(1) They are constant in form.

(2) They are characteristic for the species.

(3) They appear in an animal reared in isolation from members of its own species.

(4) They develop even if the animal is prevented from exercising the behaviour pattern in question.

(5) They are hardly ever found in one species alone at least if closely related species are in existence, but are characteristic of taxonomic groups just as morphological characters are. Thus can they be used for taxonomic purposes, as has been shown by Heinroth (1911), Whitman (1919), Lorenz (1941) and others.

Our experiments have shown that in every case in which, on the basis of criteria gained by comparative observation alone, a sequence of movements was suspected of being a fixed pattern, the co-ordination in question appeared unchanged in the animal reared in a deprivation situation, used like a ready-made tool by the inexperienced animal. Conditioning determined the way of their application only (see also Eibl-Eibesfeldt, 1956b and Eibl-Eibesfeldt and Kramer, 1958).

Fixed patterns or instinctive movements as defined by Heinroth and Lorenz are therefore not a fiction as implied by the 'anti-instinctivists', but something real, and the distinction between innate and acquired is of analytical value. The learning psychologist who does not know what is genetically determined is in a position equivalent to a geneticist performing modification experiments on genetically unanalysed material. We know, of course, that we abbreviate, when we say a behaviour pattern is inherited or innate instead of saying that its anatomical and physiological conditions are. But there is no reason for not using the term this way, as long as we remain aware of the fact that characters always *develop* on the basis of an inherited range of variation, all the more if the range of modifiability is practically nil.

Although we do not know yet what a fixed pattern is, a number of investigations have made it highly probable that they share a common physiological basis. Besides the peculiarities already mentioned, the fixed pattern is characterized by a specific spontaneity (Lorenz, 1937), which may be hypothetically explained by the assumption of neural centres creating impulses. The spontaneous activity of the central nervous system has been demonstrated by von Holst (1935, 1936, 1937), first in the earthworm in which he discovered in the isolated ventral nerve cord salvos of rhythmical impulses, corresponding exactly to the contraction of segments in the normal creeping movements. Later von Holst found that even such highly complicated inborn motor patterns like swimming in fishes are based on a central nervous system automatism. Von Holst explains this spontaneity by the hypothesis that there are groups of cells in the CNS creating impulses. These groups of cells influence each other, leading to certain forms of co-ordinated movements.

Very little is known about the neuroanatomical basis for fixed patterns but the experiments of Hess (1948), Hess and Brugger (1943) and the recent investigations of von Holst and von St. Paul (1959) strongly indicate that fixed patterns are based on an inherited neurophysiological mechanism.

Experiments have shown that fixed patterns are released by certain key stimuli which characterize simply but unmistakably the biologically adequate situation, and release the behaviour pattern even in an inexperienced animal. In other words, besides the innate ability to perform certain movements, there is an innate ability to recognize (Lorenz, 1942).

Although our investigation concentrated on the motor patterns we found that a certain stimuli situation must be given to release nest building, retrieving and prey hunting. Ignorance of this caused all Riess's errors. Wild brown rats failed to build, not because they had less unlearned responses, but because they reacted only to more specific stimuli. They needed a more covered nesting site and when I offered them little tin huts they started to build under this cover.

4. THE VALUE OF THE DEPRIVATION EXPERIMENT

Lehrmann (1953) is right in his critique, when he says that in every deprivation experiment one has to answer the question: Of exactly what has the animal been deprived? But we cannot follow him to his conclusion, that all actual behaviour of an organism is determined by the animal's experience, the only inherited basis being the bodily structures determining potential behaviour. He, as well as Schneirla and Hebb, insists that it is practically impossible to prove that experiences during ontogeny are not at work. An animal might even learn *in utero* or in the egg. To elaborate this line of thought, Schneirla (1956) and Lehrmann (1956) define as experience any influence of external stimuli on development and behaviour. According to this definition even biochemical changes or stimuli arising from growth processes, as well as any kind of external stimulation, must be termed experience. Learning is only one form of it.

The way in which such experiences may enter development is explained by Schneirla and Lehrmann on the basis of Kuo's (1932) experiment with chicks. Kuo examined the ontogenesis of the food-pecking reaction in the domestic fowl. These animals are able to peck for small objects immediately after hatching, a behaviour which we would look at as innate. But Kuo observed that in the three-day old embryo the neck is bent passively as a result of the heartbeat, which lifts and lowers the animal's head resting on the chest. At the same time the head is stimulated tactually by the yolk sac, which is moved by contractions of the amnion that are synchronous with the heart beat. One day later, the chick reacts to external stimulation by bending its head actively, and at the same time it opens and closes its beak during nodding. According to Kuo, this is due to irradiation of the neural excitation caused by the nodding. At the age of 8 to 10 days, liquid, forced into the mouth by the head and beak movements, is swallowed. The movements get more and more stereotyped and the previously more independent head, bill and throat movements become integrated into one functional pattern. According to Kuo, this is due to learning. The first arousal of the animal by visual stimuli is explained by a diffusion of impulses from the optical region in the midbrain centres which previously released the discussed behaviour to tactile stimulation (Maier and Schneirla, 1935).

Lorenz (1958) objects that this hypothesis completely leaves out of consideration one fact of the greatest importance: 'All these structures of behaviour, whether they function on the receptor or on the motor side, are adapted to innumerable environmental data. Unless one assumes a mystical "prestabilized harmony" between the organism and its environment – which would be "preformationism" indeed, information concerning all these environmental data must, at some time, have been "fed into" the organism to make this adaptation possible. This acquisition of information can have occurred only in the interaction between the organism and its environment, either during the evolution of the species or during the ontogeny of the individual.'

To uphold the hypothesis that pecking is learned in the egg in the way suggested by Kuo one would have to make at least one of three assumptions:

'The first of these is that the heartbeat and the primarily independent swallowing movements just happen, by pure *chance*, to teach the chick motor co-ordinations that can later on be used in pecking up food. The second, equally impossible assumption is that there is a *preformed harmony* between what the chick learns inside the egg and the environment with which it is to be confronted later on. The third, improbable but not impossible, is that the heartbeat and the other conditions inside the egg, have, in the evolutionary interaction between the species and its environment, been developed into a highly specialized apparatus whose function it is to teach the chick just those well adapted motor co-ordinations. In other words, the attempt to avoid the assumption of genetically fixed movements saddles us with that of an equally genetically fixated teacher!' (Lorenz, 1958).

Once we have realized the adaptive character of a behaviour pattern, we can deprive the animal experimentally of the specific information concerning the data to which the behaviour is adapted. If the animal nevertheless shows the adaptive behaviour pattern in the test situation, then we call it innate, despite the fact that learning in the widest sense, e.g. exercise of single muscle units, might have played a role during the ontogeny of the individual. This does not explain why the behaviour pattern as a whole later fits the environment.

The distinction between innate and acquired behaviour patterns, there-fore, is not at all an artificial one. If a male salticid spider needed to learn by trial and error his complicated courtship display, which enables him to approach the cannibalistic female, he would get eaten before copula-tion. A newborn baby, unable to suckle, would starve before having learned the complicated pattern of movements. On the Galapagos Islands no carnivorous land mammal exists and therefore many of the endemic birds have lost their escape reaction. They are tame, with just a few exceptions. One such exception is the little endemic Galapagos Dove (*Nesopelia galapagoensis*) which shows 'injury feigning'. As soon as one approaches a nest with nestlings, the adult bird flutters from the nest to the ground. There it runs away from the nest, fluttering its widespread wings. This 'injury feigning' is well known in birds of other countries, where its function is to attract the attention of a predator and to lead him from the nest. But on Galapagos there are no carnivorous mammals, and the behaviour pattern is normally not used. It seems rather difficult, therefore, to explain this behaviour on the basis of the learning hypothesis. From where might the animal have gathered the information about predators, to which its behaviour is adapted? Since the information could not have been acquired during the ontogeny of the individual, the only remaining possibility is that this information was acquired by the species during the course of evolution, at a time when it was confronted with predators; this 'experience' must have been preserved in the genoma of the species. It appears in the Galapagos Dove as a behavioural relict.

In the normal behaviour of an animal, innate and acquired patterns are closely linked together into functional units, so that it is very often rather difficult to distinguish the two components from each other. Nevertheless, we can deprive an organism of special information and thereby prove that certain behaviour patterns are innate. Doves (Grohmann, 1939) and swallows (Spalding, 1873) for example have been reared under conditions that made it impossible for them to use their wings and practise flying movements. Upon being released, however, these animals were able to fly as well as their siblings, who had not been deprived of the opportunity to learn flying.

How independently from learning processes certain behaviour patterns develop, can also be seen in mallards reared in isolation. With the onset of sexual maturity they will show such highly differentiated movements as grunt whistle and head-up-tail-up, without ever having seen another mallard. If we raised a tufted drake or a mandarin drake under identical conditions we should observe them performing their species specific

F

courting. In short, those movements are inherited: they mature as part of normal development in each individual of the same species in an almost identical way. While this paper was under press I continued my investigation of the ontogeny of behaviour patterns in mammals. These will be described in detail in a later publication, but I should like to mention here one more example illustrating very well a behaviour pattern in a mammal which is extremely little influenced by learning. As is well known, squirrels (*Sciurus vulgaris* L.) hide nuts in holes which they dig in the ground. They deposit the nut, stamp it into the ground by repeated blows with the front of the upper incisors and afterwards cover the hole with earth by means of the forepaws. Squirrels raised in grill cages with powder food, by a procedure similar to that described in connection with the rat experiment, were given open nuts. After they had eaten some nuts these animals immediately began to search for a hiding place. With the nut between their teeth they moved over the ground, and wherever the nut met an obstacle they started to scratch as if digging a hole. In many instances they deposited the nut, banged it down with their teeth and finally made covering movements with the forepaws, as if covering the nut with earth, although in fact there was no earth. Only rarely is such a comparatively long chain of reactions innate in mammals. This behaviour of the squirrels was filmed and a detailed analysis will be presented in the near future.

Some drawbacks of the deprivation experiments have, nevertheless, to be considered. First of all, we must always keep in mind that an animal raised artificially may not show its normal behaviour. How easily an animal is disturbed under the conditions of captivity, is well known to every animal keeper. If certain behaviour patterns characteristic for the species under observation, do not appear in the deprivation experiment, this might be a result of disturbance and not of lack of information. Strictly speaking, the deprivation experiment is conclusive only in case of a positive result. If a specific behaviour pattern comes out despite the specific deprivation situation, we can say that it is a fixed pattern. But if it does not appear, it does not necessarily indicate that the animal needs to learn it. If we keep the animal in good health we may be able to avoid such disturbances. That a certain behaviour pattern does not appear in the experimental situation might, furthermore, be due to lack of the stimuli normally releasing it. To avoid this error a normally raised control animal must be tested under the same conditions as the experimental animal and the experimental animal must be confronted with the situation in which the behaviour pattern normally appears.

GROUP DISCUSSION

EIBL-EIBESFELDT. We saw that learning plays an important role in the integration of innate behavioural elements into a functional whole. If we study such learning processes, we find that many animals are capable of learning certain tasks very rapidly. These are supposed to be of biological importance to them. Is this rapid learning a specific talent based on central nervous structures adapted to that special task during evolution or is it due to a special high motivational pressure?

GALAMBOS. Dr Eibl-Eibesfeldt asks if this is the result of prime motivation or of a special adaptive mechanism. Would you please elaborate?

EIBL-EIBESFELDT. When I studied the prey-hunting behaviour in the common toad, I found that this animal, which normally does not learn very fast, learns rapidly to distinguish between palatable and unpalatable foods. If it gets stung by a wasp or if it receives unpalatable food it needs only very few experiences to avoid such prey in the future. Is this rapid learning based on specially adapted structures of the C.N.S. or is it just due to an especially high motivational pressure? Would they learn other tasks just as fast if a similar pressure was put on them? Are there experiments where animals learned the same tasks under different motivation?

OLDS. We have experiments where certain animals learned complicated and unusual behaviour patterns. We worked with rodents too. Provided the animal by its behaviour could turn on an electrical stimulus to the hypothalamus — the animal learned with great speed, provided the stimulus was in the right part of the hypothalamus. The same animal looked very stupid if we turned the stimulus down so that it was barely above threshold. This will be clarified later when I give my paper.

HEBB. I thought Dr Eibl-Eibesfeldt was disagreeing with the idea that there is any role of learning in the instinctive patterns of behaviour. The experiments he has described clearly support the idea that learning and the constitutional structure of the animal collaborate closely, and that we are not dealing with two different and totally unrelated sorts of processes. We must not distinguish instinctive processes from processes influenced by experience.

It is my impression that we have agreement in principle on the question. I have not talked to Riess, but I am sure that Lehrmann would not disagree with any of your propositions today. It would be ridiculous to suppose today that there are no innate mechanisms, no laid-down patterns of response. What I add, reinforced by your paper, is that those laid-down patterns are what are modified by the effects of experience. In some animals little modification, in others much. The lower animal particularly is built to learn a few things and he learns them quickly. If this is the essence of the notion of instinct, this and the tendency to act in certain directions, I suggest that man's behaviour also is essentially instinctive. We are so conscious of individual differences that we do not see the extraordinary uniformities that occur through all human cultures.

EIBL-EIBESFELDT. If you read Lehrmann's paper you will see that he does not agree with all these concepts. There are certain behaviour patterns which are innate in the sense that they develop in the animal without certain types of learning being involved. We do not imply that experience plays no role at all. Lehrmann has defined experience as every impact of external stimuli on the development of behaviour, formative processes and so on. We agree that all these can influence behaviour, but behaviour is adapted to certain environmental situations. There are two possibilities to explain such an adaptation: during evolution of a species, or by learning during the ontogeny of the individual. And wherever we find that such highly adapted behaviour comes out in the animal in spite of complete lack of previous knowledge of the specific stimulus situation to which its behaviour is adapted, we speak of innate behaviour. If a male spider would need to learn its complicated courtship postures it would get eaten by the female. When a male mallard raised in isolation still shows its highly complicated courtship postures at sexual maturity it demonstrates innate behaviour, in spite of the fact that the animal might have learned something in addition to it. How our opponents argue is demonstrated in Kuo's paper. He observed that in the chick embryo the head rests on the heart and is lifted with every heartbeat. Thus nodding movements, a part of the later pecking behaviour — get induced. Later nodding becomes integrated with the previously independent swallowing movements into food-pecking behaviour which every newly hatched chick shows. Our opponents express the opinion that this behaviour was learned within the egg. (A detailed discussion is given in my paper.)

HEBB. No.

EIBL-EIBESFELDT. Yes they do. Concluding from this and similar experiments they say there is no innate motor pattern: everything is learned.

HEBB. There is no support for that extreme view. My disagreement is with the dichotomy you made earlier, between learned behaviour and instinctive behaviour.

THORPE. I agree with Dr Eibl-Eibesfeldt on this. Dr Lehrmann does not now take this view, but he certainly did appear to do so at one time. I am glad that he seems now to have come round to what I believe is the only reasonable position to take. With birds you get the same sort of thing, in regard to this interlacement of learned and innate behaviour patterns. It depends on the group as to how big these innate chunks of behaviour are. In the mammal they are small and as you go down the zoological scale they become larger, and they may be very large in insects or spiders. One other point I would like to mention is that these experiments on birds give clear evidence that the learning is too selective to be 'motivational' in this sense. A theory which relies mainly on a supposed change in the general motivational level would not carry us very far in explaining this type of learning in birds.

EIBL-EIBESFELDT (Added later): I can confirm Dr Thorpe's statement that Dr Lehrmann does not take this extreme view now. I discussed the matter with him in Cambridge at the Ethological Conference.

GRASTYÁN. I would like to know in more exact terms what is meant when you say that the animal learns quickly — How many trials?

EIBL-EIBESFELDT. It has to kill four or five rats to learn how to kill.

GRASTYÁN. If it cannot kill the first time, what happens in the next trial?

EIBL-EIBESFELDT. He tries again. If he receives a punishment stimulus, he learns faster.

GRASTYÁN. What happens if you work with a satiated animal?

EIBL-EIBESFELDT. It kills anyway. It was shown by Kuo that in cats the satiation has no influence on hunting behaviour. I still would like to ask why Dr Hebb feels that it is not justified to speak of instincts as innate behaviour in contrast to a learned response?

HEBB. My objection to 'instinct' is that it refers to a mechanism which is distinct from what enters into normal learning processes.

EIBL-EIBESFELDT. But there are differences, for example, in the physiology of these innate patterns. I would like to mention their spontaneity. Furthermore they are often released by certain key stimuli — innately. All this shows that we are justified in distinguishing innate and acquired behaviour patterns.

HEBB. The argument against that is exactly the evidence that you have in your paper. You show how closely the two collaborate. The implication of a separate mechanism is that some behaviour is controlled by instinct, some by intelligence and learning. It seems to me that it is all intelligence or all instinct. The higher species has a wider range of situation to which it can adapt, innately. The operation of intelligence and learning is within the scope of the innate aptitude. In certain cases we see the deviation from the species pattern clearly, and call that learning. But learning also operates in the things which are characteristic of the species. My objection to instinct as a term is the suggestion that we have two different kinds of mechanism controlling behaviour.

GERARD. There is a continuity from growth, through heredity, prebirth experience, to youth and ageing experience. Only in the fertilized egg have you heredity — from then on, the chromosome pattern interacts with its surroundings. If we find it useful to separate innate reflexes from conditioned reflexes, it is not meaningless to try and distinguish other different levels; some higher level reflexes common to the species we may call instinctive. What really matters in any given situation is whether the variance normally introduced by the environmental experience of the individual is relatively important compared with the variance introduced by the past experience of the race and put in the genes.

The most interesting aspect is the adaptive one, for example, the rats building nests to keep their young warm. The pattern seems innate, but the execution of the details of the pattern is clearly learned.

As an illustration of the innate character, the behaviour pattern should cease if a non-adaptive situation is brought about. For example, if you put the rat in a hot room, where the young might become overheated would it still make a nest?

EIBL-EIBESFELDT. Kinder (1927) has studied the influence of temperature on the nest-building activity of the rat. If it gets too warm, the animal stops nest-building. But that this behaviour is controlled by temperature and thus variable to a certain extent does not prove that it is not innate in the way pointed out in my paper. Pregnant rats, by the way, are less easily influenced by temperature, because of the secretion of progesterone.

GERARD. A negative result does not disprove it but if you have an instance when an animal does a complex act despite the harmful effects, it would be a strong case.

EIBL-EIBESFELDT. May I mention two examples. Turkey cocks have a highly ritualized way of fighting with rivals. They do not jump in the air and hit their opponent with the spurs, as other gallid birds do, but wrestle with their necks, grasping each other at the bill. As soon as one wants to give up it assumes a submissive posture, by lying down on the floor. In captivity it can happen that a turkey cock and a peacock get involved in a fight. Both closely related species have a similar display and therefore understand the expression movements of the preliminary display. But their techniques of fighting do not fit together. While the turkey cock expects wrestling the peacock hits him with his spurs. This leads to submissive posture in the turkey cock but the peacock unable to 'understand' continues fighting and the more he beats the turkey cock the more the latter gets latched in the mechanism of the submissive posture. He does not run away and often a fatal end results. Another example of innate behaviour misleading in artificial circumstances normally not occurring in nature is the light orientation of many insects which leads them to circle around lamps and burn to death.

Concerning the previous remark of Dr Hebb, I want to add that he himself speaks of how closely 'the two' collaborate, referring to innate and acquired patterns. Evidently he makes a distinction and only avoids the terms innate and acquired. We use them as we feel a need to distinguish those behaviour patterns which show adaptedness to specific environmental situations without the animal having experienced this situation before, from those behaviour patterns which are learned by the animal by active communication with the environment during ontogeny. We do not know if they are based on two different kinds of mechanisms and our term does not imply it. It is probable but still needs to be analysed. The separation of both by experiment is a first step towards such an analysis.

LISSÁK. The other side of the question is the humoral or hormonal background. May I mention that well-known experiment of Richter and the mouse-killing or frog-killing test of the lactating animal. The maternal aggressivity can be avoided by a simple injection of oestrone or by destroying the amygdalate. I suppose that the hormonal afferentation must have a very important role in such aggressiveness or killing experiments.

EIBL-EIBESFELDT. There exists a paper published by Koller some years ago, dealing with the hormonal control of nest-building behaviour.

LISSÁK. His method is very convenient for studying the humoral mechanism too.

MAGOUN. Are physiologists making an effort to identify activity of the C.N.S. associated with such behaviour?

EIBL-EIBESFELDT. Dr von Holst studied brain mechanism by stimulating certain areas in the brain of the domestic fowl — and he released several highly complicated behaviour patterns. He will present a paper at Cambridge in September.

THORPE. I would like to comment on one aspect which seems important in this question of learned and instinctive: that is the complexity of the stimulation to which the animal is exposed. If a bird is raised in a sound-proof room and it sings a normally elaborate song we are justified in saying that this is innate because there is no corresponding complexity in the environmental situation to which the bird is exposed which could have called forth the behaviour. One must assume that any observed complexity must come from somewhere; in this case from the animal itself. If on the other hand you can find a sufficient complexity in the sensory input to which the animal has been exposed you are inclined to put it down to the account of experience. This is a very important fundamental distinction between the two points of view. The essential point is the origin of complexity in behaviour. In so many examples of animal behaviour environmental stimuli may be acting as triggers to set off complex behaviour patterns but they are not such that they can be regarded as the full 'cause of the behaviour; the complex adjustment of it *must* be sought elsewhere and in such circumstances we are fully justified in regarding it as internal and in labelling the behaviour as innate.

HEBB. To add to the question asked by Dr Magoun, I think that it is relevant to mention the extensive neurological investigations by Beach made on instinctive patterns in the rodent. Instinct in behaviour depends on the cortex, and there is a close correlation between problem-solving capacity and sex behaviour in the male, and problem-solving capacity and maternal behaviour in the female.

REFERENCE

Lorenz, K. (1937) Über die Bildung des Instinktbegriffes. *Die Naturwiss.* 25, 289-300, 307-18, 324-31.

SOME CHARACTERISTICS OF THE EARLY LEARNING PERIOD IN BIRDS[1]

W. H. Thorpe

In the last 3 or 4 years much new work on the early learning period in birds has been accomplished so I propose in today's talk to attempt to survey some of these recent advances and to consider what lines of investigation now appear to be the most promising. I also wish to discuss the relation of modern developments in the study of bird learning to the general body of knowledge and theory concerning the flexible and individually adaptable behaviour of animals.

The acquisition of new actions and the development of skills by the process of trial and error learning has recently been the subject of a good deal of investigation. A type of behaviour which is particularly convenient for detailed analysis of this kind is the feeding technique shown by a number of species of birds, particularly tits (*Paridae*), when presented with a piece of food suspended by a thread. Individuals of many species of birds will sooner or later learn to pull up the food, the pulled-in loop being held by the foot whilst the bird reaches with its beak for the next pull. In goldfinches (*Carduelis carduelis*) at least this behaviour has been known from time immemorial. Goldfinches are so adept at the trick that they have for centuries been kept in special cages so designed that the bird can subsist only by pulling up and holding tight two strings, that on one side being attached to a little cart containing food and resting on an incline, and that on the other a thimble containing water. The keeping of birds in this type of cage was so widespread in the sixteenth century that it gave rise to the name 'draw-water', or its equivalent, in two or three European languages. Nor was this type of aviculture restricted to Europe. Dr Dillon Ripley tells me that *Parus varius* in Japan is kept as a cage bird and is taught many fancy tricks, such as the solving of little puzzles, running a betting bank, and pulling up strings. No doubt all of these depend upon trial and error learning of the kind described.

Those of us who have seen this kind of performance by wild birds at a bird table, as can so easily be done with the great and blue tits (*P. major*

---

[1] Part of this work has been published in *Nature*, **182**, 554-7, 1958, and part in *Ibis*, **101**: 337-353, 1959. Full references will be found in these two papers and in "*Current Problems of Animal Behaviour*" ed. W. H. Thorpe and O. L. Zangwill, Camb. Univ. Press, 1960.

and *P. caeruleus*) in Britain, can hardly have failed to have been impressed by the smooth easy certainty with which the complete act is accomplished. Under these conditions one seldom sees anything so suggestive of trial and error learning. On the contrary, the act appears at first sight to be a real and sudden solution of the problem from the start, as if the bird, before responding to the string at all, had seen the answer to the problem, and as if its behaviour was the planned result of this insight. But when one comes to investigate the development of such behaviour in the individual, one gets a very different picture. Far from it being a smooth and easy response, one finds instances of birds which learn with extreme slowness and difficulty, acquire some part of the response only to lose the ability again, or get to a certain point in the acquisition of the trick and are unable to complete the learning.

One point that emerges clearly, however, is that it is much easier — other things being equal — for a bird to take food from a short string than a long one; and that an essential stage in the training of birds to feed by pulling up strings is to get them to take food from a short string, say 2 inches long, where the seed is reached without the necessity of actually pulling in the string. Once this has been achieved, the problem posed by an increase of length to $2\frac{1}{2}$ inches, which must then be pulled in before the seed can be eaten, is a relatively easy one; although it of course immediately brings in a new movement, that of holding the string. Once the string has been held and the bait secured in this manner, a gradual increase in the length of string can very often be made without causing the bird any great further difficulties or setbacks.

Preliminary observations at the Madingley Field Station for the study of Animal Behaviour, Cambridge University, with captive wild-caught and hand-reared tits and finches, gave puzzling irregularities, uncertainties and differences in individual and specific behaviour. It was clear that many more factors were coming into the process of acquiring this rather striking new feeding technique on the part of the birds and that a careful experimental study of it might be expected to give results not merely of interest to the ornithologist, but of wide application to problems of animal learning in general; and possibly even to bear on problems of human learning. Miss M. A. Vince of the Cambridge Department of Experimental Psychology and of the Madingley Field Station accordingly took up this study which, although far from complete, has already yielded results of remarkable interest (Vince, 1956-59 and in press). First experiments with adult wild-caught great tits showed that the bird's first response to the experimental set-up was to keep away from it, but that with further trials the bird's positive response to bait and/or string tended to increase over a period of time. Subsequently the bird's response to both might tend to decrease and even birds which were learning well, or in which the string-pulling habit had been completely mastered, might be set back, or the habit lost, when the experimental situation was changed or the bird was moved to a new cage.

Further tests, not only with wild and hand-reared blue and great tits but also with greenfinches (*Chloris chloris*), chaffinches (*Fringilla coelebs*) and canaries (*Serinus c. canarius*), have thrown a good deal of light on what is evidently a very complex situation. It seems clear that juvenile birds tend to be superior to adults in the string-pulling situation and that this success can be correlated with the amount of time spent responding to the string and/or the bait. This amount of time responding could be due to a higher level of activity, and in tasks requiring a high level of activity (requiring, in fact, large persistence and many trials) juveniles — which are at their maximum of exploratory activity at about 13 weeks — are likely to be more efficient than adults. But positive response is not the whole of learning, and in such a task as string-pulling it is necessary also for the bird to learn to *refrain* from responding to situations in which reinforcement is absent or withdrawn. This ability to refrain is, as Vince shows, dependent on something similar to what Pavlov called internal inhibition.[1] It is weak in very young birds, develops as a result of age, and as a result of experience during the juvenile stage, is still being strengthened at an age when positive responsiveness is well past its peak and later weakens slightly again. Consequently tasks which depend less on the level of activity, and more on the ability to control behaviour by precisely timed inhibition are more likely to be mastered quickly and efficiently by older birds than by younger ones. Other experiments in which great tits were required to obtain food by opening dishes covered with white lids and refrain from opening dishes covered with black lids gave further confirmation of this view. These studies also suggest that internal inhibition is unstable in young birds and that the process of development from the unstable type of inhibition found in younger birds to the more stable type found in older birds, depends not only upon age but also on experience.

In another experiment, great tits were first trained to feed from a blue dish. When they had become habituated to the blue dish, a white

---

[1] A full discussion of the relationship between Habituation and Internal Inhibition would be out of place here; those interested will find it dealt with at some length in my book (Thorpe, 1956, 57-62).

cardboard lid was placed over it. The number of trials (i.e. the reinforced or training trials) needed for the consistent removal of the white lid was then recorded. Unreinforced trials consisted of empty dishes with black lids. When hand-reared birds were compared in this test with wild-reared ones caught as juveniles over a period of 8-20 weeks after fledging, both groups showed internal inhibition (indicated by the ability to refrain from removing the black lid) rising as a function of age and later falling slightly. But there are indications that a richer and more varied experience may change the slope of the curve, giving a sharper rise to a higher level. It seems as if, at any rate in this experimental situation, richness of early experience is an important factor in contributing to the perfect mastery of a task. Thus in a task primarily requiring superabundant activity (as, for instance, does maze learning, where a large number of different cues have to be investigated), younger animals are more likely to excel. On the other hand, a task which requires activity directed to a particular feature of the environment may well be learned better by older animals. Both these features are shown in the studies of bird learning which I have been describing.

To sum up, there are four aspects of development which have emerged from such experiments. Firstly, there is the question of responsiveness; this appears, in the hand-reared great tit, to increase with age and then decrease. Secondly, there are changes in a different type of responsiveness, namely habituation or internal inhibition. Here again there appears to be a rise and also probably a slight subsequent fall with age, but the rates of the first and second changes may be quite different, and so the variation in these two factors could well give rise to the puzzling differences in learning ability which the earlier experiments revealed. Thirdly, there is the question of the hunger drive. The birds in this work were kept under conditions such that approximately the same measure of food deprivation was experienced by all. Fourthly, the effects of early experience or environment on behaviour are clearly shown and it seems that internal inhibition may develop more rapidly and more completely in a more varied environment, presumably as a result of greater activity, greater stimulation and perhaps greater opportunity for adaptation and so on. It is plausibly assumed that aviary rearing is a richer experience than hand-rearing and that rearing in the wild is a richer experience still.

Imprinting. The phenomenon of imprinting is now so well known to the student of bird behaviour that a definition is hardly necessary. Recent experiments have confirmed that the period during which young birds can first learn to follow moving objects is strictly limited. But once a bird has learnt to follow models, the ability to transfer from one type to another can be demonstrated in birds as young as 3 days and as old as 60 days; although when first presented with a new model they will show a slight initial diminution in response, indicating that they perceive a difference and that the new model is not at first quite as acceptable as the old. With coot and moorhen, Hinde, Thorpe and Vince (1956) found that in the early days of life the following-response is stronger than the tendency (which is also present) to flee from strange objects. The result is that, in the course of the following experiments, the younger bird gets used to a number of strange objects and so its fleeing tendency is weakened by habituation. But the bird's response is always ambivalent in some degree and later the fleeing drive becomes stronger, and more difficult to habituate; and consequently, with age, a strange object becomes less likely to elicit following. In the coot, practically all the waning of a following response with age can be attributed to this growth in the fleeing drive and in these species no evidence was forthcoming for any permanent effect able to influence instinctive behaviour patterns which are to mature later. In some species, however, including some duck such as the mallard (Weidmann, 1955, 1958) and also geese, there seems little doubt that the termination of the imprinting period cannot be due solely to the development of a competing fleeing drive but there that is an internally controlled waning of the tendency to follow, independent of the development of fear responses (Jaynes, 1957).

It is clear that, in the kind of experiment which I have just described, the following-reponse can be said in some way to be 'its own reward'. All that the bird is doing in the first instance is giving rein to a need to maintain itself by its own efforts in constant spatial relationship with a moving object. This moving object can be almost anything which is not too large or too small, and which does not move too fast or too slowly.

To sum up this work on imprinting to visual stimuli, we can say tentatively that the imprinting period is initiated primarily by the maturation of an internally motivated, appetitive behaviour system which is in readiness, at the time of hatching or very soon after, to express itself in the following-response. The time during which this internally controlled tendency can find its *first* expression in action is limited, to a matter of a few hours or at most days, by internal factors; but during this time the response is ready to appear as soon as the circumstances permit it to do so. The termination of the ability to make that first response is, as we have seen, very largely influenced by the development of competing fleeing responses. Nevertheless, the evidence remains very strong that, in some species at least, an internal change directly reduces the appetitive following-drive with age. Conversely, once the following-behaviour has had a chance to establish itself, it will continue towards those models which have become associated with the achievement of the consummatory situation resulting from successful following, and may be yet further generalized to others.

It is clear that the broad nature of the stimulus to which following animals respond represents a difference only of degree from other instinctive responses, especially those of young animals. Not only does the following-tendency itself become primed through exercise and so more firmly established, but the following gives opportunity for the animal to become conditioned in various ways to the characteristics of the object which has elicited the response in the first place.

Imprinting can occur in response not only to visual stimuli but to auditory ones also. Thus an animal with an initially weak tendency to respond to both objects and sounds within a wide range may learn to pay attention to, and ultimately to follow, certain sounds which have been associated with the visual stimuli first releasing the following response. This may work both ways. Auditory stimuli may be conditioned to visual characteristics of the object, and vice versa. The recent studies of Dr Klopfer at Madingley and in the United States have given particularly good examples of this. In the first place certain surface-nesting species of waterfowl, chiefly mallard and redhead (*Aythya americana*), were examined and it was found that they were able to learn appropriate sound-signals involved in the maintenance of the brood-parent relationship as a consequence of visual imprinting. No unlearned preferences for any particular auditory signals seem to exist; they tended to approach most rhythmic repetitive signals without distinguishing between them. Nor could auditory imprinting to a particular one occur in the absence of visual stimulation. When Dr Klopfer came to investigate the wood duck (*Aix sponsa*) which is a hole-nesting species, the situation was found to be reversed: they did not initially tend to approach the repetitive signals, but exposure to a sound signal alone could produce a subsequent preference for that sound, thus demonstrating auditory imprinting. Further, the imprinted response was not reinforced or altered in any way by following or by a visual stimulus. This fact can be explained by the nesting habit of wood ducks, which require that the young duckling's first response to the mother be based on auditory stimuli. In surface-nesting birds, visual cues can play a larger role from the start, and thus assume paramount importance. The quackless muscovy duck (*Cairina moschata*) was shown to be incapable of auditory learning under the conditions of the experiment, and this striking failure in a species whose wild ancestors are closely related to the wood duck is supposed to be a consequence of domestication. Klopfer (1959) then studied the following-responses of European shelduck (*Tadorna tadorna*). Young of the species hatched and reared in sound-proof rooms showed no tendency to approach repetitive sound signals when tested at 18-26 hours of age. In this they were similar to wood ducks and domestic muscovies, and unlike any species of surface-nesting water-fowl. However, with the shelduck, exposure to repetitive sound signals in early life produced no change in the response pattern, whereas in the wood duck it did so. Nevertheless, associating the sound signals with an object or person which the ducklings were allowed to follow for short periods enabled a highly specific preference for sound to be developed, and in this shelducks resembled several species of surface-nesting waterfowl, particu-larly of the genus *Anas*. Of course this work does not prove that there are no sounds to which these birds would respond in the absence of visual and motor experience, but it does appear that a preference can be established for sounds which are linked to a visual model. As in the surface-nesters, one can suppose that the following-response serves as a necessary rein-forcement in the learning of particular sound signals. Thus the behaviour of the young shelduck does not show the pattern which would seem to be most appropriate for hole-nesting species, for whom auditory stimuli should be of much greater importance than visual ones. Moreover, hole-nesting species should either be endowed with response tendencies to specific auditory stimuli at the time of hatching, or else highly susceptible to auditory imprinting. That, for instance, seems to be true of the wood duck. It would thus seem likely that newly hatched shelducks emerge from their burrows in response to visual or perhaps tactile stimuli, with auditory cues assuming a secondary importance. The fact that shelduck will nest in thickets above ground when burrows are not readily available also suggests a possible explanation for this difference in behaviour. Here is an interesting opportunity for a field investigation which will be essential before the whole matter can be completely understood.

In nidicolous birds this particular type of following-response cannot, of course, operate. Nevertheless there is in certain song birds good evidence for something very suggestive of imprinting in the process of learning characteristic song, and indeed the vocalizations of birds can be regarded as offering particularly crucial problems concerning the acquisition of complex behaviour patterns as a result of individual learning.

The normal song of the chaffinch is an elaborate integration of inborn and learned components, the former constituting the basis for the latter.

A good example of a normal song of *Fringilla coelebs gengleri* is given in Fig. 1. The inborn component of the chaffinch song can be revealed by hand-rearing the young birds from early nestling life either in acoustic isolation or at least out of contact with all chaffinch song. Six birds thus individually isolated produced songs of an extremely simple type (Figs. 2-4) consisting of a song-burst of approximately the correct length (2-2.5 seconds) made up of about the right number of notes. The pitch, or fundamental frequency, of these notes was somewhat lower than normal and the songs produced by these isolates lacked the division into the three phrases so characteristic of the normal chaffinch song. Moreover, the final flourish and all the other fine details by which the chaffinch song is normally recognized as such were also absent. Of all the hundreds of wild and aviary-kept birds which have passed through our hands during the course of these experiments, none has produced songs of such extreme simplicity as these six birds, although such undeveloped songs are known to occur in the wild at times.

In contrast to the simple, restricted song produced by the isolated birds, we find that if, after babyhood, two or more such birds are put together in a room but still without the opportunity of hearing experienced chaffinches, they will develop more complex songs. It seems that the attempt to sing in company produces mutual stimulation which encourages the development of complexity. The members of each group of hand-reared birds thus kept together will, by mutual stimulation, build up a distinctive community pattern. The birds conform so closely to this pattern that it is sometimes barely possible to distinguish the songs one from another even by electronic analysis. The song of such birds may be quite as complex as that of a normal wild chaffinch, but its complexity tends to be of a different kind and a song thus produced may bear little resemblance to the characteristic utterances of the species. From further experiment it is clear that, in the wild, young chaffinches learn some features of the song from their male parents or from other adults during the first few weeks of life. But most of the finer details of the song are learned by the young bird when, in its first breeding season, it first comes to sing in competition with neighbouring territory-holders. There is little doubt that this is the way in which local song dialects are built up and perpetuated. In addition to this true song, the chaffinch, like many other species, has what has been called a sub-song, which is a much quiet and less aggressive affair than is the full song. It is, however, not merely a song of low intensity: it is of an entirely different pattern from the true song and

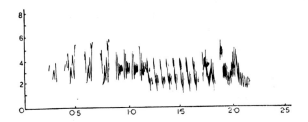

FIG. 1

'Normal' song of British chaffinch (*Fringilla coelebs gengleri*) Vertical scale: frequency in kc./s. Horizontal scale: time in seconds (Similarly Figs. 2-11).

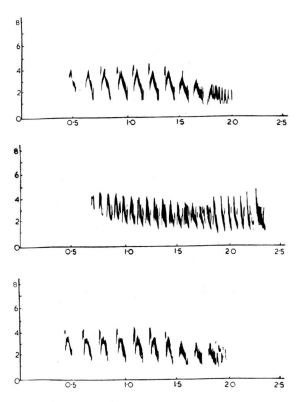

FIGS. 2-4

Song of three hand-reared isolates. GW, June 24th, 1954; B/BkY, May 25th, 1957; and BkW/W, June 24th, 1955.

G

may be described as a long succession of chirps and rattles (Thorpe, 1955, 1958; Thorpe and Pilcher, 1958). It seems to have no communicatory function and is most frequently heard in the early spring, when it is produced, so far as we know, much more by first-year birds than by older ones — the latter seeming to come into full song with much less of this preliminary sub-song. There seems little doubt, however, that the sub-song provides in some degree the raw material out of which, by practice and by the elimination of unwanted extremes of frequency, the full song is 'crystallized'. The chaffinch has, of course, like other species, a number of call notes which are in the main signals for co-ordinating the behaviour of the flock, mate and family; some of these may be used as components of both sub-song and full song. It is interesting that call notes are much more in evidence as components of the songs of isolated birds than they are in the songs of normal ones. This is presumably because the isolated birds have had a greatly restricted auditory experience to draw upon as compared with normal wild individuals.

Chaffinches are not imitative birds, in that they do not normally copy anything but sounds of chaffinch origin. Once a chaffinch has heard a chaffinch song as a young bird in the wild, it appears to have learned enough about it to refuse to copy any sound pattern which departs far from the normal chaffinch song; that is, it will learn only the finer individual variations of the song of other chaffinches. So, in the wild, chaffinches practically never, in their full songs, imitate anything but other chaffinches. Hand-reared isolated birds will learn songs of far greater abnormality, however, provided always that the tonal quality is not too far different from that of a chaffinch song. Voices as 'abnormal' as that of a domesticated canary may be learned by hand-reared birds (Thorpe, 1955), and very occasionally by wild birds; but when this happens the alien notes are kept as components of the non-communicative sub-song only; the full song is not contaminated with them.

If one catches wild chaffinches in their first autumn and keeps them until the following spring with other chaffinches, the song of which is already fixed, one gets clear evidence that the young birds have modelled their songs, in some respects at least, on those of their associates, which have probably come into song first as the spring season comes on, and which they thus hear before they themselves have got very far along the path of song production. Similarly, if, instead of exposing such wild-caught first-year birds to the songs of other chaffinches, one plays such songs to them by means of a repeating tape machine which we may call a 'song tutor', a clear positive effect is manifest. An experiment carried out in 1954-55 with four wild-caught birds given such tuition in the winter (January 6th-20th) and with three birds similarly treated in February-March showed clearly the effect of the 'song tutor', there being correct articulation of the phrases and a good approximation in pitch and quality. although there were abnormalities in length and emphasis. If, however, under these conditions one exposes the young birds to highly abnormal songs, no result is obtained. Thus in experiments in 1955-56 such birds were given tuition with a reversed chaffinch song during March. The fact that no definite effect was obtained suggested that enough of the song had

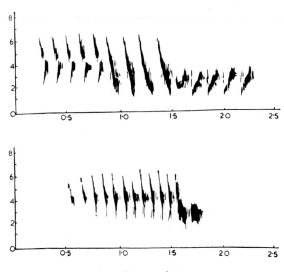

FIGS. 5 and 6
Two sons of a hand-reared auditory isolate after having been exposed to normal song on the 'song tutor' for 10 days only during November of its first year. GY/BW, April 24th, 1956.

already been learned in the autumn for the reversed song to be ineffective even with visually isolated birds. In 1956-57 a similar experiment was done using six wild-caught autumn males and exposing them in this case not to a reversed song, which was thought to be perhaps too abnormal, but instead to three different 're-articulated' songs (these are songs in which the position of the three phrases has been interchanged). In this experiment the birds were isolated in a sound-proof room. Two birds had exposures in September and October, repeated in January, two had exposures in mid- to late-October and late January and early February, and two were similarly exposed in November and February. On the whole, this experiment also had little effect, confirming the tests with the reversed song and suggesting even more strongly that the natural training which the bird had already received by the time it has reached the first winter moult has equally been sufficient to prevent it from learning after-

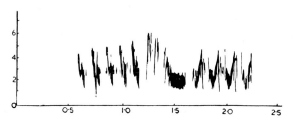

FIG. 7
Re-articulated model with 'end in middle'.

wards the rather large abnormalities characteristic of these re-articulated songs.

When we come to similar experiments with hand-reared birds, very different results are obtained. It was found that a hand-reared visual isolate can be taught features of a normal song from the tape by being exposed to it during November only of its first winter for a period of 10 days. Figs. 5

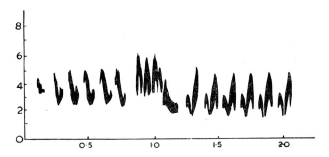

FIG. 8
Song of hand-reared auditory isolate B/BkP after having been exposed to this model for 12 days January–February and 12 days February–March. March 25th, 1958.

and 6 give the two songs developed in 1956 by such a bird treated in 1955. The first song shows clearly the influence of the 'tutor' in that it has three phrases otherwise unknown in the hand-reared isolate, having a clear stepwise descent but no end-phrase. The second song is of the isolate type plus two end-notes. These experiments thus produce evidence that tutoring, even for a short period in November, can effect the same kind of result as the normal song experience of a wild bird in the field during the autumn. Similar positive results were obtained in similar experiments with re-articulated songs carried out in 1956-57 and 1957-58. Figs. 7 and 8 show such a re-articulated model and its effect on the song of a hand-reared isolate. Hand-reared birds show similar differences from the wild-caught ones, in that if given a reversed song a considerable amount of copying is achieved. Similar experiments with other birds provide further evidence for a previous conclusion that although a hand-reared isolate is incapable by itself of producing anything approximating to a normal ending, yet if once it hears a normal end-flourish on the 'song tutor' (even though in the rearticulated song on the tape it occurs at the beginning or in the middle of the song) it will recognize it as appropriate for an ending and will attempt to place it properly in its own song.

In experiments in 1954-55 an attempt was made to indoctrinate hand-reared isolate chaffinches with the song of the tree pipit (*Anthus trivialis*) (Fig. 9), this being chosen because the spectrograph reveals that the tonal quality of the notes is similar to that of the chaffinch. The first experiment gave a doubtful result, but a repeat in 1956 resulted (Fig. 10) in the achievement of a remarkably good copy by such a chaffinch of the song of the tree pipit, producing a chaffinch song entirely unlike any other uttered in my experience by a wild or hand-reared bird. It is of interest to note that the rather long song of the model has been condensed to conform to the standard length of chaffinch song by condensing the middle phrase of the tree pipit song to two notes instead of four. This song became still further 'tightened up' and shortened by the beginning of May (Fig. 11).

The reason why chaffinches do not imitate and acquire songs from other species in the wild now seems fairly evident. There is little doubt that they restrict their imitativeness to the right models as a result of being responsive only to notes of approximately the right tonal quality. It is interesting that the imitation of the tree pipit song just referred to is the best copy of an alien song so far obtained. Here the tonal quality of the model was right, although the song itself was much too long and the phrasing of the notes of the model abnormal from a chaffinch point of view.

To summarize this work with the 'song tutor', it can be said that in eleven experiments carried out over the years 1955-57 and involving thirty-four wild autumn-caught first-year males, the only positive effect obtained (in the sense of a significant similarity between model and mimic) occurred in two experiments (seven birds) only, and in these two the model was a normal chaffinch song. Of the remaining ones (nine experiments, twenty-seven birds) the models were always abnormal — the songs being artificial, re-articulated or reversed — and the results were always negative. The contrast when hand-reared isolated birds are used is

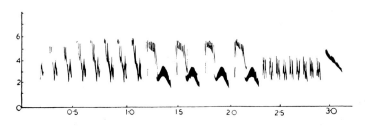

FIG. 9
Song of Continental tree pipit (*Anthus trivialis*) used for tutoring.

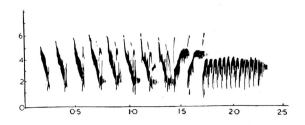

FIG. 10
'Copy' of tree pipit song produced by chaffinch R/R after tuition on 'song tutor'. April 21st, 1956.

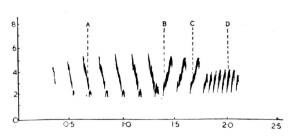

FIG. 11
'Improved' tree pipit copy. R/R, May 3rd, 1956.

striking. Thus during 1954-59, thirteen experiments involving sixteen hand-reared birds were carried out using similar song models. Of these, ten experiments (eleven birds) were positive, in the sense of yielding a significant effect. The remaining three experiments (five birds) gave a negative result.

The counter-singing that occurs between birds in adjacent territories is an important factor in stimulating and restricting the imitative abilities of chaffinches. When a chaffinch has acquired more than one song-type, each song-burst consists of a sequence of one song-type followed by a sequence of another. When songs are played back to a chaffinch, we find that those songs which it uses most frequently itself are the most effective in evoking song (Hinde, 1958). A chaffinch in the wild will thus tend to reply to a neighbour with that song of its own repertoire which most nearly resembles the song of its rival.

It is suggested that, with the more 'imitative' finches, such as the bull-finch (*Pyrrhula pyrrhula*), hawfinch (*Coccothraustes coccothraustes*) and to some extent greenfinch (*Chloris chloris*), the song, while functional in co-ordinating the breeding cycle and behaviour of the mated pair, is of less importance as a territorial proclamation. Thus in some respects it re-sembles the sub-song rather than the full song of the chaffinch; similarly, contamination with alien notes can be tolerated to an extent which might be very disadvantageous in a strongly territorial song that must maintain its character as a reliable specific recognition mark. A preliminary study of a number of species of buntings shows that many of the species, for example reed and corn buntings (*Emberiza schoeniclus* and *E. calandra*), have songs which are highly stereotyped and completely innate. The song of the yellow bunting (*E. citrinella*) appears to consist of an integration of innate and learned components much as in the chaffinch. The buntings as a whole appear to have strongly territorial songs corresponding to that of the chaffinch in function.

Apart from a very few and partial exceptions, chaffinches can learn song patterns only during the first 13 months of life, and towards the end of this time there is a peak period of learning activity of a few weeks during which a young chaffinch may learn, as a result of singing in a territory, the fine details of as many as six different songs. This special period of high learning ability is brought to an abrupt close by internal factors. It matters not whether a chaffinch has learned one or six songs by the time it is 13 months old, it can afterwards learn no more, and so remains with its one song or its six for the rest of its life. This restriction of learning ability to a particular type of object and to a sharply defined sensitive period recalls the phenomenon of imprinting.

The inborn recognition and performance of its specific song by the chaffinch involves (*a*) duration of approximately $2\frac{1}{2}$ seconds, (*b*) interval between songs of between 6 and 20 seconds, (c) tonal quality (though this last may have been learned by the experience of the bird of the qualities of its own voice). The readiness with which the bird learns to divide its song into three sections and learns to attach a simple flourish at the end as an appropriate termination shows that there must be an imperfectly inherited tendency to respond to, and perform, the features of the normal song as soon as the singer is stimulated by hearing another bird. Such an inherited tendency would explain the basic similarity of the songs of the species throughout its range.

In conclusion, I believe that recent studies of bird behaviour have added a considerable body of evidence in support of the view, now being advanced from many quarters (see Thorpe & Zangwill, 1960) that in regard to both learned and innate behaviour patterns the organism is to be regarded as 'searching' largely for cues and stimuli, consummatory situations in fact, rather than for the release of consummatory acts. This is to say that the 'goal' of the behaviour is not solely or even primarily the discharge of a specific motor-mechanism but the achievement of a specific sensory stimulation. Moreover, in this connection we must remember that the animal perceives its own consummatory acts primarily through its own interoceptors and proprioceptors, and that in the majority of cases at least it is again a special pattern of sensory stimulation, a re-afference, which is the effective reward and not simply the general level of well-being or activity resulting from the concomitant adjustment of nutritional or endocrine balance.

GROUP DISCUSSION

MAGOUN. I am trying to relate this behaviour to mechanisms of the brain. It is possible in the cat and in the monkey to introduce electrodes into the peri-aqueductal grey or the tegmentum of the midbrain and by repetitive stimulation to evoke faciovocal responses which are identical with the normal expression of emotion by these animals. These can be elicited when the brain stem is transected just ahead of this region, so evidently one is not exciting an ascending pathway to some higher level. After this region of the cephalic brain stem is destroyed electrolytically, the cat no longer vocalizes in response to an adequate environmental stimulus. This suggests that there is built into this part of the brain a mechanism for faciovocal performance in the expression of emotions, to be differentiated from the speech-mechanisms that have developed in the association cortex in the dominant hemisphere of man. This had led me to wonder whether it would be possible, by introducing electrodes into the midbrain, to evoke those patterns of vocal performance which you point out as being so specific for individual birds. Have experiments along those lines been tried? Do you think they might be feasible?

THORPE. Yes, stimulation experiments are being performed, but not so far with song birds which are, of course, very active and mostly small. We have started some ablation experiments with song birds, but these have not got very far yet. It is as yet very difficult to stimulate the brain of a very small bird so that it will behave in a fairly normal fashion and still sing. I think it will be some time before the technique is developed to the point at which significant results will begin to accrue.

FESSARD. What about parrots?

THORPE. Parrots should certainly be easier to investigate but, although they have of course an astonishing facility for vocal mimicry, would not be much good for the study of the innate sounds. In this matter of vocal imitation the Indian hill mynah excels even the parrots. But perhaps the most puzzling feature is that neither parrots nor mynahs appear to use their power of mimicry in the wild at all (Thorpe, 1959). They have stereotyped cries and calls which seem to serve for co-ordinating the movements of the flock but show no sign of mimicry. From the point of view of the study of vocal learning these species would be admirable; but not for studying mechanisms for *innate* sound production.

BUSER. It might be of interest to mention here observations made in Paris by Dr Rougeul and Dr Assenmacher, studying the electrical activity of deep brain structures in unanaesthetized ducks by stereotaxic methods: each time when simply introducing or moving up and down the Horsley-Clarke electrode, the animal would start quacking whenever a certain level was reached, lying in the tegmental midbrain. Electrical stimuli were not systematically tried and the mechanical excitation produced by the electrode appeared actually sufficient to produce the described effect.

KONORSKI. I would like to make two comments. The first one is this: As far as I know, only birds, and among mammals only man, have the ability of reproducing sounds, i.e. they possess what may be called acoustic-vocal reflexes of a specific kind. This ability seems to indicate that in these animals direct connections exist between the acoustic area and the part of motor area concerned with vocalization. We know that in man such connections in fact exist between anterior temporal area and frontal opercular region. If they are destroyed the peculiar form of asphasia ensues. The patient understands what is said to him and is even able to verbalize his thoughts, but he is not able to repeat exactly the words he hears. It is much easier for him to say something spontaneously than to repeat it. It would be very interesting to know whether such an acoustic vocal system exists in birds, and if so, to study it both from anatomical and physiological points of view.

The second point concerns the problems of imprinting. We know from extensive experimental data (the literature is given in a paper by Konorski and Szwejkowska, 1952) that classical conditioning shares one important property with imprinting, namely its partial irreversibility. By the way, this is why I do not like the term 'temporary connections' because these connections, once established, are not temporary but stable, and, as I shall discuss later, they are not obliterated by 'disuse'. If you elaborate an alimentary conditioned reflex to some stimulus, it is much more difficult to transform it afterwards into, say, a defensive conditioned stimulus by changing the reinforcement from food to shock, than to elaborate the defensive conditioned reflex to quite a new stimulus. Even after a long defensive training of the alimentary conditioned stimulus, its previous alimentary role may be detected. We explain these facts by saying that the old conditioned connections established between the central representation of the conditioned stimulus and feeding centre are by no means removed by the new training but the new connections are formed independently of them.

This suggests a form of continuity between the inborn reflexes, imprinting and normal conditioning and shows that there are perhaps no sharp limits between these phenomena. Experiments made long ago in Pavlov's laboratory by Citovitch are also relevant here. This author found that the alimentary reflex to the smell of food is not inborn but conditioned because it appears only after a few reinforcements of the stimulus, but this reflex is established very rapidly and is then very stable. I think that we could label this phenomenon either as conditioning or as imprinting.

THORPE. Some experiments have been done with deafened birds by Schwartakoff and Messmer. The production of the essential elements in an innate song is not fundamentally affected by being deafened but there may be a change in the overall 'pitch' of the song. This seems to provide a sharp distinction from conditioning.

ESTABLE. In certain species of birds, males sing more and more and differently when exhilarated by the presence of the female or when after being in the neighbourhood of the female the latter is removed from his sight. Hormonal influences have been mentioned as possible explanation of this, but though they are probably necessary, they cannot be sufficient to explain the production of such a variety of songs. Besides, an exclusively endocrine influence cannot explain the fact that the male sings better than the female; the nervous system and the sound-producing apparatus must necessarily participate.

When the male bird is in the presence of the female, it sings; if the latter is removed, it sings even more. When the female is absent it stops singing. What happens in the brain of the male bird would be interesting to know. Is there some endocrinological influence in the mechanism of the brain which conditions this behaviour? For example, the problem of the gestalt theory if the conditioned reflex is the cause, if it is first or second. I have talked on this subject with Kohler, who was a pioneer in this field. He believes that the gestalt structures precede conditioning.

SEGUNDO. To complement the observation of Dr Buser I would like to note that we have implanted electrodes in the mesencephalon of the Tero bird (*Belenopterus chilensis*). Electrical stimulation with threshold voltage produced investigation or orientation movements; with higher voltages, the bird stretched its wings, started to fly and in addition, squawked loudly. (Silva, Estable and Segundo, unpublished observations.)

GRASTYÁN. A marked following reaction could be observed in some of our experiments by stimulating the hypothalamus in cats. This behaviour seemed to be also in close correlation with the function of the rhinencephalon. You say that there is a limited period of the animal's life when this reaction can occur naturally. In which stage of maturation of the central nervous system does this reaction occur? Which structures are responsible for its integration in the birds?

DOTY. I have seen this following reaction consistently in cats deprived of all visual cortex in infancy. They will approach and follow moving acoustic stimuli and persist in this activity for minutes.

GRASTYÁN. Dr Adey has made similar observations, after the destruction of the entorhinal cortex in the marsupial phalanaen.

ADEY. After a limited reaction of the hippocampus cortex which forms the entorhinal area. The animal was tamed and at the same time would follow any moving object. This was not accompanied by any aggressive behaviour towards the object they were following. They normally attack with jaws or teeth objects that come within the visual field. This ceases after ablation of the entorhinal cortex.

MAGOUN. I am glad to hear reference to the rhinencephalic or limbic brain in this connection because I think attention should be called to the generalizations of Paul Maclean that this part of the C.N.S. is concerned with these types of behaviour which preserve the individual on feeding or aggression or defence, and which preserve the race by managing sexual behaviour.

HERNÁNDEZ-PEÓN. The curves that Dr Thorpe showed us concerning the rate of development of internal inhibition may explain the great individual variation observed during experimentally induced habituation. I wonder if he could elaborate the matter further and tell us what is the presently available evidence obtained by using a systematic approach. What kind of responses have been tested and which animals have been studied?

THORPE. The subjects were all birds of the following species: Canary (*Serinus c. canarius*), Greenfinch (*Chloris chloris*) and Great Tit (*Parus major*). These curves refer to string-pulling behaviour and to learning to take food from two types of dishes, one with a black lid and one with a white one. In the string pulling the wild bird, if it learns the trick at all, often behaves with extreme precision and the whole movement appears highly organized. In experimental studies, however, the birds present very varied behaviour. This, we hope, will be explained in the future as a result of this discovery of the different rates of change of these factors, namely the level of responsiveness and of internal inhibition, which are themselves partly an expression of the previous experience of the bird.

SOME ASPECTS OF THE ELABORATION OF CONDITIONED CONNECTIONS AND FORMATION OF THEIR PROPERTIES

E. A. Asratyan

Much in the field of conditioned reflexes was achieved by Ivan Pavlov and his pupils and by his other followers in many countries of the world. Nevertheless, many aspects of this problem have not yet been satisfactorily investigated and require further experimental study and theoretical elaboration. At present, many scientists in the U.S.S.R. and elsewhere are studying, as Pavlov's scientific heritage, the elaboration of conditioned reflexes, the formation of their properties, their preservation, and the significance of various factors acting favourably on these processes. My collaborators and myself are among them.

At present the main trend of our experimental and theoretical investigations in this field is the study of the role of the strength of stimuli and their sequence in the elaboration of conditioned reflexes and the formation of their properties. The purpose of this paper is to report our findings and present our interpretation of them.

The important role played by the relative strength of the excitatory processes which take place in nervous structures and especially in the cortex, is generally known. Pavlov has stated: 'Prime importance must be ascribed, of course, to strength relations in the activity of the cortex.'[1] He also repeatedly emphasized the great importance of the pattern of combinations of stimuli in time for the elaboration of conditioned reflexes. He stated that 'since conditioned stimuli play the role of signals, they must become effective only when they precede the signalized physiological activity.'[2]

Our collaborators investigated these problems in dogs in the usual semi-soundproof chambers designed for the study of conditioned reflexes. In order to elaborate conditioned reflexes with definite functional properties, we combined in various ways either two so-called 'indifferent' stimuli, or two different unconditioned stimuli, or one 'indifferent' and one unconditioned stimulus. The characteristic feature of our experiments

---

[1] I. P. Pavlov, *Complete Works*, vol. III, 1949, p. 382.
[2] I. P. Pavlov, *Complete Works*, vol. III, 1949, p. 381.

was the attempt to select and apply only those 'indifferent' stimuli which provoke in experimental animals reflex reactions which can be objectively observed and graphically recorded.

I. In 1958, our collaborators Varga and Pressman performed a series of experiments in dogs in which they combined two so-called 'indifferent' stimuli, namely, a sound and a passive lifting of the animal's leg. In some of these experiments stimuli were always applied in the same stereotyped sequence, in others in a variable sequence. The advantage of a passive movement of the leg as one of the 'indifferent' stimuli is that it gives direct and immediate indication of a connection between the combined stimuli when the movement of the leg or the electromyogram of its muscles is observed. In addition, with these indicators the investigators were able to study directly the whole process of formation of conditioned connections when these stimuli are combined from the very beginning of the connections to any subsequent stage of their evolution.

(a) In experiments by previous investigators of this problem (Podkopayev and Narbutovich (1936), Zeliony (1928), Oreshuk (1950), Rokotova (1952), Karmanova (1955), Bregadze (1956), Sergeyev (1957) and others, this was not possible. The reason was that they used only the method of intermediated and, besides, sporadic indication of the process of elaboration of connections between 'indifferent' stimuli. Data obtained by Varga and Pressman clearly show that between the brain points of these stimuli a double (or two-way) 'associative connection', i.e. actually a conditioned reflex connection is established. This occurs not only when sound and passive lifting of the animal's leg are combined in a variable sequence, but also when they are combined in a stereotyped one. (Fig. 1) Further, in the course of their experiments, Varga and Pressman also obtained data which on the one hand corroborate facts previously established by other workers, and on the other are new. For example, they have shown, in conformity with the findings of other authors, that the connections between 'indifferent' stimuli are characterized by extreme fragility and instability. After being established, they rapidly begin to weaken and soon disappear after a period of more or less regular function. They recover again for a very short time but only after a certain interval, during the experiment, or when an alimentary conditioned reflex has been elaborated in response to one of the combined stimuli.

(b) At the same time the experiments of Varga and Pressman established other facts which illustrate the great significance of a definite sequence in combining stimuli. Their experimental data show that although the above-mentioned properties — fragility and instability — are characteristic for both conditioned connections between the brain points of two stimuli, they are not inherent in these reflexes in an equal measure. When sound and passive lifting of the animal's leg are combined in a variable sequence, the conditioned connections arising between them are almost equivalent in their rate of formation, consolidation, stability, resistance to extinction, etc. But when these stimuli are combined in a stereotyped sequence, the resulting conditioned connections essentially differ from each other in all of the above-mentioned criteria. A direct or forward conditioned connection, i.e. a connection leading from the preceding stimulus (P) to the

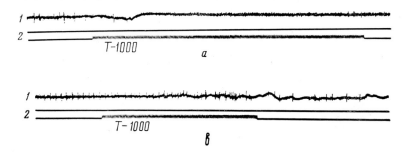

FIG. I

Conditioned connections resulting from various combinations of a sound and a passive lifting of the dog's leg. (*a*) Active lifting of the leg (indicated by the rarefaction or disappearance of electrical potentials in the extensor of the leg, i.e. in the gastrocnemius muscle) in response to the application of a tone after its thirty-seven combinations with a passive lifting of the leg in the stereotyped sequence: 'tone — passive lifting of the leg'; (*b*) reaction to a tone after twenty-eight combinations of a passive lifting of the leg with this tone in experiments with a reverse sequence, i.e. 'passive lifting of the leg — tone'.

    I. — electromyogram of the gastrocnemius muscle; 2. — mark of conditioned stimulation.

subsequent one (S) becomes elaborated more easily and is more powerful and resistant to extinction and other altering factors, than a reverse or backward conditioned connection, i.e. a connection leading from S to P. Further, a direct connection recovers more rapidly than a reverse one after an acute extinction or when, following their natural disappearance, a break is made in the experiment, or when one of the combined stimuli turns into an alimentary conditioned signal. Essentially similar results were obtained by Varga and Pressman in a series of experiments on other dogs in which they combined passive lifting of the animal's leg with the blowing of air into the animal's eye which evoked the blink reflex. The advantage of the combination of these two stimuli over those applied in the previously described experiments was that both stimuli (and not only one of them) called forth effects which could be recorded objectively. Moreover, as shown in the course of the experiments, the new stimulus, a puff of air in the animal's eye, applied in the given combination, proved to be stronger than the stimulus (sound) applied in the previous combination. With this technique, it proved possible to demonstrate the elaboration of direct and reverse connections in a more distinct, graphic and what is particularly important, direct form. This was possible both when one of the combined stimuli was applied first in stereotyped sequence, and

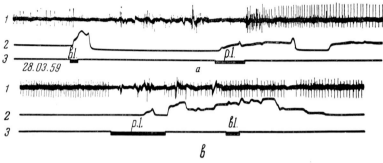

FIG. 2

A two-way connection resulting from the combination of a passive lifting of the leg with the blowing of air into the eye. (*a*) A conditioned motor reflex arising when the combination is applied in the stereotyped sequence — 'blowing of air into the eye — passive lifting of the leg'. In response to the blowing of air into the eye (*d*) the dog blinks and lifts the leg which is testified to by the disappearance of action potentials in the gastrocnemius muscle. The lifting of the leg (p.p.) is again accompanied by blinking which testifies to a reverse connection; (*b*) A conditioned eyelid reflex arising when the combination is applied in the stereotype sequence 'passive lifting of the leg — blowing of air into the eye'. In response to the passive lifting of the leg (p.p) the dog blinks. After the blowing of air into the eye (*d*) there is observed, along with the blinking, a disappearance of action potentials in the gastrocnemius muscle, which testifies to a reverse connection.

    1. — action potentials of the gastrocnemius muscle; 2. — movement of the eyelids; 3. — marks of stimulation (long line — passive lifting of the leg; short line — blowing of air into the eye).

when the other stimulus was applied first (Fig. 2). As a puff of air in the animal's eye proved to be a stronger stimulus than sound, the direct conditioned connections were much more stable than when sound was combined with a passive lifting of the animal's leg. To some extent this also applies to reverse conditioned connections.

    II. New facts related to this problem were established by Lyan-Chi-an, who continued the investigation of a very pressing problem which Varga (1953) had previously studied in our laboratory.

    Using dogs, Varga combined in a strictly alternating sequence two classical unconditioned stimuli of moderate intensity, namely, presentation of food and electrical stimulation of the leg. She established the possibility of elaborating a stable double (or two-way) conditioned connection between cerebral nervous structures corresponding to these two stimuli. It should be noted that under standard experimental conditions (strictly alternating sequence of combination of stimuli, relative equality of their intensity, observance of the routine conditions of maintenance of the experimental animal, etc.) these conditioned connections are practically equivalent as regards sign, strength, stability and so on.

On the contrary, in the experiments of Lyan-Chi-an, two unconditioned stimuli were combined in a stereotyped sequence. In other words, he combined in a stereotyped sequence a defensive motor reflex of a fore-leg, evoked by applying an electric shock of moderate intensity, with an alimentary reflex to the presentation of a moderate portion of powdered meat and bread. In certain series of experiments, performed on one group of dogs, application of the electric shock preceded presentation of food, while in other series, performed on another group, presentation of food preceded application of the electric shock. Both series of experiments yielded essentially similar results which agree in some respects with the data of Varga and of Pressman and Varga, but differ in some essential points. In the experiments of Lyan-Chi-an, double (or two-way) conditioned reflex connections between the brain points of the combined unconditioned stimuli were also formed. This is shown in Figs. 3 and 4. However, here also, as in the similar Varga and Pressman experiments, direct and reverse conditioned connections between these points were far from being equivalent. In comparison with Varga and Pressman's experiments those of Lyan-Chi-an showed a considerably more pronounced difference in the rate of elaboration of conditioned connections leading from the preceding (P) to the subsequent (S) stimulus, than from (S) to (P). In both series of Lyan-Chi-an's experiments, the direct conditioned reflex connection between the combined unconditioned stimuli is formed slightly more rapidly than the reverse conditioned reflex connection. This connection is also of much greater strength and stability and is characterized by a considerably greater regularity than the reverse connection. In contradistinction to a direct connection between two indifferent, i.e. physiologically weak stimuli, a direct connection between two unconditioned, i.e. physiologically strong stimuli, forms easily, consolidates increasingly from day to day and persists if the conditions which have given rise to it are maintained; namely, when these stimuli are combined in the given sequence.

H

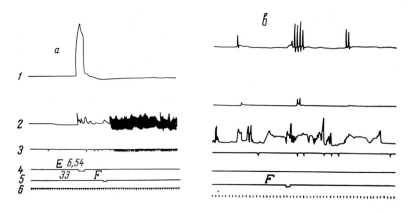

FIG. 3

An alimentary conditioned reflex to an electric current. A dog to which an electric current and the presentation of food were applied in the stereotyped sequence 'electric current — food'. (*a*) A conditioned salivary alimentary reflex to the application of electric current (direct connection); (*b*) movements of the leg during the presentation of the food receptacle (reverse connection).

From top to bottom: 1. — mechanogram of movement of the left foreleg; 2. — mechanogram of masticating movements; 3. — salivation in drops; 4. — mark of electro-cutaneous stimulation; 5. — mark of presentation of the food receptacle; 6. — time in seconds.

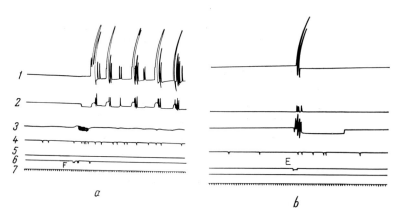

FIG. 4

Electro-defensive motor reflex to presentation of food. A dog to which presentation of food and electrical current were applied in the stereotyped sequence 'food — electric current'. (*a*) A conditioned motor defensive reflex to the end of the act of eating (direct connection); (*b*) a conditioned alimentary reaction to the electric current (reverse connection).

From top to bottom: 1. — mechanogram of movements of the left foreleg; 2. — mechanogram of movements of the right foreleg; 3. — mechanogram of masticating movements; 4. — salivation in drops; 5. — mark of electro-cutaneous stimulation; 6. — mark of presentation of the food receptacle; 7. — time in seconds.

The matter is entirely different with a reverse conditioned reflex connection between unconditioned stimuli. They greatly resemble, especially in their fragility and irregularity, conditioned connections between indifferent stimuli. It must be pointed out that a reverse connection, is so feeble, so unstable, multiphasic and diverse in its manifestations and depends on so many factors for its functioning that initially we even doubted its conditioned reflex nature.

Some of the peculiar features revealed by the experiments of Lyan-Chi-an in the functioning of reverse conditioned reflex connections are of special interest. For instance, (S) evokes more easily the reflex corresponding to (P) if the strength of (P) has been increased or if the excitability of the central nervous structures is raised. By strengthening (P) or by an increase in the excitability of the relevant nervous apparatus it becomes possible to revive and activate the reverse conditioned connections even when under usual experimental conditions they cease to manifest themselves. A similar result is obtained if (S) is weakened, or the excitability of the corresponding nervous structures is lowered. For example, in an experiment in which stimuli are applied in the sequences 'electrical shock — food', the presentation of food evokes a conditioned reflex lifting of the animal's leg more frequently and more distinctly if the leg was previously stimulated by a stronger shock than usual, or if, prior to the experiment, the dog was deliberately fed to satiety. The feature common to these two different preliminary experimental manipulations is that they both lead to the same picture of relative excitability or excitation of the central nervous structures corresponding to these two stimuli.

In contrast to this, a preliminary strengthening of (S) or increase in excitability of the nervous structures corresponding to its reflex leads to inactivation of the nervous connection even when under usual experimental conditions they function regularly and satisfactorily. Similar results are obtained by a preliminary weakening of (P) or by a preliminary decrease of the excitability of the relevant nervous structures. Let us, for example, take again the type of experiments thoroughly studied by Lyan Chi-an in which stimuli were applied in the sequence: 'electric shock — food'. Here the presentation of food evokes no conditioned lifting of the leg if the animal is in a state of fasting before the experiment, or if it is given appetizing food at the beginning of the experiment, or if its leg is first stimulated by a weak electric shock. It may be noted that although these preliminary experimental manipulations are different, they have something in common: in different ways they lead to the creation of the same picture of relative excitability or excitation of the central nervous structures of these two stimuli.

III. New and interesting data obtained by our collaborator Struchkov (1958) also relate to the problem under discussion. While elaborating conditioned reflexes in dogs, he combined 'indifferent' stimuli with an unconditioned stimulus. This special method is known in the literature as the method of 'covering'. In this method the 'indifferent' stimuli are applied against a background of action of the unconditioned stimulus. Struchkov used food as an unconditioned stimulus and chose only those 'indifferent' stimuli which by themselves evoke in the organism specific reactions that can be objectively observed and recorded. For example, in one series of experiments he applied a passive lifting of one of the dog's hind legs and in another a momentary cooling of a limited area of the skin on one side of the animal's body, which evokes a local vasomotor reaction. This sequence of stimuli was applied systematically in all experiments of each series. The following very interesting facts were brought to light. After repeated combination of an alimentary reflex with one of the 'indifferent' stimuli, presentation of food alone began to evoke reactions peculiar to these stimuli. In one series of experiments the reaction was an active lifting of the leg, and in another a local vasomotor reflex. This is shown in Fig. 5. In other words, in Struckhov's experiments the classical unconditioned stimulus — food — played the role of a conditioned or signalling stimulus, while the so-called 'indifferent' stimuli — passive movement of the leg or local cooling of the skin — appeared as reinforcing stimuli. These remarkable experiments show that it is precisely the position in time of the preceding stimulus (P) which determines the acquisition by the food of a signalling significance in relation to other reflexes, that is, the formation in one case of a somato-motor conditioned reflex to the presentation of food, and in the other case a vasomotor conditioned reflex. It may be assumed therefore that this is the consequence of the formation of a direct conditioned reflex connection between central nervous structures of the alimentary reflex and corresponding structures of the somato-motor or vasomotor reflexes. It was subsequently established that in these experiments there also arises a double (or two-way) conditioned connection between the unconditioned and indifferent stimuli which are combined in a definite, stereotyped sequence. This means that with the direct conditioned reflex connection there exists a reverse connection which conducts excitation from the nervous structures corresponding to (S) (i.e. to the movement of the leg or local cooling of the skin) to the nervous structures corresponding to (P) (i.e. the alimentary stimulus). This is clear from the fact that passive lifting of the leg or local cooling of the skin also acquire a signalling significance (i.e. the faculty of evoking an alimentary reaction in a conditioned reflex way when repeatedly combined with food, according to the method of 'covering' applied in

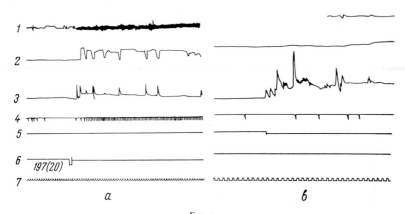

FIG. 5

(*a*) A motor conditioned reflex evoked in the dog by the act of eating (direct connection); (*b*) an alimentary reflex evoked by the passive lifting of the leg (reverse connection).

    1. — Mark of masticating movements; 2. — mark of placing the leg on a bench; 3. — mark of movements of the same leg; 4. — mark of salivation; 5. — mark of passive movement of the leg; 6. — mark of presentation of food (figure indicates the number of combinations); 7. — mark of time — in seconds.

the experiments discussed above. This is demonstrated in Fig. 6. The data obtained from these experiments show that here too there is a considerable difference between the specific features of direct and reverse conditioned connections, and that, furthermore, it is the same kind of difference as is observed when two 'indifferent' or two unconditioned-reflexes are combined. Thus, in a given case the direct conditioned reflex connection is formed more rapidly than the reverse conditioned reflex connection and is much more powerful, stable and effective.

    The fact demonstrated by Struchkov that only weak and unstable conditioned reflexes become indifferent stimuli when 'covered' by un-conditioned reflexes, has been known since the work of Pimenov (1908), Krepa (1933), Pavlova (1933), Vinogradov (1933), Petrova (1933) and others; but these authors regarded it as an indication of the elaboration of an ordinary one-way conditioned reflex connection possessing certain specific features. In Struchkov's experiments this fact appears in quite a different light, namely, as a particular case of the general phenomenon of elaboration of a reverse conditioned reflex connection (along with the direct connection) when two stimuli are combined in a stereotyped sequence. The transitory character of this connection, which was pointed out long ago by many workers and was regarded by Pavlov as an enigmatic phenomenon in conditioned reflex activity, may, to a considerable degree, be interpreted as a result of its systematic non-reinforcement during the periodic application of a stimulus for the purpose of testing a conditioned reflex to it.

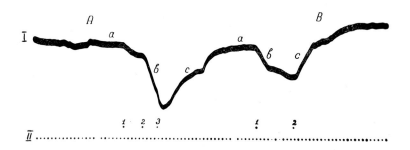

FIG. 6

Conditioned and unconditioned reflex local changes in the skin temperature.

A. Decrease of skin temperature in the dog under the action of food during 60 seconds and subsequent application of cold. I. Record of skin temperature. II. Time — 12 seconds; (*a*) background; (*b*) decrease of temperature during the process of eating and application of cold; (*c*) recovery of skin temperature after the process of eating and action of cold. 1. — mark of presentation of food and beginning of the act of eating; 2. — mark of application of cold; 3. — mark of the end of eating and application of cold.

B. Conditioned reflex decrease of skin temperature during the process of eating. (*a*) — background; (*b*) — decrease of skin temperature during the process of eating; (*c*) — recovery of skin temperature after the process of eating. 1. — mark of presentation of food and beginning of the process of eating; 2. — mark of the end of eating.

IV. The significance of a definite sequence in the combination of stimuli for elaboration of new conditioned reflex connections and for preservation of existing ones is graphically shown in the experimental data obtained by our collaborator Pakovich.

From the earlier investigations of American psychologists, Schlosberg (1928), Hilgard (1937), Wolfle (1930), Bernstein (1934) and others, which were carried out on human beings, it was known that when the indifferent stimulus precedes the unconditioned stimulus by 0.1 second and less, the elaboration of a conditioned reflex is impeded, and sometimes even becomes impossible. In recent years, Pakovich has made a thorough investigation of this question in dogs, on motor reflexes which can be objectively recorded with a sensitive mechanographic device, and in some experiments also by electromyography. His data show that when a combination of a sound of moderate intensity with an electrical stimulation of the animal's legs is used, a motor conditioned reflex is not elaborated if both stimuli begin and cease to act strictly simultaneously within a period of 1 to 5 seconds. According to Pakovich's findings, hundreds of combinations of these stimuli do not lead to the formation of the conditioned reflex even when sound precedes the electric current within a limit of about 100 msec. and when they cease to act simultaneously. The picture does not change if the intensity of the stimulating current is considerably increased. A conditioned reflex becomes elaborated only when the interval between the onset of the sound and that of the electrical stimulation of the skin exceeds this time-limit. This is illustrated in Fig. 6. Other data obtained by Pakovich show that the time factor expressed in such micro-values makes itself felt also at a certain distance from the above-mentioned peculiar demarcation line. Pakovich established in particular that the latent period of the newly formed conditioned reflex, as well as its strength, duration, stability and other properties, depends to a considerable degree on the interval between the onset of action of the two stimuli, the indifferent and the unconditioned.

Pakovich established another very interesting fact: a firmly established and regularly evoked electro-defensive motor reflex disappears in the dog if the conditioned stimulus is applied synchronously with the unconditioned one in the course of a series of experiments. The same occurs also when the interval between onset of the conditioned and of the unconditioned stimulus is reduced to less than 100 msec. The conditioned reflex reappears only when these conditions of combined action of both stimuli are changed and when the interval between the onset of the two stimuli again exceeds 100 msec. The restoration of the conditioned reflex proceeds more rapidly and is more complete when this interval is somewhat higher than its threshold value.

Recently, Pakovich carried out an experimental analysis of the disappearance of the established conditioned reflex when conditioned and unconditioned stimuli were applied synchronously.

He found that this phenomenon is due to the sporadic application in the course of his experiment of the conditioned stimulus alone for the purpose of testing its conditioned effect. It seems, therefore, that simultaneous application of the conditioned and unconditioned stimuli leads to such a weakening of the conditioned reflex that it disappears even after a few extinction trials.

The following fact is noteworthy. Although a strictly simultaneous action of both stimuli or a certain minimal precedence of action of one of them creates such conditions that the cerebral nervous structures cannot elaborate new conditioned connections, or even abolishes all previously conditioned reflexes, this does not preclude the possibility of a negative and even positive interaction between the cerebral structures which correspond to these stimuli. Pakovich demonstrated that even in conditions of a synchronous action of sound and electrical current there may take

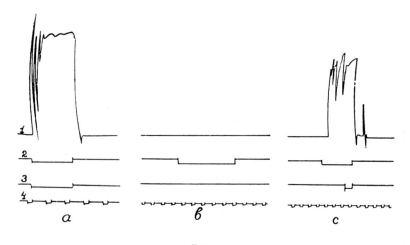

FIG. 7

Motor reflexes arising from different combinations in time of two stimuli — a tone and an electric current. (*a*) — a motor reaction resulting from a strictly simultaneous action of the stimuli; (*b*) — absence of a conditioned reflex to the tone after 582 strictly simultaneous applications of it in combination with an electric current; (*c*) — emergence of a conditioned reflex to the same stimulus after fourteen applications of it in combination with an electrical current delayed for 2 seconds.

1. — record of movements of the leg; 2. — mark of conditioned stimulation; 3. — mark of unconditioned stimulation; 4. — time in seconds.

place both a reciprocal inhibition and a summation of excitation provoked by each of these stimuli in corresponding central nervous structures. The reciprocal inhibition is observed predominantly in the first period of the combined action of the stimuli, when the orienting reaction to sound is still strong. As to summation of excitation, it is observed predominantly following the combined action of the stimuli. During these periods a subthreshold excitation evoked by an electro-cutaneous stimulus applied separately turns into an above-threshold excitation when an electric current of similar intensity is applied in combination with a sound. In the same conditions of combined action of both stimuli a weak above-threshold excitation evoked by a weak electric current becomes considerably intensified, etc. Finally, it must be noted that according to these findings, the phenomena described above and the determining factors observed in the formation of conditioned reflexes are not connected to any appreciable degree with typology, age or other features of the experimental animals; it follows that they belong to the category of basic phenomena and determining factors which are characteristic of the conditioned reflex activity of higher parts of the central nervous system.

How are all these findings to be interpreted and generalized?

Experimental psychologists, neurophysiologists and animal trainers have for long known a number of facts which prove the formation of a two-way nervous connection and have provided a basis for the formulation of corresponding theories on this question (Goltz, 1884; Bekhterev, 1887; Ebbinghaus, 1911-13; Kalisher, 1912-14, Savich, 1918; Zeliony, 1929; Beritov, 1932; Konorsky and Miller, 1936; Narbutovich and Podkopayev, 1936; Rosenthal, 1936; Petrova, 1941; Kupalov, 1948; Fiodorov, 1952; Voronin, 1952, and others). In this connection special mention must be made of the theories of Pavlov (1949) concerning double (or two-way) conditioned connections, advanced by him in recent years and based on original facts brought to light in his laboratories. Pavlov stated that 'when two nervous points are connected, or associated, the nervous processes developing between them proceed in both directions'.[1] At that time, however the founder of the theory of conditioned reflexes was of the opinion that the important question of two-way conditioned connection was still not sufficiently elaborated, experimentally or theoretically, and that it required further investigation. It appears to us that the facts recently obtained in our laboratory increase to some degree our knowledge of this problem. They reveal new aspects of direct and reverse connections, and, in particular, new aspects of the role played in this process by the physiological strength of the stimuli and by the sequence of their combination.

All these facts, in addition to the previously known data of other investigators, lead to the assumption that the formation of a double (or two-way) conditioned connection is not a limited phenomenon peculiar only to a certain group of conditioned reflexes, but is widespread, if not universal for this class of reflexes. This creates, so to speak, a structural basis for a two-way functional connection and for a circular conditioned reflex interaction between the connected nervous points, approximately in the

[1] I. P. Pavlov, *Complete Works*, 1949, vol. III, p. 452.

same manner as was assumed by Lorente de Nó (1934, 1938) and his followers for the activity of the central nervous system in general. In any case, there are sufficient grounds for this assumption during the stage of formation of conditioned reflexes and for the initial period of their functioning. Subsequently, depending on a number of circumstances, evolutionary development leads to different results: to the inhibition of both conditioned connections, to the inhibition of one of them, and sometimes to the preservation of both connections in a state of stability and efficiency. In this case a usual one-way conditioned connection can be regarded as a derivative of a double conditioned connection, as resulting from the subsequent inhibition of one of the paired connections.

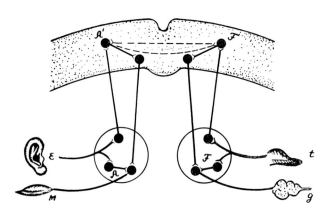

Fig. 8
Schematic representation of a conditioned reflex arc.

I should like also to point out that all the factual material described in this communication, as well as the appraisal of its scientific significance, may also be regarded as corroborating the proposition we advanced many years ago, that the primary conditioned reflex results from the synthesis of combined inborn reflexes evoked by both unconditioned and 'indifferent' stimuli (Fig. 8).

Of course, at present, we are far from a satisfactory interpretation of these facts. Nevertheless, some purely hypothetical statements can be made. In particular, we are inclined to believe that the elaboration of a double conditioned connection may be accounted for by the relative equality of intensity of the excitations which arise in the corresponding central nervous structures under the influence of the combined stimuli. It goes without saying that this basic condition can be observed best when two stimuli of almost equal physiological strength are combined (for example, two 'indifferent' stimuli, two unconditioned stimuli, or one 'indifferent' and one unconditioned stimulus). This is also possible when two paired stimuli are combined in a variable sequence. Such a combination of these two factors can secure the formation and existence of double conditioned

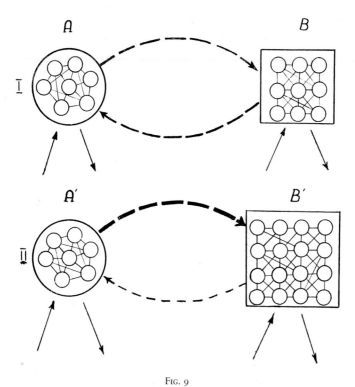

FIG. 9

I. Diagrammatic representation of a double conditioned connection with equivalent components.

II. Diagrammatic representation after development of non-equivalence.

connection with absolutely equivalent components (Fig. 9 I). But when these paired stimuli are combined in a stereotyped sequence, the basic condition is not fulfilled, which, in our opinion, leads to the development of non-equivalence in the direct and reverse conditioned connections (Fig. 9 II). We explain it in the following way. When the (P) and (S) stimuli are applied in a stereotyped sequence, the central nervous structures corresponding to (S) become more excited after the emergence of conditioned connections than the central nervous structures corresponding to (P). This is due to the fact that the structures corresponding to (S) are in this case excited by two sources — by (P) in a conditioned reflex way and by (S) in an unconditioned reflex way. There does not exist the initial relative equality in intensity of excitation of the central nervous structures which corresponds to the combined stimuli. The excitation of the nervous structures of (S) prevails to a great extent over the excitation of the nervous structures corresponding to (P). As a result the direct conditioned connection begins to prevail over the reverse connection in all characteristics. This explanation was corroborated by Varga in a series of experiments (1958) in which she demonstrated that the transition from a variable sequence of combined stimuli to a stereotyped sequence entails a considerable increase in the excitability of the central nervous structures which correspond to (S) and prevalence in this respect over the one corresponding to (P).

We are inclined to offer a similar explanation for Struchkov's findings concerning the conversion of food to a signalling stimulus for somatomotor and vasomotor reflexes. In the first phase of combining food (which is the preceding stimulus (P)) with a passive lifting of the paw or a local cooling of the skin (which is the subsequent stimulus (S)) the central nervous structures corresponding to the latter stimuli become excited to a relatively high degree on account of the novelty of the stimuli for the experimental animals. Owing to this, the level of excitation of the central nervous structures corresponding to these stimuli approximates the level of excitation of the central nervous structures of the alimentary reflex which is the preceding stimulus. This creates favourable conditions for the elaboration of the double conditioned connection between these structures. Subsequently, after elaboration of this double connection, the above-mentioned factor comes into effect, namely, a more intense excitation of the central nervous structures of (S) coming from two sources by way of summation — at first, from the food in a conditioned reflex way, and then, against this background, from adequate stimuli of the nervous structures (a lifting of the paw or cooling of the skin) in an unconditioned reflex way. This maintains the previously created relative equality in levels of excitation of the nervous structures corresponding to the combined stimuli, i.e. the precondition necessary for maintaining the double conditioned connection is preserved.

Facts concerning relatively different duration of efficiency for the conditioned connections arising after combination of various stimuli of different biological significance (two 'indifferent' stimuli, two unconditioned stimuli, or one 'indifferent' and one unconditioned stimulus) can be best understood when considering the important role of the concrete physiological strength of the corresponding stimuli. There are grounds for assuming that this factor plays an important role in the further fate of the conditioned connections, whereas the relative strength of excitation of the central nervous structures corresponding to these stimuli and the sequence of application play an outstanding role in elaborating these connections and forming some of their properties. If we assume that the level of excitation of the central nervous structures originating conditioned reflex connections expresses approximately the number of functional units which come into activity, and that the strength of the conditioned reflex connection is its derivative, the following conclusion may be drawn: for maintenance and functioning of conditioned connections it is necessary that they should possess a certain threshold strength, i.e. consist of a definite 'threshold' number of functional units. Weak conditioned connections, that is, connections consisting of a small number of functional units, become rapidly fatigued and exhausted even after moderate activity; a protective inhibition occurs which blocks them. At present we are unable to explain satisfactorily why such inhibition develops in structures corresponding to weak conditioned connection. We can point out, however, with some justification, that there is a similarity between this phenomenon and the rapid development of inhibition during a protracted action of weak conditioned and even indifferent stimuli. This phenomenon was known a long time ago, from numerous investigations carried out by Pavlov in his laboratories. Moreover, the development of inhibition in connection with a protracted action of weak stimuli seems to belong to the category of phenomena which are common to all nervous structures.

For the time being we cannot give a satisfactory explanation for the facts obtained by Pakovich, which show that a conditioned reflex cannot be formed when two combined stimuli act synchronously. Nor can we explain the disappearance of an existing conditioned reflex when a conditioned stimulus and an unconditioned one are combined in a similar way, although in this case the possibility of a positive and negative interaction of these stimuli remains. It is possible that a certain role in this respect is played by mutual inductive inhibitory influences of the simultaneously excited cerebral structures upon each other. These influences, however, do not preclude the summation of excitations that have originated in them.

KONORSKI. The problem investigated by Professor Asratyan and his group is very important, and has not been solved as yet, although it has been studied for many years. This is the old problem whether the so-called backward conditioning exists, or not. Both in Russia and in America there were authors strongly supporting the idea of backward conditioning, as well as strong opponents of this view. While the first group of authors claimed that *any* association between stimuli (both forward and backward) leads to the formation of connections between them, the second group argued that the phenomena of backward conditioning were only pseudo-conditioning due to sensitization. In fact, while the biological role of forward conditioning is obvious, the biological significance of backward conditioning could hardly be understood.

Professor Asratyan has brought out more extensive material concerning this problem than any other author. According to his data backward conditioning does exist, although the connections formed in the direction from the subsequent stimulus to the preceding one are much weaker than those established in the opposite direction. This is also in agreement with the results obtained by Czech authors on chimpanzees, and recently by Mrs Budochovska in the Psychological Department of the Nencki Institute on man.

CHOW. I would like to ask Professor Asratyan how these very interesting experimental results are to be incorporated, if they are to be incorporated, in the concept of reinforcement during the formation of the conditioned reflex.

ASRATYAN. These conditioned reflexes also need reinforcement. If one of the stimuli is applied without any other, this leads to the extinction of the reflex in every case. But in cases where we have a weak stimulus, the so-called 'indifferent stimulus' — I say so-called because I think that these indifferent stimuli are only relatively indifferent — indeed if they evoke a reaction at all in the organism they cannot be indifferent. They are indifferent in relation to another reaction evoked by another stimulus but by themselves they also originate reflexes like unconditioned stimuli, although their histological sign and their strength are different. When we combine two indifferent stimuli, or weak stimuli, in these cases absence of reinforcement leads to a more rapid extinction than in the case of strong stimuli. Reinforcement is necessary.

NAQUET. How do you explain the limit of 100 msec.?

ASRATYAN. I am afraid we cannot answer this question in a satisfactory manner. It may be a question of mutual influences, facilitation and inhibition, not elaborated connections. I really don't know. But it should be pointed out that facilitation alone is not sufficient for the elaboration of conditioned connections.

FESSARD. I believe that new connections within the central nervous system cannot be formed unless the associated afferent messages converge towards common neurones so that the limit of 100 msec. might be explained by the recovery period of these neurones, at least of those having discharged after the first of the afferent signals reaching them.

NAQUET. I think 100 msec. represents the recovery time of the reticular excitability and you may have some facilitation which permits the establishment of conditioning.

HEBB. I have been very interested for a long time in the problem of the sequential aspect of cerebral function. It may find its simplest, its most experimentally attackable form in the apparent ordering in time of the conditioned stimulus and unconditioned stimulus. I was going to ask Professor Asratyan what speculations he was making about possible neuronal action that might explain this. It seems to me that Professor Fessard's point is excellent but yet there is the further problem that conditioning is not good unless there is *some* overlap. It is as if the line had to be busy to a certain extent, or in certain circumstances.

I would like to say also that I found the paper very interesting in the study of relatively unimportant, biologically unimportant, stimulations. So much of human behaviour is composed of reactions to biologically neutral stimuli, or very nearly neutral.

ASRATYAN. First of all I should like to remind you that we are quoting from our data. In the case of stereotyped sequences of application of the stimulus the significance of these two conditioned connections is different. Dr Konorski also mentioned this in his remarks that direct conditioning in all cases is much stronger and steadier and more regular than backward conditioning. This illustrates the biological differences between these connections and the significance of the sequence of combination. How does one explain this? Originally both nervous points of both stimuli are equally stimulated, however once the connection is established and the stimuli inverted, one point, namely the second point, receives stimuli from two sources, whereas the other receives only its original stimulus. This is the reason for the reinforcement of forward conditioning and the difficulty of backward conditioning.

In answer to your second question, in cases of biologically weak stimuli, as for example in cases when we combined two so-called indifferent reflexes, giving rise to the elaboration of weak two-way conditioned reflex, these reflexes disappear very rapidly. Occasionally in our cases we have been able to prolong their duration. Why these conditioned weak reflexes disappear we don't know. Our theory, our 'fantasy', is that it is due to the lower threshold level of excitation, to the small number of cells activated in both coupled nervous points during the elaboration of reflexes. As a result of the activation of such reflexes, their weak connections easily become exhausted and fatigued and soon disappear. A strong stimulus would call into play a larger number of cells and consequently a steady conditioned reflex is elaborated.

THE PHYSIOLOGICAL APPROACH TO THE PROBLEM OF RECENT MEMORY

Jerzy Konorski

It is a striking fact that the investigations of higher nervous activity of animals carried out both in physiological laboratories by methods of conditioned reflexes, and in psychological laboratories by use of such other methods as maze learning, discrimination box, etc., have been almost exclusively concerned with the problem of stable memory. In fact, in all these investigations the animal is routinely trained to perform a particular task or a set of tasks and then various properties of the acquired reactions, or the very process of their acquisition, are studied. But it is easy to conceive that the performance of the more or less firmly established conditioned responses, in the broadest sense of the word, and, of course, unconditioned responses, does not exhaust the whole behaviour of the animal. We know from everyday observation of animals and man that a large part of this behaviour is often based on transient memory traces which persist for some time and then are partially or even totally abolished. Recently the clear realization of a probable difference between the mechanisms of stable and transient memory traces has turned the attention of investigators to the latter category of phenomena and has given an impetus to their studies.

I intend in the present paper to present a brief review of the methods used so far in the study of phenomena of recent memory, to propose some new methods which may be applied in this field, to examine the relations between stable and recent memory and to discuss the problems of a probable physiological mechanism of recent memory, versus that of stable memory.

I. TRACE CONDITIONED REFLEXES

As a matter of fact, the phenomena of recent memory have been implicated for a long time in some conditioned reflex (CR) studies, although their significance in this respect was not clearly understood. I have in mind the so-called trace CRs which were studied by several research-workers of the Pavlov school (Pimenov, 1907; Grossman, 1909; Dobrovolskij, 1911; Feokritova, 1912; Pavlova, 1914) in the first decade of the work in this field. These workers established that if a given 'indifferent' stimulus is reinforced not during its action but some time — of a range of seconds or minutes — after its cessation it *is* possible to establish in a dog the CR not to the stimulus itself but to a short period of time just preceding the moment of reinforcement. Thus, if for example a dog repeatedly receives food 3 minutes after the cessation of the conditioned stimulus (CS), he learns to salivate not earlier than about half a minute before the moment of feeding. In a variation of such experiments the animal receives food simply at constant intervals and learns to expect it at the proper moment — 'the CR to time'. The end of the act of eating plays in this experiment a role of a trace CS.

Facts of this kind mean that (1) the CS produces some changes in the CNS which persist some time after its cessation, and (2) that the animal is able to 'measure' somehow the time elapsed after it.

The process of elaboration of a trace CR is such that first both the CS itself and the whole period between the stimulus and the reinforcement evokes salivation and then gradually the conditioned reaction is more and more postponed. This shows that first there is a generalization of the CR to all moments following the CS and then differentiation of these moments occurs.

A peculiar property of trace CRs is that they are very widely generalized: even the application of new stimuli, much different from the original CS, produces salivation in the appropriate moment after their cessation; for example, when the original trace CR was elaborated to a tactile stimulus applied to one spot of the skin, it is produced by tactile stimuli applied to quite different spots and also in response to auditory stimuli. This property of trace CRs seems to suggest that they are formed not to the traces of the given exteroceptive stimulus itself, but rather to some of its consequences which are common for various sorts of stimuli. As any external stimulus elicits an orientation reaction it may be that the proprioceptive stimuli generated by this reaction form the true basis for elaboration and occurrence of trace CRs. We shall return to this question in a later section.

2. DELAYED RESPONSES

Nearly at the same time Hunter (1913), according to the suggestion of Carr, introduced into behaviouristic psychology another method of investigation of recent memory based upon the so-called delayed responses. The general principles of this method are roughly these: the animal is taught to receive food in two or more different places (or run to the food through several different ways). When the animal is restrained in the cage or attached on the starting platform, a signal heralding that the food is presented in a particular place is given; in many experiments such a signal is provided simply by baiting one of the bowls in front of the animal. Then after a number of seconds or minutes the animal is released and if he remembers which signal was given, he will go to the corresponding place and be reinforced there.

After the first paper by Hunter appeared, a number of authors studied the delayed responses in various species, attempting to find the maximal delay periods which can be achieved, the cues which are used by the

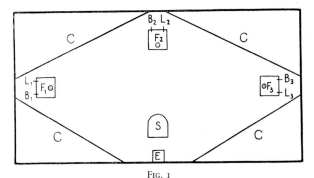

Fig. 1
Experimental setting used in our study.
F_1, F_2, F_3, left, middle, and right food tray. The bowls are automatically moved into position by the experimenter using an electromagnetic device. E, table and seat for experimenter. S, starting platform. B_1, B_2, B_3, buzzers, L_1, L_2, L_3, lamps situated on the respective food trays. (After Konorski, J. and Ławicka, W., 1959. *Acta Biologiae Experimentalis*, **19**, 175-198).

animals to solve the task, and the way in which the delay period is 'bridged' by the animal (Walton, 1915; Yarborough, 1917; Cowan, 1923; Yerkes and Yerkes, 1928; Tinklepaugh, 1928; McAllister, 1932). This form of experimentation grew in importance in the 'thirties of this century when Jacobsen (1936) showed that delayed responses are dramatically impaired or abolished by prefrontal lesions in monkeys and apes. The results of these studies will be discussed in a later section.

The delayed responses have been recently studied in our laboratory by Ławicka and Konorski (Ławicka, 1957, 1959; Konorski and Ławicka, 1959; Ławicka and Konorski, 1959) in dogs and cats by using the experimental setting presented in Fig. 1. The animal was on the leash or in the cage on the starting platform and a signal, visual or auditory, which we shall call a 'preparatory stimulus', from one of three food trays was given. When after being released the animal ran to the proper food tray, the bowl with food was automatically presented. In certain series of experiments the source of preparatory stimuli was situated not on the food trays but at the starting platform, and the animals had to learn by trial and error which signal denoted food in which food tray.

Here are some results of these experiments (Ławicka, 1959).

1. In response to the preparatory stimulus the animal as a rule displays an *orienting reaction* (of the whole body, of the head or only of the eyes) *towards the corresponding food tray*. This is true even in those experiments in which the source of the preparatory stimulus is not situated in the direction of the goal.

2. As shown earlier by other experimenters, the preservation of the bodily orientation towards the given food tray during the delay period is, as far as normal animals are concerned, not at all necessary for the correct reaction after release. In fact, during this period the animals nearly always change their position many times and take different attitudes which does not in the least affect their post-delay reaction.

3. During the delay period normal animals may be distracted in many different ways, by presentation of extra-stimuli from different places, by screening the food trays, by giving the animals food on the starting platform, or by taking them out of the experimental room, and in the majority of trials these measures will not prevent them from running to the correct food tray.

4. If in the triple-choice delayed response method two preparatory stimuli are given one after another in the same trial, the animal, after being released, is able to go to both food trays and ignore the third one.

These data seem to suggest that the 'locating' of the food tray in space during the action of the preparatory stimulus constitutes the cue the animal uses in the post-delay run. Since the bodily orientation is not maintained during the delay period — the animal may even have been removed from the room — the memory of this cue is based purely on the intracentral nervous processes going on in the brain during the delay period, which processes are precisely responsible for those forms of phenomena which are called recent memory.

3. RECENT MEMORY TESTS FOR VARIOUS SORTS OF STIMULI

From what has just been said about the delayed response test it can easily be seen that this test concerns a *particular kind* of recent memory, namely the recent memory of directions in space. Although we do not know exactly which sorts of stimuli are involved in determining these directions (labirinthine, proprioceptive, or a compound of them) we do know that these stimuli were acting when the preparatory signal was applied and the animal remembers them during the delay period. But obviously not only these kinds of stimuli but also exteroceptive stimuli and their various modalities can leave their transient memory traces which may be easily detected in human beings, by use of introspection. However, as far as animals are concerned, the methods for examination of recent memory of these stimuli are not so obvious because we must be sure that the given test really concerns the stimuli in question and not their proprioceptive effects. We have seen for example in Section 1 that even in trace CRs we cannot be sure that the animal remembers the exteroceptive stimulus itself and we have some reason to believe that rather its proprioceptive counterpart constitutes the basis of this form of reflexes. In order to study the recent memory of various modalities of exteroceptive stimuli the following test has been devised (Konorski, 1959).

We choose a certain group of stimuli $S_1, S_2 \ldots S_n$ whose recent memory we wish to examine − e.g. tones of various pitch, lights of various intensity, tactile stimuli applied to various places of the body, etc. − and apply them according to the following schedule: the compound composed of *the same* stimulus, whatever it is, repeated twice ($S_x S_x$) is reinforced, while the compound composed of two different stimuli, whichever they are ($S_x S_y$), is not reinforced, or vice versa. And so when the first component of the compound is applied, the animal does not 'know' whether he will get reinforcement or not because this depends on comparison with the second component which is presented several seconds after the first one. Consequently, the animal has no possibility of preparing himself beforehand for a particular kind of reaction, and thus to make use of proprioceptive cues, as is the case in delayed responses or in some other tests in which the first element of the compound determines by itself the character of the conditioned reaction.[1]

The test described was applied by Chorążyna (1959) in dogs for the study of recent memory of tones, and by Stępień and Cordeau (personal communication) in monkeys for the study of recent memory of rhythms of acoustic and visual stimuli.

[1] For instance, in conditioned inhibition the CS alone is reinforced, while the same stimulus preceded by another stimulus (conditioned inhibitor) is not reinforced. In this case already during the action of the conditioned inhibitor the animal takes the negative attitude towards the food tray and preserves it − or remembers it − during the action of the CS.

4. ON THE PHYSIOLOGICAL MECHANISM OF RECENT MEMORY

It is now almost generally accepted that recent memory is based on the activity of reverberating circuits of neurones which are connected with a group of neurones excited by the actual operation of a given stimulus. Such activity causes this group to continue to be excited for some period after the cessation of the stimulus itself (Hebb, 1949), and either dies out spontaneously within a lapse of time or is knocked out by some inhibitory influence arising from other foci of antagonistic excitation (the so-called external inhibition).

In order to develop this hypothesis a little further and make it more precise, the following well-known facts from the field of CR studies should be taken into account.

1. If a CS is suddenly discontinued before the moment of its usual reinforcement, the conditioned response proceeds uninterruptedly almost with the same intensity as if the CS were still acting (Kupalov and Lukov, 1932). On the contrary, if the reinforcement is usually presented several seconds *after* the CS is discontinued, the conditioned response appears already *during* its operation. This shows that a high degree of generalization exists between the actual action of a stimulus and its traces.

2. If an actual stimulus is not reinforced, but the 'trace stimulus' is, then differentiation of the two stimuli is gradually established. As a result the animal always displays the conditioned response only after the cessation of the stimulus.

3. The animal is also able to differentiate early traces from late traces of the stimulus (cf. section 1). This differentiation is, however, much more difficult than that between the stimulus itself and its traces.

If we hold the view developed in detail elsewhere (Konorski, 1948) that generalization, or similarity, of stimuli is due to the overlapping of their central representations, while differentiation of them is possible when in at least one of these representations there are elements which do not belong to the other one, then the above facts can be understood as follows:

According to the vast evidence of facts concerning the responses of various nerve-cells to the incoming impulses on all levels of the nervous axis, we may admit that the central representation of a given stimulus consists of the following types of neurones: Neurones which are activated only at the beginning of the operation of the stimulus (pure on-elements, group 1a); neurones which are activated during the whole action of the stimulus but not after its cessation (group 1b); neurones which are activated not only during the operation of the stimulus but also, by virtue of reverberating circuits connected with them, some period after their cessation (group 2); neurones which are activated only after the cessation of the stimulus (pure off-elements (group 3)). This is illustrated in Fig. 2.

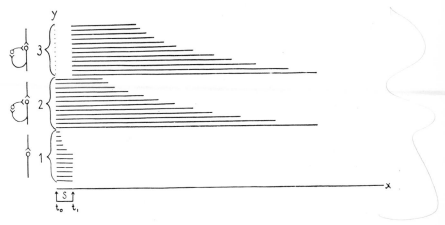

FIG. 2

Diagrammatic representation of the physiological structure of a trace stimulus.

The x axis represents time, t_0 is the beginning of the operation of the particular stimulus, t_1, its termination.

Along the y axis are represented three groups of neurones: (1) a group of neurones activated during, and only during the operation of the stimulus; (2) a group of neurones activated both during the operation of the stimulus and, owing to the reverberating circuits of neurones, for some time after its termination; (3) a group of neurones activated *after* the cessation of the stimulus (off-neurones). All off-neurones are represented as acting for some time after the cessation of the stimulus by way of reverberating circuits. On the left the respective type of neurones of each group is indicated. The horizontal lines represent the periods of excitation of each particular neurone. The whole group 1 is activated only during the operation of the stimulus, some quickly adapting on-elements being also shown. Group 2 is activated during the operation of the stimulus and after its cessation, gradually becoming less active in the course of time. The whole group 3 is activated by the cessation of stimulus and then becomes gradually less active as in the case of group 2. Further explanations in text. (After Konorski and Ławicka, 1959. *Acta Biologiae Experimentalis*, **19**, 175-198.)

As we see the neurones of group 1, being activated only *during* the operation of the stimulus, but not after its cessation, are responsible only for its actual effects; group 1a — i.e. the pure on-neurones group — causes the beginning of the stimulus to have a greater reflexogenic strength than its continuation — a well-known fact from CR experiments. On the other hand neurones of group 2 continue to be activated after the cessation of the stimulus and thus form a basis of the recent memory traces of that stimulus. As far as neurones of group 3 are concerned — pure off-elements — they account for the *active role* played by the cessation of a stimulus (again well known from the CR experiments) and also for the recent memory traces of this cessation. And so while neurones of group 2 account for *common* features of a stimulus and its traces and provide a basis for their mutual generalization, neurones of group 3 account for diversity of the stimulus and its trace and form a basis for their possible differentiation. Various moments of the trace of the stimulus differ among themselves in that with a lapse of time fewer and fewer elements of groups 2 and 3 are activated. And so the more remote the trace of the stimulus, the less its reflexogenic strength, a fact which is again supported by much experimental evidence.

We have a strong inclination to believe that the 'sense of time' of men and other animals, i.e. the sense of the varying durations of time which have elapsed since a definite event, is based on nothing else than the strength of traces left by this event at various moments after its cessation. The weaker these traces the more remote in time the given event seems to be.

5. THE PROBLEM OF LOCALIZATION OF REVERBERATING CIRCUITS

If the above hypothesis is correct then the problem arises as to where the reverberating circuits responsible for recent memory are situated. The simplest assumption is that they are localized in the associative areas of the cerebral cortex — as decorticated animals possess hardly any recent memory — in close vicinity to the respective sensory projection areas. In consequence we may expect that the destruction of these associative areas should lead to the abolition of recent memory for stimuli in the given sensory modality.

Let us analyse from this point of view the functions of the prefrontal area, i.e. that associative area which was first recognized as having to do with recent memory in the classical experiments by Jacobsen (1936). As is well known this author demonstrated that after bilateral ablations of the prefrontal area in monkeys delayed responses are abolished and he attributed this defect to the loss of 'immediate memory', as contrasted with the full preservation of 'stable memory'. The results of Jacobsen were afterwards confirmed by many authors, but his interpretation was subjected to much criticism. It was argued that the impairment of delayed responses is due not to the lack of 'immediate memory' but to the enhanced distractability of prefrontal animals (Malmo, 1942; Wade, 1947; Harlow et al., 1952), to their hypermotility (Wade, 1947) or to the impairment of associative functions (Nissen et al., 1938; Finan, 1942).

In our experiments on delayed responses with dogs (Ławicka and Konorski, 1959) we used an experimental setting (Fig. 1) which allowed us to observe and analyse the changes in animal's behaviour after operation more clearly than was possible in the Wisconsin apparatus. We have found that after ablations of the frontal poles rostral to the presylvian sulcus (Fig. 3) the animals, completely or almost completely, lose their

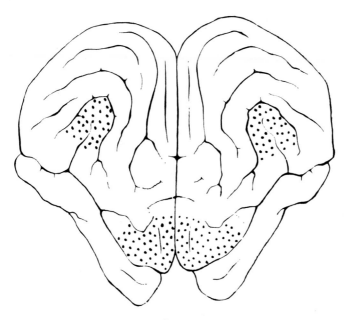

FIG. 3

The cerebral cortex of dog represented in two dimensions (if the sheet of paper is bent along the longitudinal axis, the three-dimensional picture of the cortex is obtained). The prefrontal associative areas and temporal associative areas removed in corresponding experiments are stippled.

capacity to remember in which direction they have to go in the delayed response test. Being released after the delay period they 'follow their nose', i.e. go to that food tray to which they are just turned. If the delay period is short and no distracting stimulus has intervened, the dogs are able to preserve their bodily orientation towards that food tray which was signalled and then they are able to react correctly; we have called this type of reaction a 'pseudo-delayed response' since it is due not to the recent memory of the cue but to the actual direction of the body and head. But if the animals' attention is diverted for a moment, so that they change their bodily orientation, then they will go either in the other direction or will not go anywhere. Of course they are also not able to go to the proper food tray after receiving food on the starting platform, or after being taken out of the room. When two signals are given, one after the other, the dog after release, if not distracted, goes correctly to the last signalled food tray and does not go to the other one. In other respects the general behaviour of our prefrontal dogs does not differ from that before operation, in particular they do not display any hyperactivity or exaggerated reactions to new stimuli.

Our experimental data seem to support the original idea of Jacobsen that the impairment of delayed responses in prefrontal animals is due to the loss of recent memory. However, this statement requires one substantial qualification, namely, that not *all* kinds of recent memory are impaired after prefrontal lesions but only recent memory of *directional cues*. In fact we have so far no evidence to show that other sorts of recent memory are also affected by these lesions and we have already some evidence that it is not so. One bit of it is provided by Mishkin and Pribram (1956) who have found that delayed responses in simple go-no-go tests were not impaired in prefrontal monkeys. Another one will be presented later.

The important problem arises as to why it is that only the recent memory of directional cues is destroyed after prefrontal lesions. We think that a tentative answer to this question can be given.

The extensive study made recently by Sołtysik in our laboratory (in preparation) concerning the effects of caudate lesions on delayed responses revealed that these lesions produce striking disorders of orienting reactions. The animals either do not visibly pay any attention to the auditory stimuli, or are not able to locate correctly the source of the stimulus even during its operation. When after some time this deficit is compensated the delayed responses are as much destroyed as in prefrontal animals. These animals are also severely impaired in all locomotor CRs, not being able to find their way to the familiar places they ran to hundreds of times before operation.

Although premotor cortex was not specially studied from this point of view, nevertheless as observed by I. Stępień et al. (in preparation) premotor lesions, and even more so premotor-prefrontal lesions, also produce striking defects in the animal's orientation in space and orienting reactions. The connections between caudate nucleus and pericruciate region were emphasized by several authors (cf. Purpura et al.).

All these data show that both premotor area and the rostral part of caudate nucleus play an important part in general orientation of animals in space, i.e. in reacting correctly to directional cues and in formation and retention of locomotor CRs. Therefore, it is quite reasonable to believe that the prefrontal area, or rather some yet undefined part of it, is closely functionally connected with these regions supplying the reverberating circuits responsible for recent memory of those cues which subserve this orientation.

But it seems that much more precise analysis of the relations between projection areas and adjacent associative areas can be carried out with respect to the recent memory of exteroceptive stimuli on the basis of the test described in section 3. The corresponding experiments were performed by Chorążyna and L. Stępień in our laboratory (unpublished). After the dogs were trained to differentiate between pairs of identical tones (S_xS_x) and different tones (S_xS_y), the areas situated ventral to the auditory projective area, namely gyrus sylviacus anterior and posterior (Fig. 3), were bilaterally removed. After this operation the dogs lost completely and irreversibly the ability to differentiate such pairs, although not only *simple* differentiations, but even conditioned inhibition (see footnote on page 6) was fully preserved (Fig. 4). In other words, the animal was able to differentiate between the auditory stimulus S — positive CS — and the auditory compound S_oS — inhibitory CS — because stimulus S_o elicited a negative *attitudinal* reaction which was retained or remembered during the action of S.

On the other hand ablation of the prefrontal area did not impair the performance of our test.[1] This shows that the prefrontal area has probably nothing to do with recent memory of auditory stimuli. It is of interest to note that partial bilateral ablations of the auditory projection area also did not affect this test.

Similar results were obtained by Goldberg *et al.* (1957) in cats. After bilateral removal of ventral parts of the temporal region discrimination between groups of tones which differed only in temporal patterning was lost, although simple tonal discriminations were preserved.

Even more convincing experiments were recently performed by Stępień *et al.* (personal communication). These authors, as mentioned before, used our test for investigating visual and auditory recent memory in monkeys. After the animals were trained to differentiate between pairs of identical and different rhythmical stimuli, both acoustic (clicks) and visual (flashes), different parts of the temporal lobes were bilaterally

[1] After prefrontal ablation the animal was disinhibited for several weeks (Brutkowski *et al.*, 1956) and therefore displayed a positive reaction to both excitatory and inhibiting stimuli, but this defect was soon totally compensated.

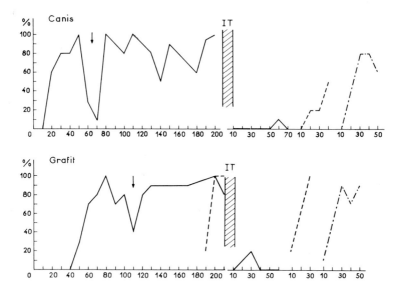

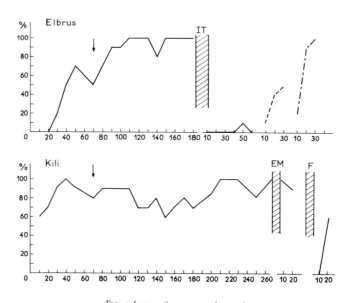

FIG. 4 (*see caption on opposite page*)

removed. After ablation of the anterior parts of the first and second temporal gyri the differentiation of the pairs of auditory stimuli was lost, while the performance of the same test with visual stimuli was preserved. The opposite was found after the ablation of the posterior parts of the second and third temporal gyri and gyrus fusiformis.

6. RELATIONS BETWEEN RECENT AND STABLE MEMORY

It is now generally accepted that recent memory is based on the activity of reverberating chains of neurones, whereas stable, or permanent memory is due to some structural changes produced in the brain. The kind of changes with which we have to do here has been a matter of much speculation. One of the possible hypotheses is that put forward long ago by Tanzi (1893), Ramón y Cajal (1911), Ariens Kappers (1917), Child (1921), Coghill (1929) and others, and recently adjusted to the CR experimental evidence by Konorski (1948). According to this hypothesis when an indifferent stimulus is reinforced by an unconditioned stimulus, the 'potential connections' established in ontogenesis between the corresponding groups of neurones are transformed into 'actual connections'. This is accomplished by growing and multiplication of synaptic contacts between the axons of the neurones representing the CS and bodies and/or dendrites of neurones representing the UCS.

Without going more deeply into that problem one must notice that all structural theories of conditioning have so far encountered one major difficulty: it is well known that quite often a CR is formed and proves to be stable even after a single reinforcement, the so-called 'one trial learning'. This means that a few seconds' simultaneous operation of the two stimuli would be sufficient for the formation of stable connections between the respective groups of neurones.

FIG. 4
The effects of cortical lesions on acoustic recent memory in dogs.
Each graph represents the percentages of negative (correct) responses, i.e. lack of movement for each dog to the inhibitory CS-i in successive blocks of ten inhibitory trials.
IT, infratemporal ablation, EM, ablation of gyrus ectosylvius medius, F, prefrontal ablation. Continuous lines, responses to inhibitory compound stimuli, S_xS_y (acoustic recent memory test). Dashed lines, responses to inhibitory stimulus in simple acoustic differentiation. Dashed-dotted lines, reactions to inhibitory compound of conditioned inhibition, S_0S.
Arrows in the course of tone-relation differentiation (S_xS_x vs. S_xS_y) denote the end of preliminary training in which only particular pairs of tones were applied.
In the first three dogs tone-relation differentiation was totally abolished after infratemporal lesion. Both differentiation and conditioned inhibition were easily established after operation. In the fourth dog bilateral removal of middle ectosylvian gyrus did not affect the tone-relation differentiation; the removal of prefrontal areas caused the general syndrome of disinhibition which was soon compensated.

This difficulty can now be overcome if we take into account the fact that each of the stimuli taking part in conditioning leaves transient traces in the nervous system such that the respective central representations of the stimuli are excited for a much longer time than the duration of the stimuli themselves.

If the proposed mechanism of the transformation of recent memory traces into stable memory traces is correct, then one should predict that cutting the first ones short in some way or other, for instance by electro-convulsive shock, would lead to slowing down or even preventing the process of conditioning.

Such experiments were in fact performed by a number of authors and gave clear positive results. Duncan (1949) was the first to apply ECS after each conditioning trial in rats and he showed that the closer the application of the shock is to the trial, the stronger is its disrupting effect upon learning. Later the co-workers of Gerard (1955) and Thompson and Dean (1955) applied ECS at various times after a single session of discrimination learning and again proved that the shorter the interval between the learning session and the shock, the poorer is the animal's retention after 24 hours.

All these data show that after the termination of the learning trial, or a massed series of trials, the consolidation of the CR continues and that this phenomenon depends on some on-going process in the nervous system. It is quite reasonable to believe that this is exactly the same process which is involved in the recent memory phenomena described in earlier sections.

The important role played in the formation of CRs by recent memory may explain some other facts connected with learning which would otherwise be difficult to understand. It has been shown by Chow (1951), Mishkin and Pribram (1954) and others that the ablation of posterior ventral parts of the temporal lobes in monkeys abolishes or greatly impairs visual discriminations established before operation. However, Orbach and Fantz (1958) found recently that if before operation the animals were given prolonged, post-criterional overtraining, then the discrimination habit suffered little or no decrement after inferotemporal lesions. If we assume that the 'learning to criterion' of a visual discrimination is largely based on recent memory, i.e. that the animal remembers from trial to trial and from day to day which figure is positive and which negative, then this would explain why after a partial destruction of the visual association area the habit is greatly impaired. On the other hand if with long training the habit becomes based on stable memory, then no post-operative deficit would ensue. It is worth while to stress that the ablation of the same area in monkeys produced a total abolition of recent memory of visual stimuli tested by our method in recent experiments by Stępień et al.

To sum up, we believe that the inferotemporal area in monkeys contains reverberating chains of neurones connected with the visual projection area and therefore lesions in this area produce the deficit of recent memory observed either directly by using our test, or indirectly by using not very firmly established visual discrimination habits.

To end this section it is necessary to draw attention to the striking deficits of recent memory found in recent years in humans after hippo-campal lesions (Milner and Penfield, 1955; Scoville and Milner, 1957; and others). Similar results were recently obtained after hippocampal lesions in monkeys by Stępień et al. with respect to both visual and auditory stimuli. The physiological mechanism of these deficits seems to us so far not clear and they require more detailed investigation.

SUMMARY

In this paper the general review of the existing experimental material concerning recent memory in animals is presented and possible mechan-isms of this phenomenon are discussed.

It has been shown that recent memory is involved in trace CRs (section 1), in delayed responses (section 2) and in those forms of CRs in which, in order to display a correct response the animal has to compare two succes-sive stimuli (section 3). It has been assumed that the mechanism of recent memory depends on throwing into activity reverberating circuits of neurones, connected with neurones engaged in perception of a given stimulus, and probably situated in the so-called association areas surround-ing the given projection area (section 4). As delayed responses appear to be based on the recent memory of directional cues, it is understandable that they are destroyed after lesions in prefrontal cortex situated in the vicinity of premotor area and caudate nucleus, structures directly concerned with the animal's orientation in space. Similarly acoustic recent memory is destroyed by lesion in gyri sylviaci in dogs and cats and anterior parts of temporal gyri in monkeys; visual recent memory is destroyed after inferotemporal lesions in monkeys (section 5).

Recent memory plays a prominent role in the consolidation processes of conditioning, since it causes a much more prolonged activation of groups of neurones concerned in a given conditioning than is provided by the actual operation of the corresponding stimuli (section 6). Therefore, the more powerful is the reverberating system of neurones within a given analyser in a given species, the more perfect and long lasting is the recent memory of the corresponding stimuli and the more rapid is the process of consolidation of the respective CRs.

GROUP DISCUSSION

ROSVOLD. I would like to ask Dr Konorski, from the point of view of the position put forth in his paper, how he would account for the fact that in the literature there are many papers that deal with the impairment of sensory discrimination following frontal lobe lesions.

KONORSKI. As we have established in our laboratory, prefrontal ablations produce two different sorts of impairment: one is that discussed in this paper, namely the loss of recent memory of directions involved in delayed response tests; the second is the impairment of inhibitory conditioned reflexes. While the first one is, according to our data, irreversible, the second one is, on the contrary, compensated with further training. It is clear that the symptom described in Rosvold and Mishkin's paper belongs to the second category. We suppose that both these symptoms are of different origin and mechanism, and we try now to check this supposition by experiments.

ROSVOLD. With reference to the permanence of these deficits, I would say that contrary to Jacobsen's earlier statements, in the chimpanzee the deficit is not permanent. Instead with training the animals gradually recover their ability to perform very well on tests of recent memory. The chimpanzee tells us another thing: a subjective thing to be sure, but we can see in watching the animals no evidence that orientation is a critical factor for those tests. In fact it is not unusual for the animal to be standing on his head when looking at the stimulus, and then turn completely over and respond correctly. Thus, even though this notion of proprioceptive recent memory being the unique function of the frontal lobes is intriguing, I am not entirely convinced that it is the answer to delayed response deficit. As Dr Konorski stated, we simply do not know what the stimulus factors in the delayed response problem really are. We have assiduously tried to determine what it is in this problem that the animal is responding to or by what means he is responding. We have not been able to demonstrate definitely what it is in the test situation that the animal uses as the basis for his solution of the problem. This is why there is so much speculation about the probable function of the frontal lobes. Probably the only resolution is the development of a test method in which the stimulus and response variables will be clearly delineated.

HEBB. I would like to add to this that bilateral total removal in another species produces no sign of defect: even better than in the chimpanzee.

KONORSKI. In man, yes.

ESTABLE. I am very much interested in Professor Konorski's communication that gives rise to so many problems. Obviously the only objection, if it can be called that, is that we have on one side techniques to study the central nervous system and on the other side techniques to study psychological problems, and the bridge is always there, but it is hard to correlate and the passage from one to the other is hard to interpret.

One must be precise with terms and when one says centre, for instance, one must not think that the centre of the spoken word means that the spoken word is generated there. If a cortical area is destroyed and the spoken word is perturbed or disappears, all that one can say is that the cortical area is necessary but not sufficient for the reproduction of the spoken word.

The fact that neurones are incapable of reproducing themselves is perhaps the price we have to pay to have memories and habits and other learned capacities which persist throughout life. If neurones died and were substituted by others, it is hard to conceive how these functions could be preserved.

Reverberation circuits may be the basis of learning but perhaps they are not enough. Do you, Dr Konorski, conceive as different phenomena: habits, organic memory and memory itself?

KONORSKI. As far as I know in dogs and in monkeys the loss of recent memory of directions after prefrontal ablations is irreversible. Moreover, in some of our animals, there was only a partial deficit of recent memory, due perhaps to smaller lesions. Why in Dr Rosvold's chimpanzee the deficit of recent memory is reversible, should be explained by further experimentation. As far as patients with pre-frontal lesions are concerned, they are able to solve the delayed response test very well. We believe that it is so because their memory of directions is supported, or even based, on visual cues and also on verbal recent memory which in man, is very powerful.

I agree that we are not able so far to state definitely which sorts of cues are responsible in delayed response tests, although it seems that this problem may be solved by further experimentation.

To answer Professor Estable, I would like to stress once more that, according to our view, conditioned reflexes, including habits as a particular form, are chiefly based on stable or static, or organic memory, while such forms of behaviour which are involved in delayed responses are based on transient or dynamic memory.

OLDS. I wish to address myself to the experiments where the so-called auditory association areas were removed, and where Dr Konorski says his experiment was on recent memory, for an auditory stimulus. I wish to suggest the possibility that these were not experiments on recent memory at all, but possibly on the animal's ability to compare two stimuli. It seems to me that the way this could be tested is to have the stimulus and the comparison stimulus (another S_x or S_y) presented somehow simultaneously. If the deficit is in the animal's ability to compare, he will fail this test. If it is in recent memory, he will pass. One might also ask the question of the delayed response technique again here and ask if it is really fair to reject the delayed response as a test for recent memory of a particular (e.g. auditory) stimulus. One might develop some text in which a given tone S_x would not signify a direction but an abstract contingency and find whether excision of the auditory association areas prevented an auditory memory which involved no comparison.

KONORSKI. As to the first question of Dr Olds I agree that the test proposed by us is based on comparison of two stimuli, which is rendered impossible by the loss of recent memory. Whether or not there is any special function which may be called 'comparison' — I do not know.

As to the second question I would remind that, as shown in my paper, the removal of pre-frontal areas did not impair the recent memory of particular auditory stimuli, as proved by our recent memory test.

K

ANOKHIN. I should like to make two comments on Dr Konorski's very interesting report. The brain, as a specific substance has two possibilities for 'remembering', each of which can be related to what Dr Konorski relates to 'recent memory'. There is first of all the ability of a nervous substance to associate any successive stimuli coming from the inner or outer world of the organism. On account of its ability to conduct stimuli rapidly and multilaterally and of its ability to retain in the synaptic systems the molecular changes which have taken place, the nervous tissue 'remembers' any succession of stimuli brought upon it. That is the most direct and universal memory which fits under the name of 'recent memory'.

This memory, however, represents a specific advance effected by the nervous system in relation to the acting agents of the outside world.

For a given association to become stable, it has to end by a strong emotional discharge, i.e. has to end by some event which is meaningful for the life of the organism.

Thus in my view, to study the physiological mechanisms of 'recent memory' consists basically in discovering those concrete processes which occur as a result of emotional discharges and spread in the direction of the cerebral cortex, retaining there fleeting temporary associations.

As is shown by the unavoidable extinction of desynchronization when training for the association 'sound-light', a final consolidation of such ephemeral associations is indispensable.

ASRATYAN. Food boxes are very important factors in recent memory. Do you think the rule of the tonic conditional reflex, as we name it, plays a role in this recent memory?

BUSER. I wish to ask Dr Konorski if he has some information on the thalamic connections of the cortical areas which were ablated in his experiments.

KONORSKI. I think that Asratyan's 'tonic conditioned reflexes' are based on the same principles as ordinary conditioned reflexes, i.e. when firmly established, they are due to stable memory traces.

Our lesion producing the loss of delayed responses comprised gyrus proreus, subproreus and the anterior part of gyrus orbitalis. The vessels in presylvian sulcus were usually spared. These lesions produce degeneration in dorso-medial nucleus of the thalamus. Other degenerations were not so far studied.

CONDITIONED REFLEXES ESTABLISHED BY COUPLING ELECTRICAL EXCITATION OF TWO CORTICAL AREAS[1]

R. W. DOTY AND C. GIURGEA

Is the mere coincidence of action of two stimuli sufficient to form a learned association between them, or is some motivational factor also required? This has been a persistent question in psychology (and psychiatry) and is of major importance in any attempt to solve the riddle of the neural mechanisms subserving learning. Human experience is too complex to provide an answer despite the long history of 'associationism' as a science. In animal experimentation, on the other hand, it has been difficult to demonstrate learning or establish conditioned reflexes when motivation or 'drive reduction' have been unequivocally absent.

The pertinent evidence has been reviewed elsewhere (Giurgea, 1953a). The experiments of Loucks (1935), however, are of special interest since they are the direct antecedents of our own. In several dogs Loucks stimulated the 'motor' cortex through permanently implanted electrodes effecting a movement of one of the animal's limbs. With each animal on as many as 600 occasions over several days he preceded the motor stimulation with an auditory conditional stimulus (CS). The CS never came to evoke the movement with which it was so thoroughly paired, nor any other movements. A food reward was then introduced to follow the CS and the induced movement. Within a few trials the animal began moving to the CS. Loucks drew the justifiable conclusion from these experiments that the motivational element was essential to the formation of conditioned reflexes and these results have had a wide and well-deserved influence on psychological theory since that time.

Louck's position was apparently confirmed by Masserman (1943) who failed to obtain any signs of conditioning when stimulation of the hypothalamus was used as US. However, Brogden and Gantt (1942) were able to produce movements by presenting a CS alone after repeated pairing of CS and stimulation of the cerebellum. In some animals the 'conditioned response' (CR) so elicited was very similar to the movement induced by cerebellar stimulation. Motivation seemed to be absent here.

[1] New research reported here was supported by grants to R. W. Doty from the Foundations' Fund for Research in Psychiatry and the National Institutes of Neurological Diseases and Blindness (B-1068), and by a travel grant to C. Giurgea from the Academy of the Rumanian Peoples Republic.

In 1951, while working in the laboratories of P. S. Kupalov seeking further confirmation of the hypothesis of 'shortened conditioned reflexes', it was discovered that conditioned reflexes could readily be formed by pairing stimuli at two cortical points (Giurgea, 1953 a, b). Stimulation of occipital cortex which is initially without apparent effect ultimately produces movement highly similar to that elicited by the stimulation of the sigmoid gyrus with which it is paired. This direct contradiction of the results of Loucks seems best explained by differences in the timing of presentation of stimuli. In all his experiments Loucks (1935) used intertrial intervals of 2 minutes or less, usually 30-60 seconds, whereas an intertrial interval of 3-5 minutes was used in our experiments. If the intertrial interval is reduced to 2 minutes even after such CRs have been established, the CRs disappear in the majority of dogs tested so far (Giurgea, 1953 a, b), although the unconditioned response (UR) is unaffected.

Continuing these studies, it has been shown that formation of CRs by cortical stimulation is not dependent upon sensory endings in the meninges since the CR may be readily established after destruction of the Gasserian ganglion (Raiciulescu, Giurgea and Savescu, 1956). A CR established to stimulation of parietal-occipital cortex as CS was also elicited by a tonal or photic CS (Giurgea and Raiciulescu, 1957). In two animals with total, histologically confirmed section of the corpus callosum CRs were established even though CS and US were applied to different hemispheres (Raiciulescu and Giurgea, 1957; Giurgea, Raiciulescu and Marcovici, 1957). The electrical activity recorded from the US area does not appear to be changed by this conditioning procedure and is within normal limits of low voltage, fast activity very shortly after the US is applied (Giurgea and Raiciulescu, 1959). In none of these experiments does the behaviour of the dogs indicate even the slightest element of motivation. This impression has now been confirmed objectively in the experiments reported below.

TECHNIQUE

The experiments at Michigan have so far been performed on four dogs, two cats and two cynomolgous monkeys. The dogs are restrained easily by placing their legs through plastic loops (e.g. Fig. 1). Cats are held by placing their heads through a heavy plastic stock leaving their limbs free. Monkeys are kept permanently seated in a Lilly-type chair (Mason, 1958). All animals are adapted to restraint prior to electrode implantation. During the experiment the animals are isolated and observed through a 'one-way' glass.

The cortex is stimulated through platinum electrodes, usually resting on the pial surface or just beneath it although in some dogs the thickness of the skull made such adjustment difficult. Two of four electrodes are carried in 7 mm. diameter plastic buttons which are held in trephine holes by means of screws (Doty, Rutledge and Larsen, 1956). Flexible 0.5 mm. diameter polyethylene insulated wires connect the electrodes to an 18 or 34 contact receptacle permanently secured to the skull by stainless steel posts (Doty, 1959).

Stimulation consists of 1 msec. rectangular current pulses at a frequency of 50/sec. and is monitored on a cathode-ray oscilloscope with a long-persistence screen. Great care is taken to keep the stimulating circuits and the animals isolated from ground and to avoid any other possibility of stimulation outside that intended.

Prior to pairing CS and US the effects of stimulation are observed for each electrode pair. It is advantageous to have several pairs of electrodes in 'motor' cortical areas so that the chances are increased for procuring a relatively simple movement to serve as an UR. By means of automatic and silent control the CS is presented for 3-4 seconds and is slightly overlapped by the US of 1-1.5 seconds duration. Six to ten combinations of CS and US are made daily.

After study of CS-US coupling is complete, the animals are trained in the same experimental chamber to press a lever to obtain food. The lever is then connected to administer cortical stimulation with each press.

RESULTS

Dog Alpha. All stimulation in the 'motor' cortical regions produced stiff, complex and unnatural movements. That finally chosen as an UR was a lifting and extension of the right hind leg, a slight lifting and curling of the tail, and a rotation of the head to the midline and down (Fig. 1). The US was 1.8 mA. applied just posterior to the left postcrucial sulcus. The CS of 1.1 mA. was applied to the left posterior suprasylvian gyrus. It elicited no response for the first forty-two CS-US pairings. The CS current was then increased to 2.2 mA. and elicited an opening of the eyes and turning of the head to the right, a response judged to be inherent to stimulation of this area. It was still obtained, when, later in the experiment, the CS was again reduced to 1.0 mA. The first distinct CR was seen on the thirtieth post-operative day after 108 CS-US pairings. It was a turning of the head to the midline and down, a movement similar to the head movement seen to the US and in opposition to that inherently evoked by the

CS. Movement of the leg or tail was never elicited by the CS. This CR subsequently occurred up to 100 per cent of the time in some sessions and had a threshold of about 0.3 mA. It could also be elicited by 0.4 mA. applied to a second pair of electrodes about 2 mm. distant from the original CS pair.

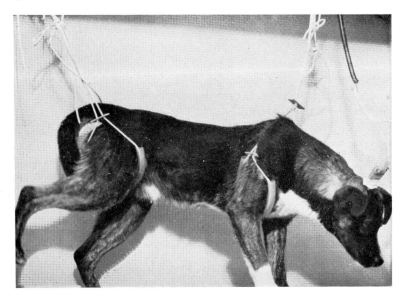

Fig. 1

Unconditioned response of *Dog Alpha* to stimulation just posterior to left postcrucial sulcus.

The same CR was evoked by a CS of 3/seconds clicks after one session (eight trials) combining this CS with the UR. A second UR was coupled with 9/seconds clicks as CS. This at first produced the previous CR which gradually became modified to a sidewise oscillation of the head with nose pointing down. This new 'CR', however, had nothing in common with the second UR.

It was very difficult to teach this dog to eat in the experimental situation. Once trained, however, the animal pressed the lever repeatedly despite accompanying CS or US stimulation which in the case of the US produced violent movements. In contrast, if the side of the cage was tapped gently each time the lever was pressed, two or three taps abolished all pressing for the rest of the session.

Dog Beta. A US of 2.0 mA. at the right postcruciate gyrus produced a brisk, well-integrated flexion of the left hind leg as its only apparent effect. The CS at the right marginal gyrus gave no overt sign at intensities up to 2.2 mA. The first sign of movement to this CS occurred during the sixth session, forty-fifth pairing. The slight tossing of the head and indefinite movements such as stepping or shifting posture seen then subsequently became very common. On the sixty-sixth pairing two 10-cm. flexions of the left hind leg, held for about 1 second each, were seen as the only movement to the CS. This was the first CR. This type of CR occurred seventy-four times in 171 subsequent CS presentations (including extinction) and had a threshold of 0.95 mA. It was not extinguished by eighty-four presentations of the CS alone at 2-3 minute intervals for eleven sessions. These CRs were also obtained to stimulation of the right posterior ectosylvian gyrus indicating some generalization had occurred.

Technical difficulties prevented testing this dog in the lever-pressing situation. However, the animal was extraordinarily sensitive and yelped violently even when grasped gently by the scruff of the neck. Yet there was no evidence of pain or emotion during the training sessions, and the animal ran each day to the experimental room and jumped into the enclosure to be harnessed.

Dog Gamma. Stimulation at 0.4 mA. 1.5 mm. above the right pyramid in the field H_1 of Forel was used as US. It produced a forceful extension of the neck and rotation of the head over the right shoulder, wider opening of the eyes, flaring of the nostrils and occasionally a lifting of the right lip (Fig. 2). This response was elicited sixty-eight times in ten sessions with no particular alteration in the animal's behaviour. Pairing of the US with a CS of 3/second clicks was then begun. A CR of turning the head up and 130° right was elicited by the CS on the sixteenth trial and similar CRs occurred on forty-eight of ninety-six subsequent presentations. The CS also evoked great agitation, whining and yelping. Both the CRs and this agitation to the CS were extinguished in three sessions totalling twenty-two presentations of the CS alone.

Lever-pressing behaviour was little altered by coupling with stimulation of the postcruciate gyrus producing a hind-leg left. It was slowed greatly by the click CS or other sounds, and abolished immediately by the US.

Dog Epsilon. Stimulation at right or left postcruciate gyri produced well co-ordinated, maximal flexions of left or right forelegs respectively. Stimulation of left posterior ectosylvian gyrus with 1.8 mA. or right mid-marginal gyrus with 1.6 mA. produced no response when tested initially. Stimulation at the latter points was then used as CS and at the former as

US. For convenience the prefix 'R' or 'L' will be used to designate to which hemisphere the stimulus was applied, e.g. L-CS with R-US means CS applied to left posterior ectosylvian gyrus, US to right post cruciate.

For the first forty pairings of R-CS with R-US there was no response to the R-CS. During the next few sessions the R-CS frequently elicited a lowering of the head and flexion of the right foreleg as shown in Fig. 3, i.e. the limb opposite that in which the UR was induced. The first left

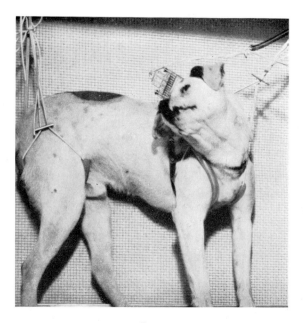

FIG. 2
Unconditioned response of *Dog Gamma* to stimulation in right
field H_1 of Forel.

foreleg CR occurred on the eighty-first presentation of R-CS and in the next 113 trials occurred fifty-eight times. These CRs were discrete, 4-20 cm. elevations of the left foreleg held for several seconds and frequently returned to the floor prior to the UR. The threshold for CR elicitation was 0.5-0.7 mA. Other movements, not so specific, occurred regularly, so that movement now occurred 95 per cent of the time to this CS.

L-CS was now paired four times with R-US, and except for the first presentation produced flexions of the right foreleg (again opposite to the UR) each time. Two sessions later differentiation was begun and continued

TABLE I

INITIAL FAILURE OF DIFFERENTIATION IN DOG EPSILON

Stimulus location	Total differentiation trials	LFL CRs	RFL 'CRs'
R-CS, R-US	50	11	7
L-CS, no US	44	14	5

for twelve sessions with results as shown in Table I. Obviously no differentiation occurred under these conditions; CRs were maintained to stimulation of either area though the percentage of occurrence to R-CS may have
declined.

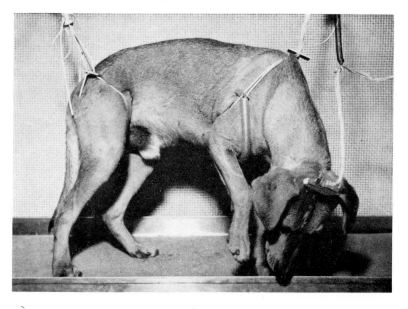

FIG. 3
One of the first conditioned responses of *Dog Epsilon* to stimulation of right marginal gyrus.
At this time the CR is in the 'wrong' leg, but in subsequent trials the left foreleg, the one lifted
to the US, lifted to this CS (Doty, 1959).

It is characteristic of these animals (Giurgea, 1953 a, b) that just prior to
the appearance of the first CRs and frequently thereafter, movements of
the affected limb occur sporadically during the intertrial period. This
phenomenon was observed in Dogs *Beta* and *Epsilon*. These movements

might possibly arise from some 'irritative' process consequent to the repeated presentation of the US, but the following experiments show this is not the case. Using the usual timing and parameters, the L-US alone was presented 100 times in twelve sessions producing a forceful right fore-leg flexion each time. No spontaneous lifts of this limb occurred in this period. Another 150 presentations were then given in which L-US preceded L-CS by irregular intervals. Initially L-CS still gave some left foreleg CRs or other movements, but these reactions were extinguished by this procedure since for the last seventy presentations there was no response whatever to L-CS. Orthodox temporal relations for L-CS and L-US were then used. At first this restored the nonspecific movements, then left foreleg CRs and ultimately right foreleg CRs occurred about 50 per cent of the time to L-CS at a threshold of 0.7 mA.

The R-CS was then presented for the first time in 79 days. The left foreleg was lifted 15 cm., flexing at the wrist, and was held so for about 5 seconds. Ultimately it was possible to obtain right leg flexions to L-CS and left leg flexions to R-CS.

Coupling L-CS, L-US or R-US with the animal's lever-pressing had no effect, whereas auditory stimuli or R-CS completely abolished pressing. The effect of R-CS had been predictable on the basis of behaviour changes seen as soon as the use of R-CS was resumed (after the hiatus described above). Since more than 5 months had then elapsed from time of electrode implantation it seems likely trigeminal fibres had grown into this medial electrode location.

Monkey 1. The CS of 1.0 mA. applied to the left occipital pole consistently produced movement of the eyes, and sometimes the head down and to the right. At any time during this stimulation, however, the eyes might be moved elsewhere if attention was so directed. The 0.2 mA. US (300/second) in the left precentral cortex produced a smooth, vigorous flexion of the right forearm and contraction of the muscles on the right side of the neck and face causing the mouth to open (Fig. 4). Coupling of the CS and US was begun 2 weeks after surgery and continued for 4 weeks, 200 trials in twenty-four sessions. In these 200 trials the right arm made random movements during the CS eleven times. Obviously there was no conditioning. During the next 25 weeks the animal was used sporadically for testing various lever-pressing procedures with fruit juice rewards.

Coupling of CS and US was then resumed. The effects of these stimuli were still exactly as they had been 7 months earlier. Using a two-minute intertrial interval for the first fifty-one trials in five sessions there was no sign of conditioning. A four-minute interval was then used for trials

52 to 84. The first CR was seen on the sixty-seventh pairing. The right arm was flexed to the level of the restraining collar, then extended along its lower surface with fingers fluttering as though seeking an object. In the next forty-seven trials a movement similar to this occurred to the CS thirty-one times. At the threshold current of 0.55 mA. or during the later phases of subsequent extinction sessions the movement was more likely to be a simple flexion very similar to that evoked by the US (Fig. 4). Even when the movement was vigorous, it often terminated prior to the US.

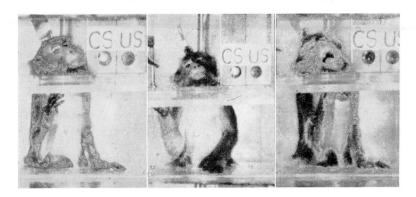

FIG. 4

Responses of *Monkey 1*, enlarged from a 16 mm. colour film which was taken through a one-way mirror. *Left* and *centre*: conditioned flexions of right forearm to CS at left occipital cortex. The slight inclination of the head to the right, which also imitates a movement of the UR, was sometimes seen with high intensities of the CS before conditioning was begun and hence cannot accurately be considered a part of the CR, although its consistency and threshold of elicitation may have been altered by the conditioning procedure. The CS and US signal lights were used only during photography. *Right*: unconditioned response to stimulation of left precentral cortex. Note similarity of end point of this response to that obtained by Delgado from stimulation of the rhinal fissure (Delgado, 1959, Fig. 1 top).

In ninety-one presentations of the CS given in five sessions without the US this CR was elicited fifty-six times. One-minute intervals were frequently employed. In two sessions after repeated presentations of the CS without the US, the CR was absent for five or more consecutive trials. The head and eye movements evoked by the CS were still present during this period of extinction. On several occasions it was noted, however, that the eyes closed at the onset of the CS and the animal appeared to drowse even though the eyes could be seen moving beneath the lids.

Stimulation with an electrode pair within 2-3 mm. of those used as CS gave no eye movements if the polarity of the stimulus was negative for the electrode separated from the others by a small sulcus. None the less the

CR was evoked from this pair with this polarity three times in six stimulations, never using the US. Stimulation in the right posterior parietal lobe elicited eye and head movements which were almost the exact counterpart of those elicited by the CS save they were to the left. No CRs were elicited by this stimulation in nine attempts during two sessions.

With four-minute intervals and the same US there was no CR to an auditory CS despite 110 pairings in nine sessions. After this, giving the auditory CS simultaneously with the CS to the occipital pole often produced 'external inhibition' of the CR to the latter stimulus. Seventeen tests with the auditory CS alone (plus the US) elicited no CRs even though the tests were given randomly throughout twenty-four presentations in which simultaneous auditory and cortical CS (plus US) was used.

The effect of coupling various stimuli with lever-pressing was then studied. On July 11th the animal pressed the lever forty-one times in a five-minute period and with each press received a US of 0.4 mA. (double the intensity used routinely) which produced violent movements, and often convulsive after-discharges, with each press. There was no hesitation whatever in lever-pressing behaviour beyond that attributable to the physical handicap consequent to the induced movement (e.g. Fig. 5). Coupling with cortical CS was similarly without effect. On the following day, as seen in Fig. 5, a novel clicking stimulus completely disrupted the behaviour when coupled with each lever-press.

The animal was then taught in sessions of twenty trials per day to press a lever to avoid a shock to its tail. The first response to a tonal CS occurred on the thirty-third trial and a criterion of twelve avoidances in twenty CS presentations was reached in 128 trials. Generalization to 20/sec. and 5/sec. clicks as CS was immediate. The cortical CS, however, produced the former CR, a flexion of the right hand towards the chin rather than the extension to press the lever at the level of the abdomen. After twenty-five combinations of this cortical CS with the tail-shock, the animal began making lever presses to avoid this US. It took more than 100 trials, however, before the former CR was fully extinguished under these conditions. The threshold for the shock-avoidance response to cortical CS was 0.2 mA. which is significantly less than the 0.55 mA. threshold at the same electrodes for the flexion CR established without motivational context.

Monkey 2. The CS and US elicited responses very similar to those seen in *Monkey 1* save that the seizure threshold was much lower in this animal and the UR was frequently followed by a few clonic movements. The animal struggled almost continuously in the experimental situation (even when being given fruit juice) and no CRs were ever observed. Using

MONKEY # 1

12 JULY 59

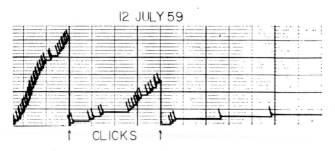

↑ CLICKS ↑

14 JULY 59

"MOTOR" CORTEX
0.4mA

15 JULY 59

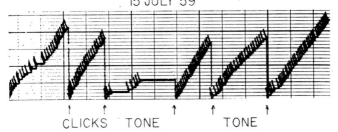

↑ ↑ CLICKS TONE ↑ ↑ TONE ↑

FIG. 5

Records of lever pressing for grape juice. The animal is rewarded for each press and this is recorded by an upward excursion of the trace. On July 12th for the five-minute period labelled 'clicks' between the arrows each lever-press turned on a clicking sound for 3 seconds in addition to operating the solenoid dispensing the juice. No tests were made on July 13th. On July 14th coupling a cortical US with each lever-press produced no disturbance in pressing behaviour beyond that attributable to the violence of the UR. On July 15th the same clicking sound used on July 12th now no longer disturbs pressing behaviour, but introduction of a 2000 cycle tone with each press brought this behaviour to a halt. Started again pressing without the tone by administration of several 'free' millilitres of juice, the monkey continues to press with only a minor slowing of rate when the tone is presented during a second period.

three-minute intervals ninety-one couplings were administered in twelve sessions. Then after a hiatus of 25 weeks another 116 combinations were given with two-minute intervals in three sessions and eighty-five combinations at four-minute intervals in four sessions. Finally, 265 couplings were given automatically at four-minute intervals in two overnight sessions, but still without indication of conditioning.

The animal was then conditioned to avoid a shock to the tail by pressing a lever. The first CR to a tonal CS required 105 trials and 238 trials to attain twelve avoidances in twenty CS presentations. Generalization to other auditory conditional stimuli was immediate and complete. The cortical CS was then employed. For 300 combinations of this CS with the tail-shock US there was, judging by the animal's general behaviour and visually observed respiration, no anticipation whatever of the impending shock during a four-second CS. Yet on every presentation the CS was patently effective since the eyes moved persistently down and to the right during each stimulation. The first CRs occurred after the CS was increased to 1.2 mA. The threshold was ultimately determined to be 0.6 mA. for the elicitation of this CR.

Cat 425. Conditioning with cortical stimulation was likewise a failure in this animal; but so too was conditioning using an auditory CS and foot-shock as US. The animal was also seizure-prone. A total of 345 pairings of a right middle ectosylvian gyrus CS with right ansate gyrus US produced no CRs, and 420 pairings of a tonal CS with foot-shock US was almost equally ineffective although a few CRs were seen.

Cat 489. This animal has been thoroughly studied by Allan Minster. The CS applied to right middle ectosylvian gyrus usually elicited no overt response initially at the currents used. At higher currents the animal looked up and to the left. The US in the right ansate area produced an abrupt turn of the head to the left and flexion of the left foreleg. The first CR occurred on the thirty-ninth pairing, fifth session. These CRs, however, never became consistent from one session to the next. In 100 trials after the first CR there were a total of only thirty-two and fifteen of these were made in three of the fifteen sessions. At first, the CR was a vigorous lifting and extension of the left foreleg, but after the seventy-second pairing the right foreleg executed this same movement to the CS more often than did the left. The threshold for CR elicitation by stimulation of middle ectosylvian gyrus was probably about 0.8 mA. Stimulation of the right posterior ectosylvian gyrus at 0.35 mA. yielded seven right and one left foreleg CRs in eleven presentations. To date, ninety-seven pairings of the right ansate US with a CS applied to left middle suprasylvian gyrus produced only four leg lifts that could equivocally be called CRs, yet the current for this suprasylvian CS has been kept high enough that head movements initially seen to this stimulation still occurred frequently.

Ten-channel EEG records taken for each trial in this cat have not yielded much new information. Confirming Giurgea and Raiciulescu (1959) there is rarely any electrical abnormality even in the immediate vicinity of the electrodes following either CS or US. No changes characteristic of the conditioned state could be detected and it could not be predicted from the electrical record whether a CR would or would not occur. The CS in middle or posterior ectosylvian gyrus usually produced immediate electrocortical arousal whereas slower patterns frequently persisted through most of the middle suprasylvian CS. The arousal produced by CS and US, however, was minimal since 8-12/sec. rhythms returned often within 1-2 seconds after stimulus cessation.

INTERPRETATION OF RESULTS

There can be no question that conditioned reflexes can be established with cortical stimulation as US. To the thirty dogs successfully conditioned in this manner in the laboratory in Bucharest and the cats observed by Nikolayeva (1957) can be added the animals of this study extending the phenomenon to the monkey and to a wide variety of cortical electrode placements. The vagaries in the appearance of this phenomenon undoubtedly arise not only from its complexity but from ignorance of its nature and the procedures most favourable for its induction. Such problems are not unknown in the study of more usual types of conditioning.

With equal assurance one can state that, in the usual sense of the word, there is no motivation involved in the formation of CRs by coupling cortical stimulations. The animals tested so far have remained entirely insouciant to self-administered cortical stimulation of near convulsive strength inducing violent movement, yet were profoundly inhibited by moderate and innocuous auditory stimuli. There is little reason to expect the cortical stimulation might be rewarding, and there was nothing in our observations to suggest this. On the other hand where motivational factors were expected as with the possible meningeal involvement (*Dog Epsilon*) or in the field of Forel (*Dog Gamma*), the method readily confirmed this impression. It is of some interest that in *Dog Gamma* the presence of this aversive factor did not preclude some form of motor conditioning.

Besides the direct evidence gained from coupling the cortical CS and

US with lever-pressing there is equally convincing circumstantial evidence for the absence of motivation in these conditioning procedures. The extreme brevity of electrocortical arousal following the CS–US combination in *Cat 489*, or *Monkey 1* closing its eyes to doze with onset of the CS, is scarcely expected from motivational stimuli. Nor are these CR movements purposeful; rather they are physiological absurdities. They seldom prepare the animal posturally for the ensuing UR and more often than not the CR is terminated before the UR begins. Watching *Monkey 1* day after day raise its arm to stimulation of its 'visual' cortex one could not escape the feeling that this nonsensical yet persistent movement was somehow analogous to the compulsive movements of neurotic humans.

The work of Segundo and his colleagues, reported at this meeting and elsewhere (Segundo, Roig and Sommer-Smith, 1959), in which a tonal CS evokes movements similar to those elicited by electrical stimulation of centre median or the mesencephalic reticular formation as US, provide excellent confirmation of our observations — movements produced by central stimulation can be conditioned. Masserman's failure to obtain such results from hypothalamic stimulation (Masserman, 1943) stands in sharp contrast to the results with *Dog Gamma* and the work of Segundo *et al.* Obviously the hypothalamus must be carefully re-examined in this regard. The US in the experiments of Segundo *et al.* probably produced motivational effects in some of their animals, but in others it appears less clear. In any event it would be difficult to ascribe some 'biological significance' or appropriateness to the movements induced by the CS. It is equally difficult to find a motivational basis for the 'backwards' type of conditioning linking the US with the CS as analysed by Asratyan in this volume.

Since CRs can be established without a motivational factor, there is more hope that the basic phenomena of learning can be sought in neural systems sufficiently simple for meaningful analysis, perhaps with purely electrophysiological techniques. The temporal factor appears to be critical and the experiments with *Dog Gamma* and especially *Dog Epsilon* show the conditioned state is not established by the repeated, randomized excitation of US and CS systems.

Several observations support Sperry's hypothesis (1955) that the significant alteration is to be sought in the effector system. In motivated conditioning an alteration in excitability specific to the limb being conditioned can be observed some time before any CRs appear (Doty and Rutledge, 1959). In the present and earlier experiments (Giurgea, 1953 a, b) movements similar to the CR, never seen previously in the animal's behaviour, often appeared spontaneously at about the same time that CRs were first noted. The threshold of the neural heirarchy controlling the complex CR thus seems to have been lowered. The frequent generalization of these CRs to other stimuli supports this view and in *Dog Epsilon* and *Cat 489* it was observed that convulsions induced accidentally by high-current CS began with remarkably prolonged CRs.

Some animals seem to have inherently low thresholds for particular movement complexes so that stimulation at widely separated points within the nervous system will evoke the same response. For instance in *Cat 523* stimulation in sensorimotor cortex, posterior ectosylvian and middle suprasylvian gyri, and the caudate nucleus produced an abrupt turning of the head which was highly similar for the different stimulus points. Stimulation in middle ectosylvian gyrus, ventral anterior and ventral posterolateral nuclei did not produce this effect but a convulsion elicited from middle ectosylvian gyrus began with prolonged turning of the head 180° to the rear. In *Cat 365* flexion and, at higher currents, attack movements of the foreleg could be elicited by stimulation in the anterior portion of the caudate nucleus, septal region, ventral hippocampus, and periaqueductal grey. This motor response was not correlated with the motivational effects of this stimulation since caudate and septal stimulation increased lever-pressing, periaqueductal stimulation was avoided and hippocampal stimulation was 'neutral'. Stimulation of the median forebrain bundle, pyriform area and habenula which produced aversive effects in this animal did not elicit the foreleg attack movement.

The data are too limited to know whether electrodes in these areas in any cat would give these responses. The impression is gained, however, that they would not and that somehow a particular type of movement has in a given individual come to be 'prepotent' over others. The stimulating electrodes may thus be revealing the existence of 'individually acquired reflexes' (Beritoff, 1924) established through the animal's own activities. At least they are not different from the individually acquired reflexes deliberately given the animal by the stimulating electrodes during the course of our experiments. However, the relation, if any, between these phenomena must, as so many questions raised by these experiments, await further experimental analysis.

GROUP DISCUSSION

SEGUNDO. I shall first comment on the finding that motor cortical stimulation is relatively 'indifferent'. It agrees with other observations, for excitation of this region in the sleeping monkey produced no arousal unless a generalized seizure

L

occurred and, under the latter conditions, one should doubt whether wakefulness derived from stimulation itself or from proprioceptive 'feed back' resulting from clonic movements. The same 'indifference' was shown by the visual area: when the animal was awake, excitation with few volts produced investigation movements directed towards the contralateral field; when the animal was asleep, stimulation of up to 80 volts produced no effect. A different result occurred when excitation was applied to temporal pole, cingular cortex or hippocampus: with low voltages, animals were immediately aroused, both behaviourally and electroencephalo-graphically (Segundo, Arana and French, 1955). Therefore, and as far as we can infer from the influence of animal brain stimulation upon sleeping state or tendency to excite itself, certain areas are 'indifferent' and others are not.

Dr Doty mentioned that stimulation of subcortical structures may be conditioned. In our laboratory, brief tones have been reinforced by direct excitation of mesencephalic reticular formation, centre median, basolateral amygdala or head of caudate nucleus and learned responses to tones have eventually appeared. In some cases (centre median, mesencephalic reticular formation, certain amygdaloid or caudate placements) conditioned effects were practically identical to the absolute responses. In other cases, responses from different points in caudate or amygdala, could not be conditioned *in toto*; some of their components, however, could and consequently conditioned responses were similar to a part of the absolute response. In a third group of animals (also caudate or amygdala) the conditioned reaction, though consistent, was completely different to the absolute effect. This variable relationship has been found in other types of conditioning and, therefore, though difficult to interpret here, is not altogether surprising (Hilgard and Marquis, 1940).

To summarize we can say that stimulation effects of certain areas of the brain can be conditioned. The latter term seems justified in the sense that the process has many features (technique, effects, inhibitions) of classical conditioning. These studies may help to understand the physiology of learning and that of tested nuclei (Roig, Segundo, Sommer-Smith and Galeano, 1959; Segundo, Roig and Sommer-Smith, 1959).

CHOW. In your monkey work, do you worry about whether your stimulus would activate the pain sensation in your animal?

DOTY. We are very much aware that the factor of meningeal stimulation must be considered. Dr Rutledge and I have shown that stimulation of the dura mater of the saggital sinus in the cat can serve as a conditional stimulus and is undoubtedly also a nocuous stimulation. However, I feel satisfied that, as outlined in the text, this factor can be detected by the self-stimulation procedure employed and was present only as stated. In addition, Dr Girugea has established these responses in dogs after destruction of the Gasserian ganglion.

HERNÁNDEZ-PEÓN. The conditioned response obtained by Dr Doty using cortical stimuli as conditioned and unconditioned stimuli provides a method for testing definitely whether there might be some cortico-cortical connections in some cases of conditioning. And I wonder whether he has done transcortical cutting isolating the respective cortical areas and testing whether these conditioned responses persist after the transection or not.

DOTY. I think the experiments of Girugea and his colleagues showing these conditional reflexes to be established after callosal section when the conditional stimulus and unconditioned stimulus are in different hemispheres, indicate that a subcortical pathway is likely to be involved in the production of this phenomenon. Perhaps pertinent also are experiments which Dr Rutledge and I have been doing using electrical stimulation of marginal gyrus in the cat as conditional stimulus and shock to the foreleg as unconditioned stimulus. If the stimulated cortical zone is circumsected so that most of the pathways available for intracortical elaboration of the excitation are severed, conditioned reflexes still occur to the cortical conditional stimulus. If, on the other hand, the stimulated cortical zone is undercut for a total length of more than about 8 mm. the conditioned reflexes are lost. They often return, however, after about a month of training. The critical factors are not fully determined in the reappearance of conditioned reflexes after this undercutting of the stimulated cortex, but it may be that 'U' fibres are necessary. It is also not certain whether that mere passage of time is sufficient or whether it is the retraining which is critical.

KONORSKI. Did you try to extinguish these reflexes that you have established and how did you obtain the extinction?

DOTY. Dr Giurgea taught me a lot about extinction. Apparently it is extremely difficult to bring about a total extinction of a salivary conditioned reflex. Those 'temporary connections' are surprisingly permanent. Hence a technique of 'acute' extinction is used wherein the conditional stimulus is presented as one might expect without the unconditioned stimulus, but also at much shorter time intervals than employed during the establishment of the conditioned state. I objected that this alteration of procedure would not yield a proper comparison so we tried extinguishing by rather long intervals between conditioned stimulus presentations. In *Dog Beta* we got no extinction in eighty-five presentations. Hence in *Monkey 1* shown in the film, we used shorter intervals of 1-2 minutes and on the two occasions produced 'acute' extension in which the conditioned reflexes were totally absent to the conditional stimulus and in five or more consecutive presentations of the conditioned stimulus, although the animal remained alert. Giurgea has also published extinction data on some of his dogs. Our *Dog Gamma* in which an aversive factor, was present in the unconditioned stimulus showed rapid extinction.

ANOKHIN. Much of the recently gathered data points to the possibility of obtaining 'conditioned responses' by an association between the most distinct points of the brain. In fact, this trend of thought covers also some of the better-known conditioned reflexes, as the one induced by training with sound and light.

Yet a question comes reasonably to our mind: what aspect of the activity of the brain, taken as a whole, do such facts reveal? Dr Doty's interesting experiments may be taken as instances of the brain tissue's ability to act as a specialized substratum, and to establish instant links between any two stimuli which affect it simultaneously.

Our team considers that such aptitude proves the capacity of the nervous tissue to unite any separate elements during stimulation. This capacity is the basic physiological ground of any spontaneous conditioned response. But if we assume at the start that conditioned responses are a physiological function of the animal, we must consider them as the outcome of a complex physiological system, leading necessarily to an adaptation process which involves the organism as a whole.

Dr Doty tells us that he finds it difficult to draw objectively a difference between the leg-lifting response which he has induced, and the one obtained in the classical

Pavlovian test by direct application of an electric shock to the animal's paw. Yet to us, the difference seems considerable. In Pavlov's test, the subject draws away the paws from the source of stimulation, thus displaying an adaptative behaviour, which terminates in a reverse afferent drive, in our sense of the word, indicating that the animal has avoided the impact of the electric current. Besides, Dr Doty in his experiment shows the movement of limbs as the mechanical effect of a stimulation which, after having been subject to association, is now conveyed outwards onto the motor system. This proves admirably the capacity of the brain tissue to register any sequence of induced stimuli.

I wish, in concluding, to draw your attention to one important factor, which is of particular relevance, to Dr Hernández-Peón's remark on the possibility of showing pure cortico-cortical connections. Our laboratory has shown that the most insignificant stimuli, as well as lesions of the cortical tissue will instantly involve subcortical formations, and possibly, reticular ones. This is why, by the very nature of the process, no subsequent effects of stimulation can be *only cortical*.

DOTY. In reply to Dr Anokhin — I think we must simply adopt the mechanistic, objective approach which Pavlov used so successfully. If I form a conditioned reflex by using an avoidable, painful, 'biologically significant' stimulus to a forepaw so that the animal lifts it when a tonal conditional stimulus is sounded, and for the other paw proceed as Giurgea and I have done so that the other paw is lifted when the 'auditory analyser' is stimulated directly at the cortex, you would be unable to tell me simply by looking at the animal's behaviour, which conditioned reflex was which. True, by careful analysis I suspect you would find great differences in the autonomic nervous system responses to the stimuli employed, at least during some stages of the training. But their absence in the latter case only proves them to be an unnecessary complication in the process of establishing the neural alteration responsible for the change in effect of the conditional stimulus. Both tone and direct electrical stimulation of the 'auditory analyser' are initially without effect on somatic musculature save possibly for an 'orientation reflex' which is soon lost. Both become effective on the same motor apparatus in approximately the same number of trials. Both states are subject to the laws of conditioning, i.e. there is no apparent backward conditioning, there can be external inhibition, they can be extinguished. Why then call them different states or infer for them different mechanisms?

We have shown that if the ventral roots are crushed and an animal immobilized with bulbocapnine, it can still be conditioned to make conditioned reflexes with its hind leg even though the leg has never moved during conditioning. Thus we can show proprioceptive feedback from the unconditioned reflex to be unnecessary for the formation of conditioned reflexes. This does not say, that such factors are not normally present; only that they need not be. Such experimental simplification of the situation certainly does not alter significantly the process we desire to elucidate, nor change its name. In similar vein the elimination of motivational factors must not be construed to infer qualitatively different processes to be operative in 'cortical-cortical' conditioning as compared to the more usual procedures which involve such unknowns as 'biological purpose' or unanalysable emotional and subjective factors.

REFERENCES

Doty, R. W., Rutledge, L. T. and Larsen, R. M. (1956) Conditioned responses established to electrical stimulation of cat cerebral cortex. *J. Neurophysiol.* *19*, 401-15.

Giurgea, C., Raiciulescu, N. and Marcovici, G. (1957) Reflex condition — at interhemisferic prin excitarea directa corticala dupa sectionarea corpului calos. Studiu anatomo-histologic. *Revista Fiziol. Norm. Patol.* *4*, 408-14.

Doty, R. W. and Rutledge, L. T. (1959) Conditioned reflexes elicited by stimulation of partially isolated cerebral cortex. *Fed. Proc.* *18*, 37.

Beck, E. C. and Doty, R. W. (1957) Conditioned flexion reflexes acquired during combined catalepsy and de-efferentation. *J. comp. Physiol. Psychol.* *50*, 211-16.

INTERFERENCE AND LEARNING IN PALAEOCORTICAL SYSTEMS[1]

J. Olds and M. E. Olds

Recent stimulation and single-unit studies in our laboratory have convinced us that the hypothalamus with its projections to palaeocortical and related structures bears some very special relation to mechanisms of instrumental learning, and possibly to associative mechanisms in general.

INTRODUCTION

In one sense all animal-learning experiments involve response learning, for it is a changed response that signifies to the experimenter that some learning has occurred. Nevertheless, it is possible to distinguish between a type of learning that is mainly response learning, and another type that is mainly a learning of associations. The former is evidenced when an animal learns how to get food in a problem box; he has learned a new response, he has learned what to do. The latter is evidenced when an animal learns to salivate when a bell announces the present arrival of food; he does not salivate to get food but because the bell is associated with food, and the animal salivates as though the bell meant food.

In the study of learning, two basic procedures have been used with respect to these two types of learning.

In instrumental conditioning, response learning is the salient feature of the procedure. The experimenter has only one stimulus at his disposal (a reward or punishment). He awaits the response which interests him, and, when it occurs, proceeds to stimulate or to withdraw stimulation. If he stimulates with what is called a 'reward', the response in question has its repetition frequency augmented, and if the animal is rewarded again and again, the response may quickly come to dominate the animal's repertory.

In Pavlovian conditioning, association receives the emphasis. The experimenter imposes first an 'irrelevant' stimulus and then a 'relevant' one. Eventually, the irrelevant response makes the animal 'think' of the relevant one, or at least perform some response that we take as oblique evidence of such a thought. Pavlovian conditioning is thus conceptualized,

[1] The research reported here was supported by grants from the Foundations Fund for Research in Psychiatry, the National Institute of Mental Health, and the Ford Foundation.

153

usually at a hidden and unexpressed level, in terms of the association of ideas. A new association in the environment is imprinted on the animal, and we observe the conditioned response not mainly as a measure of the animal's adaptive behaviour but rather as a measure of the degree to which we have impressed the association on the animal.

Whether there is one basic mechanism with two aspects or two or more basic mechanisms is still almost entirely a matter to be decided by further experiments, although there is considerable argument pro or con association or response learning. At any rate, our experiments have taught us something rather definite about the physiological processes underlying response learning. It appears to us that our studies also have relevance to the broader problem of associative learning, but that has not yet been established. Any argument that there is only one basic mechanism with these two different aspects in the learning process will, we believe, make it even more likely that these studies involve one very important basis of learning in general.

I. SELF-STIMULATION EXPERIMENTS ON LEARNING

Self-stimulation tests (Fig. 1) described in detail elsewhere (Olds, 1958) indicate that electric stimulation in medial-forebrain-bundle regions of the hypothalamus, or in related structures of basal ganglia, paleocortex and tegmentum (Fig. 2), causes positive reinforcement of learning to the degree that animals will spend long times turning on the stimulus to the brain in preference to all other pursuits. Animals will learn to run in a runway (Fig. 3) with such stimulation as the only reinforcement; they will cross an electrified grid (Fig. 4) to reach a pedal and stimulate their brains; and they will learn rapidly to perform without errors in a multiple choice maze (Fig. 5) (Olds, 1956) with the electric stimulus to the brain as the only incentive. Both acquisition and extinction curves on all these problems compare favourably with those where the positive reinforcement (or unconditioned stimulus) is a food object. It is clear, therefore, that stimulation in these regions promotes repetition of a learned response.

II. INTERFERENCE-STIMULATION AND LEARNING

The question we went on to ask was a question that has troubled physiological psychology for some time: is there any sense in saying learning mechanisms are somehow localized in these fields? Or before we ask that, is learning localized at all?.

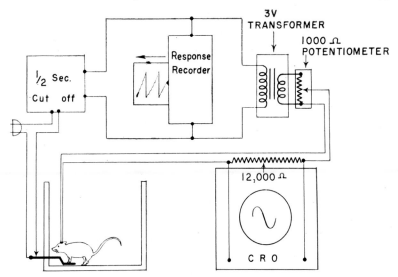

FIG. 1

Self-stimulation experiment. Animal's lever response causes $\frac{1}{2}$-second cut-off device to deliver 60-cycle current as long as lever is depressed up to $\frac{1}{2}$-second maximum, after which the animal must release and press again for more current. Current causes cumulative recorder to register response (thereby converting response rate into the slope of a graph) and causes via transformer and potentiometer a stimulus to the rat's brain which passes on the way through a constant resistor across which it is measured by cathode-ray oscilloscope. Rats respond with rates up to 12,000 responses per hour with electrodes in medial-forebrain-bundle regions.

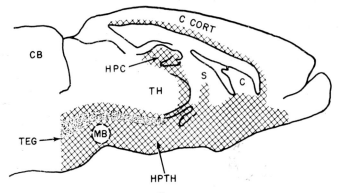

FIG. 2

Map of self-stimulation and some escape points in rat's brain. The former are indicated by cross hatching, the latter by stippling. Self-stimulation region extends from baso-medial areas of tegmentum through baso-lateral hypothalamic areas into telencephalon and then up through the basal ganglia to the whole palaeocortical system. Escape regions plotted here include the dorsal posterior hypothalamus and similarly placed points in the gementum. The escape system is now known to extend forward too.

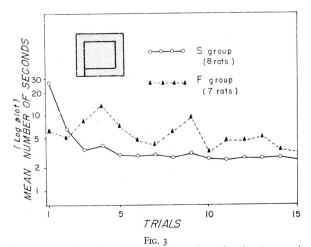

FIG. 3

Runway experiment in which animals ran faster for electric reward (solid line) than a control group running for food (dotted line) (Olds, 1956).

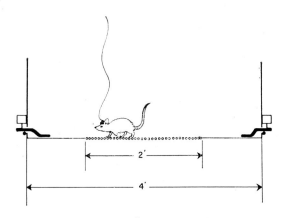

FIG. 4

Obstruction box in which animals were required to cross grid with shock to feet to reach pedal to stimulate brain. After three self-stimulations on one side, pedal became inoperable and animal crossed the grid again to get three more self-stimulations on the other side. Animal continued to shuttle as shock increased until foot shock became so high as to inhibit further self-stimulation behaviour. Foot shock of 60 μamp. stopped most rats running for food; however, one hungry rat took almost 300 μamp. for food reward. Self-stimulating rats took over 400 μamp. for hypothalamic stimulus as reward.

In some earlier attempts to answer this question following the example of Lashley (1929), surgical lesions were used, the neocortex was the primary locus of the search, and each animal learned only once so he could not serve as his own control. Very often, surgical lesions appeared to leave parallel structures to do the job; the neocortex seems *ipso facto* a narrow constraint upon the search; and individual as well as surgical differences

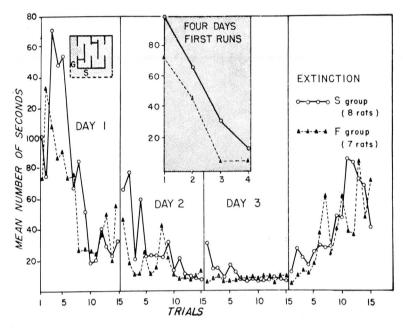

FIG. 5

Multiple-choice maze in which animals improved performance from trial to trial and from day to day, the only reward being an electric stimulus below the septal area (solid line). They are compared with a control group running for food (dotted line). Insert shows day-to-day improvement in terms of first run of the day indicating that no primer-stimulation is necessary to get rats running for electric reward.

from animal to animal make it desirable for animals to serve as their own controls.

Thus we turned to an electric stimulation (cf. Thompson, 1958; Mahut, 1957; Stein and Hearst, 1958) to 'jam' the network, to cause, that is, a temporary disarrangement of pattern which is believed to function as a temporary (reversible) lesion. We believe this has three advantages: (1) it is reversible; (2) it can be expected to project to parallel structures and thus cause a diffuse interference; and (3) utilizing penetrating implanted electrodes, we are in a better position to get beyond the neocortex.

Furthermore, we use a discrimination reversal experiment, to be described below, so that after preliminary training the animal can learn and re-learn the same problem day after day, eliminating errors each day in roughly the same number of trials. This methodology allows us to test animals one day on rate of learning under the electric 'lesion' and another day to test the same animals on control; and we may repeat the process as often as we choose.

METHODS

To date, 150 rats with implanted electrodes have been tested in a problem box where they had to learn over again each day which pathway and lever would activate a feeding mechanism. The problem box is shown in Fig. 6. A red plastic lever on the left activated the food magazine one day, and a white metal lever on the right activated it the next. Each day the rat had to learn anew which lever worked. This took a small number of runs, after which the animal would run only to the correct level. After each pellet was discharged, the animal had to go to the magazine and eat (thus breaking the photo-beam) before the magazine would work a second time. Thus animals could not stay at the pedal discharging several pellets and then go to the magazine to eat them all, but were forced to run the maze both ways for each pellet. Ten consecutive responses on the correct lever was the criterion of learning. All animals were put through extensive preliminary training (running every day for more than a month) before being used in experiments. By the end of this training period, animals would always begin each day by distributing runs randomly to right and left; then they would stabilize on the lever that activated the food magazine. Depending on the animal, this would take from three to twenty-five runs each day. Animals were not used in experiments until progressive improvement in this daily score had ceased. During training and tests, animals were maintained on a feeding schedule with 23 hours of starvation and 1 hour of feeding each day. They were tested after 22 hours of deprivation.

The data were plotted in terms of cumulative response curves (see Fig. 7). Solid lines were used to indicate correct responses, dotted lines, to indicate errors. The slope of the line indicated the speed of responding (on the correct or error pedal). When the dotted line flattened out, this indicated that the animal had stopped making errors. Every test consisted of 2 days, one with the left lever correct (indicated by graph on left), the other with the right lever correct (indicated by graph on right), to rule out position

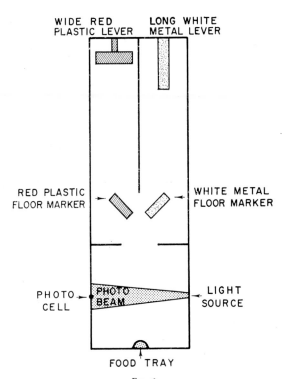

WIDE RED PLASTIC LEVER

LONG WHITE METAL LEVER

RED PLASTIC FLOOR MARKER

WHITE METAL FLOOR MARKER

PHOTO CELL

PHOTO BEAM

LIGHT SOURCE

FOOD TRAY

FIG. 6

Problem box. Response on correct lever causes food magazine to operate. Animal must retrace steps and break photo-beam in order for correct lever to work a second time. Correct lever changes from side to side from day to day. After about a month of preliminary training, each animal daily achieves criterion (ten correct runs in a row) in about three to twenty-five trials.

preference. In the six tests shown in Fig. 7, errors level off in all cases, while correct responses continue to cumulate.

In the first test, there was no stimulation. Then stimulation was introduced in an effort to interfere with the learning mechanism. For this purpose a series of $\frac{1}{2}$-second trains of sine wave current (60 o.p.s.) was introduced at a constant rate of one for every three seconds. A pair of tests were given at each of five electric current levels, 10, 20, 30, 40 and 50 μamp. r.m.s. It is believed that the 50-μamp. stimulus sets up a supra-threshold electric field in the brain of about 1-mm. diam. (Olds, 1958). The stimulation was divided into $\frac{1}{2}$-second trains separated by $2\frac{1}{2}$ seconds of no stimulation because it was found that such a discontinuous

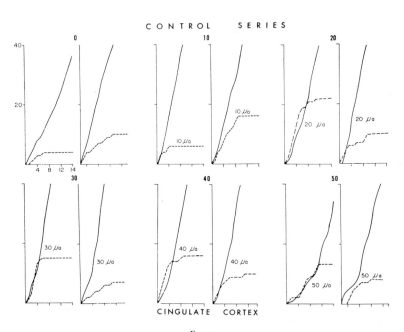

CONTROL   SERIES

CINGULATE   CORTEX

Fig. 7

Daily response curves. Slope of black line indicates rate of correct responding; slope of dotted line indicates rate of incorrect responding. Cumulative response totals are plotted along ordinate, minutes along abscissa. When dotted curve flattens, errors have been eliminated and only correct responding continues. Left curve in each pair indicates a day when left lever is correct; right curve indicates a day when right lever is correct. Large numbers above each pair indicate electric current setting in microamperes of the interference stimulus. In this series with cortical stimulation, the stimulus does not interfere materially with animal's ability to learn.

train caused few seizures and caused greater stimulus effects in other respects.

Some animals were also given a series of special tests which will be described in more detail later. These were (1) a self-stimulation test for positive reinforcing effects; (2) a memory-performance test for confusion after criterion is reached each day; (3) a reinforcement-confusion test to find whether confusion persists when electric stimulation is programmed so as to reinforce learning; and (4) in a very small number of cases, an escape test to discover negative reinforcing effects of stimulation.

After learning experiments were complete, each animal was sacrificed, and his brain was sectioned and stained to determine the precise location of stimulation.

RESULTS

(1) *Differences*. — The results indicate a definite division of the brain into (1) a larger set of regions where electric stimulation has very little effect on this learning behaviour, (2) a smaller (but very extensive) region where electric stimulation has very devastating effects and (3) a region where effects are ambiguous.

First, when electrodes are implanted in the neocortex and in many parts of the adjacent cingulate cortex, stimulation from 10 to 50 µamp. does not cause any major deficit in behaviour (Fig. 7). Similar effects are often seen with electrodes in the thalamus (left of Fig. 9). In all these cases, there is learning, with, of course, some day-to-day differences. Stimulation may cause some increment in errors, but it does not prohibit performance or learning. Animals run well, eat well, and learn well whether the stimulus is going or not.

Second, when electrodes stimulate in other places, quite different results are obtained (Fig. 8). It appears totally impossible for animals to reach criterion with the stimulus going in these areas. Except for confusion of learning, the animals perform well. They run almost as fast as usual; that is, the total number of runs is about equal for the stimulated and control series. The animals eat food well when the correct response activates the food magazine. But they cannot learn to eliminate errors on days when the stimulus is going. Because the animals continue to run and to eat, it is assumed that there is no interference with behaviour or drives. The interference has to do only with the ability to eliminate errors. The stimulus in these cases is very small, interfering usually at levels of 20 µamp. or less. Finally, it should be noted that the stimulus does not merely cause or enhance a position preference, for errors on right or left levers are both caused to increase greatly by the electric stimulus.

Third, there are sometimes effects which make it impossible to make a satisfactory test: (1) animals stop running when the stimulus is introduced: (2) the stimulus produces seizures so that no test can be made; (3) the animal stops eating so that it is no longer possible to assume motivation for learning; and (4) the stimulus causes some definite confusion which is so mild or unstable as to be ambiguous or a forced position habit renders results ambiguous (see caudate placement in Fig. 9).

(2) *Mapping.* — Mapping these effects, we find the surprising result that

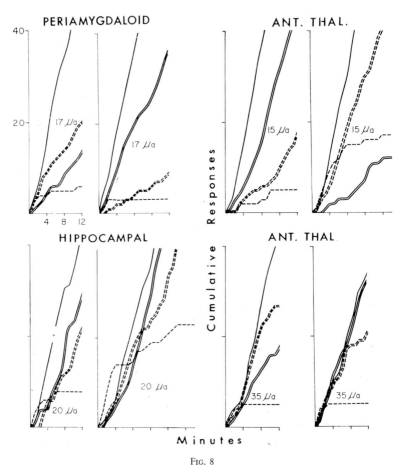

Fig. 8

Interference effects. Control curves (in background) show errors eliminated (dotted lines), correct responses cumulating (solid lines). On days when animals run under effects of stimulation (double lines in foreground), errors are not eliminated.

the medial-forebrain-bundle regions of the hypothalamus, its extensions into the tegmentum and basal ganglia, and the related structures of the palaeocortex are the places most apt to yield confusion upon electric stimulation. Stimulation in the neocortex, sensory thalamus, and large

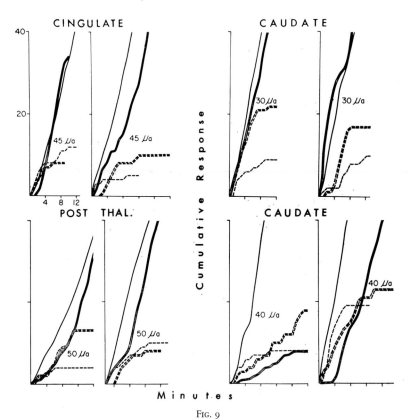

FIG. 9

Stimulation with very little effect (cingulate and posterior thalamic electrode, left) and mild effects (two caudate points, right). With stimulation in cingulate or posterior thalamus, responding is sometimes slowed, and errors sometimes increase. But learning is not prevented. In two cases with electrodes in the caudate nucleus, results are ambiguous. At the top, the stimulus causes the number of errors to double (thus stimulation interferes with learning); but errors are eventually eliminated (thus learning is not prevented by stimulation). In the other animal with caudate electrodes, stimulation sometimes caused such a great decrement in correct responding that it was impossible to tell whether learning occurred or not. In this case, it may also be noted, the decrement caused by electric stimulation seemed to involve a position habit forced by stimulation, so that the animal failed when the left lever was correct, but succeeded when the right was correct.

parts of the reticular activating system cause no detrimental effects at all. And moderate or ambiguous effects are yielded in the borderline structures such as the caudate (Fig. 10). And this is practically the same map as was obtained for self-stimulation effects (Fig. 2).

Is it true, then, that the points of positive reinforcement, far from facilitating learning, actually inhibit it?

M

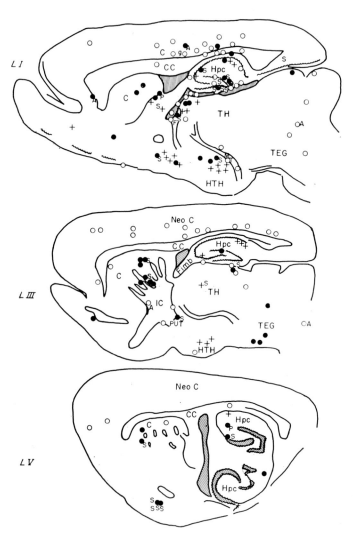

FIG. 10

Mapping of interference effects. Plus marks indicate complete interference with learning, i.e. more than three times normal number of trials without meeting criterion. Open circles indicate no effect of stimulation. Closed circles indicate ambiguous effects as noted in text. Other notations are: S — seizure, P — forced position preference, A — activation.

(3) *Correlation with Self-Stimulation.* — In an effort to test for such a correlation, forty-six animals with electrodes placed diversely throughout the brain were tested first for interference and later for the self-stimulation effect. The result was a most remarkable correlation. Of eighteen animals completely confused by the electric stimulus, fifteen were self-stimulators. Of seventeen animals unaffected, fourteen were non-self-stimulators (Fig. 11). Of eleven animals moderately impaired by the stimulus, seven were self-stimulators. All told, there were only three cases of definite impairment that were non-self-stimulators; and there were four cases of ambiguous impairment.

A first answer is, therefore, that points yielding the most interference in a learning experiment are the points which also cause self-stimulation. A question arises, however, whether the points which cause interference but no positive reinforcement occurred by chance, or whether they follow some pattern. Mapping the points (Fig. 12), we see that there is a design. Of the twenty-nine points yielding complete or ambiguous impairment, we have satisfactory histological localization on twenty-six. The points which yield both confusion and self-stimulation are scattered throughout the hypothalamic-palaeocortical system, but the points which yield only confusion are clustered along the hippocampus proper (that is, as distinct from the dentate gyrus), plus one in the anterior thalamus. We may guess, then, that there are two kinds of confusion points: (1) the self-stimulation points, and (2) a second kind located mainly in the hippocampus proper.

(4) *Memory Test.* — A further difference between these two kinds of points appears when we test for confusing effects of the stimulus on on-going performance, after criterion has been reached on a given day. We have called this, perhaps wrongly, a memory test because we introduce the jamming stimulus after learning has occurred, and we look to see if the animal can still 'remember' the correct way. We might equally well call it a performance test, inasmuch as the stimulus might interfere with correct performance even if some hypothetical 'memory' were intact.

At any rate, the test shows up a striking difference between two kinds of placement. If electrodes are in placements which produce avid self-stimulation, the stimulus causes a complete relapse to errors (and errors continue indefinitely) when stimulation is introduced after learning. But if electrodes are in the interference points where this is dissociated with self-stimulation, the result is different. The animal may make a few errors upon initial introduction of the stimulus, but correct performance is readily resumed (Fig. 13).

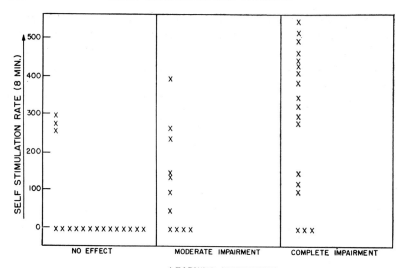

FIG. 11

Correlation of interference with self-stimulation. Each point stands for one electrode pair. The position on the ordinate indicates the self-stimulation rate for an 8-minute test period (current set at optimal level in 10- to 50-μamp. range). Three categories on abscissa indicate no interference, ambiguous interference, and total interference.

Self-Stimulation Test of 26 Points Which Yield Confusion

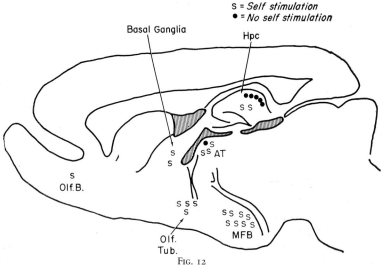

FIG. 12

Points where self-stimulation electrodes (S) and non-self-stimulation electrodes (●) yielded confusion.

Of seventeen self-stimulators given this test, fifteen showed total failure to regain criterion; the other two were moderately impaired. Of six non-self-stimulators given the test, three were moderately impaired, and three were unaffected (Fig. 14). All animals were significantly impaired on the initial learning test. This suggests that the points where impairment is dissociated from self-stimulation are points involved in learning but not in later memory or performance.

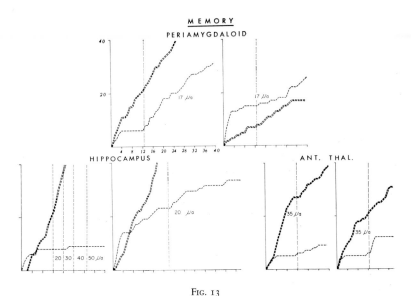

FIG. 13

Memory test. Cumulative-error curves are shown for days when stimulation started at onset of test (double lines) and days when stimulation did not start until after criterion was reached (single lines). Vertical dotted line indicates onset of stimulation for latter case. When stimulation starts at onset of test, errors are not eliminated in any of these cases. When stimulation is introduced after criterion, it causes complete relapse with electrodes in periamygdaloid cortex, but not complete relapse with hippocampal or anterior thalamic electrodes.

Now the question arises whether, in places where self-stimulation and confusion are associated, the confusion results from the extreme reward (which might render the food reward unimportant), or from some additional pattern disruption over and above this reinforcing effect.

(5) *Reinforcement-Interference Test.* — To attempt an answer to this question, a test was devised in which the 'interfering' stimulus was so correlated with the correct response as to constitute to some degree an

added incentive. This was accomplished by having the wrong lever terminate the series of stimulations, and the correct lever re-start the series. Thus the animal making all correct responses would be stimulated as before, $\frac{1}{2}$ second on, $2\frac{1}{2}$ seconds off. But during learning, each day, the sequence would be interrupted every time an error occurred, and restarted only by the next correct response (Fig. 15).

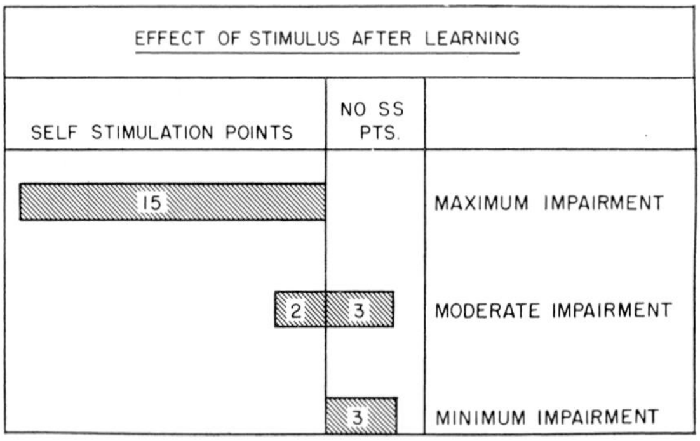

EFFECT OF STIMULUS AFTER LEARNING		
SELF STIMULATION POINTS	NO SS PTS.	
░░░░░░15░░░░░░		MAXIMUM IMPAIRMENT
2 ▨3▨		MODERATE IMPAIRMENT
	▨3▨	MINIMUM IMPAIRMENT

FIG. 14

Memory test for twenty-three points, all of which yielded impairment on learning test. Seventeen cases were self-stimulators. Six were non-self-stimulators. The figure shows that fifteen of the self-stimulation points yielded maximum impairment when introduced after learning; the other two self-stimulation points yielded moderate impairment. Of the non-self-stimulation points, three yielded moderate impairment, and 3 yielded almost no impairment.

When this test was applied to the confused self-stimulators, those with very rapid rates of self-stimulation were no longer confused. Several of the slower self-stimulators appeared, however, to be still confused (Table I). The possibility remained that those still appearing confused were in fact making errors to terminate negative reinforcement; i.e. they were receiving both positive and negative reinforcement from the same stimulus (Roberts, 1958). To test for this in a very preliminary fashion three of them were given tests for escape responding yielded by the electric stimulus, and these three did give evidence of escape. Thus we cannot find from these tests any support for the notion that the self-stimulation points cause a bona-fide confusion. Rather, it appears that the large reinforcing effect of the electric stimulation somehow overrides the smaller positive reinforcing effect of the food. When food and electric reinforcement pull the same way, the animal can achieve criterion, and can run perfectly.

There is still room for doubt, however, because (1) the animals appear to be running and searching for food during stimulation trials in the learning and memory test, and they eat the food rapidly when they get it; (2) it is

TABLE I

REINFORCEMENT–INTERFERENCE TEST COMPARED WITH SELF–STIMULATION SCORE AND ESCAPE TEST. POINTS IN THE O COLUMN SHOWED NO IMPAIRMENT ON THE REINFORCEMENT–INTER-FERENCE TEST. POINTS IN THE PLUS COLUMN WERE COMPLETELY IMPAIRED. SELF–STIMULATION SCORES ARE RANK-ORDERED FROM TOP TO BOTTOM OF THE TABLE; THESE ARE RATES FOR AN 8-MINUTE TEST PERIOD. THE EVIDENCE SHOWS THAT POINTS YIELDING HIGH SELF–STIMULATION RATES CAUSED NO INTERFERENCE IN THIS TEST. THREE POINTS WHERE INTERFERENCE OCCURRED WERE TESTED FOR ESCAPE, AND THESE TESTS INDICATED THAT NEGATIVE REINFORCE-MENT ACCOMPANIED POSITIVE REINFORCEMENT AT THESE POINTS

O	+	
S. St.	S. St.	Esc.
550		
500		
468		
450		
	370	
	350	+
325		
300		
	280	
270		
	150	
	100	+
	122	+

not clear why animals which have reached criterion in the memory test proceed to make errors upon introduction of stimulation, when the same animals, having reached criterion under the reinforcement-interference conditions, can run and eat perfectly under the same electric stimulation; and (3) in the reinforcement-interference test the added incentive of the goal might cause the animal to override the confusing effects of the stimulus, rather than proving there were no confusing effects in the first place. We have often seen animals become 'brighter' as the 'reward' potentiometer is turned upwards in maze experiments.

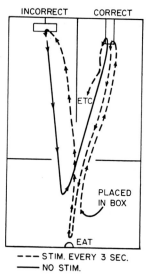

FIG. 15
Reinforcement–interference test. Interference stimulus starts when animal is placed in box and continues unless error pedal is pressed. At that point it is terminated and does not start again until correct response occurs.

DISCUSSION

At the end of the first set of experiments we were well aware that the hypothalamic–rhinencephalic system was most likely the central core of the positive-reinforcement mechanism. And we also thought in terms of positive reinforcement as involving (1) some close relationship to learning (a concept we still hold) and (2) some peculiar virtue in promoting learning, sharpening the wits, oiling the course, or stamping in the right response.

The second set of experiments surprised us at first, indicating as it did that the most efficacious way to interfere with the learning mechanism was to hyperstimulate the same system which we had formerly thought to promote learning. We should not have been surprised, of course, for this finding emphasized what we should have known at first: response learning involves, first, cessation of wrong behaviours, secondly, commencement of correct ones, and thirdly, repetition of correct ones. A stimulus causing repetition of behaviour would only promote the third stage of the process, which in a sense is not learning at all but its antithesis.

But again there was still room for doubt. Our stimulation of the large hypothalamic system causes repetition and inhibits adaptive changes in behaviour. In a sense, this is one and the same thing; by repeating, the animal cannot be adaptive, changing. This is consistent; but we must sometimes beware of consistency.

Our animals could repeatedly get the brain stimulus (which is all the repetition they want) and yet adopt the correct response to get food at the same time; and they appear to be trying to get food. Why does the response fail to become stereotyped down one lane? One might say there is a reinforcement of the antecedent 50 per cent probability. But then why in the memory tests where the learning occurs first does the stimulus cause return to 50 per cent probability? Or even more strikingly, why, after the animal learns in reinforcement-interference tests, can he run successfully under stimulation, to food and back, with no errors even though the stimulation continues? The same animal running currently in the memory test starts and continues to make errors upon introduction of the stimulus.

The possibility we want to suggest is this: our stimulus might cause some confusion in addition to the output of positive motivation. In the reinforcement-interference test, the strong positive motivation emanating from hypothalamic stimulation keeps behaviour in line. But minor problems cannot be solved because of confusing effect. It might be, then, that total activity in this hypothalamic-rhinencephalic system determines the positive-reinforcement function; but the pattern of activity in the same system is precisely the more or less lasting process that is altered by learning.

Giving up, then, the idea that positive reinforcement promotes learning, we are left with alternative notions: either it is a simple inhibitor of learning or else it is somehow a function of the same neural aggregates which are chiefly involved in learning; but quantity is most important from a standpoint of reinforcement, the patterning most important from the standpoint of learning.

From the latter point of view, stimulation of the system could be said to augment the positive reinforcement and the repetitiousness of the whole system, but to disrupt the patterns formed by association of mild cues.

The final experiment we have to report searched for ways of causing learned changes in neural patterns by operant-conditioning techniques.

III. THE OPERANT CONDITIONING OF SINGLE-UNIT RESPONSES

A most important contribution of behavioural psychology to the brain and behaviour field is the conception that a response is not merely something to be elicited, observed, characterized, and recorded. In operant-behaviour analysis, a response is more than that: it is something to be conditioned. The single-unit response is, on the face of it, precisely the type of categorical and clearly defined event that should be amenable to operant-conditioning techniques. We report here initial successes in this endeavour.

METHODS

In these studies, rats were prepared first with self-stimulation electrodes in medial-forebrain-bundle regions. Preliminary tests established that very high self-stimulation rates were achieved, and no tendency to escape from stimulation was present. Rats which failed to meet these requirements were eliminated. Each rat was then placed in a stereotaxic instrument under barbiturate anaesthesia. A hole of 3-mm. diameter was drilled in the skull, usually 1 mm. behind, and 1 mm. lateral to the bregma. The dura was pierced repeatedly with a sharp instrument. Then tungsten microelectrodes of 1-μ diameter (Hubel, 1957) were lowered 1mm. into the cortex.

As the animal recovered from the barbiturate anaesthesia, still in the stereotaxic instrument, he was given repeated doses of isopropyl meprobamate (Soma, Wallace Laboratories). Each dose was 80 mg./kg. The dose was repeated whenever any tendency of the animal to try to escape from the instrument appeared. Previous tests had shown that an almost paralysing dose of isopropyl meprobamate (100 mg./kg.) fails to block self-stimulation (Olds and Travis). From this point on, the electrode was advanced downwards through the cortex, hippocampal formation, thalamus and so forth, stopping whenever a clear spontaneous response appeared. Output from the microelectrode was led through a cathode follower into a Grass a-c amplifier and thence into a Dumont cathode-ray oscilloscope. Responses of single nerve cells appeared as 200- to 500-μv. negative spikes, lasting about 1 msec. They were identified mainly by their duration, by being repeated responses of constant amplitude, and by their disappearance upon movement of the microelectrode by about 200 microns.

Unit responses were not considered satisfactory for these experiments if their resting frequency was more than about 2 per second; and they were preferred if this were something less than 1 per second. When such a response was observed, a three-step experiment was performed: first, after several minutes of waiting, a 30-second record was made on moving photographic paper of the resting rate of the unit response. Second, an elicitation test was made. A series of twenty ½-second trains of stimulation (sine wave 60 c.p.s., 50 μamp.) was introduced via the medial-forebrain-bundle electrodes at a repetition rate of 1 every 2 seconds. These were not correlated with single-unit response. Instead, there was an explicit effort

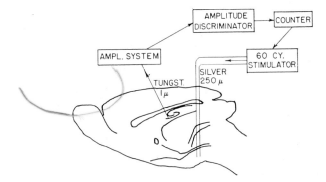

FIG. 16

Schematic diagram of single-unit operant-conditioning apparatus. Single-unit response is amplified and fed into amplitude discriminator which disregards all lesser signals, but yields an output whenever the single-unit response occurs; the output then goes to a counter. The counter is preset to activate a stimulator and reset whenever it reaches some number from 1 to 9. At this point, a ½-second train of 60-cycle stimulation (50 μamp. r.m.s.) is delivered to the medial-forebrain-bundle 'reward' point. During the stimulation, the counter is disengaged so that it will not count stimulus artifact. Immediately afterwards, it commences to count again until the preset ratio is again reached at which point it delivers another 'reward' stimulus.

made to stimulate only in the absence of single-unit responses. Immediately after this test a second 30-second record of activity was made on film. In the event of elicited effects, each stimulation produced a series of responses from the unit, and no further tests were made. The microelectrode was then advanced until a new unit response appeared. In the event that elicited effects were not found, the experiment continued. Third, a reinforcement test was made. The experimenter awaited a single-unit response and, each time it appeared, immediately delivered a stimulus to the hypothalamus. When this was done by hand, reinforcement could be applied after one appearance or after several appearances of the unit response. It was usually applied after each appearance of the response with a delay of about $\frac{1}{2}$ second (this was the experimenter's response time).

The design of the experiment, when the stimulus was presented auto-matically, is shown in Fig. 16. The output from the oscilloscope amplifiers was led into an amplitude discriminator circuit, and the output from the circuit activated an electronic counter which could be preset to deliver stimulation after a preset number of responses from 1 to 9. In this case, the delay of reinforcement was about 3 msec. Each activation of the stimulator was recorded on a cumulative response recorder, so that the response rate was retained on a permanent record.

In the case of a positive experiment, the single-unit response rate was greatly augmented by either the hand or the mechanical reinforcement procedure. The increased rate outlasted the procedure by a variable period of time. Immediately after this procedure, a third record of the unit's activity was made on film. It is the comparison of the three films that comprises our data.

In the event of failure to reinforce, by manual techniques, the unit was often put on the automatic reinforcement procedure, and sometimes positive reinforcement bypassed by the former procedure was discovered after long runs with the latter method. Because of the close temporal relationship between the control picture and the augmented picture, when the manual technique was successful, it was always the more convincing.

RESULTS

The first point to emphasize is the difference between the neocortex and the palaeocortical structures studied. Palaeocortical units often appeared to 'learn with ease'. Neocortical units never yielded any similar rapid modi-fication when subjected to reinforcement techniques. The details of this difference will be clarified below. Most often, stimulation caused neo-cortical unit responses to disappear, never to return; but sometimes, rein-forcement caused slow augmentation of response.

Where stimulation had any effect other than inhibition, it produced one of four kinds of changes in the pattern of single-unit response: (1) conver-sion of a sporadic grouped response to a continuous response by the reinforcement procedure; (2) augmentation of the response rate of a sporadic response by reinforcement; (3) elicitation of activity imme-diately after the stimulus, but only when it was given as a reinforcement; and (4) elicitation of activity by the stimulus irrespective of its use as a reinforcement.

The most striking cases were of the first type (Figs. 17 and 20 I, II, IV). They were recorded mainly from areas such as the dentate gyrus, fimbria regions, and mammillo-thalamic tract regions, which appeared to be 'seizure-prone' in our previous experiment (Fig. 10). In these cases, the unit was originally responding in a sporadic pattern with single responses or groups appearing at less than one per second. Stimulation when

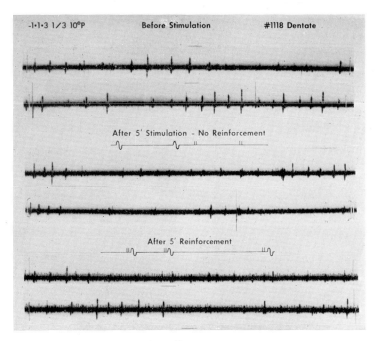

FIG. 17

Experiment on single-unit response recorded from dentate gyrus. Small unit response (almost lost among larger slow waves) occurs at rate of approximately one per second before stimulation, and rate is not greatly increased by uncorrelated stimulation. When stimulation is correlated as reinforcement for unit response, however, continuous firing (at rate of about 30 per second) ensues. Time base as in Fig. 18.

introduced during silent periods did not cause any elicited firing. Such stimulation could be continued for periods of 5 minutes or more without materially augmenting the response rate. Then, if the stimulation was withheld and delivered only after the appearance of a single or grouped response, ten to twenty reinforcements would often suffice to cause a sudden burst of activity; the unit would respond continuously at rates as high as 30 per second. This burst would sometimes last for a period of only

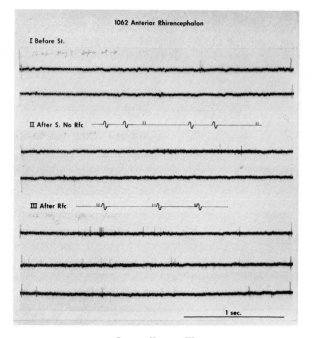

I   II   III

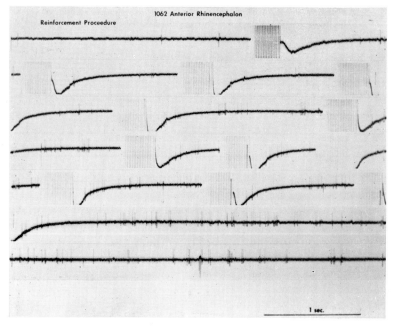

IV

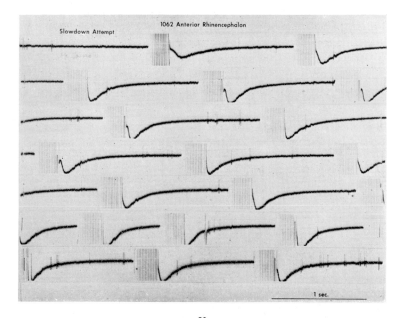

V

FIG. 18

Series of experiments on single-unit response recorded from anterior rhinencephalon. I. Before stimulation. II. After stimulation without reinforcement. III. After reinforcement. IV. After waiting for unit to slow down (about 5 minutes), reinforcement procedure is undertaken a second time, and a photographic record is made during reinforcement; large lattice-type artifact indicates 60-cycle sine wave stimulus. V. Still later, after another wait, attempt is made to correlate stimulation with pauses, but this is unsuccessful. Later an electronic device was made to correlate stimulation with long silent periods, and the procedure caused some unit responses to cease altogether.

several minutes, with response amplitude decreasing in an orderly fashion. Then the unit response would disappear for a period of some minutes, to return at the original amplitude. At other times, the repetitive activity would continue at a high level for longer periods. One might suspect that a hippocampal seizure had been started by the reinforcement procedure, except for the fact that movement of the electrode in these cases reveals no similar activity in neighbouring cells.

The second type of changes (Figs. 18 and 20 III) were not greatly different from the first, but in these cases, the rapid responding caused by reinforcement seemed much more like the original sporadic responding, although its frequency was far greater. There was no tendency for the rapid responding to be accompanied by decrement in amplitude. It appeared to follow much more ordinary acquisition and extinction patterns, augmenting at each reinforcement, slowing upon cessation of the reinforcement procedure, often coming to rest at a higher firing rate than the original rate, but lower than during reinforcement.

Changes of this type were graded along a dimension of rapid or slow conditioning. With units in the anterior rhinencephalic cortex, condi-

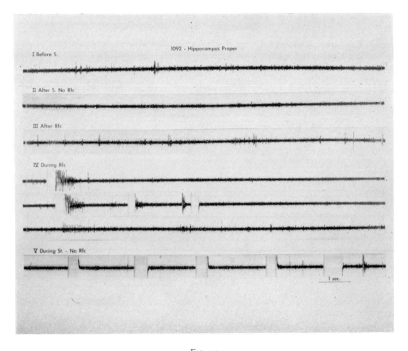

FIG. 19

Experiment on single-unit response recorded from hippocampus. It is noteworthy that stimulation which closely follows a unit discharge (see IV) causes a burst of activity which is not seen when stimulus occurs against a background of no-firing (see V).

tioning was quite as fast as with type I units in the dentate gyrus. But the response was more moderate. Some 'learning' of a much slower order occurred with points estimated to be at the base of the neocortex. There was never any possibility of augmenting the rate by manual reinforcement with electrodes, here, but, left on automatic reinforcement for long periods of time, the unit response rate would sometimes increase gradually. This seemed quite like the conditioning of a skilled act in its time course, an idea possibly forced on us by the fact that the final conditioned unit activity was often accompanied by some minute movement of an extremity. One animal learned to move his tail to the right while remaining, otherwise, absolutely still.

In contrast to the conditioning of cortical units which sometimes seemed like conditioning the muscle output itself, the conditioning of subcortical units often led us to feel that we were observing the basic mechanism of instrumental conditioning itself. This was the case first in the conversion of dentate responses to seizure-like tempos as in type 1. But also the type 3 modification, observed in the hippocampus and diencephalon, appeared to involve some basic mechanism of learning.

With microelectrodes here, the stimulus had quite different effects when given immediately after a unit response from those it might have against a background of silence (Figs. 19, and 20 IV). When it followed the unit, the stimulus would invoke either a further burst of response in the same unit, or a burst of very high potential activity not easily characterized. If the same stimulus was applied at some temporal distance from a single-unit response, there were no similar effects.

It may be relevant that stimulation did sometimes elicit in hippocampal electrodes a high-voltage, repetitive, positive discharge of somewhat longer duration than the single-unit response.

Finally, there is of course the type 4 modification: the stimulus causes an elicited effect so that reinforcement cannot be tested. It is hard to estimate how frequent this occurrence is because these effects have been quickly by-passed in our experiments in search of areas where elicited effects are absent. It is certainly clear that these cases increase in number as the microelectrode approaches the point of stimulation in the posterior hypothalamus (Fig. 20 V).

SPECULATIONS

It is certainly tempting to speculate at this point, so long as it is understood that no scientific factual import should be attached to these speculations.

Ashby (1953) has suggested that perhaps each neurone is in itself a negative feedback system, at least a system that modifies its output depending on the feedback it gets from previous outputs. We have perhaps shown something of this kind here.

There is of course nothing in our work to determine that the unit is the conditioned entity; perhaps it is simply our method for identifying a

N

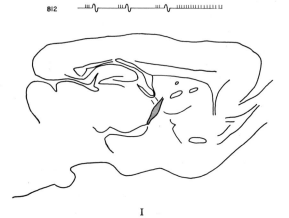

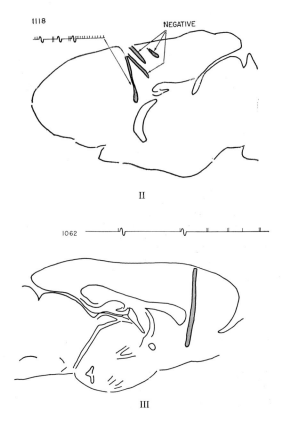

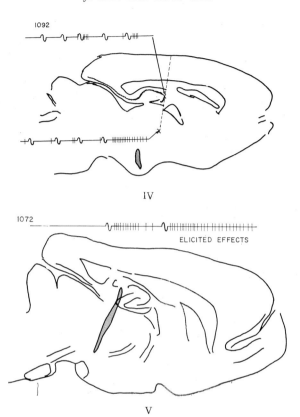

FIG. 20

Localizations of microelectrode points yielding various effects. I. Point in or near mammillo thalamic tract yielding reinforcement to continuous firing (schematically symbolized by unit-sinewave pairings followed by repetitive unit discharge). II. Point in fimbria yielding reinforcement to continuous firing, plus three cortical points yielding negative results. III. Point in anterior rhinencephalon which augmented firing rate greatly during reinforcement procedure. IV. Point in hippocampus where reinforcement caused firing after the stimulus; and point in mammillo-thalamic tract region of thalamus where reinforcement yielded continuous firing. V. Point in dorsal posterior hypothalamus where stimulation elicited unit firings.

larger integration which we proceed to condition. However, we do have anecdotes which suggest that a unit discharge started by pressure (as our microelectrode enters an area) can be maintained active by reinforcement. If stimulation with the microelectrode can be performed systematically, it will at least be shown whether the unit response needs to be started by some afferent system to be conditioned.

Supposing for a moment that the unit itself is the conditionable entity in these experiments, we would then be provided with some sort of a trace system. We could suggest that instrumental conditioning techniques leave a changed pattern of repetitive discharge in these units, a suggestion which someone more given to theorizing than we might inflate into a model for a brain.

SUMMARY

Three sets of experiments have been reviewed here, suggesting first obliquely and then more directly that the hypothalamic-rhinencephalic system is more intimately related to instrumental conditioning than the other parts of the brain.

First, self-stimulation experiments which show that stimulation in this area can serve as a strong positive-reinforcement or unconditioned stimulus in Skinner box, runway, obstruction box, and maze experiments were cited. These suggested that somehow a good deal of activity emanating from this system might foster at least the repetition of preceding responses, if not the learning of responses themselves.

Second, interference-stimulation experiments were conducted to find where electric stimulation might interfere with performance in a T-maze type of test. It was found that precisely the same system was implicated. Stimulation in positive-reinforcement points appeared to cause confusion because of the prepotency of the electric brain-stimulus 'reward' over the food reward to the hungry rats. But other points in the hippocampus proper caused confusion without any accompanying positive-reinforcing effects. These points were also distinct from positive-reinforcement points in that interference occurred only during learning but not during later performance.

Third, instrumental-conditioning experiments were carried out on single-unit responses in cortical, palaeocortical and subcortical regions. Units in subcortical and palaeocortical structures were often readily conditioned. Only rarely and with great difficulty were cortical units conditioned. Conditioning in lower centres often appeared to suggest basic mechanisms, as stimulation after a unit discharge would have different effects from those it would have against a background of silence, or, several stimulations after a unit discharge, would cause seizure-like repetitive discharge.

The data from all three experimental programmes might be summarized by the hypothesis that the quantitative measure of activity in the hypothalamic-palaeocortical system is a measure of the positive reinforcement, the tendency to repetitive behaviour. The pattern of repetitive firing in the units of this same system is the residual process which is modulated by instrumental-conditioning techniques.

As to whether the same changing pattern of residual processes might serve as a model for associative conditioning, we will suspend judgment.

GROUP DISCUSSION

GERARD. In what manner are your experiments different in principle — obviously they are more elegant in degree — than ones using any other kind of effector response? Any response obviously must involve the discharge of some unit somewhere in the brain.

OLDS. Two answers. In the case of the cortical unit and even in the case of the anterior rhinencephalic unit that I showed, my impression is that there is no difference in principle at all. My feeling is, in both these cases, that the animal decided that doing something was getting him reinforced and so he did it. In the case, however, of the fimbria and dentate gyrus units and in the case of some of the hippocampals, I had a feeling that here is the mechanism, so to speak, so that you would say 'this is the stuff decisions are made out of'. That here we were playing with something that just automatically had its response rate augmented if we stimulated the hypothalamus right after it has discharged.

GERARD. Did you say that stimulation of the fornix in the rat, under your conditions, interferes with learning?

OLDS. No. The answer is that in the hippocampus proper we interfered. But in the fimbria and often in the fornix our stimulation usually produced seizures before we could get any experimental tests.

GERARD. I raised the point only because of the recent report of an unfortunate operation on man, in which the fornix was cut bilaterally. Recent memory was completely abolished.

OLDS. I have a hunch that response learning and recent memory are somehow very closely related. And that if we said response learning and recent memory involve palaeocortical and hypothalamic systems we might be on to something, and the more structured memory might be, it seems to me, in the neocortex and the classical thalamic system.

GRASTYÁN. By stimulation of the hippocampus we got similar observations in somewhat different experiments. On the background of already established conditioned reflexes we obtained always an inhibition. The interpretation of these observations was, however, always very problematic. It is well known that the hippocampus is one of the structures that has the lowest threshold for eliciting afterdischarges. I see that you disregard the experiments in which you elicited afterdischarges. I am still not absolutely convinced, however, that by stimulating the hippocampus you did not get any after-discharge in the hippocampus itself. Sometimes when recording in various parts of the hippocampus we got after discharges when we did not see any sign of after-discharge in other structures. I am not convinced that these effects represented a physiological inhibition. I have to admit at the same time that we had some observations in which we did not elicit any after-discharge in the hippocampus and we still obtained inhibition. I would be very interested to know what might be the physiological meaning of this inhibition. According to our supposition, the hippocampus inhibits the orientation reflex, which is a necessary step in the development of the conditioned reflex.

OLDS. We found that if we were on the surface of the hippocampus itself, so that we were stimulating the hippocampal cells proper, we very rarely got grand mal seizure perceptible in the animal's behaviour. When we were in dentate we almost invariably did get grand mal at such low thresholds that it was impossible to do any research at all. Now as to whether our results in the hippocampus proper might be from hippocampal seizure which could be recorded although not observed I certainly would not be at all surprised if that were true. I have often conceived of these experiments in the light of trying to find the place where localized seizures would have the same effect as a generalized electro-convulsive shock. We are trying to look for a place where we can, so to speak, jam the network by excessive activity.

ADEY. I was very interested in Dr Olds's observations of the role of the anterior hippocampus in this particular type of activity. I wonder whether he has also examined the ventral parts of the hippocampus arch and whether he has come to any conclusions about the relative significance of the more ventral zones of the hippocampus as opposed to the dorsal. My reason for asking this is primarily that we have studied quite extensively the course of the normal wave discharges in the hippocampus in the course of various learning procedures. I would mention that there does not appear to be a homogeneity of the whole aspect of the hippocampus in this regard, and that, briefly, the dorsal hippocampus and the entorhinal cortex are regions which appear to be particularly concerned in the type of behaviour in which we are interested, to the point where one might summarize by saying that the region between the hippocampal pyramidal cells and the dentate gyrus, where Dr Olds mentions this extreme sensibility to seizure, this region and the adjacent entorhinal cortex appear to be concerned in what we might term the execution of planned behaviour, basing that opinion on certain very regular slow-wave discharges. If I might raise one further point, that is the question of these curious polyphasic discharges which Dr Olds saw when he was recording from the vicinity of the dentate gyrus. I wonder whether he may not be seeing in fact a muscle discharge if his microelectrode recording set-up is the typical one with the monopolar method of recording. The absence of the normal muscular paralysing agents will very often produce volume conducted muscular effects that may be extremely confusing in the interpretation of the micro-electrode recording.

OLDS. In all cases that we have reported, in which are found this special phenomena of peculiar effects immediately after the stimulus we have very careful control showing that we do not get these effects except when we apply the stimulus immediately after the unit response. In all other respects, I assure you this looks like artefact. And it is only because it has this physiological significance, namely that the proximal unit has to fire before we apply our stimulus in order for us to see this response, it is only for that reason that I even mention it.

Let me go back to following the hippocampus around to its posterior arch. To me it looks like the hippocampus all the way around has the dentate gyrus facing it. I did show three sagittal sections in my large map and if you had looked carefully you would find that in all cases if the electrodes were placed just above the arch of the hippocampus proper, we got the rather total inhibitory effect without self-stimulation. Finally, as to your notion that the dentate might be involved particularly in planned behaviour, I had very much a similar notion after this work because we interfered completely with stimulation in hippocampus and I felt that the hand-in-glove arrangement between hippocampus and dentate cannot be for nothing. In the single unit studies we found the most remarkable mechanism-like effects in the outflow from the dentate itself where we could give two or three stimulations in a reinforcing position, that is following the response, and then multiple firing would suddenly ensue.

MAGOUN. Stimulating ascending pathways to the rabbit's hippocampus evokes an undulating slow-wave discharge whose frequency is around 5 to 7 a second. Unit recordings from the hippocampus, by Dr John Green, often show firing in some relationship to this ryhthm. Did you elicit such a rhythm from stimulating reinforcing sites? if so, could you correlate unit firing with the slow waves?

OLDS. We do not have fair data to answer that. Because wherever we got an elicited effect we went on very rapidly to another unit. Quite often units would respond on slow waves, this being rather hard to see when you have a lot of filters, but still it was rather obviously there and it made the unit an unlikely one for further recording. We did not spend much time with units that were associated clearly with slow waves. Thus in a sense we have worked out of our population a lot of material which you would like to have and we will certainly go back and look at it later.

SEGUNDO. It seems opportune to mention observations performed upon human subjects that illustrate contrasting features of archi- and palaeo-cortices. Firstly, excitation effects of hippocampus or fornix that included somnolence or even slight blurring of consciousness, a result has that not been encountered in extensive exploration of the human neocortical mantle (Penfield, and Rasmussen, 1950; Segundo, Arana, Migliaro, Villar, Garcia-Guelfi, and Garcia-Austt, 1955). Secondly, the report by Grünthal of dementia produced by hippocampal atrophy (Grünthal, 1947); neocortical lesions of comparable size do not provoke dementia. This material stresses the manner in which interference with hippocampal mechanisms affects behaviour, thus supporting Dr Olds's observations.

KONORSKI. Did you try to use as reinforcing agent self-punishing points instead of self-rewarding ones? It is interesting to see whether in this case the units, whose activity you observe, will behave in the same way as in your experiments or, on the contrary whether they will stop firing, when their activity is negatively reinforced.

OLDS. The positively reinforcing points interfered with learning. Then we have anecdotes on the negative reinforcing points which show they do not interfere with learning in any similar fashion. But we do not have full evidence, just anecdotes, which make us sure that we will find that the negative reinforcing points do not interfere with learning.

As for slowing the units, I believe again on the basis of anecdotes, the answer will be yes. In the early days of this experiment we had animals that were tested for self-stimulation but we did not find whether they were also escaping and I have had an animal that I worked on for a period of almost 24 hours and every unit that I ever tried to reinforce was slowed. Since then I think that when we do study the negative reinforcement we should find that it will work.

BUSER. I wish to mention here some observations made on rabbits, by Dr Cazard and myself, on the effect of repetitive stimulation of the dorsal hippocampus on neocortical evoked potentials. It appeared that a short tetanization of the hippocampus (subliminal for producing any hypersynchronic or paroxystic phenomenon), was followed by a net increase (lasting up to 30 minutes) of the amplitude of cortical sensory responses (primary as well as motor irradiated evoked potentials). These effects were obtained on acute (chloralose or curarized unanaesthethized) as well as chronic preparations.

OLDS. I believe that that sounds extremely pertinent. Of course under anaesthesia the evoked potentials are also augmented, is that true?

BUSER. Yes, under anaesthesia and also in caudate rabbits.

OLDS. So it does look as if the same function could be involved in both of our situations.

ROSVOLD. I was wondering whether there is any difference in your results between the caudate and the hippocampus or whether you think they are very similar.

OLDS. There is a difference. Of course, because of the internal capsule it is very difficult to know when you are stimulating caudate and not internal capsule too. We found that all our caudate stimulators produced associated movements of one sort or another. Very often in the case of the ambiguous caudate results we were quite sure that the animal was trying to do one thing and being forced to do another by the stimulus. We found that also inevitably with caudate stimulation the running ceased, that is, the animal simply would not run at all. It looked more like total disruption. I might even be tempted to say that even long-term memory was disrupted in these cases.

ROSVOLD. Do you suppose that the stimulation of the hippocampus jams the function of the hippocampus or excited it?

OLDS. I think it is interfering. I find it hard to think of a stimulation in a learning experiment of doing something to organize a pattern, though stimulation of certain places of the reticular formation has been shown to augment certain kinds of perceptual tasks, but I regard this as an exception.

MYERS. What proportion of your attempts to condition rhinencephalic neurones has resulted in failure?

OLDS. We have never had a failure of the sort we have had with cortical units with rhinencephalic units. We have had a failure of the experiment either because we reinforced too soon; its activity remained high and we could not use it further, because we could not find whether we had elicited it or not. Similarly we have had cases where we thought we had something to work with but after trying to reinforce silence, the response did not come back. But this cannot be said to be a failure to reinforce. With cortical units, we have had the unit going for periods of 5, 10, 15 minutes, reinforcing regularly and failed to augment its firing rate. This has happened many times with neocortical units but never with palaeocortical units so far.

MYERS. Have you seen evidence that the conditioning of one unit has any influence on the conditioning of other units in the neighbourhood.

OLDS. Yes. This is a definite thing. Quite surprising and I don't know quite how to put sufficient constructions on the situation to explain it. We found some situations where we had one unit in an area, and reinforced it. Eventually it went into continuous firing. Its amplitude decreased and it finally disappeared and it subsequently was replaced and we reinforced the other one, and those two then alternated. Another thing has happened, we seemed to be reinforcing a slow wave and a unit, and then we moved the electrode and then we found that now for perhaps a millimetre we could not get rid of the slow wave, and other units firing on it; this should have been mentioned in connection with Dr Magoun's earlier question.

A NEW CONCEPTION OF THE PHYSIOLOGICAL ARCHITECTURE OF CONDITIONED REFLEX

P. K. ANOKHIN

The present conception has taken shape over a period of more than 30 years as the result of the work of the author and his pupils on the physiology of higher nervous activity.

The conception proposed in this paper eliminates a number of contradictions that have accumulated in the physiology of the conditioned reflex in recent years; it opens new avenues of research in the mechanisms of the conditioned reflex discovered by Pavlov, who revolutionized the study of the behaviour of animals and man.

The generally accepted view of the mechanism of the conditioned reflex rests on Descartes's reflex theory expressed in the concept of the 'reflex arc'. According to this view, the excitation evoked by a conditioned stimulus constitutes the afferent part of the conditioned reflex arc. In the central part of the arc the excitation is transferred from the analyser to the effector part of the reflex and, finally, the excitation reaches the efferent part of the reflex arc where it stimulates some working organ or combination of organs to action.

This classical concept has three characteristic features.

1. In the reflex arc the excitation spreads according to the linear-translational principle: at each successive moment it spreads to new neural elements and never returns to the course already traversed.

2. The reflex arc ends in an adaptive action which, from the point of view of these ideas, forms as an entirely new phenomenon in the path of the linear-translational spread of the conditioned excitation.

3. The formation of the reflex action in the peripheral working apparatuses is conceived as a process *completing* the reflex arc and, consequently, the very adaptive result of the reflex action is not the decisive factor for the dynamic alternation of the processes of excitation and inhibition in the reflex arc.

The conception proposed below does not exclude the reflex as a principle of the organism's activity and its relation to the external environment. The reflex invariably constitutes the nucleus of our new ideas.

189

However, this nucleus is considerably expanded and supplemented by new links physiologically conceived as components of an integral neurodynamic and *not linear* organization, which we have named the 'functional system'.

The formulation of our concept became possible only when the basic classical method of investigating conditioned reflexes had been supplemented by additional techniques which enabled us to reveal the other aspects of conditioned reactions and their physiological substrate.

The 'secretomotor method', the method of studying conditioned reflexes proposed by us, has been of particular importance in the elaboration of the new concept. Owing to a special design of the stand this method made it possible to record simultaneously the secretory and motor components of the conditioned reflex, the motor component constituting not a mere manifestation of movement towards food but a movement of choice towards one of the two or four feeding troughs connected with the given conditioned stimulus (Fig. 1).

The special design of a two-sided experimental stand made it possible to connect various conditioned stimuli with the different sides of the stand and to compare the secretory and motor components in the most diverse experimental situations.

Since by the classical secretory method this had not been possible on a wide scale, the first experiments conducted in our laboratory with our method revealed new aspects in the physiological architecture of the conditioned reflex (Anokhin, 1932, 1933). All the results of our investigations were published in detail in some of our generalizing papers (Anokhin, 1949, 1955, 1958).

To solve the problem of the physiological architecture of the conditioned reflex we have made extensive use, since 1937, of the electroencephalographic method. A method of recording the EEG in a perfectly natural environment in the study of conditioned reflexes was first used in our laboratory (Laptev, 1941, 1949). Recently these aims have been considerably furthered by the numerous investigations of the physiological peculiarities of the brain stem reticular formation so brilliantly begun in the laboratories of Magoun, Forbes and Moruzzi and later applied to the elaboration of conditioned reflexes in the laboratories of Jasper, Hernández-Peón, Morrell, Gastaut, and our own (Jasper, 1957; Morrell, 1958; Hernández-Peón, 1958; Gastaut, 1957, Ioshii, 1956).

Our conception of the general physiological architecture of the conditioned reflex is best considered fragmentally, so that at the end of this report it may appear before the reader in its totality.

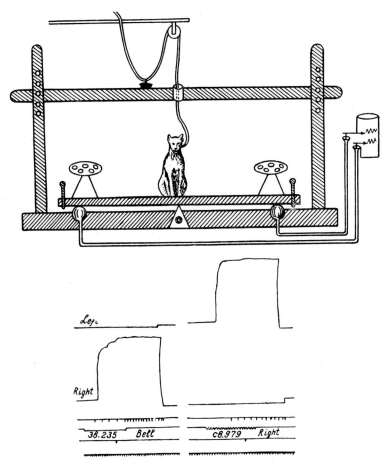

Fig. 1

A. Two-sided stand with two feeding-troughs making it possible to record simultaneously the secretory and motor components of the conditioned reaction ('Secretomotor method'). Pneumatic transmission.
B. Sample of kymograph record showing movement to the left (1) and right (2) and the conditioned secretion of saliva in drops.

I. CONCEPT AND MECHANISM OF AFFERENT SYNTHESIS

According to the reflex theory the role of the afferent influences on the central nervous system consists in the fact that the external stimulus usually serves as the *impetus* for the beginning of some reflex action. This conception ascribes the decisive role to an isolated stimulus, something that has found expression in the evaluation of the conditioned stimulus as a decisive factor in determining the quality and strength of the conditioned reflex effect.

However, one physiological phenomenon which has considerably shaken this widespread idea was described in detail in Pavlov's laboratory. I refer to the phenomenon of the *dynamic pattern* (Pavlov, 1932).

As is well known, a definite and precise sequence of the selfsame conditioned stimuli, trained without any alterations over a long period of time, becomes the principal factor determining the quality and strength of the conditioned reactions. Conversely, the role of the *individual* conditioned stimulus is eliminated and the latter serves only as a *non-specific impetus* for the appearance of the conditioned reflex, whereas the quality and nature of the conditioned reaction does not depend on any conditioned stimulus in particular. This stimulus does not even have to be a conditioned stimulus, but may be an entirely new, i.e. indifferent (in Pavlovian terminology) stimulus. Nevertheless, it will evoke the conditioned reaction characteristic of the absent conditioned stimulus which was always used in the former experiments *at the given point of the dynamic pattern* (Pavlov, 1932).

Thus these experiments already revealed that the conditioned reflex, as regards its quality, strength and time of appearance, is a *synthetic result* of the action of the conditioned stimulus and the preceding action of a greater sum of afferent stimuli representing the *conditions of the experiment as a whole*.

A direct EEG analysis of the processes of the cerebral cortex conducted in our laboratory has shown that a sound stimulus, applied at the point of the dynamic pattern where light was always used, causes a desynchronization of cortical electrical activity, although applied at its usual place 15 seconds previously it did not produce such desynchronization (Fig. 2) (Anokhin, 1956). Thus a real sound cannot alter the electrical activity of the cerebral cortex, this activity alternating according to the preceding training of the dynamic pattern.

This dependence of each conditioned reflex on the synthetic nature of the external afferent influences was particularly clearly revealed in a special experiment conducted in our laboratory. The *selfsame conditioned stimulus* (bell) was reinforced by food in the morning and by an electrocutaneous pain stimulus in the evening (Laptev, 1937). In the end the dog elaborates a perfectly clear differentiation: experimented upon in the morning it responds to the bell with pronounced food reflexes, whereas in the evening in response to the *same* bell in the *same* chamber the animal shows a pronounced defensive reaction.

In this experiment the difference in the reactions clearly does not depend on the conditioned stimulus which has retained only the *non-specific trigger* action because both reactions emerge only in response to the action

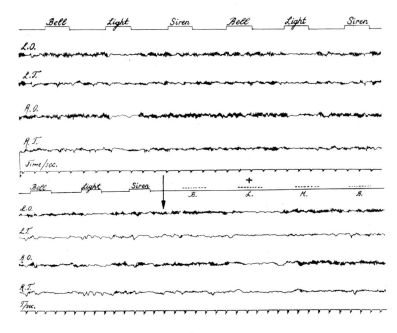

Fig. 2

A. EEG of the dynamic pattern of 'Bell-Light-Siren'. The regular light (+) is suddenly replaced by a bell, but a desynchronization corresponding to the application of light at this place is evident just the same.

B. Application of all the stimuli of the dynamic pattern (↓) is discontinued. Further development of cerebral activity in total conformity with the structure of the pattern can be seen. Complete desynchronization can be seen in place of the absent light (+).

of the bell, whereas in the intervals between the conditioned stimuli the animal sits quietly.

Nor are the conditions of the experiment as a whole a differentiating factor since they are the same in both experiments and only the *time of day*, as one of the components of the conditions of the experiment, is the determining factor.

If we take into consideration the fact that the time of day becomes an active factor the moment the dog is placed in the stand and the reaction emerges only at the moment the bell comes into play it will become clear that the time of day, being a special stimulus, determines the quality of the reaction because of the creation of a specific *subthreshold* dominant state of the central nervous system (according to Uchtomsky) which spreads to the working apparatuses owing to the trigger action of the conditioned stimulus.

The synthetic nature of the relations between the conditioned reflex and the external conditions of the experiment, both as a whole and of its individual components, may also be revealed under the usual conditions. Suffice it to transfer the animal, that until then had responded with good conditioned alimentary reflexes, to other surroundings (for example, a lecture-hall for demonstration to students) and the conditioned stimulus loses its conditioned reflex effect. In this case the synthesis elaborated from the tonic afferent action of the usual experimental situation and the trigger action of the conditioned stimulus is disturbed and the conditioned reflex disappears.

The following question arose in our laboratory: does this process of the synthesis of the situational and trigger afferent influences have any preferable localization in the cerebral cortex?

The experiments of our associate Shumilina, conducted over many years and consisting in extirpation of the frontal lobes in dogs who had conditioned reflexes elaborated in the two-sided stand, have shown that the frontal lobes have a very definite relation to this function of synthesis of the afferent stimulations of different quality. During the experiment all the normal intact animals in the two-sided stand behave rather monotonously, with certain insignificant variations. Since the different conditioned stimuli are reinforced by a single portion of food on the different sides of the stand, the animals elaborate an expedient habit of sitting quietly during the intervals between the conditioned stimuli *in the middle of the stand.*

After removal of the frontal parts (six to eight according to Brodman) all the intact animals begin to behave in a characteristic way immediately following the operation — they keep running from one feeding trough to the other as long as the experiment lasts. We have named these movements 'pendular' (Fig. 3).

It might be assumed that these movements were one of the forms of 'motor restlessness' described by many authors after they had removed the frontal areas of the animals' brains. However, a direct analysis of the mechanism of these pendulous movements has shown them to be directly

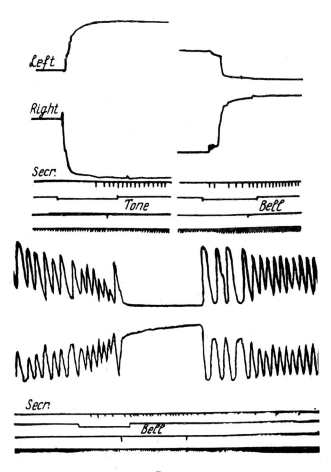

FIG. 3

A. Normal discrimination of the sides of the stand in response to corresponding conditioned stimuli. Stable movements to the left and right sides and quiet attitude in the middle of the stand during the interval between the stimulations.

B. Continuous 'pendular' runs to the opposite sides of the stand after removal of the frontal divisions of the cerebral cortex. Stops only during feeding. Conditioned secretion is the same as before the operation.

dependent on the nature of the afferent influences suffered by the animal under the conditions of the given experiment.

For example, if we elaborate in the animal conditioned reflexes *only to one side of the stand*, i.e. set up the conditions of Pavlov's classical method,

O

after the removal of the frontal parts of the cerebral cortex this animal behaves perfectly quietly during the intervals between the applications of the conditioned stimuli: *it sits on one side of the stand and performs no pendular movements.*

However, if we feed this quiet animal from the opposite feeding trough but once, it immediately begins to perform the well-known continuous pendulous movements to both sides of the stand.

These experiments suggest that the 'pendular' movements are a direct result of the situation stimulation which includes conditions of alternate choice and behaviour.

Why then does the intact animal sit quietly in the middle of the stand during the intervals between the applications of the conditioned stimuli?

The interest of this phenomenon consists precisely in the fact that the numerous stimulations of the experimental conditions (situational afferentation) affect the nervous system all the time, whereas the conditioned reaction manifests itself only at the moment the conditioned stimulus begins to act (trigger afferentation). At the same time the extreme change in the experimental situation convinces us that the situational stimuli form an organic component part of the afferent integral. Thus it becomes clear that all forms of afferent excitations affecting the animal's nervous system at the given moment undergo a synthetic processing and that *only after this* stage does the efferent complex of working excitations begin to form.

In recent years, neurophysiological studies have convinced us that all the afferent influences on the organism come to the cerebral cortex along two channels: (1) the specific or lemniscus pathway and (2) the non-specific, i.e. the brain stem reticular formation. The latter excitation is an indispensable condition for any interaction and interconnection of specific excitations on the level of the cerebral cortex.

Specially for the physiology of the conditioned reflex this means that any form of association of stimulations acting on the organism simultaneously or successively becomes possible only if the activating effect of the reticular formation has spread to the substrate of the cerebral cortex. The constant mediator between the new external conditions and the associative activity of the cerebral cortex and subcortical structures is the orienting-investigatory reaction of the animal taking place under an uncommonly high activation of the apparatus of the brain stem reticular formation (Hernández-Peón, Shumilina, Havlíček).

The physiological and biological purport of the orienting-investigatory reaction was very well revealed by Pavlov himself (Pavlov, 1925). It has now been shown that it occurs under a constant excitation not only of the cerebral cortex but also under an efferent excitation of the peripheral apparatus of the sense organs (Granit, Dell, Livingston). Owing to the rapid alternation of this efferent stream from one analyser to another the afferent synthesis stage preceding the very conditioned reaction is considerably enriched by afferent impulses, something that determines a finer and more adequate (for the given conditions) formation of effector processes of the conditioned reflex.

Naturally, after the stage of elaboration of the conditioned reaction this primary period of the multifarious efferent influences on the sense organs, increasing the excitability of the latter, is in large measure eliminated, owing to which the apparatus of the very conditioned reflex are simplified during the stage of its complete automation (see Fig. 4).

Electrophysiological studies of the orienting and investigatory reaction have shown that it is able continuously to maintain a high level of excitation in the cerebral cortex and at the same time maintain in an active state the newly formed temporary bonds (Anokhin, 1957; Karazina, 1957). Recently Professor Lindsley published a remarkable paper in which direct stimulation of the brain stem reticular formation demonstrated the tremendous role played by the reticular formation in the discriminative function of the cerebral cortex for rhythmic flashes of light (Lindsley, 1958).

Thus we believe it completely proved that *the power basis for the all-round synthesis of the numerous external and internal, situational and trigger afferent influences on the cerebral cortex is the ascending generalized activation of the brain stem reticular formation.*

The role of the reticular formation in refining afferent analysis also manifests itself in the fact that at this moment an alternate increase in the excitability of various receptor structures at the periphery takes place (Granit, 1957; Dell, 1957; Snyakin, 1958).

All told this makes it absolutely necessary, in analysing conditioned reflex adaptations, to set apart an independent stage of afferent synthesis.

The significance of this stage consists first of all in the fact that before its completion the flow of effector excitations to the functioning organs cannot be formed. The composition of these effector excitations and, consequently, the nature of the adaptive act itself are directly dependent on the way in which this stage of the afferent synthesis is completed.

At this point I must emphasize that the decisive role of the afferent function, as a 'creative' function of the cerebral cortex, was repeatedly indicated by Pavlov (Pavlov, 1928). The proof of this decisive role of the afferent function of the cerebral cortex is, in our opinion, the *afferent synthesis stage* which, as we shall see below, determines all the subsequent stages in the formation of the behaviour of man and animals.

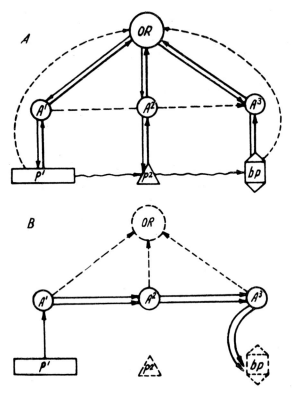

FIG. 4

General scheme illustrating the role of the orienting-investigatory reaction in the formation of the conditioned reaction, i.e. in the establishment of the chain of afferent traces from the stimulus to the acceptor of action.

A. At each stage of the animal's movement towards the reinforcing factor the orienting-investigatory reaction contributes to the production of return afferentation.

B. Final form of bonds. The conditioned signal aids in the almost instant spread of excitations along the afferent traces fixed in the past by means of the orienting-investigatory reaction.

2. SPECIFIC ACTIVATING EFFECT ON THE CEREBRAL CORTEX AND PROCESSES OF AFFERENT SYNTHESIS

The *specific* activating function of the brain stem reticular formation plays a special part in the processes of afferent synthesis (Anokhin, 1958).

There is a widespread opinion that the activating effect of the reticular formation on the cerebral cortex is of a non-specific nature. According to this view, the non-specific influence on the cerebral cortex is always of the

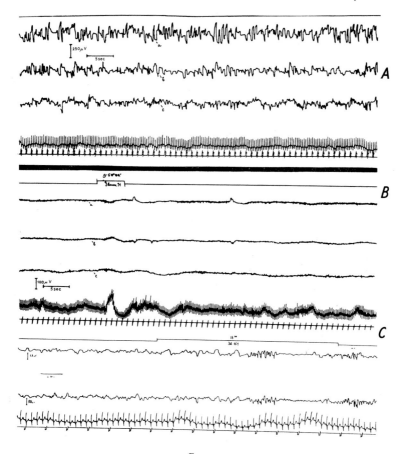

FIG. 5
A. Normal EEG of the rabbit in an experiment *without a pain reinforcement.*
B. EEG of the same rabbit *after application of several pain reinforcements* during elaboration of a conditioned defensive reflex. Very strong desynchronization of electrical activity can be seen not only at the moment of application of the conditioned stimuli but also during the intervals between them.
C. After chlorpromazin injection.

same physiological nature regardless of the reactions of the integral organism taking place in the given situation (Moruzzi and Magoun, 1949; Magoun, 1952; Magoun, 1958; *et al.*).

This point of view undoubtedly finds justification in the facilitating effect which develops in the cortical cells for the excitations coming to the cortex along the specific lemniscus system. This conclusion is also favoured by the phenomenon of 'awakening' or desynchronization of the cortical electrical activity which is always of a generalized nature and seems to be independent of the biological quality of the unfolding reactions.

However, along with these remarkable generalizations, our laboratory has obtained facts attesting that the non-specific activating effect of the brain stem reticular formation on the cerebral cortex *is organically connected with the biological specificity of the given conditioned reaction*. It proved possible to block by means of chlorpromazine (aminasine) the activating effect of the reticular formation for the conditioned *defensive* reaction, at the same time retaining the activating effect on the cortex for the *alimentary* reaction, i.e. for a reaction of another biological quality. At this moment the animal can greedily eat the food offered to it (Gavlichek, 1958) (Fig. 5).

Similarly blocking the defensive activation of cortical electrical activity by chlorpromazine fails to eliminate the animal's waking state which, as is well known, is also maintained by the activating effect of the brain stem reticular formation on the cerebral cortex (Fig. 6).

Thus it was demonstrated beyond all doubt that there are several activating influences on the cerebral cortex and that *each of them may be blocked individually because of the different chemical specificity of the nervous substrate on which each of these biologically different reactions occur*.

What is the significance of this varying biological specificity of the activating influences on the cerebral cortex occurring during the afferent synthesis which precedes the formation of the conditioned reaction itself?

In the first place it contributes to the *selective* rise in the excitability ('facilitation') of the neural elements in the cerebral cortex, which in the given animal were historically associated, by the principle of conditioned coupling, with the inborn subcortical reaction of the given biological quality (positive or negative).

Owing to this selective involvement of the cortical elements the mobilization of the numerous cortical systemic connections, which help to complete the stage of afferent synthesis, proceeds much faster and more efficiently.

Our view of the specific, i.e. selective, activating influence of the reticular formation on the cerebral cortex *with the perceptible generalized desynchronization of its electrical activity* fits in with the remarkable experi-

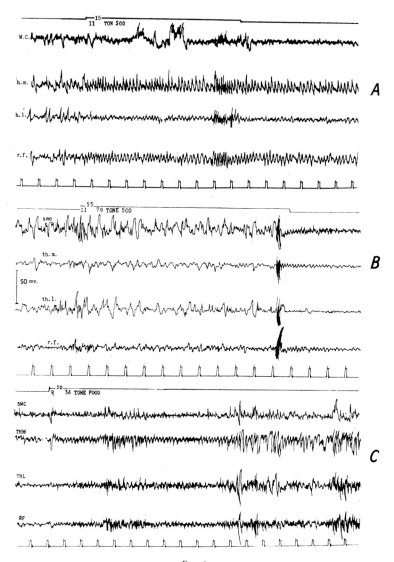

FIG. 6

A. Shows the presence in the reticular formation of a specific rhythm of electrical activity (4-6/sec.) corresponding to the animal's defensive state.

B. Elimination of the specific reaction by an injection of chlorpromazine. Application of the conditioned defensive stimulus no longer produces the generalized activation of the EEG.

C. Cortical and subcortical EEG of the food conditioned stimulus (tone).

ments performed by Jasper, Kogan and our own collaborator Polyantsev (Jasper, 1957; Kogan, 1958; Polyantsev, 1959) (Fig. 7).

These authors have shown that, when cortical electrical activity is in a state of generalized desynchronization, the various individual cortical elements are in absolutely different states of activity. Some of them may be excited, others inhibited, while still others may change the form of their activity several times during the entire desynchronized state. These data can be understood only in the sense that each activated state of the

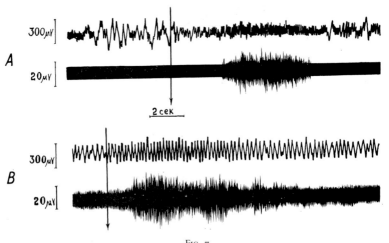

FIG. 7

A. Simultaneous lead-off with the same electrode, i.e. from the same point of the cerebral cortex, of slow EEG activity and impulse activity. The apparent lack of coincidence between the two forms of activity shows a certain independence of the cellular impulse activity on the EEG.

B. An even more demonstrative lack of coincidence is revealed by leading off the two indices from the same point of the reticular formation. Here the EEG does not have the usual desynchronization at all but the cellular impulse activity emerges just the same.

cerebral cortex (according to the desynchronization index) has a corresponding system of selective excitation of cortical bonds. It is just this that constitutes the physiological basis for the extensively ramified process of afferent synthesis.

This first stage in the formation of the physiological architecture of the conditioned reflex may be represented schematically as in Fig. 8.

This Figure shows that the afferent synthesis, as a physiological process, draws its energy from the ascending activating influences of the brain stem reticular formation. These influences reach the cerebral cortex in the

form of facilitating influences both at the moment of the action of the
external stimulations and, especially, at the moment of the appearance of
the orienting-investigatory reaction.

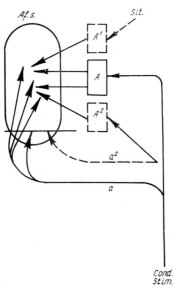

FIG. 8

Schematic representation of the constituent
processes of the afferent synthesis stage. The
scheme shows the constant activating influence of the brain stem reticular formation
on the afferent synthesis. It manifests itself
during the action of the experimental situation as a whole and during the episodic
action of the conditioned stimulus.
A^1, A^2. Analysers through which the
situation stimuli produce their effect.
a^2. Collateral action of the same stimuli
through the reticular formation.
A. Analyser of the conditioned stimulus.
a. Collateral action of the conditioned
stimulus through the reticular formation.

3. PHYSIOLOGICAL MECHANISMS FORMING THE APPARATUS OF THE ACCEPTOR OF ACTION

In this part of our report we shall describe a new mechanism of the
conditioned reaction noticed and elaborated in our laboratory. In its
physiological essence this mechanism is the end result of the afferent

synthesis stage, like the subsequent formation of the effector apparatus of the conditioned reaction itself. However, it forms, in large measure as an independent, physiological formation and has, as we shall see later, a special *afferent* significance.

In its physiological content this apparatus consists essentially of the afferent excitations which in their totality reflect precisely the sum of afferent excitations that must enter the cerebral cortex only at the end of the reflex action. It follows that the acceptor of action, as an afferent reflection of the results of future action, is a physiological apparatus of so-called 'anticipation'.

The tremendous importance of this apparatus in the behaviour of animals consists primarily in the fact that forming immediately after the end of the afferent synthesis stage *it considerably forestalls the process of formation of the reflex action as well as the completion of this action.*

The acceptor of action makes its appearance so soon after the end of the afferent synthesis that it may be argued that this apparatus is a direct and immediate result of precisely the afferent synthesis stage.

From a psychological point of view this moment, i.e. the end of the afferent synthesis corresponds to the emergence of the 'idea', 'intention' or 'aim' to perform the given action.

I believe it is necessary to observe at this point that the various reports that I have published on the physiological mechanisms of this stage in the development of conditioned reflex actions, have shown that many investigators do not as yet adequately understand that in a psychological sense the emergence of an 'intention' to perform some action *is an absolutely indispensable* stage which antedates the action itself and that, consequently, we, physiologists of the nervous system and higher nervous activity, must strive to analyse the physiological correlates of this 'intention'.

The physiological content of this apparatus consists of the entire past afferent experience of the animal or man concretely related to the given behaviour pattern. Basically it is a certain integration of the afferent impulses which arise from the *results* of some reflex action or act of behaviour.

For example, grasping a pitcher of water is connected with the reception of a series of afferent influences of a varying modality.

Our brain receives specific tactile impulses reflecting the form and mechanical properties of the pitcher, temperature impulses, kinaesthetic impulses suggesting weight and, consequently the fact that the pitcher is filled with water, etc. The impulses also include a visual afferentation suggesting the movement of the hand towards the pitcher.

The aggregate of all these afferent impulses arises only when the pitcher is grasped and, consequently, may be referred to as *afferentation of the results of the action*, in the true sense of these words.

From the morpho-physiological point of view such an aggregate of afferent influences forms in the cerebral cortex and subcortical apparatus a system of strong bonds which, by virtue of a number of repetitions of the given act acquires properties of an organized, integral afferent formation. It is precisely this system of bonds that becomes active owing to the rapid selective spread of excitations at the moment the afferent synthesis stage is being completed and that constitutes the physiological basis of the acceptor of action.

At this point we are consciously leaving out of consideration the aggregate of the internal and external influences which, after the afferent synthesis stage, have, on the whole, conditioned the emergence of the very intention 'to grasp the pitcher'.

It stands to reason that this intention is only a separate stage in a series of other 'intentions' which are finally completed through the stage of a subjective 'quenching of thirst' by a drop in the osmotic blood pressure.

At this point it is important to note that, as soon as the afferent synthesis stage was completed, the cerebral cortex immediately exhibited an active excitation of the entire system of the aforesaid afferent bonds which had become consolidated on the basis of the past experience of the afferent results of the act of grasping the pitcher.

In other words, the afferent apparatus, which we have named the acceptor of action, forms under any action of a conditioned stimulus before this reflex action has occurred and consequently constitutes an absolutely integral part of the cyclic architecture of any conditioned reflex action.

It may be assumed that the anticipatory formation of the acceptor of action has become the decisive factor in the organization of the adaptive behaviour of animals because it eliminates chaos in the choice and elaboration of the individual acts of this behaviour (Fig. 9).

Containing all the *afferent results* of the past reinforcements, i.e. containing at the moment of action of the conditioned stimulation the afferent results only of the future (!) action, the acceptor of action becomes a peculiar control apparatus which establishes a physiological correspondence between the completed action and the initial 'intention' to perform this action.

There are several forms of experimental proof of the existence of such an afferent apparatus which forestalls the appearance of the conditioned reflex action, as well as its afferent results.

The first and most demonstrative form of experiment consists in the fact that the *experimenter suddenly replaces the quality of the unconditioned alimentary reinforcement.*

In conducting these experiments we reasoned as follows: if the prepared conditioned excitation of the afferent cells in the cortical representation of the unconditioned centre precisely reflects the properties of the *future*

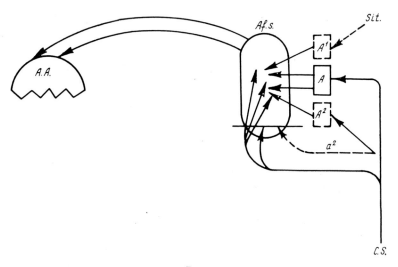

FIG. 9

Stage of formation of the 'acceptor of action' consisting of the afferent traces of past reinforcements. At this stage the reflex action itself has not formed as yet.

return unconditioned excitation and the normally elaborated behaviour of animals is based on this adequacy, the latter must infallibly change if we replace the unconditioned stimulus. Owing to this replacement the anticipatory conditioned excitation in the additional afferent apparatus would be of one quality (on the basis of the former reinforcements) while the real unconditioned stimulus would suddenly (!) be of another quality and, consequently, because of such a combination of the conditions the composition of the nervous impulses of the return afferentation coming to the cerebral cortex from the real unconditioned stimulus would not correspond to the conditioned excitation prepared there. What will the actual behaviour of the animal in this case be?

This idea was applied in our laboratory (Anokhin and Strezh, *Soviet Journal of Physiology*, No. 5, 1933) on the basis of a bilateral alimentary reinforcement allowing these peculiarities of higher nervous activity to be demonstrated.

The experiment was conducted in the following manner. Only two conditioned secretomotor reflexes were elaborated in the animal: to the tone of 'A' with a reinforcement on the right side of the stand and to the tone of 'F' with a reinforcement on the left side. Both reflexes were reinforced by 20 g. of dry bread and were sufficiently well consolidated. After a brief latent period the animal would rush to the corresponding side of the stand and wait there for the unconditioned stimulus. At this stage of the experiments the animal no longer exhibited any erroneous motor reactions.

At the beginning of an experimental day dried meat was placed in one of the plates on the *left side* and thus, against the background of the usual dried-bread reinforcements, the animal was to receive a meat reinforcement to one of the regular stimulations with the tone of 'F'. On the basis of the aforementioned peculiarities of the afferent apparatus of conditioned excitation we must assume that for some brief space of time the new unconditioned stimulations *which do not coincide in their visual, olfactory and gustatory qualities with the already emerged conditioned excitation* must lead to a lack of coincidence in the two excitations and then to the development of an orienting-investigatory reaction. The latter should be the more strongly pronounced the more the prepared conditioned afferent excitations and the available afferent excitations from the true unconditioned stimulus fail to coincide.

These expectations were justified by experiment. When the unconditioned stimulus is thus replaced it usually gives rise to an orienting-investigatory reaction which, depending on the strength of the stimulatory action of the suddenly used inadequate unconditioned stimulus, either changes to an active alimentary reaction (when bread is replaced by meat) or retards the alimentary reaction and the animal even refuses the food (if the meat is replaced by bread).

The foregoing experiment enabled us to observe both forms of the reaction.

The second form of the experiment aimed at proving the existence of the acceptor of action is based on the peculiarities of the experimental method in the two-sided stand proposed by us (see Fig. 1).

Several conditioned secretomotor reflexes firmly fixed by training are elaborated in the animal. To each of the stimuli used at any given moment the animal responds with a positive motor alimentary reaction to a feeding-trough either on the right or left side according to the side on which the animal was fed during the application of the given conditioned stimulus.

Let us assume that with a flash of light the dog was always fed from the right-hand trough, whereas with the sound of the tone of 'C' it was given food in the left-hand trough. According to the law of the conditioned reflex, the animal responds to this form of experiment by elaborating precise conditioned motor reactions to the right and left sides of the stand.

As soon as these conditioned reactions are firmly fixed the food is suddenly (!) given to the flash of light on the left rather than on the right side of the stand.

In other words, an operation is performed or, in the terminology of the Pavlovian laboratory, the conditioned reflex is 'reshaped'.

In this form of experiment it is possible to see that the animal frequently fails to take food from the trough on the side that does not correspond to the conditioned signal. For a long time it looks alternately to the right and left feeding-troughs (orienting-investigatory reaction) and begins to eat the food only after a long latent period. Additional investigations of the animal's respiratory component, when the side on which the food rein-forcement is made is suddenly changed, show the animal to exhibit an uncommonly pronounced orienting-investigatory reaction with a strongly marked inspiratory tonus in breathing.

The only cause that could be thought of for this pronounced reaction was the *lack of correspondence between the sudden feeding (return afferentation) and the already prepared complex of afferent excitations in the cerebral cortex in accordance with the place of the old and usual feeding* (acceptor of action). The same conclusion is suggested by the fact that both food reinforcements, on the right as well as on the left sides, are essentially of the same signifi-cance to the animal, the distances from both feeding-troughs also being the same.

The only remaining cause is the lack of correspondence between the already prepared acceptor of action and the afferent influences emerging when the animal is fed on the inadequate side.

The method of sudden replacement of the reinforcement may be used in most diverse variations, especially in experiments on human adults and children. For example, by showing some dainty to a child and placing this dainty, so that the child sees it, in a 'problem box' from which the child extracts it, it is possible finally to establish adequate correlations between the sight of the dainty and the subsequent reinforcement which occurs when the child opens the box. However, if a *dainty of another quality* is imperceptibly placed in the box, upon opening the box the child immediately develops a reaction of 'surprise' ('What is it?', according to Pavlov) which occurs with different variations depending on a number of conditions. The child may carefully examine the box from all sides, shake it in the hope of receiving the *expected* reinforcement, etc. It is perfectly clear that all these actions are a direct result of the *lack of correspondence between the fixed afferent excitations in the form of the acceptor of action and the afferent influences coming to the central nervous system from the inadequate appearance of the new dainty when the box is opened.*

The third way of proving the emergence of afferent excitations in the acceptor of action forestalling the formation of the action itself is the electroencephalographic method. As stated previously the systems of afferent excitations forming part of the acceptor of action are mobilized much more rapidly than the effector part of action. At times, a very complex reflex action is formed. It follows that the *ascertainment of the preparatory excitations in the area of the cerebral cortex, which must, in the future, receive the return afferentation from the results of the action*, should become one of the methods of studying the physiological mechanisms of the acceptor of action.

A typical example of the anticipatory spread of excitations over the cerebral cortex is the generally known, so-called, electroencephalographic 'conditioned reflex' which manifests itself when sound and light are combined. As is well known, after a number of such combinations the sound alone causes a desynchronization of the α-rhythm in the occipital area of the cortex *before the appearance of the light.* Here the sound sets off a chain of excitations in the cerebral cortex, which spreading rapidly reaches the elements in the visual cortex that will not receive adequate visual excitation from the periphery until a few seconds later (Jasper, 1937; Livanov, 1937; Karazina, 1957; and many others).

Any acceptor of action for any, even very complex acts of behaviour, is formed absolutely according to the same type. Any act of behaviour is represented in the cortex by the development of an uninterrupted chain of afferent excitations received from the individual stages of this act to the final reinforcing factor inclusive. It is precisely this chain of traces of the past afferent excitations that is a peculiar 'conductor' for the rapid spread of the excitations from the conditioned stimulus to the system of excitations *which is the afferent reflection of the results of the as yet forthcoming action.*

Examples of such a spread of the afferent excitations may now be obtained from most diverse papers in which the authors themselves did not intend to study precisely this problem.

We may cite data from the work of Jasper who points out that in a number of cases the secretomotor area of the cerebral cortex exhibits a depression of its rhythm much ahead of the real movement of the arm, this desynchronization sometimes appearing in the person tested at the thought of the forthcoming movement alone (Jasper, 1958).

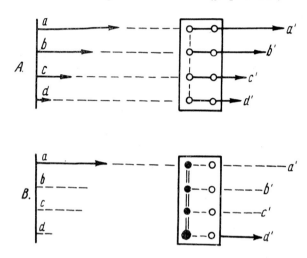

Fig. 10

Schematic representation of the 'anticipatory' spread of excitation and its significance in the formation of the acceptor of action.

A, a, b, c, d, → successively developing action of the external stimulations of which d is the reinforcement with food. Orienting reactions a¹, b¹, c¹ and d¹ emerge correspondingly.

B. Correlation of the processes after training. The action of the one initial stimulus a is enough for the process of excitation immediately to spread along the afferent traces to d which is the 'acceptor of action' in this case.

We find indications of similar facts in the studies of Gastaut concerned with depressing the rolandic rhythm (Gastaut, 1957).

In his recent detailed review of the studies of the reticular formation O'Leary also cited data to the effect that the 'idea' of the forthcoming movement alone may lead to a desynchronization of the electrical activity of the cerebral cortex (Fig. 10).

All the data culled from the literature, as well as our own observations, indicate that after the application of a stimulus or the reading of instructions the selective impulse process of excitation, which ensures the formation of the conditioned reflex, spreads with uncommon speed through all the chains of the past afferent stimulations which reflected the continuity in the development of some act of behaviour. This process of the anticipatory propagation of afferent excitations until the moment the acceptor of action is formed may be shown diagramatically as in Fig. 9.

4. FORMATION OF THE CONDITIONED REACTION EFFECTOR APPARATUS

The stage of formation of the conditioned reaction effector apparatus is directly dependent on the course or end of the afferent synthesis. The latter is always an integral whole and contains in its composition both somatic and vegetative components (motor component, respiratory component, cardiac component, vascular component, hormonal component, etc.).

The characteristic feature of this effector integration is the fact that each of its functioning peripheral components is harmoniously related to the other components and together they constitute the given act of behaviour or the conditioned reflex.

For example, the respiratory component of the conditioned reflex was subjected to systematic analysis for the first time in our laboratory (Balakhin, 1930-35; Polezhayev, 1952; Makarov, 1958; et al.). It was shown to be of an entirely specific character corresponding to the biological quality of the animal's given reaction as a whole. In the defensive conditioned reflex the respiratory component exhibits a high inspiratory tonus and frequent respiratory movements of the thorax.

In a well-fixed alimentary conditioned reflex the respiratory rhythm is, on the contrary, quiet and only at the moment when the conditioned stimulus is applied does the orienting-investigatory reaction temporarily raise the activity of the respiratory component (Fig. 11).

A comparative evaluation of the secretory, motor, respiratory and cardiovascular components of the conditioned reflex shows that they are all harmoniously adapted to the biological significance of the whole reaction. If the reaction requires general activity and tension (as, for example, the conditioned defensive reaction) all the vegetative components, as many as there are, unite into an integrated whole, each of them corresponding to the tasks of the given adaptive act. This means that the intensity of the vegetative components of the conditioned reflex, which provide the entire reaction with power resources, is directly dependent on the degree of the *forthcoming* expenditure of these resources.

This state, revealed particularly clearly as early as 1935 in the studies of

P

our associate Balakin, was recently confirmed by special forms of experiments.

In our laboratory Dr Kasyanov has shown that the respiratory component of the conditioned reflex is the first conditioned reflex component to form in the effector pathways (Kasyanov, 1950). The cardiovascular complex reaches the effector pathways almost simultaneously with the respiratory component. Gantt's studies have shown, however, that the cardiac component of the conditioned reflex appears somewhat ahead of the respiratory component (Gantt, 1952).

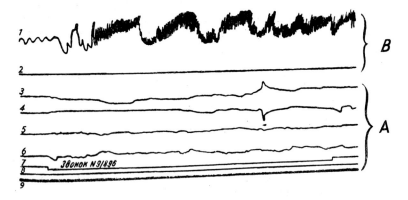

FIG. 11

Dissociation between the generalized and local excitation of the motor apparatus of the dog after bilateral extirpation of the sensorimotor areas of the cerebral cortex. The generalized reaction (A) is on hand, while the local raising of the hind limb is totally absent (B).

The recent studies conducted by Shidlovsky in our laboratory with the aid of up-to-date cardiographic apparatus ('Cardiovar', 'Barovar', etc.) have confirmed our former observations and have shown the respiratory component to reach the effector pathways somewhat ahead of the cardiac component (Shidlovsky, 1959).

It should be noted, however, that these insignificant differences in the appearance of the vegetative excitations in the peripheral organs, where they are detected by suitable apparatus, are of no fundamental importance. They may be due to different lengths of the pathways the excitations must traverse from the centres to corresponding organs, to the number of synapses in these pathways, and, lastly, to the peculiarities of the recording apparatus.

But some aspects of this phenomenon, constant for all types of conditioned reactions, are undoubtedly important. For example, the vegetative components in general reach the terminal effector components in the form of components of specific qualities (secretion for the alimentary conditioned reaction, movement for the defensive conditioned reaction) before the conditioned reflex reaction manifests itself. The other important aspect of what we call 'vegetative outstripping' consists in the fact that all these components in their totality are of a conditioned reflex nature and reflect precisely the energy requirements of the forthcoming conditioned reflex action.

Shidlovsky devoted a special experiment to this problem. He recorded the cardiovascular components of the conditioned alimentary reaction in two different situations: in one case, the animal had to overcome a small obstacle to get at the food received as reinforcement, thus exerting a muscular effort, while in the other case the food was brought directly to the animal's muzzle. Thus, in the first case, the conditioned signal warned the animal not only of the forthcoming feeding but also of *certain muscular efforts* it had to exert before receiving the food.

In total conformity with these conditions the respiratory and cardiovascular components of the conditioned reaction are vigorously activated in the first case. Conversely, in the second case, the same vegetative components manifest no such changes and deviate but slightly from the level of the resting state (Fig. 12).

All the experiments performed in this direction clearly show that the conditioned reaction, as a manifestation of the integral organism, affects the periphery through very numerous terminal neurones involving most diverse somatic and vegetative components.

An evaluation of the physiological composition of this integral efferent formation should take into account its three physiological peculiarities:

(*a*) it is a direct result of the afferent synthesis stage;

(*b*) it forms during the entire course of elaboration of the given conditioned reflex (see below);

(*c*) it has a vertical physiological architecture, since it infallibly includes cortical and subcortical components.

The last of the foregoing propositions is clearly demonstrated by the very participation of vegetative components in the conditioned reflex. Since these components reflect the integral character of the total reaction and are formed through the terminal pathways of the hypothalamus and the brain stem reticular formation, it is possible to chart the general distribution of the nervous impulses within the entire efferent stream of excitations, including the functioning organs.

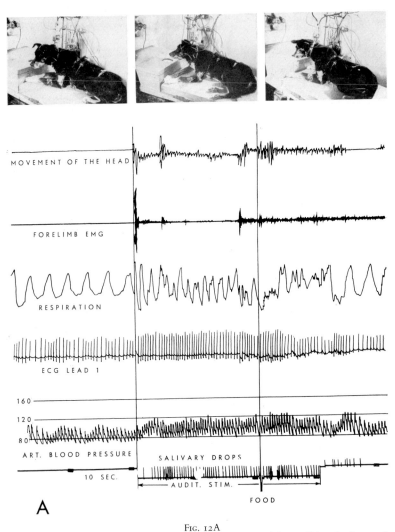

Illustration of the dependence of the vegetative components of the conditioned reflex on the forthcoming energy expenditures signalled by the conditioned stimulus.
A. Reaction to the conditioned stimulus with the animal in close proximity to the food.

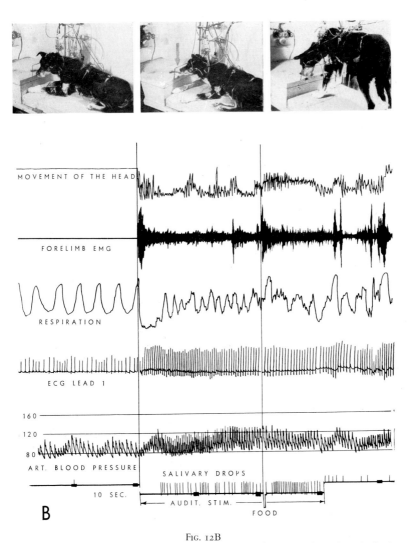

FIG. 12B

B. Reaction to the conditioned stimulus when overcoming a difficulty before taking the food. The latter case shows much greater activity of all the vegetative components of the conditioned reaction.

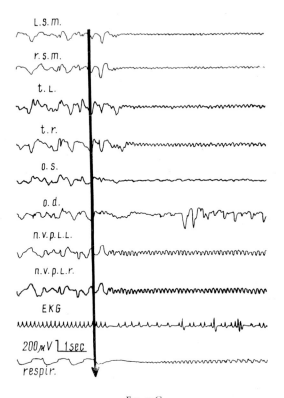

FIG. 12C

C. Confrontation of different components of a response to direct stimulation of the brain stem reticular formation. Abbreviations: l.s.m. — left sensorimotor cortex, r.s.m. — right sensorimotor cortex, t.l. — left temporal cortex, t.r. — right temporal cortex, o.s. — occipitalis sinistra, o.d. — occipitalis dextra, n.v.p.l.l. — n. ventralis posterior lateralis, left, n.v.p.l.r. — n. ventralis posterior lateralis, right, EKG, respir. — respiration.

The latest data on the representation of vegetative functions in the cerebral cortex once more emphasize the importance of precisely the vertical plan in the structure of the effector complex of excitations in the conditioned reflex. I am referring primarily to Papez's view of the 'visceral cortex' and to the studies of a number of other authors directed towards the same aspect of the subject (Papez, 1958; Maclean, 1954; Bard, 1948; Green, 1958; Adey, 1958).

On the basis of authentic facts indicating representation of vegetative

functions in the limbic, orbital, girus cinguli and other parts of the cerebral cortex it might be assumed that the whole effector part of the conditioned reflex, including the vegetative components is elaborated in some
form at the level of the cerebral cortex.

However, the manifestation of the vegetative components during the
first fractions of a second in the action of the conditioned stimulus warrants
the assumption that this first reaction of the well-fixed conditioned
reflex forms at the level of the subcortical apparatus.

With this question we closely approach the problem of localization of
conditioned reflex coupling. On the basis of electroencephalographic
experiments Fessard, Gastaut and Yoshii reached the conclusion that the
coupling of the conditioned bond occurred primarily in the area of the
reticular formation and that only later, already as a vertical 'projection',
did the conditioned reflex process became cortical (Fessard and Gastaut,
1958; Gastaut, 1958). The very rapid changes in the respiratory
component, revealed in our experiments, also seem to indicate this
localization of the process of coupling of conditioned bonds. This seems
the more probable since the brain stem reticular formation, which receives
along collaterals the afferent impulses from the lemniscus-conditioned
excitations, contains all the fractions of the respiratory and cardiovascular
centres.

Moreover, the unconditioned excitations also come to the reticular
formation. Thus all favourable conditions for the coupling function seem
to be set up in the area of the brain stem reticular formation whose neural
elements have extensive possibilities for the convergence of afferent
excitations (Moruzzi, 1956; Amassian, 1958; Fessard, 1958). Nevertheless,
considering the particular role of the orienting-investigatory reaction in
the formation of the conditioned reflex, it is difficult to agree with the
idea of a primary subcortical coupling of the conditioned bond (Anokhin,
1957; Anokhin, 1958).

The question of the composition of the effector complex of the conditioned reaction came particularly clearly to the fore in our experiments
during the studies of the conditioned motor reflex. In this case we are
referring to the local motor-defensive conditioned reflex reinforced by
electric current and manifesting itself in lifting the hind limb.

In our laboratory it was established long ago that this 'local' reflex, its
seeming simplicity and 'localness' notwithstanding, is a result of extraordinarily complexly integrated effector excitations selectively propagated
to the peripheral motor apparatus according to very definite stages in the
formation of the conditioned reaction. It was found that, before the

animal lifts its corresponding limb in response to the conditioned stimulus signalling pain stimulation, the excitations are rapidly redistributed along the axial musculature of its body. Owing to this rapid process, the animal assumes a new posture with new relations between the points of support and the centre of gravity, enabling it to raise the corresponding limb (Shumilina, 1939).

An electromyographic analysis of the antagonistic muscles in the different limbs of animals and man made it possible to show that this excitation, which we have named 'positional excitation', very rapidly reaches the extensors of the limbs, and the entire body shifts to three points of support within several fractions of a second before the limb previously stimulated by electric current is raised (Shumilina, 1949; Kasyanov, 1950).

In this interesting phenomenon we thought it possible to analyse the composition of the effector complex of excitations in so commonplace a conditioned motor act as the jerking away of the hind limb.

For the physiologist interested in higher nervous activity and animal behaviour this phenomenon of the dual nature of excitations in the motor conditioned reflex is important because both the first and second stages *are clearly of a conditioned reflex character despite their different central localization*. As a matter of fact, the rapid redistribution of the tonic tensions in the axial musculature of the body and the proximal parts of the limbs is not 'diffuse' in the ordinary physiological sense. This positional excitation is distributed over very definite motor neurones which shape the animal's posture precisely corresponding to the *future* raising of one of the limbs. From the biomechanical point of view we know very well that, if it had not been for this preliminary phase of shift of the centre of gravity in accordance with the basic points of support, the dog would fall, in attempting to raise the hind limb, as a bronze statuette falls when one of its legs is broken.

A conditioned motor reflex may be elaborated for any of the dog's four limbs by reinforcing it with electric current, and in each individual case the positional excitation will be distributed over the body segments anew, i.e. depending on the limb which will be lifted within several fractions of a second after the application of the conditioned stimulus. This fact is the best proof that both stages in the development of motor excitations are of a conditioned reflex nature.

At the same time we know very well that the central localization of both excitations is not the same. Whereas the positional excitation forms at the level of subcortical centres, especially in the neural elements of the reticular formation (Magoun, 1952; Moruzzi, 1956, *et al.*), the local limb lifting, i.e. the local conditioned motor act is effected by the pyramidal tract and has a definite cortical localization.

The question is: how do both these organic components integrate in the animal's integral conditioned motor act? We endeavoured to answer this question by means of a number of variations of conditioned reflex experiments.

In order to trace the very fact of the shift in the centre of the body's gravity during the stage of formation of the positional excitation we

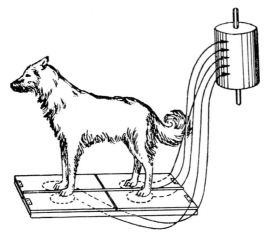

FIG. 13

Stand designed with four separately recorded stages. In addition to recording the spread of positional excitation this stand permits of recording the secretion of saliva and the vegetative components.

designed a stand by means of which we could record the pressure exerted by each of the four limbs (Fig. 13). The experiment showed that the moment the conditioned stimulus was applied there was a rapid and rather complex redistribution of muscular efforts, which could be easily recorded kymographically and electromyographically (Koryakin, 1958). It also showed that, if the conditioned motor defensive act was effected, say, by the right hind limb, the lifting of the paw was always preceded by an uncommonly stable complex of relations in the excitations of the brain stem. Now, if both sensomotor areas of the cerebral cortex are removed, an interesting dissociation between the positional and local stages of the conditioned motor reaction are observed. Whereas in response to the conditioned stimulus the positional complex is retained in total conformity with its former nature, the local motor act is completely absent. This selective injury to the local component of the conditioned motor act indicates that positional excitations are really of a subcortical origin. (Fig. 14).

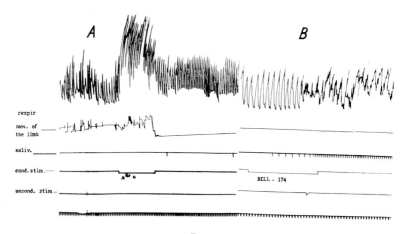

FIG. 14

Comparison of the respiratory component of two conditioned reactions — defensive (A) and alimentary (B).

The question of how a clearly subcortical complex of excitations could acquire a conditioned reflex nature cannot be dealt with at present, since it would lead us away from the subject under consideration. Here it is important only to note that our various experiments with the orienting-investigatory reaction have convinced us that the *conditioned reflex nature of the subcortical reactions is not primary*. It becomes such only after the active interference of cortical control at the stage of the very strong orientating reflex (Anokhin, 1949; Livingston, 1958; Hernández-Peón, 1958, 1959; *et al.*) (Fig. 15).

I presume that this part of my report illustrates sufficiently clearly two propositions: (1) the intricate complex of the effector excitations of the conditioned reflex is always very extensive and includes the cortex, as well as subcortical apparatus, and (2) this complex can be understood only by assuming the existence of a stage of synthesis of all the afferent influences affecting the animal at the given moment.

5. RETURN AFFERENTATION OF THE RESULTS OF CONDITIONED REFLEX ACTION

The conception of 'return afferentation' had developed in our laboratory long before the cybernetic trend of thinking led to the formulation of the 'feedback' idea, now being transferred into neurophysiology and proposed for the self-regulating technical systems.

Studying the problem of compensation of organic functions after the production of cross anastomoses we came to the conclusion that the creation of any new functional system of the organism in place of a

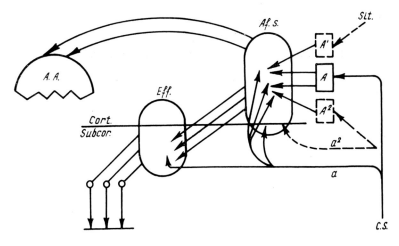

FIG. 15
Further development of the conditioned reflex architecture. Integrated effector excitations reach the functioning organs, and formation of the adaptive action.

previous system that has been abolished required constant interference of return afferent impulses from the results of the performed action themselves.

The physiological meaning of return afferentation consists in the reflection in minutest afferent impulses of the minutest details of the results of a given action. These results may direct the information to the central nervous system through the most diverse receptor apparatus. However, this afferentation as a whole constitutes a peculiar integral which reflects in the stream of afferent impulses the aggregate results of the given reflex action (Anokhin, 1935; Anokhin and Ivanov, 1933). Since it is directed *back* to the central nervous system to the neural formations just activated we found it most convenient to name it the 'return afferentation'.

In the existing literature afferent impulses of this type are ascribed mainly to proprioceptive formations. At this point I want to stress the fact that this conception has nothing in common with that of return afferentation. Proprioceptive signalling is also of a return nature, but it regulates the trend of the very action in the sense of its biomechanical characteristics. Proprioceptive signalling will never be able to inform the brain of the results of the adaptive effect obtained by means of the given movement. As a matter of fact, we cannot assay by means of a proprioceptor whether we have grasped a knife or fork, although the impulses of a tactile nature, suggesting that the hand has touched the object and the visual impulses fixing the moment of grasping the object, by means of return afferent impulses together ensure exhaustive information of the fact that the movement has ended in a certain positive result.

Here we approach the most critical point of the physiological architecture of the conditional reflex from which all the new adaptive acts, yielding more perfect results of action, begin. We shall ask the question in the following manner: where is the return afferentation of the results of the action directed to, what apparatus of the central nervous system perceives it and, so to speak, 'assays' the correspondence of the result achieved with the result of the afferent synthesis performed by it earlier?

The experiments and considerations discussed above, as regards the formation of the afferent apparatus of the acceptor of action, have led us to the conclusion that the meeting of the excitations of the acceptor of action and of the return afferentation from the results of the performed action is the moment at which the organism is always informed of the satisfactory precision of the act of behaviour that has taken place. It is precisely at the point where these two excitations — the excitation of the acceptor of action and the stream of return afferentations from the results of the action — meet that, in our opinion, the necessary condition for any co-ordinated and regulated relation of the animal and man to the external environment lies. Only when these two streams of excitation exactly coincide do the effector excitations cease to reach the functioning apparatus and is the given behaviour stage in the chain of individual reflex actions completed (Fig. 16).

Conversely, if the streams of return afferentations entering the brain along different analysers fail to coincide with the system of excitations, which has formed at the end of the afferent synthesis and is the apparatus of the acceptor of action, this lack of coincidence immediately involves other reactions, primarily, the orienting-investigatory reaction. By its very essence the orienting-investigatory reaction leads to an accumulation

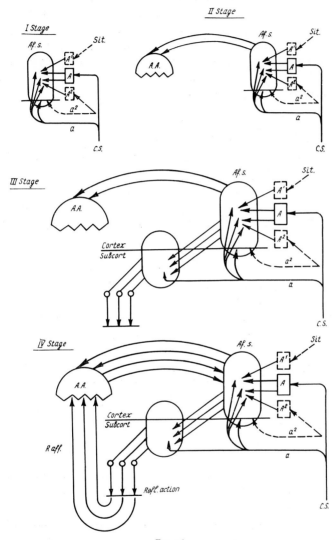

FIG. 16

Completion of the conditioned reflex physiological architecture. The figure shows the successive stages in the development of the architecture.

of new afferentations from the external environment, to a repetition of the afferent synthesis stage already at a new level and, lastly, to the formation of new effector complexes. On their part, these latter lead to some new act of behaviour and thus determine streams of new return afferent impulses which usually correspond in larger measure to the established acceptor of action. In any act of behaviour this cyclic process, beginning with the afferent synthesis stage and ending in the confrontation of the return afferentations and the excitations of the acceptor of action, continues until

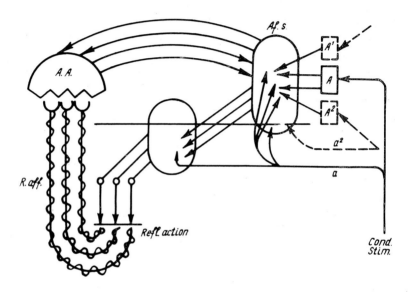

FIG. 17
Example of lack of correspondence between the acceptor of action and the return afferentation
'Discordance'.

both excitations fully coincide. In human behaviour, which, in our opinion, unfolds, even in its higher forms, according to the foregoing physiological architecture of the conditioned reflex, this final moment may be formulated as a 'coincidence of the results of action with the initial intention'. It is in this that the definite significance of the conception proposed by us for the physiological understanding of a number of phenomena of a psychological nature lies.

An analysis of most of the experimental situations, especially conducted in the way of the integral behaviour of the animal by the 'free runs' method, shows that very many forms of behaviour are elaborated according to the aforesaid physiological architecture of the conditioned reflex (Fig. 16). The diagram shows the completion of the whole stream of excitations, which arose as a result of the afferent synthesis and of determined and particular adaptive effect. Practically every act in the life of man develops according to this architecture. Both as regards erroneous actions and the initial period of learning new actions, the only criterion of the correctness of the action is, in our opinion, the coincidence of the assigned excitations with the stream of the return afferent impulses which bring information of the results of the action performed at the given moment. This is particularly well seen in cases in which some erroneous act is performed. How do we detect the errors of an action if the latter has ended 'safely' from the point of view of all the demands made on it by the classical reflex theory? Everything seems to be on hand here: the stimulus, the central apparatus, as it is usually understood, and, lastly, the reflex action. By means of what additional apparatus then does man or the animal discover that the action they have performed is inadequate or erroneous? (Fig. 17).

The physiological architecture of the conditioned reflex proposed by us, like that of any 'voluntary action', offers a sufficiently objectively grounded answer to all these questions. At the same time it offers a real basis for a further scientifically objective analysis of the complex behaviour reactions of man and the animals.

CONCLUSION

The concept discussed above is an attempt to unify some of the available information on the physiology of the central nervous system and to combine it with the facts obtained in direct studies of the neurophysiological mechanisms of the conditioned reflex.

It is but natural that, with such a synthesis of the vast number of facts, we had to introduce several new conceptions which correspond to certain mechanisms discovered by us.

To begin with these conceptions include that of the *afferent synthesis*. The absence of stress on this stage of the complex treatment of all the multiform and numerous afferent influences on the organism by the central nervous system rendered unintelligible the very process of formation of the *efferent* complex of excitations, always of an integrative nature, i.e. always harmoniously combining the functioning components of the whole conditioned reaction.

To be sure, on the basis of what mechanisms does the given combination, rather than any other out of the millions of possible combinations of
excitations developing in the cellular elements of the central nervous
system, become integrated?

On the basis of what mechanisms is a very definite end effect of adaptation chosen and fixed out of the many probable end effects of adaptation,
this end effect being precisely the one which exactly corresponds to the
aggregate of the afferent influences affecting the organism at the given
moment?

We have become convinced that the key to the solution of these
problems lies in the extremely fine and multiform processes of accumulation of afferent information from the external and internal environments
of animals and man. This is followed by a dynamic interaction and
synthesis of this afferent information and, on the basis of these processes,
one of the most intimate processes of any form of conditioned behaviour
– the formation of the complex integrations of the effector apparatus.
This process truly deserves the picturesque designation given to it at one
time by our teacher Pavlov who named the afferent function of the brain
the 'creative' function.

We see that it is indeed 'creative' if we take into account the enormous
number of qualitatively heterogeneous afferent stimulations acting on the
organism at each given moment and if we add to this that for man it
infallibly ends in what may be psychologically termed the formation of
the 'intention' of action.

Many physiological factors contribute to this remarkable process.
Here we may include the rule of *convergence* of heterogeneous afferent
stimulations in the selfsame element of the stem reticular formation
(Fessard, 1958; Moruzzi, 1958; Amassian, 1958), the activating effect of
this system on the cortical level of elaboration of the afferent signals
(Moruzzi and Magoun, 1949), the integrating action of the frontal
divisions of the cerebral cortex on this synthetic process (Shumilina, 1944;
Anokhin, 1949) and, lastly, the controlling action of the cerebral cortex
on all the subcortical and spinal entering elements for the afferent impulses
(Anokhin, 1949; Livingston, 1958). All the above, put together, serves
the highest synthesis – the formation of the conditioned bond!

Application of the term 'creative' to this process does not exclude the
fact that all its details, as well as the process as a whole, are structurally and
physiologically determined and, consequently, may become the subject
of a strictly objective scientific analysis.

This latter proposition is illustrated by the fact that it is precisely the physiological methods of research that enabled us to discover the existence of a special apparatus — the acceptor of action. As may be observed it co-ordinates behaviour during the second stage of the conditioned reflex, i.e. during the formation of the efferent act and the emergence of the return afferentation on the adaptive results of this act.

The entire architecture of the whole conditioned reflex offered for your consideration shows that this physiological analysis may be continued. It shows how living nature in the long evolutionary process mastered the *future* and fixed in material forms — structural and dynamic — the possibility of the animal's adaptation to *forthcoming events* in the external en-vironment.

The conditioned reflex is the expression of the higher adaptation formulated by Pavlov in the *principle* of signalling, i.e. the possibility of adaptation of the animal and man to future events by just the *remote signal* of these forthcoming events alone.

Of course, it would be wrong to assume that the foregoing material exhausts the entire content of the physiological architecture of the condi-tioned reflex. The material presented is undoubtedly only the beginning of its study. However, it is important that its features be outlined precisely as those of an *integral physiological architecture* and for us it serves as the point of departure for further analysis.

Making a positive evaluation of our concepts of the physiological architecture of the conditioned reflex in one of his recent works, Alfred Fessard expresses the opinion that a further fine neurophysiological elaboration of the 'main points' of this general architecture will make an essential contribution to the development of these concepts (Fessard, 1958).

We fully agree with this opinion and, as may be judged from the fore-going material, we are doing all we can to concretize physiologically the various aspects of this general architecture.

We also think it possible that further analysis and accumulation of facts in the study of the neurophysiological bases of the conditioned reflex may make us change some of our present-day views and form new concepts concerning the concrete physiological mechanisms. This is the essence of scientific progress.

We believe, however, that any study of the intimate processes of the conditioned reflex by means of analytical and very fine methods and techniques may prove much more successful if it is correlated with the general physiological architecture of the conditioned reflex. And it is just this that prompted us to make this general architecture of the condi-tioned reflex, as we conceive it today, the subject of discussion.

Q

GROUP DISCUSSION

OLDS. I would like to address myself to the remarks on the reticular formation and its differentiation. We also found differentiation in the reticular formation based on the dichotomy between the aversive and approach behaviour. We find that stimulation in the dorsal medial tegmentum produces escape. Stimulation in the ventral lateral tegmentum produces approach of the self-stimulation variety — in between there are overlaps.

First — the type of electrical activity which Dr Anokhin showed as typical of aversive stimulation did not appear in the ventral lateral placements but did appear in dorsal medial placements. The type of electrical activity which he showed as characteristic of alimentary stimulation did appear in the ventral lateral placements, but not in the dorsal-medial placements. My question is whether the electrodes used by Professor Anokhin were in the same parts of the reticular formation or in different parts.

My second question is: We have applied chlorpromazine and we have obtained results which are superficially in conflict with Dr Anokhin's results and we have checked our data. This is it: Chlorpromazine inhibits the self-stimulation response *totally* in the rat at 2 mg. per kilogramme — a dose which has very little effect on the escape reaction produced by stimulation of the dorso-medial tegmentum. This is different from Neprobamate and Nembutal which inhibit the escape reaction and have little effect on the self-stimulation response.

ANOKHIN. I suppose that the difference here is to be found in the specific localization of the stimulation. A given reaction may be induced from different points of the functional system; it can be provoked by natural stimuli, as by electrical ones. Yet, if electric stimulation is applied to a given spot of the reticular formation which is on the excitation pathway, after synapses which have been made sensitive to chlorpromazine, it may happen that the drug will have no blocking effect on the animal's defence reaction, which had been induced by direct excitation.

GRASTYÁN. I am in perfect agreement with Professor Anokhin about the conception of the functional specificity of reticular activating influences. I think we also obtained in our own experiments evidence confirming this supposition: we found that the stimulation of different points in the reticular formation in the hypothalamus had always a specific influence in the sense that it activated only certain behavioural acts, but inhibited others, antagonistic to those of the activated ones. The only point with which I do not agree is the interpretation of the electrical activity recorded in the reticular formation. I cannot believe that it represents a specific activity of the reticular formation (I refer to the 4-6 cycles per second activity see *slides 6 and 7*). It must be recorded very close to the substantia grisea centralis in the mesencephalon and in my opinion it reflects a special projected activity of the rhinencephalon to the brain stem (hippocampus, entorhinal cortex). It was shown by Dr Adey that abundant connections exist between these two areas. Moreover I have seen this activity to appear in the same point of the reticular formation in both alimentary and defensive conditioned reflexes; thus in my opinion it could not be regarded as representative of a specific function of this reticular subcentre.

ANOKHIN. I can give Dr Grastyán the following answer: Comparison of the slow rhythms of the reticular formations of the hippocampus and of the different regions of the cerebral cortex shows that the specific slow rhythm of 4-7 per second occurs as a general rule in connection with direct painful stimuli of either the sciatic nerve or the skin of the foot. With other forms of stimuli, for instance, stimuli due to food, one does not get this rhythm. As has been shown by simultaneous recordings of EEG and of nervous impulses of individual nerve cells from one and the same point of the brain, the main characteristic of this rhythm is its persistence and its regularity.

As soon as the rhythm changes even for a fraction of a second, the cell impulses disappear or diminish.

We believe that this rhythm originates in the reticular formation and after a very short time (0, 1-0, 3 seconds) spreads to the corresponding region of the cortex, the parietal and the visual region. I suppose that our disagreements with Dr Grastyán are basically due to the fact that under normal experimental conditions our laboratory animals are always under some painful influence or in a state of fear. A specific rhythm can always appear on the electroencephalogram according to the degree of fear. In normal animals, which are awake, it is very difficult to suppress this rhythm and it can be achieved only after working several months with a pleasant food reinforcement. It may be that all these conditions were fulfilled in Dr Grastyán's experiments.

I think that in the future we also shall endeavour to bring about conditions under which this rhythm appears more often.

GALAMBOS. The data from Dr Grastyán's experiments resemble ours closely. I am not sure, however, that the term 'conditioned response' should be applied to these data. Choice of term is of course merely a matter of definition, and since a stimulus followed by a reinforcement here yields a changed brain response, the brain event fits the usual definition for a CR. We view the electrical event, however, as more probably indicating an elementary process in a chain of processes, that, when completed, yield learning. The phenomenon in question probably indicates that the brain is being prepared for the specific change that will occur and is not the signal of the actual change itself.

CHANGING CONCEPTS OF THE LEARNING MECHANISM

Robert Galambos

GENERAL CONSIDERATIONS

Animals almost invariably learn when placed in a situation where an opportunity to do so is provided, and yet they can learn no more than their capacities permit or make possible. It is, in other words, as unprofitable to try to teach an animal a task beyond his capabilities as it is to try to prevent his learning it when he has been prepared by nature to do so. Such essential facts as the inevitability but limited scope of learned responses were well known to Darwin (e.g. *Descent of Man*, Chapter 3) and to other astute observers before and since. Herrick, taking this broad biological view, has comprehensively summarized the more recent work (1956).

In the analysis of how animals come to learn, scientists from several disciplines generally agree now that they (*a*) sense environmental events, (*b*) react 'reflexly' to them, and (*c*) modify their subsequent behaviour in the light of those experiences. Much study and an enormous literature have developed around these phenomena and current work on the brain events occurring during learning seems to be directed towards answers for the following three major questions:

I. What is the nature of the neural organization that enables, permits and indeed requires the organism to make contact with the environment through its senses for the purpose of analysing it? Much effort has been spent on defining the physical nature of the energy exchange that occurs at the sensory end organ – e.g. the transmutation into nerve impulses of mechanical motion in the inner ear and of electromagnetic radiation in the eye. Beyond this many investigators have been trying to specify the analysis performed within the sensory afferent pathways; much of this work has been done in anaesthetized or otherwise reduced preparations. Besides this, effort in increasing amount is being devoted to uncovering the basis for the evident ability of normal, intact organisms to respond preferentially to input from one rather than another of its sensory inputs – the problem of 'attention' and its converse 'habituation' if you will.

Finally, there are the matters of how different 'perceptions' arise merely because the input energy arrives, say, via the ear rather than the eye, and how it can be that these perceptions become permanently stored as 'memories'. The data about the brain needed for dealing scientifically with these last objective behavioural events are meagre or nonexistent, but progress in the development of new and relevant information is obviously accelerating and inevitable.

II. What is the essential nature of the neuronal organization which makes the innate 'reflex' responses inevitable for the animal? It is not a chance matter that dogs breathe and swallow, and salivate when food is put into the mouth, and withdraw the paw when an electric shock is applied to it. Neither, one must admit, is it accidental or by chance that they learn when exposed to the world about them. As is true of every living animal, dogs come naturally equipped to do things of this sort. There are many such innate behavioural responses displayed commonly throughout the animal kingdom, and in addition patterns peculiar to each species are clearly recognizable. Thus dogs bark, not mew; and they are adapted behaviourally to do many other things not in the repertoire of pigeons and cockroaches. Experimenters on brain function generally assume that comprehensible neural correlates exist for both the species-specific behavioural displays and for the ones which the different species commonly exhibit. It is unnecessary to point out, however, that while exact descriptions of such behaviour are available from many sources, satisfactorily comprehensive neural generalizations for dealing with them certainly are not.

III. What is the new neuronal organization created within the animal by an experience with the world around him? The dramatic commonplace phenomenon we call learning must be explained, it would appear, as a more or less permanent change of the nervous system. An astonishingly large amount of searching has gone into attempts to specify the exact nature of that change, and it is clear that physiologists, rightly or wrongly, consider this process of learning to be of paramount interest and importance to an understanding of brain physiology. The scientific analysis has largely proceeded by attempts to describe where in the brain, and when in time, the brain change takes place, and there are several current ideas of the essential features of the process. Furthermore, much new information is being developed, as this Conference will demonstrate. Some ideas seem to be growing in favour while others decline, and it is towards a critical evaluation of both the ascendant views and the classical ones that I would direct your attention in what follows.

CONCEPTS ABOUT THE BRAIN CHANGE IN LEARNING[1]

The classical view holds that the neocortex is where the specific changes accountable for new learned responses occur. I shall not list the arguments in favour of this view; the reader will instead find below several experiments that raise objections to this generalization and others that may provide concepts for our possible further enlightenment.

1. There seems to be no universally accepted definition of learning. 'Learning' is common to octopus, cat and bee despite the large differences in their neural apparatus. In particular the mammalian cerebral cortex is obviously not needed since animals wholly deficient in this structure display behaviour that by any reasonable definition is 'learned'.

2. Some mammalian habits can be abolished by decortication and then be relearned. The pre- and post-operative CRs seem to be the same, and if we make the plausible assumption that the cortex participated in the original habit it is evident that the second one is mediated by extracortical structures.

3. The cortex, however, is clearly the site of a durable change in certain other kinds of habits. This conclusion emerges, for example, from the learning experiments in which the corpus callosum is sectioned at a crucial state (Myers). These studies show that some essential event does indeed occur in the cerebral hemisphere for habits involving visual discriminations at least.

4. Different amounts of neocortex seem to be required according to the degree of complexity of the learning problem. If a two-tone pitch discrimination and a three-tone pattern discrimination are taught to a cat, removal of its auditory cortex abolishes both, and only the 'simple' pitch discrimination can be relearned (Neff and Diamond). Some neural events responsible for the 'complex' tone-pattern CR have been eliminated by partial decortication but the necessaries for a 'simple' CR remain. (What is meant by simple vs. complex learning has not to my knowledge been adequately defined.)

5. Recent experiments on various neuronal aggregates within the brain (e.g. the reticular and limbic systems), while suggesting remarkably distinctive functions for each of them (e.g. attention, emotion), indicate also that these separate cellular aggregates combine in some orderly way to create the brain change that ultimately yields learned behaviour.

---

[1] This section closely follows a portion of an unpublished manuscript by R. Galambos and C. T. Morgan, 'The Neural Basis of Learning', prepared in 1957 for *Handbook of Physiology*, scheduled for publication in 1960.

Consideration of the time course of acquisition will illustrate this concept. A monkey learning to avoid shocks by pressing a lever at a signal appears to pass through a series of behavioural stages in the process. At first the signal arouses much 'emotional' activity such as pilo-erection and vocalization. Later, when learning has progressed to 50 per cent correct responses, this 'emotional' behaviour can be partly replaced by an 'alert or attentive' attitude. The fully trained animal, in final complete command of the situation, seems undisturbed 'emotionally' by the signal and sits relatively 'inattentive' as he delays making the correct response until the very last moment. These successive behavioural stages presumably reflect a progressive reorganization of brain structures or processes during acquisition. If this is true, brain events measured at a particular place in the early stages of learning might be absent there later; while at another brain locus characteristic brain events might appear only when learning has become complete. Evidence accumulates that learning is just such a dynamic orderly march of events that involves much or all of the neural apparatus the organism possesses.

6. There is reason to believe that there are different kinds of learning, that the brain changes accounting for these are not uniform or identical, and that what happens in the brain during solution of one problem need not happen in the solution of the next one. As has been adequately shown (Brady and Hunt) a rat trained both (a) to press a lever to get a drop of water (an instrumental or Type II response) and (b) to 'expect' a shock at the termination of a signal (a classical or Type I response), loses only the second of these habits after experiencing a number of convulsive seizures. Furthermore, the lost habit returns after a time without retraining. That convulsive seizures temporarily abolish one CR while leaving another entirely intact defines a large and presumably highly significant difference in the neural basis of the two CRs.

7. All problems are not equally easy for animals to learn. Teachers know that what one child learns easily another may never acquire, and everyone will concede that speaking, writing and reading are much more readily learned by man than by any other species. Besides the obvious species and individual differences in learning capacities which are apparent upon a moment's reflection, there is the fact that whereas many or very many combinations of CS and US are ordinarily required to establish a CR, a single exposure to CS alone produces lifetime retention in the case of imprinting (Hess). What are the neural events in this exceptional instance, where for only a few hours in the life history of an organism its brain is prepared to make a particular set of functional connections? The

answer to this question would undoubtedly provide highly useful clues applicable to 'ordinary' learning as well.

8. Wholly unlearned complex behaviour like that of newly hatched birds which are said to scatter for cover at the first presentation of specific sounds or moving shapes may represent simply the ultimate with respect to the neural processes we would like to understand. Reflexes and instincts emerge because some neuronal organization is handed down, like body shape, as part of an organism's phylogenetic heritage. Conceivably this neuronal organization has much in common with or is actually identical to the one achieved through experience. If this were so, the same physiological principles would suffice equally well for explaining the behaviour built in at birth and that acquired during life. Darwin's choice of the term 'inherited habit' for the unlearned response would in that event turn out to have been peculiarly apt. For a full discussion of this problem by the author the reader is referred to the 2nd Macy Conference on *The Central Nervous System and Behavior*, where the neural mechanism of vomiting was considered.

DATA ABOUT THE BRAIN CHANGE IN LEARNING

For reasons of convenience or of convention the mammalian brain seems to have become the principal object of study and the facts make it increasingly clear that within it the neural change of learning is not a single event occurring at a single point in time but rather a sequence of events occurring over a more or less prolonged interval in widespread brain locations. Acquisition of the learned response takes time (Duncan), and not only is the appropriate classical analyser system activated but so also are the reticular core of the brain stem and the limbic system as well (e.g. Anokhin, Buser and Roger, Galambos *et al.*, Hernández-Peón *et al.*, 1958; Trofimov *et al.*). Within the anatomical limits of a classical analyser system, furthermore, variation in response to the conditioning stimulus is commonly encountered during the learning process not only at the cortical termination but also at the first synapse (Galambos *et al.*, Gersuni *et al.*, Hernández-Peón *et al.*, 1956), a fact presumably related to action of the efferent sensory systems. With large and microelectrodes new electrical events uniquely related to learning have been described (Jasper *et al.*, Kogan, Livanov, Morrell and Jasper, and Yoshii *et al.*), and experimental evidence is even being marshalled to support Coghill's insight (Herrick) that it is 'neuropile' modification that produces learning (e.g. Gastaut). Finally, recent observers (e.g. John and Killam) have begun to cast some light upon the dynamic course of events during acquisition according to which responses grow and fade in one structure after another until at last a stable pattern of brain activity associated with the fully elaborated CR becomes established. Any concept, therefore, that holds that the essential events in conditioning and learning occur at a particular instant in time and exclusively in the cerebral neocortex struggles against an already impressive and continuously growing body of contrary facts.

As for the work in our own laboratory, the research effort in which Drs Sheatz, Hearst, Bogdanski, Vernier and several others have collaborated has been directed towards a descriptive analysis of the electrophysiological events associated with acquisition, retention and extinction of learned responses. It is our feeling that much new information remains to be collected before we can comprehend even the simplest basic events in learning, and we would do this with minimum reference to the preconceptions of the processes involved that we ourselves invent or that we have inherited in the form of 'syntheses' achieved by students now long dead. Our experimental plan and essential results have already been described and need not be repeated here (1st Macy Conference); we have been observing evoked EEG responses in simple learning situations. Our modest progress to date may be summarized under several general headings.

1. In normal cats and monkeys the EEG response evoked by a brief acoustic or visual signal of constant strength is not constant in size or duration. This variability in response is not restricted to the cortical terminus of the specific analyser but can be measured in widespread cortical and subcortical regions as well. Presumably the observed variability reflects the processes underlying the 'orienting response' intensively studied in many laboratories, and is related to what others call 'attention' (Galambos, Sheatz and Vernier).

2. Reinforcement of these auditory or visual signals (CS) by shock, food or mildly noxious stimuli like a puff of air in the face (US), remarkably increases the probability that the response to the CS will be large in amplitude and prolonged in duration at all sites where it is recordable. Fig. 1 illustrates this phenomenon as well as other relevant points.

3. If, however, the CS is a signal that an operant response (e.g. pressing a lever) will avoid shock or procure food, the brain activity evoked by the CS tends to become reduced during acquisition and may disappear in the fully trained animal (Hearst et al.). The evoked activity returns, however, when the behavioural response is prevented (e.g. by moving the lever out

of reach of the animal). It is evident, therefore, that the CS can evoke a large or a small response from the brain of a conditioned animal depending on the kind of training he has received. This fact may explain the varia-' tions in results obtained by others using this method of study (Kogan).

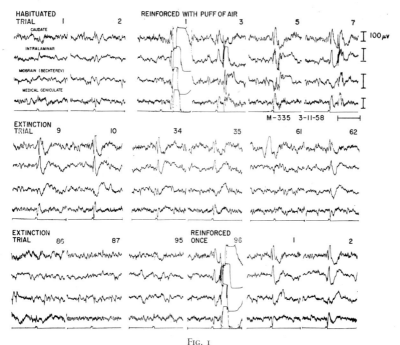

FIG. 1

Effect of classical conditioning procedure on amplitude and duration of response evoked by click. Rhesus monkey, chronic bipolar electrodes implanted in four brain areas as indicated. The fifth line in each record signals delivery of acoustic click whose intensity remained constant throughout. Record to be read from left to right, and top to bottom. In Habituated Trials (1, 2) the click evoked small modest responses at all electrode locations. Effect of reinforcing click with puff of air to face is to increase amplitude and duration of click response in all brain loci. After discontinuation of reinforcement (Extinction Trial) response amplitudes and durations decrease progressively until they revert (Trials 87, 95) approximately to control values. A single reinforcement (96) restores response amplitude once more (1, 2).

4. There are many subcortical areas in which remarkably similar activity is aroused by both visual and auditory CSs after their reinforcement. This is in contrast to the well-known fact that in certain regions (e.g. the classical visual cortex) only one of the stimuli proves effective. Brain locations where a common event is produced by different sense modalities in learning situations include midbrain reticular and limbic

structures at least, and the exact specification of where this occurs would appear to be valuable information to collect (Galambos and Sheatz).

5. Anaesthetization profoundly modifies the brain response to click or flash. Several waves disappear from the cortical record; the earliest one persists as the well-known evoked response of the deeply anaesthetized cortex. Furthermore the number of brain locations where responses appear becomes smaller as the anaesthetic constricts activity into approximately the limits of the classical afferent pathway.

6. Whereas several years ago we felt the evoked response variations here under discussion might reflect the specific changes connected with the formation of the 'temporary connection' we presently view them, in agreement with many others (e.g. Voronin *et al.*), as more probably related to attention, orientation responses and the like. This conclusion does not at all diminish our interest in them, however, for the brain processes they signify unquestionably underlie the one we originally set out to study. The brain is somehow primed or prepared for the specific event it undergoes when learning is achieved, and an exact definition of the factors responsible for this is a necessary first step.

CONCLUSION

Observation and experimental analysis are said to be of value only in so far as they provoke a new and more comprehensive synthesis. If what has gone before in this essay can be called an analysis it is surely a small and imperfect one and the syntheses to be derived from it are merely speculative questions. One may observe, however, that physiologists are perhaps overly impressed by the learning abilities of man; deeply involved in the search for an explanation for his unusual capacities they seem to reject the thought that human learning almost surely represents merely an extension and elaboration of a general capacity possessed by most living animals. While the principles in operation may indeed work more efficiently or to a more elaborate degree in man with his highly developed neocortex, it seems only reasonable to assume that the same principles operate not only to produce his learned reactions, but also to guarantee performance of his unlearned responses (e.g. breathing) and to make possible the learning displayed by animals with simple nervous systems as well (but see Pantin, p. 193 for an opposite view). It could be argued, in brief, that no important gap separates the explanations for how the nervous system comes to be organized during embryological development in the first place; for how it operates to produce the innate responses characteristic of each species in the second place; and for how it becomes reorganized, finally, as a result of experiences during life. If this idea should be correct, the solution of any one of these problems would mean that the answer for the others would drop like a ripe plum, so to speak, into our outstretched hands.

GROUP DISCUSSION

MAGOUN. Dr Galambos's demonstration that reinforcement leads to a widespread generalization of afferent signals within the CNS, together with an increment in their amplitude and configuration, makes the third such report to appear recently. Drs Killam and John found that the central distribution and amplitude of responses to a series of flashes were increased during reinforcement in avoidance conditioning. Drs Worden and Marsh found the same thing using tones as signals and a food reward as reinforcement. This alteration of the conditioned signal induced by reinforcement may provide the situation which, in Dr Fessard's opinion, is pre-requisite for the formation of a novel connection: namely, the elaboration of a stage in which convergence of the conditioned and unconditioned signals can occur. At the Moscow colloquium, Dr Gastaut stressed the importance of subcortical brain mechanisms in this regard, because these then provided the only known sites at which the conditioned and unconditioned signals might converge upon common neurones. With the demonstration that a reinforcing stimulus opens widespread regions of the brain to an incoming signal, we need not search for focal sites where such convergence might occur, for many possibilities then emerge. The role of reinforcement, in generalizing and increasing the amplitude of the responses of the central nervous system to afferent signals, represents an outstanding achievement of recent electrophysiological investigation of the processes of learning in the brain.

GALAMBOS. May I add that it was Artemyev and Bezladnova 10 years ago who dealt first with the problem [Artemyev and Bezladnova (1952). Electrical reaction of the auditory area of the cortex of the cerebral hemisphere during the formation of a conditioned defence reflex. *Trudy Inst. Fiziol.* **I**, 228-36.]

PALESTINI. I would like to know whether you notice any difference in the rate of development of habituation by recording in different sites of the brain.

GALAMBOS. I cannot give a precise answer. The extraordinary variation in response amplitude encountered during the experiments has thus far prevented the precise measurements that would be required.

PALESTINI. In our laboratory we have observed some difference in the rate of habituation, between the specific and non-specific sensory pathways; the habituation is faster for the non-specific responses. The places we recorded at were the reticular formation, the mesencephalon, the centrum medianum and the non-specific responses in the cortex. We also found that both habituation and conditioning are better shown in the slow late potentials.

THORPE. I think the suggestion that an investigation of the organization of the 'centres' for instinctive behaviour may throw a light on the process of learning, is a very important one. Often when you are dealing with animals which have fairly elaborate innate behaviour, learning consists chiefly in making a fine adjustment to these innate behaviour patterns, and so in studying instinctive behaviour one often sees that the animal seems set to learn one particular thing and nothing else. The instinctive mechanism is ready to take it just so far along the line towards perfection of the particular performance but no further and from there on learning takes over. In such a situation the suggestion that the fundamental mechanisms are of the same kind seems valuable. Also, it has been suggested that when animals are not in perfect health the innate behaviour may fail to come out automatically in its full perfection but can nevertheless be perfected by learning. But there is one point where I think the differences are great: in innate motor patterns the action is often highly elaborate and the innate adjustment may be very fine; but the innate receptive mechanism by which responses are released is seldom or never capable by itself of coping with complex stimuli. In other words releasers, if they have to be recognized innately, without any learning coming into the process, must be very simple. So in complex releasing situations learning has perforce to take a correspondingly more important part, since the innate component cannot take the animal very far. In this respect of complexity there does seem to be a significant difference between the mechanisms for organizing motor patterns and those controlling perceptual recognition.

ECCLES. Dr Galambos refers to overlapping neuronal fields for various functions of the medulla and suggests to us that some new stimulus or new input will galvanize this group of neurones into an entirely new response. There need be no mystery about this if you consider the mode of operation of neuronal networks. I don't think we have considered these properties sufficiently. We must think of the nervous system as composed of immense assemblages of neurones with patterns of connections at each synaptic relay. If an impulse is going to be propagated, there must be convergence — and therefore there must be a lot of collusion (if you like) in neuronal operations. In any kind of possible connections in neuronal networks it can be demonstrated that if you alter the input, you alter the output. The particular situation that Dr Galambos mentions provides an example. In the whole of this medullary assemblage of neurones there are all kinds of pathways and the particular input you get by pharyngeal tickling operates in one particular way to give you the vomiting output. We have to think of neuronal patterns and how varying inputs give varying outputs and how modifications can be produced in this way by habituation and learning.

GALAMBOS. There are of course several models one could use as one attempts to visualize the principle of organization at work in neuronal networks and nuclei. Dr Eccles prefers the input-output model in which the essential phenomena involved are exclusively synaptic transmissions and excitation and inhibition. Surely there is no law, however, against looking for some other organizing principle. No less an authority than that grand old man of American comparative anatomy, C. Judson Herrick, has said something is going on in the neuropile that we do not understand.

OLDS. From Dr Galambos's slides, it seems that a common message pervades the system at a certain stage of learning before the response is fully developed. We used to think that the message was coded by the place to which it was projected, or by the system of units to which it was projected, but this pervasiveness suggests that the message may somehow be characterized by its pattern. This brings me to my question — is there any characteristic difference observed between this complex event, depending on the nature of the input signal or the nature of the reinforcement, or both. Does a difference in this complex event ever arise when the stimulus is changed, say from click to light?

GALAMBOS. Again, we do not have the information for answering this question precisely. The evoked response seems to be identical in many brain loci with different stimuli, but in other places this is not so. One of our current problems is to obtain just the data required to answer the question Dr Olds asks.

HERNÁNDEZ-PEÓN. I would like to ask two brief questions — I noticed that during anaesthesia there was an enhancement of one of the waves of the auditory cortical potentials. I would like to know what is the interpretation of this fact. The other question is: where was the puff of air applied, because probably its localization is of some importance in conditioning. For example, if it is applied to the eye, the response is probably not extinguished or habituated. But we have observed at the spinal V sensory nucleus that the potential evoked by a puff of air is decreased with repetition of the stimulus — and the habituation disappears by giving anaesthesia. We also found that the pinna reflex evoked by giving repetitive puffs of air disappears, but if we anaesthetize the cat the pinna reflex returns and is not habituated under anaesthesia.

GALAMBOS. I had not considered the possibility that the exact region to which the air puff reinforcement was delivered might make much difference. We have simply blown the air into the animal's face. As to your question of whether the evoked response amplitude increases with anaesthesia, the answer is a somewhat qualified yes. In the awake animal two electrical events are identifiable in the first 20 or 30 msec. of the cortical response to a click. One of these disappears with anaesthesia. Since the two sum algebraically, removal of one allows the other — the well-known 'evoked response' — to stand alone, and it often seems then to have grown in size.

SEGUNDO. So far work on electrographic aspects of conditioning has analysed changes that occur in the direct response to the indifferent and later conditioned stimulus (Anokhin, 1958; Fessard and Gastaut, 1954). It seems opportune to mention that, as a consequence of training, the conditioned signal also became capable of modifying the response to the absolute stimulus (in somatic sensory cortex and perhaps mesencephalic reticular formation). Namely, the potential evoked by a painful stimulus is larger when preceded by its conditioned signal than when not preceded by it: in terms of human experience, it is larger when 'expected' than when 'unexpected'. (Segundo and Sommer-Smith; Galeano and Roig, 1959).

Finally, I would like to ask the interpretation for the short latency of visual cortical responses to clicks. And if shapes of cortical and sub-cortical responses are similar to shapes encountered in primary sensory cortex?

GALAMBOS. We are presently closely comparing cortical and subcortical records for similarities and differences in their morphology and duration. Published data confirm our own impression that such records show remarkable similarities throughout a period of 0.5 to 1.0 seconds following the conditioned stimulus. If this should turn out to be correct, some new unexplained phenomenon existing in large parts of the brain of the conditioned animal would have to be assumed. Such a phenomenon would certainly be worth careful study.

THE SIGNIFICANCE OF THE EARLIEST
MANIFESTATIONS OF CONDITIONING
IN THE MECHANISM OF LEARNING[1]

E. Grastyán

In the electrophysiological investigation of the temporary connection there are at least as many incongruous observations between behavioural and electrical manifestations as there are consistent ones. The significance of these inconsistencies, however, is at least as important as that of the consistencies, since they disclose the limitations of our classical methods of observation.

In the majority of our experiments we are looking for electrical correlates of well-defined types of behaviour. Sometimes, however, our attention is first attracted by a definite and consequent electrical change which has no conspicuous behavioural correlate, or has a correlate which was concealed, or one which we had not hitherto regarded as important. Sometimes phenomena, which from a behavioural aspect seem to be identical, prove to be distinct in the course of the electrophysiological investigation. In other cases the boundary of well-separated behavioural manifestations becomes indistinct from the aspect of the electrical events. I am convinced that behind these discrepancies the possibilities of further development lie and that they deserve special attention. Let me demonstrate the problem with some concrete observations.

According to the classical Pavlovian conception, the orientation reflex represents a typical unconditioned phenomenon. This view is nowadays generally accepted. According to this assumption the orientation reflex can easily be elicited by every new, unknown stimulus. The essence of the reaction consists of characteristic movements by means of which the animal turns with all of his receptors towards the situation or the source of the stimulus in order to ensure a better acquaintance with it. The orientation reflex was also called a 'what is it reflex' by Pavlov. This, I think, expresses the essence of the reaction better than its accepted English equivalent, the orientation reflex, which does not imply necessarily the idea of motion. Below I will use the orientation reflex in this Pavlovian sense.

[1] A part of this study was carried out under a Fellowship from the Foundations' Fund for Research in Psychiatry at the Department of Anatomy, University of California at Los Angeles.

The observations to be reviewed were made on cats with chronically implanted electrodes during the elaboration of conditioned alimentary and avoidance responses. By means of a careful analysis of the motion pictures taken synchronously with the electrical recordings, it was established that the orientation reflex was invariably accompanied by a series of characteristic slow potentials (4-7 c/s) in the hippocampus and in some points of the reticular formation. Attention to this reaction as a peculiar kind of archicortical arousal was directed by Green and Arduini (1954). According to our observations, this theta activity was an excellent indicator of the orientation reflex, since it invariably and synchronously appeared with the orientation, irrespective of whether it manifested itself spontaneously or was elicited by a conditioned stimulus.

So far these observations do not represent any contradiction of the classic conception. Later, however, a careful analysis of the electrical recordings disclosed a challenging fact. It turned out that unfamiliar stimuli, even at their first application, elicited neither the hippocampal slow potentials nor behavioural orientation in the great majority of the cases. The unfamiliar stimuli elicited in these cases a desynchronization in the hippocampus quite similar to that in the neocortex. The characteristic slow potentials did not appear until after several presentations of the stimulus to be conditioned, and were also accompanied by typical orienting and searching movements.

From these consistent observations we were compelled to conclude that the orientation reflex cannot be an unconditioned phenomenon but must be an extremely rapidly developing conditioned manifestation. This surprising conclusion seems to be supported by the long known fact that the orientation reflex can be easily extinguished, like conditioned but unlike unconditioned reflexes.

On the basis of these considerations we have to conclude that for the elicitation of the orientation reflex, the stimulus has to be familiar in a certain measure. I should like to emphasize the attribute of the 'certain measure' since the significance of the conditioned stimulus at the time of appearance of the orientation reflex is still uncertain in the animal. It has some motivational effects, but it does not evoke the proper conditioned reflex yet, or only with a very long latency. In other words the animal performs orientation movements for the very reason that he 'does not know' the exact meaning of the stimulus. (What is it reflex.)

In perfect agreement with this, it has been observed that at the stage of stabilization of the conditioned reflex, when the conditioned movements become automatic, both the hippocampal slow waves and the orientation reflex disappear. In this stage the significance of the stimulus becomes 'certain' and as a consequence the 'what is it reflex' loses its biological usefulness.

It is very easy, however, to regain the orientation reflex after this stage also, if we make a slight change in the learning situation. This happens for example, if we introduce a differentiating stimulus or during extinction. As a consequence of the application of the unreinforced stimulus, the effect of the positive stimulus transiently regresses, i.e. it elicits again the characteristic slow waves in the hippocampus and the orientation reflex.

At the time of stabilization of differentiation, the slow potentials again disappear and desynchronization will be elicited by both kinds of stimuli; however, in some cases when the differentiation proves to be too difficult, remnants of the slow potentials can be observed to the very last.

The conception that the orientation reflex corresponds to a conditioned phenomenon seems to be contradicted by the common experience that every new and unfamiliar stimulus is capable of eliciting the orientation reflex if it is strong enough. However, I believe that the problem of intensity of the stimulus requires special consideration. It seems probable that with strong stimuli the conditioned factor is represented by the intensity in itself, which is independent of the quality or the modality of the stimulus. The animal in natural conditions often meets strong stimuli signalling danger. The unknown amount of natural conditioned reflexes, however, makes it difficult to decide in every case whether a stimulus is new or not. By means of the tendency towards generalization, probably considerable numbers of stimuli become more or less familiar to the animal in natural conditions. As a consequence, it is sometimes very difficult to find a completely indifferent stimulus for a mature animal.

In asserting that the orientation reflex represents a conditioned manifestation, I have no intention of implying that the unfamiliar stimulus has no effects at all at its very first application. Disregarding the well known electrical reactions, marked somatic reactions can often be observed too. These reactions, however, are not orientation movements, or at least are not identical with those observed following the reinforcement of the stimulus.

The most common effect elicited by a new stimulus is the well-known startle response, or a transitory form between the startle and orientation, a quick, phasic movement of the head towards the stimulus. The startle reaction has aroused the attention of several researchers in the past, and its significance in relation to the temporary connection has recently been reviewed by Gastaut (1957). Let me give a short account of some of our recent observations concerning this problem made in Long Beach in collaboration with Drs Lesse and Eidelberg.

The first question arising here, too, is whether the startle response is an unconditioned or a conditioned reaction, and also what is the relationship between the startle response and the orientation reflex. I think that the solution of this problem is beyond the scope of a simple terminologic question. Thus, if it becomes apparent that the organization of these two reactions is not an inborn property of the nervous system, then we are facing the two simplest and most basic forms of the learning process, the understanding of which must be an indispensable condition for the approach to more complex conditioned patterns.

Prosser and Hunter in 1936 and later Landis and Hunt (1939) established that the startle response could easily be conditioned. According to our own observations in a well-isolated, sound-proof experimental situation, a single reinforcement of a click stimulus (which in itself does not evoke the startle response) results in a long-lasting and stable conditioned startle response. The extremely fast development of the conditioned startle response makes it highly probable that a great majority of the startle responses elicited by moderate stimuli through the telereceptors represent conditioned phenomena. The question arises, however, whether they really represent true conditioned reflexes or only sensitization phenomena, i.e. a pseudoconditioning. It is known that repetition of a strong stimulus eliciting startle response in itself might increase the general excitability for every kind of stimuli without any pairing of them (Grether, 1938). In addition it is an everyday experience that in hyperexcited states every stimulus may elicit startle responses. The arguments of Larssen (1956), however, seem to contradict this supposition.

He has shown that the unconditioned stimulus could not bring about an increase of the response to the conditioned stimulus unless the two stimuli were paired with a definite interval. Moreover, the conditioned reactions could be inhibited differentially. On the basis of these observations he rejects the explanation of sensitization for his own experiments. Our own observations also throw doubt on the hypothesis of simple sensitization; because no electrical or behavioural signs of increased excitation could be observed before the critical second application of the conditioned stimulus. The fact that many stimuli, similar to the one reinforced, also elicit the startle response is a consequence rather of generalization and so does not exclude the true conditioned nature of these reactions.

For the correct estimation of the general excitatory level of the CNS or, better, the excitatory level of the unconditioned mechanisms and drives, we have an excellent indicator in the rapid (40 c/s) oscillations of the baso-lateral amygdaloid complex discovered by Lesse (1957). In our experi-ments the presence of this activity did not seem to be prerequisite for the elicitation of the conditioned startle response.

On the basis of these considerations we have to conclude that, for the establishment of the most simple form of the temporary connection, a single reinforcement of the conditioned stimulus may be sufficient.

The extremely rapid development of the startle response is surprising when compared with the development of the classic conditioned processes. This difference suggests that the conditioned reflex, considered as simple is in reality a very complex chain of reflexes. Under natural conditions an extremely rapid development of relatively complex conditioned reflexes is often observed. From this it is obvious that the conditioned stimulus, used in general laboratory practice, takes a highly artificial place among the natural signals which necessarily accompany the unconditioned stimulus and which cannot be removed from the experimental situation. As a consequence our artificially attached conditioned stimulus will represent a second, third or many-fold order signal of the unconditioned factor.

At the present time all the theories of learning are based on the view that repetition is an indispensable condition for learning. The compelling evidence presented by these rapid forms of learning obliges us to revise our concepts, because they might require a very different explanation from those suggested so far. Let me quote in this respect the extremely clearly defined concept of Lashley: 'The basic problem of learning is what we call "incident memory", learning in one trial. We have to seek the explanation of learning and memory somewhere else than repetition. All the neurological theories dealing with the learning process, that I have seen, have assumed an effect of repetition on synaptic nerve endings, but the fact is that most learning does not involve repetition.' Only one thing which I have to add to this as a small disagreement is, that incidental and instant learning does not exclude necessarily the existence of repetitive synaptic events.

The startle response and the orientation reflex represent the earliest manifestations of the development of the temporary connection, or as I tried to make evident, they represent already true conditioned manifesta-tions, so that the investigation of their intimate neural mechanisms would have basic importance. Unfortunately in this respect our possibilities — except for some basic facts — are still limited to speculation and conjecture.

The differences showing themselves between the somatic accompani-ments of the startle and orientation reflex suggest already highly different neural mechanisms. The startle response is characterized essentially by a tendency to generalized flexion, and whereas the orientation reflex is not exactly the contrary of this, its more complex nature indicates a basically different biological character. The essential characteristic of the startle response is protective, it has a tendency to exclude influences coming from the environment, but in the orientation reflex on the contrary, the readiness to accept the influence is the most typical.

From these absolutely contrasting features it is evident that the two phenomena cannot be regarded simply as quantitatively different representatives of an essentially identical mechanism. Supporting evidence is offered for this assumption in the older literature, according to which the intensity of the startle response is not in a causal relationship with the appearance of the orientation reflex. (Secondary manifestations of the startle (Strauss, 1938.)) During the continuous reinforcement of the conditioned stimulus the startle response progressively decreases, or disappears. It could not be excluded that it is even this inhibitory process which makes possible the appearance of the orientation reflex.

According to earlier observations (Forbes and Sherrington, 1914) typical startle responses could be observed on decerebrated animals. This observation clearly shows that the basic mechanism of the startle response is located somewhere in the lower brain stem. It does not mean, however, that in an intact animal higher processes do not play a role in the integration of the startle response. This is supported by the observation of Gastaut and Hunter (1950) that startle responses elicited by flicker are modified by the removal of the occipital cortex, further by the observations of Haas et al. (1953) who established that the motor cortex plays a similarly important role in the integration of experimental myoclonus.

Considering that every kind of stimuli can be used for the conditioning of the startle response, its organization must occur in a structure which has the capacity to integrate these stimuli. On the basis of this requirement the reticular formation offers itself as a suitable region in the brain stem (Moruzzi and Magoun, 1949; Starzl, Taylor and Magoun, 1951; French, Amerongen and Magoun, 1952). This supposition finds strong support in the earlier observations of Muskens (1926) that lesions of the medial reticular formation alone result in a permanent disappearance of the startle response.

The origin and nature of the inhibition of the startle response represent a more difficult problem than its primary integration. Adey, Segundo and Livingston (1957) established the important fact that descending hippocampo-cortical impulses exert a profound inhibitory influence on ascending reticular conduction. This inhibition seems to be mediated chiefly through the entorhynal cortex and stria medullaris system (Adey, Merrillees and Sunderland, 1956; Adey, Sunderland and Dunlop, 1957; Adey, 1957). Similar inhibitory influence has been shown by our laboratory (Grastyán et al., 1956, Lissák, et al. 1957). Unfortunately no direct observations have been made in these experiments on the startle response. As we shall see later the inhibitory role of the hippocampus has to be considered in the inhibition of the orientation reflex too.

A further inhibitory mechanism which might be responsible for the inhibition of the startle response is offered by the observations of Hernández-Peón (1955) and Hernández-Peón, Scherrer and Jouvet (1956). This inhibition seems to control the effect of incoming impulses in the first sensory relays. At present, however, we are still uncertain about the exact structural origin of this inhibition. Some evidence has been furnished that it originates in the reticular formation.

An important inhibitory mechanism of diffuse neocortical origin, controlling reticular influences on peripheral reflex function, has recently been discovered by Hugelin and Bonvallet (1957). This inhibitory mechanism has to be considered first as responsible for the brief, phasic character of the startle response. However, its possible role in the extinction of the startle response as well as its relation to the archicortical inhibitory mechanisms mentioned above, remains a matter of speculation at the present time.

A definite difference between the mechanisms of the startle response and the orientation reflex is reflected by the accompanying electrical manifestations of the two responses. These differences are particularly characteristic in the hippocampus. As I already mentioned, the appearance of the startle response is accompanied in the hippocampus by a desynchronization. At the appearance of the orientation reflex a marked change occurs; the characteristic theta rhythm replaces the former desynchronization. In the course of regular reinforcement of the conditioned stimulus, the latency of the starting of these theta potentials gradually shortens, and finally the stimulus elicits them instantaneously.

The hippocampal evoked potential undergoes a similar marked change during the development of the orientation reflex. At the time of the manifestation of the startle response, the changes of the amplitude of the evoked potential seem to be rather inconsistent; at the appearance of the slow waves, however, in the great majority of cases a significant decrease in amplitude or even disappearance of the potentials can be observed.

These marked electrical changes would suggest that the hippocampus played an active role in the integration of the orientation reflex. Unfortunately this cannot be stated with certainty because the functional interpretation of the otherwise significant electrical happenings is still extremely uncertain. The only thing which can be established with certainty is that something important happens in the hippocampus at the time of appearance of the orientation reflex. Let us consider what suggestions are offered by the stimulation experiments.

An orientation reflex most similar to the natural one can be elicited in the freely moving animal by stimulation of the hypothalamus and reticular formation (Grastyán, Lissák and Kékesi, 1957). The same stimulation is one of the most effective in eliciting the theta rhythm from the hippocampus (Green and Arduini, 1945). Stimulation of the hippocampus, on the other hand, effectively inhibits the orientation reflex and conditioned reflexes (Grastyán et al., 1957). This stimulation is accompanied in the contralateral hippocampus by a clear-cut desynchronization. From these observations it would follow that during the appearance of the rhythmic slow waves the function of the hippocampus is inhibited. These observations, together with the fact that the orientation reflex disappears at the stabilization of the conditioned reflex and at the same time a desynchronization (presumably representing a more active state) takes place in the hippocampus, would suggest that the hippocampus inhibits the orientation reflex. Since the inhibition of the orientation reflex is a necessary condition for the final stabilization of the conditioned reflex, this inhibitory function would provide the hippocampus with a role in proportion to its morphological importance.

This supposition is, however, valid only if the interpretation of the electrical events and the behavioural effects elicited by stimulation of the hippocampus are correct.

An inhibitory function of the hippocampus is suggested by some interesting observations of John and Killam. These authors observed that during the presentation of a negative conditioned stimulus (repetitive flicker) definite following can be observed with a predominance in the hippocampus; while during the presentation of the positive stimulus (which is of the same modality as the negative one, differing only in frequency) no following can be recorded in the hippocampus.

Our own observations concerning the disappearance or decrease of the hippocampal evoked potentials during the presence of the slow waves seem to offer additional supporting evidence. The decrease in the evoked potential might be an expression of the inhibited state of the elements responsible for the evoked activity.

Unfortunately we have very little and incomplete information about the importance of the diffuse thalamic projection system in the elaboration of the startle response and orientation reflex. Recently Eidelberg (1959) made an important observation that a lesion of the centrum medianum irreversibly eliminates the possibility of eliciting the hippocampal rhythmic slow potentials. According to this observation the role of the thalamus is crucial in the control of hippocampal function. Unfortunately, no direct observations are available concerning the effects of this lesion on the startle response and orientation reflex.

The greatest difficulty is found at the present time in understanding the mechanism responsible for the transition of the startle response to the orientation reflex and the orientation reflex to the proper conditioned reflex. When we consider that the most dramatic electrical changes during this period of time can be observed in the hippocampus, it seems very probable that the solution to these questions is more or less identical with the understanding of the generation of the hippocampal slow potentials.

In reviewing the above facts my first intention was to demonstrate the highly complex nature of the manifestations preceding the establishment of the most simple conditioned reflex. I am convinced that for the approach to the neural mechanisms of conditioning, an inescapable requirement would appear to be the breakdown of the learning process into its most elementary components, as was necessary in research on the spinal cord. That is the only way in which we may secure a more exact correlation between electrical and behavioural phenomena.

GROUP DISCUSSION

MORRELL. Dr Fessard has asked me to begin the discussion of Dr Grastyán's report and to present some of the material partially reported at the Moscow symposium and which has not yet appeared in print. Some of this material agrees beautifully with that now before us and may serve to underscore the lack of behavioural correlation with some electrographic criteria of conditioning and perhaps indicate in some measure why this is so. In addition I think we can illustrate some features of hippocampal participation in the conditioning process.

As Dr Grastyán has so well pointed out, it has been difficult to assign specific excitatory or inhibitory connotations (with reference to cell discharge) to the electrical activity recorded with large electrodes from various ganglionic regions. This is perhaps one of the more important reasons for the great ambiguity in relating the previously discovered electrical signs of conditioning to any aspect of behavioural learning. Causally related interactions between various levels of the central nervous system as well as the degree of participation of these elements in the total integrated response are probably better expressed as changes in a rate of unit discharge than in terms of the slow oscillations reflecting dendritic polarizations. Because the latter may be non-propagated, they are perhaps less likely to

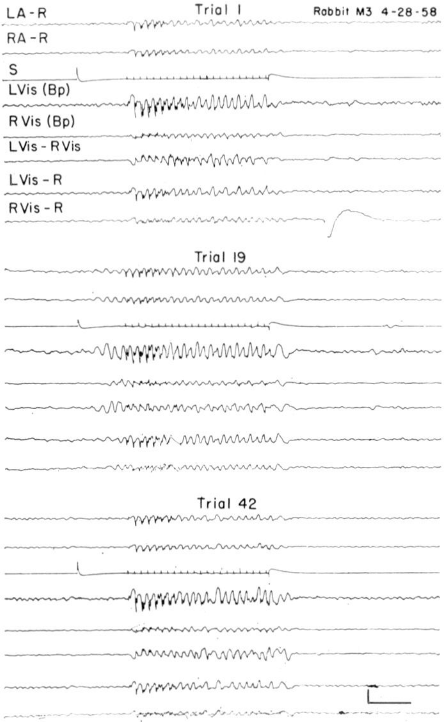

FIG. I

Sample conditioning trials illustrating responses before conditioning (Trial 1), repetitive response (Trial 19), and localized desynchronization of Stage III (Trial 42). Desynchronization is barely visible because of the low amplifier gain necessitated by simultaneous tape recording. The repetitive response of Stage II, however, is clearly evident. Equally evident is the lack of repetitive response in Stage III. The signal channel (S) indicates by the first deflection the onset of the conditional acoustic signal. A photoelectrical cell records the light flashes superimposed on the signal channel and the final deflection indicates the cessation of tone. The onset of the tone precedes the light by 2 seconds and is continuous with it for a further 5 seconds, both signals going off together. This convention is followed in the succeeding figure as well. Calibration: 200 microvolts and 1 second. Channel designations are as follows: left auditory to reference, right auditory to reference, signal, left visual (bipolar), right visual (bipolar), left visual to right visual, left visual to reference, right visual to reference. The electrodes were implanted over the respective cortical regions prior to this examination. The animal is unanaesthetized but restrained in a comfortable hammock. (From Morrell, Barlow, and Brazier. Analysis of conditioned repetitive response by means of the average response computor. *Biological Psychiatry*. In Press.)

influence other neuronal systems. Our use of microelectrodes implanted in cortical and subcortical regions was designed to evaluate relationships in unit discharge characteristics of these structures during the course of a developing conditioned response.

In previous studies (Morrell and Jasper, 1955; Morrell, 1957) we have described the historical development of electrocerebral conditioning to combinations of sound and intermittent light as consisting of three stages. The first evidence of conditioning is manifested by a generalized desynchronization produced by the conditioned stimulus in all cortical derivations. Next there is a brief transitory stage when the conditioned stimulus evokes a repetitive response which is at or close to the frequency of the imposed stroboscopic light if that frequency is within the

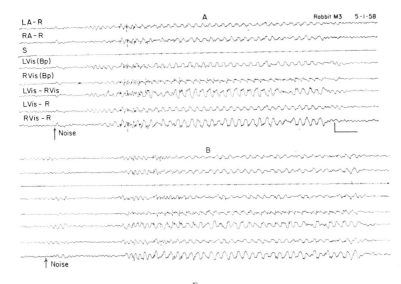

FIG. 2

Recurrence of repetitive response in Stage III after adventitious noise. Note that the noise itself may elicit rhythmic discharge (B). Calibration: 200 microvolts and 1 second.

range of 3-12 per second. The third stage is characterized by localized desynchronization in visual derivations elicited by the acoustic conditioned stimulus. Since this discussion was not foreseen, I have not brought adequate illustrations of all of these stages for demonstration. However, some features may be illustrated by examples from a study on cortical conditioning carried out with Dr Barlow and Dr Brazier of the Massachusetts General Hospital and the Massachusetts Institute of Technology. Fig. 1 provides two bits of pertinent information. If attention is directed to the tracing labelled trial 19, one may see a good example of the repetitive response to an acoustic stimulus. This is the pattern characteristic of Stage II of the conditioning procedure. In the tracing labelled trial 42 all trace of the conditioned repetitive response has disappeared, to be replaced by the localized desynchronization characteristic of Stage III. The latter cannot be clearly seen in this figure because the gain has been greatly reduced in order to avoid blocking of the amplifiers in a tape recorder fed through the EEG machine by the high voltage transients.

INITIAL PRESENTATION

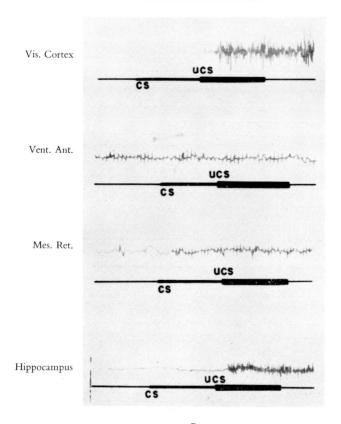

FIG. 3

Simultaneous microelectrode records from the cortex and subcortical regions in a cat during electrocerebral conditioning. Onset of the conditioned stimulus (tone 500 cycles per second) is indicated by the first widening of the signal channel. Onset of the unconditioned stimulus (intermittent light 10 per second) is indicated by the second widening of the signal channel. This convention applies to all the microelectrode figures. The derivations also apply to the same figures and they are all tracings from the same animal.

In the light of Dr Grastyán's comment that the slow rhythms in the hippocampus may be caused to reappear by a change in the stimulus situation after they have disappeared, I might add that we have observed a similar phenomenon with respect to the slow waves which constitute the Stage II response. If, during Stage

III, when the repetitive response had completely disappeared, an extraneous noise is introduced into the experimental room, a prompt reappearance of the conditioned repetitive response to the acoustic signal may be observed on the very next conditioning trial (Fig. 2). Indeed the noise itself may elicit some vestige of these slow rhythms (Fig. 2b). Our repetitive response is derived from cortical rather than hippocampal regions, but it may have a significance similar to that envisaged by

HABITUATION

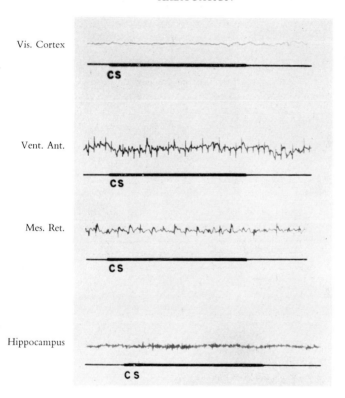

FIG. 4
Pattern of response after habituation. (See text for further explanation.)

Dr Grastyán. The relationship of these stages to behavioural learning is not fully understood although there is some evidence that the Stage II repetitive response is not adequate for behavioural transfer (Chow, Dement and John, 1957) while Stage III or localized desynchronization may be correlated with a motor response (Morrell and Jasper, 1956; Gastaut et al., 1957).

The initial microelectrode investigation involved a survey of unit discharge in various subcortical nuclei compared with stages in the evolution of the conditioned electrocerebral response. The stages were defined by changes in the surface electrical activity according to the scheme just outlined. Simultaneous recordings were made from the visual cortex, nucleus ventralis anterior of the thalamus, the periaqueductal portion of the mesencephalic reticular system, and the hippocampus. The signal stimuli were bright intermittent light (UCS) and low intensity pure tone (CS) delivered in the same pattern as illustrated in the previous figures, except

STAGE I

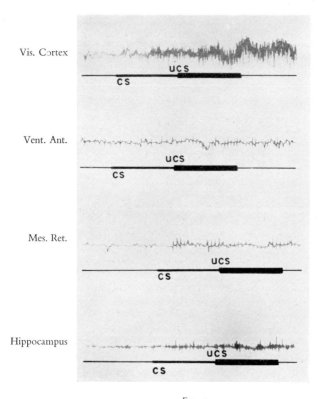

FIG. 5
Pattern of response during Stage I of the conditioning procedure. (See text for further explanation.)

that the duration was shortened so that the entire trial could be included on a single sweep of the oscilloscope. Thirty-four animals, both cats and rabbits, were used. All observations were made during acute experiments. Ether anaesthesia was used for tracheotomy and craniotomy. Animals were immobilized under Flaxedil and placed in the Horsley-Clarke stereotaxic instrument after injection of procaine into points of pressure and contact. Tungsten microelectrodes of the type designed by Hubel (1957) with a tip diameter of 1-5 μ were used. For sub-cortical recordings these electrodes were encased in a glass micro-pipette in order to avoid damage to the needle tip. The electrodes were connected to capacity-coupled amplifiers having a moderately long time-constant (0.04 seconds) so that some slow components could be visualized. Attempts were made to use DC recording for simultaneous observation of steady potential states but we were

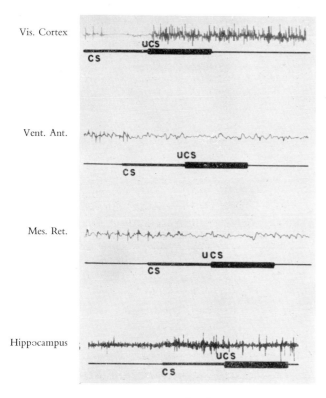

STAGE II

Vis. Cortex

UCS

CS

Vent. Ant.

UCS

CS

Mes. Ret.

UCS

CS

Hippocampus

UCS

CS

FIG. 6
Pattern of response during Stage II of the conditioning procedure. (See text for further explanation.)

usually unsuccessful in resolving single units with that method. Indeed, even capacity-coupled amplification did not always provide discrete resolution. Nevertheless, the recording system was adequate to determine the presence or absence or change in frequency of unit discharge at the sites sampled and, in many cases, individual units were clearly identified. Most of you are aware of the tremendous technical difficulties one faces in attempting to record simultaneously from several microelectrodes and will bear with us in these early faltering steps. The results must be viewed as only first order approximations since adequate statistical analysis awaits the accumulation of more data with the use of multiple microelectrodes concurrently sampling the same cellular population.

As soon as conditioning trials were begun, it was obvious that there was wide

STAGE III

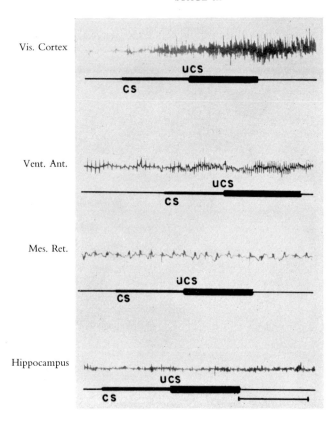

FIG. 7
Pattern of response during Stage III of the conditioning procedure. (See text for further explanation.) Calibration: 250 msec.

variation in the pattern of unit discharge to both conditioned and unconditioned stimuli. This was true even of different but adjacent units in the same ganglionic grouping within any given stage of the conditioning procedure. For this reason the results to be demonstrated can be considered valid only in a rough statistical sense. For example, we define 'increased firing' as meaning that more than 50 per cent of the units recorded in a given area at a given stage of conditioning showed an increase in discharge frequency. The following figures are taken from a cat in which the sequential pattern to be described was particularly prominent.

On the initial presentation of the signal stimuli before conditioning (Fig. 3) the visual cortex is observed to respond only to the unconditioned stimulus, i.e. intermittent light. Units in ventralis anterior did not respond either to the conditioned or to the unconditioned stimulus, whereas units in the mesencephalic reticular formation responded with increased discharge to both stimuli. At this stage units in the hippocampus were observed to respond only to the unconditioned stimulus. Habituation trials were then carried out in which the conditioned stimulus was presented repeatedly without reinforcement. Habituation was considered complete when no change in unit discharge occurred in any area on presentation of the conditioned stimulus (Fig. 4). Paired trials were then reintroduced until the

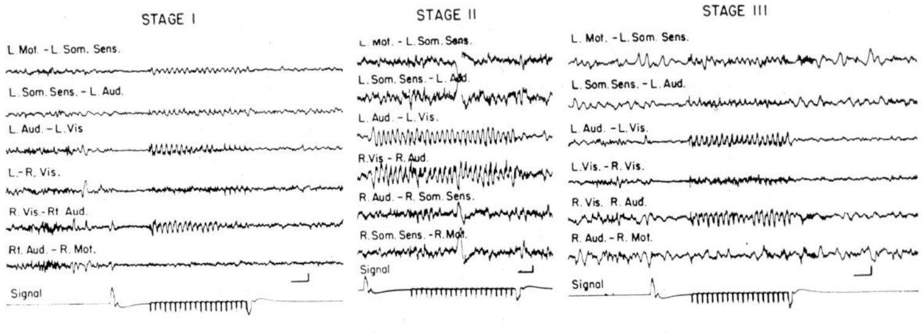

FIG. 8

Examples of EEG tracings from surface cortical electrodes for each of three stages of electro-cerebral conditioning. Unanaesthetized animal. Derivations are from implanted electrodes at the sites indicated. First upward deflection on the signal channel indicates onset of 500 c/sec. tone. A photocell records the stroboscopic flashes superimposed upon the signal line. The final downward deflection indicates cessation of tone and light. Calibration: 50 µV and 1 second.

first signs of conditioning were observed. In Stage I (Fig. 5) which was character-ized by generalized desynchronization in the cortical surface tracing, units in the visual cortex responded to both the conditioned and unconditioned stimulus. Units in the ventralis anterior showed no change in response to the conditioned stimulus but had now developed distinct increase in discharge frequency to the uncondi-tioned stimulus. Units in the mesencephalic reticular system again responded to both stimuli. At this stage, however, it was noted that hippocampal discharge occurred in response to the conditioned stimulus as well as the unconditioned stimulus. Stage II (Fig. 6), characterized by the appearance of a repetitive response in surface cortical tracings, was correlated with suppression of discharge in the visual cortex when the conditioned stimulus was presented and also in ventralis anterior during presentation of both of the signal stimuli. Spontaneously firing units in the mesencephalic reticular formation were also suppressed by both stimuli, while in contrast, those of the hippocampal formation were increased in discharge frequency during both conditioned and unconditioned signals. The development of Stage III (Fig. 7) was defined by the appearance of desynchronization limited to

S

visual cortex derivations. Unit discharge in the visual cortex was observed to increase upon the presentation of both conditioned and unconditioned stimuli and the same augmented response to both signals was noted in a spontaneously firing unit of nucleus ventralis anterior. Units in both the mesencephalic reticular formation and the hippocampus no longer responded to either stimulation nor did any further responses develop even when trials were continued to as many as one hundred.

TABLE I

PATTERN OF UNIT DISCHARGE DURING DEVELOPMENT
OF CONDITIONED ELECTRICAL RESPONSE

		Response to:	
	CS		UCS
Initial presentation	o	Visual Cortex	↑
	o	Vent. Ant.	o
	↑	Mes. Retic.	↑
	o	Hippocampus	↑
Habituation*	o	Visual Cortex	
	o	Vent. Ant.	
	o	Mes. Retic.	
	o	Hippocampus	
Stage I (Trial 32)	↑	Visual Cortex	↑
	o	Vent. Ant.	↑
	↑	Mes. Retic.	↑
	↑	Hippocampus	↑
Stage II (Trial 39)	↓	Visual Cortex	↑
	↓	Vent. Ant.	↓
	↓	Mes. Retic.	↓
	↑	Hippocampus	↑
Stage III (Trial 78)	↑	Visual Cortex	↑
	↑	Vent. Ant.	↑
	o	Mes. Retic.	o
	o	Hippocampus	o

* Relay nuclei in Auditory System not monitored.
↑ > 50 per cent increased firing.
↓ > 50 per cent decreased firing.
o No change.

Table I presents a summary of these data. The findings suggest that some sequential pattern of involvement does indeed exist. However, the interplay of these ganglionic systems, if changes in one can be assumed to be related to changes in any other, does not provide evidence of any one-to-one relationship such that excitation of one area can be assumed always to inhibit or activate another area. For example, the proposal of Lissák and Grastyán (1957) that the hippocampus exerts an inhibitory influence on the ascending reticular activating system is borne out only in a record of Stage II. In Stage I both mesencephalic reticular formation and the hippocampus show increased discharge. Thus the relation between hippocampal and reticular discharge could not be described as reciprocally inhibitory but rather changed with change in stage of conditioning. On the other hand, the evidence does support the contention of Gastaut (1958) and Yoshii (1957) that participation of elements in the thalamic reticular system is essential for the final development of a conditioned response and that some form of thalamo-cortical linking forms the substrate of a fully developed learned response. As Dr Grastyán has already noted, our results as well as his own, tend to support the impression of John and Killam (1959) with respect to the particular role of the hippocampus in the early stages of conditioning.

In different ways it would appear that both hippocampus and mesencephalic reticular formation are concerned in the initial steps which determine what events will or will not become crystallized as engram. In no case where this entire sequence has been observed did the thalamo-cortical linkage appear without prior activity in hippocampal and mesencephalic systems. Of particular interest was the fact that definite inhibitory sequences were always evident (in the form of suppression of resting unit discharge) in the course of acquisition of the simple positive temporary connection. The fact that these inhibitory unit events were highly correlated with the development of the so-called frequency-specific repetitive response in the gross surface electrical tracing may help explain the lack of correlation between this particular electrical manifestation and behavioural transfer.

It may well be that these conditioned changes in discharge patterns of single nerve cells are a different order of phenomenon from that understood as behavioural learning. Yet it would seem that ultimately alterations in behaviour of the total organism must be related in some way to changes in behaviour of nerve cells. It is in this sense and in this context that we believe that we can demonstrate learning (defined as a change in discharge frequency consistently related to an experimentally imposed signal pattern) in single cells of the central nervous system.

JOUVET. Dr Grastyán, I agree with you that extinction of the orientating reflex may come from some upper level. I have also been studying extinction of orientation reflex in chronic decorticate cats and in chronic mesencephalic cats. I could never habituate the startled response in decerebrated animals. Sometimes after as many as 800 stimuli I still obtained startled responses. Concerning decorticate cats but with paleocortex remaining, I could not get a true extinction of orientation reflex and in other cats after removing the frontal lobes I found that this also would cause a disturbance in the extinction of the orientation reflex. I expect to show that this inhibitory influence may come mainly from the neo-cortex and from the frontal lobes. I think this is in agreement with Dr Konorski. But of course there must be some relationship between the hippocampus structure and the diffuse thalamic nucleii. I feel that the cortex is absolutely necessary, at least some part of it, for this inhibition of the orientation reflex.

HEBB. One of the things that arouse orientation is the 'strange' object. But it is not one that has never been presented before. It acquires its capacity to arouse. This is seen clearly in Riesen's chimpanzees reared in darkness. The visual event in the form of a light flash, would produce a startle response; but otherwise the visual event, which by definition was strange, had no capacity at all to produce an orientation reflex. The tenor of Dr Grastyán's paper is that we need pay attention to the history of the stimulus when we apply it to the animal and I think this should be extended also to his comment about immediate learning, rapid one-trial learning, in the higher species. It is a different matter in the lower species — in the higher species it is not done with unfamiliar material. You are dealing with something that has a long history, as far as the elements of the response are concerned. One weakness of many investigations of learning is their disregard of the past naturalistic history of the animal. The study of learning without regard to the past history of the animal is totally unrealistic.

PALESTINI. I want to add some observations regarding the pretrigeminal preparation, that is to say, a cat with a midpontine transsection. These cats remain permanently awake. There is a desynchronized activity of the cortex and they present ocular vertical movements of the eyes. We believe that these movements are purposeful, because when a mouse is presented to the cat, the cat follows it with its eyes. These movements are maintained during the whole period of stimulation by the passing object. This contrasts with the normal intact cats. We think that in the lower pons and medulla there exist inhibitory structures, which exert an ascending inhibition towards higher levels. We believe that lower structures also must be taken into account in explaining all the inhibitory phenomena.

GERARD. I wanted to talk on the same subject as Dr Hebb. Dare one draw the conclusion that, because a single event has led to a permanent trace, this excludes the need of some continued activity to produce morphological, chemical and other changes in the neurone pattern? A single impulse may continue to cause activity, by reverberation or other mechanisms, for very long times. This has been demonstrated by sending brief stimuli to several centres, which then continue discharging for months. Further, there is a continued dynamic state, with responses, memories, etc., which is still quite different from the permanent structured engramme which is established and endures long after the dynamic memory has gone. The fact that one can get a permanent change after one stimulus does not exclude the reverberation type of mechanism in establishing fixation.

CHOW. We have prepared cats with lesions in the n. centrum medianum bilaterally and these cats have been presented with learning problems before lesion. After lesion they can still remember these problems.

SEGUNDO. It appears to me that Dr Grastyán made a distinction between 'orientation' and 'startle' responses. Does he believe the difference to be qualitative or simply quantitative in the sense that they constitute different intensities of response to novel, or significant stimuli.

HERNÁNDEZ-PEÓN. Have you done any lesion experiments on the hippocampus and observed the effect on the extinction of orientation reflex?

GRASTYÁN. I think that Dr Morrell's observations are partly in agreement with my own — namely the second stage in which the big increase of unit discharge is observed in the hippocampus and disappearance of unit discharge in the reticular formation. There seems to be a discrepancy concerning the first stage when both structures show an increase in firing. Unfortunately we don't know the relationship of this firing to the gross electrical recording and the behaviour manifestations. Perhaps this is a transitory stage in which both structures were activated. In the third phase — and this would be an answer to Dr Hernández-Peón as well, the unit activity in the hippocampus disappeared completely — which might correspond to the picture we got during the final phase of extinction, when the stimulus ceased to elicit changes. I agree with Dr Jouvet that after decortication of the animal the extinction of the orientation reflex becomes very difficult. We made exactly the same observation after extirpation of both hippocampi. The animal can still learn, but you cannot extinguish its orientation reflex — it remains always the orientation reflex which mediates the final act.

BUSER. I wonder if Dr Grastyán could give us some more details about Dr Eidelberg's experiments on coagulation of centre median. What was the behaviour of those animals? My question is in connection with the observation made on one animal with very large bilateral destruction of the medial thalamus (including centre median): this animal would show strong orientation as well as startle reactions.

GRASTYÁN. Dr Eidelberg's experiments were carried out on the rabbit. After bilateral lesion of the centre median — the slow potentials irreversibly disappeared entirely from the hippocampus. In some cases after unilateral lesion it disappeared on the same side.

BUSER. What about behaviour?

GRASTYÁN. He did not make any observations on behaviour.

ROSVOLD. It is comforting to hear of these electrical effects because they help to explain the findings that human memory is affected by hippocampal damage, and that the monkey with hippocampal damage has difficulty in solving problems involving memory.

BEHAVIOURAL AND EEG EFFECTS OF TONES
'REINFORCED' BY CESSATION OF PAINFUL STIMULI[1]

J. P. SEGUNDO, C. GALEANO, J. A. SOMMER-SMITH AND J. A. ROIG

Major contributions to the neurophysiology of learning have issued from the study of so-called 'signal responses' established by way of systematic association of two stimuli (one indifferent, one effective), a combination leading frequently to a change in responses provoked by the former (Anokhin, 1957; Pavlov, 1941). In most work, initiation of the indifferent (later conditioned) stimulus IS was followed, after a brief interval, by initiation of the absolute excitation AS (Fig. 1A). It has been suggested and/or established that other combinations also are useful: for instance, tone cessation – pain initiation (Fig. 1B), tone initiation – cessation of eating, etc. (Galeano, Roig, Segundo and Sommer-Smith, 1959; Konorski, 1948; Rowland, 1957; Segundo, Roig and Sommer-Smith, 1959; Zbrozyna, 1958; Zeleny cited by Pavlov, 1951). In the present series, a brief indifferent tone was systematically followed by cessation of a prolonged painful stimulus SS (Fig. 1C): this routine was capable of inducing a learning process and animals came to respond behaviourally (in a manner similar to the effect of pain substraction) and electroencephalographically (with reduction of sensory cortical potentials) to tones treated in this fashion.

MATERIAL AND METHODS

Experiments were performed upon seven cats carrying electrodes implanted chronically in: (i) subcutaneous tissue of foreleg (for stimulation); (ii) extradural space overlying both somatic sensory and, sometimes, one acoustic and/or visual cortical receiving areas (for recording) (these leads shall be referred to as 'cortical'); (iii) subcortical structures as nucleus medialis dorsalis of thalamus (NMDT), mesencephalic reticular

[1] This work, published in abstract fashion in the XXI Physiological Congress Volume (Sommer-Smith, Galeano, Roig and Segundo, 1959), was supported in part by grants from Rockefeller Foundation (58122) and U.S.A.F. Office for Scientific Research (AF49-638-585).

formation (MRF) and/or mesencephalic central grey matter (MCG) (for recording and/or stimulation).

Details of electrode construction and implantation will be described elsewhere (Roig, Segundo, Sommer-Smith and Galeano, to be published). Main technical points were: (1) placement of recording 'cortical' and of stimulating subcutaneous electrodes was controlled electrographically until a complete response (including early positive spike and later waves) occurred in the former to single shock excitation of the latter; (2) electrodes were implanted in subcutaneous foreleg tissues and carried per-

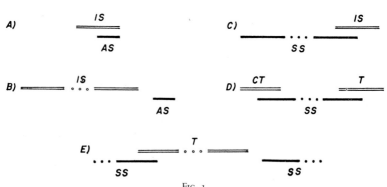

FIG. 1

TEMPORAL RELATIONSHIP BETWEEN ABSOLUTE AND INDIFFERENT STIMULI (modified from Konorski, 1948). (A) Initiation of indifferent stimulus IS followed by initiation of absolute stimulus AS. (B) Cessation of indifferent stimulus followed by initiation of absolute stimulus. (C) Initiation of indifferent stimulus followed by interruption of feeding or of subcutaneous stimulus SS. (D) Interruption of SS preceded by application of tone T; initiation of SS preceded by application of a different frequency (conditioned) tone CT (see text). (E) Alternation of subcutaneous stimulus SS and of tone T (see text). AS, absolute stimulus; IS, indifferent stimulus; SS, subcutaneous stimulus; T, tone.

manently by animals, thus permitting repeated excitation of same area in consistent fashion (this assumption was borne out by study of evoked responses, characteristics of which did not vary over weeks or months). Therefore, throughout the entire procedure recordings were derived from the primary cortical representation of one same excited region.

Sessions were carried out daily in a relatively sound-proof room in which animals did not see the investigator but were observed by him. EEG was recorded with a Grass IIID machine; amplified signals were also led from after the first stage of the power amplifier (outlets J5 and J6) through a 0.02 μfd. condenser (to reduce movement artefacts) and then in parallel to both beams of a Dumont 322-A cathode ray oscilloscope. Triggering by stimulators enabled display (and photography) of cortical evoked potentials: in upper beam, control potentials during silence immediately preceding tone initiation; in lower beam, responses during tone immediately following tone initiation. Grass S 4 models (with SIU 4A isolation units) served as stimulators. Tones were generated by a Hewlitt Packard 200A audio-oscillator connected with a loudspeaker.

Training proceeded in two stages.

Stage I. A tone T and a subcutaneous stimulus SS were applied independently and exhibited no constant temporal relationship. T was kept constant for each preparation (frequency, 200-2000 c.p.s.; duration, 4-10 seconds). SS lasted from 30 seconds to 30 minutes and consisted in rectangular pulses (applied singly or in pairs separated by 10-100 msec.) with the following characteristics: voltage, 1.5-15 volts; pulse duration, 0.1 msec.; frequency, 2.5-8 c.p.s. Voltages were adjusted so as to obtain visible manifestations described below; choices between single or paired shocks and between different frequencies were decided in each animal depending on what parameters elicited larger late, slow and labile cortical phenomena (see below).

The first presentation of T occurred either alone (three cats) or during SS (four cats): behavioural and EEG effects were noted. Thereafter, T was applied independently of SS and repeatedly until no response occurred: when habituation had thus ensued, it was again tested against a background SS.

Stage II. The basic feature of the training schedule was that prolonged SS were interrupted systematically 2-5 seconds after initiation of T (Fig. 1C): hence, T initiation consistently preceded SS cessation. Sessions lasted up to 90 minutes and involved up to twenty-five such combinations.

Acquired responses to T were eventually established (see below). Since they involved simultaneous behavioural and EEG effects, the possibility arose that the latter were a result of the former: T electrographic effects were tested in trained animals immobilized by intravenous Flaxedil (artificial respiration; rectal temperature over $36°$ C.).

'Learned' effects produced by T application (during SS) were compared with effects of agents known to affect cortical sensory responses, as: (i) voltage reduction (or cessation) of SS (seven cats); (ii) MRF stimulation (Grass S 4 model and SIU 4A: voltage 0.25-2 volts; pulse duration, 0.1 msec.; frequency, 200 c.p.s.; total duration, 1-2 seconds) (two cats);

(iii) same T when novel (on first presentation) (four cats); (iv) intense crashing sound (three cats); (v) different frequency tone (CT) that signalled SS initiation (tone conditioned in the usual sense) (Fig. 1D) (two cats).

Specificity of learned effects was tested by comparing them with consequences encountered in slightly dissimilar circumstances as: (i) effect of different frequency tone upon response to same SS (four cats); (ii) effect of same T upon response to SS applied to different limb (three cats); (iii) effect of same T upon response to different modality stimulus (repetitive flash) (two cats).

In three preparations, T and SS were alternated so that T initiation preceded SS cessation by 5 seconds and T cessation was followed, 5 seconds later, by SS initiation (Fig. 1E): behavioural and EEG effects of T initiation were identical to those encountered in remaining animals of this group (in which tone cessation did not signal shock application.[1]

RESULTS:

(1) EFFECT OF SUBCUTANEOUS STIMULI (SS)

(A) *SS application.* When prolonged SS were applied, extreme voltage values proved inadequate: relatively low ones evoked little or no behavioural manifestations; relatively high ones produced notorious and even violent signs of discomfort (cats moved and mewed continuously, tried to escape and attacked cables or cage; jerks of limb, body and head were prominent). Hence 'intermediate' values (1.5-15 volts) were used: under these conditions, SS effects though variable, composed a list that was limited and included for the group an initial startle followed by head depression or rotation, ear retraction, eye closure or blinking, plaintive mewing, shoulder hunching, general position shift and obvious 'concern' with the excited forelimb that currently exhibited flexion jerks synchronous with shocks and was regarded and/or licked. Responses usually consisted in an aggregation of various individual movements, each cat exhibiting a short number of characteristic combinations that could differ from one animal to another. Two cats in the group responded in a stereotyped and consistent fashion to SS initiation by adopting a 'tense' attitude (head depressed, ears retracted, eyes closed, body bent forward) that, except for minor shifts, was maintained for the duration of SS (Fig. 2).

Comments on the electrographic consequences of SS will be restricted to general EEG effects and to potentials evoked by SS in contralateral

[1] Observations pertaining to effects of tone cessation in these (and other) cats will be discussed elsewhere (Galeano, Roig, Segundo and Sommer-Smith, 1959).

BEHAVIOURAL AND EEG EFFECTS

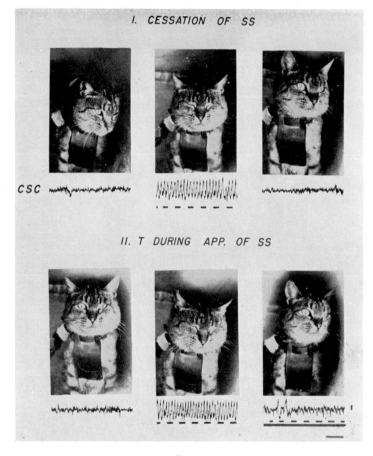

FIG. 2

BEHAVIOURAL AND EEG EFFECTS. (I) CESSATION OF SUBCUTANEOUS STIMULUS. Left, control; centre, SS effect; right, SS interruption effect. (II) TONE APPLICATION DURING SUBCUTANEOUS STIMULUS. Left, control; centre, SS effect; right, influence of T on SS effect. Note similarity of consequences of SS subtraction (without previous T) (top line) and of T application (during SS) (bottom line). In this and in other figures using EEG records, application of SS and of T are indicated by broken and by continuous bars, respectively and calibrations represent 50 μv. and 1 second APP., application; BEHAV., behavioural; CSC, contralateral sensory cortex.

sensory cortex. A detailed report covering cortical evoked potentials in free, unanaesthetized cats is in preparation (Roig, Segundo, Sommer-Smith and Galeano, to be published): it will indicate that, in 'chronic' cats cortical responses to single subcutaneous shocks consisted (when recorded as described above) in a succession of positive (P) and negative

POTENTIAL EVOKED BY SUBCUTANEOUS SHOCK
ON CSC

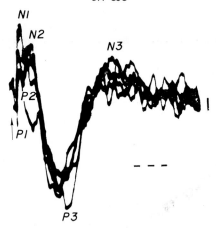

FIG. 3

POTENTIAL EVOKED BY SINGLE SUBCUTANEOUS SHOCK ON CONTRALATERAL SENSORY CORTEX: (unless specified otherwise, records from all figures are from sensory cortex contralateral to peripheral shocks). As recorded with equipment described in text, potentials consisted in a succession of positive (downward deflections P) and negative (upward deflections N) peaks named, according to polarity and chronological order of presentation, P1, N1, P2, N2, P3 and N3. Arrow indicates application of subcutaneous shock. Calibrations: 20 μv., 50 c.p.s. (as in all figures using cathode ray oscilloscope), CSC, contralateral sensory cortex; SUBCUT., subcutaneous.

(N) peaks, tentatively named as follows (Fig. 3): P1 (initial positive spike) was comparable to that encountered regularly but designated variously and ascribed to presynaptic activation in specific terminals (Figs. 3, 6, 8, 9, 11, 12). N1 was similar to first part of subsequent negative wave (Figs. 3, 6, 8, 9, 10, 11, 12). P2, N2 and P3 constituted a variable sequence exhibiting similarity with 'augmenting' complexes; when N2 was absent,

P2 was practically continuous with P3 (Figs. 6, 11); as N2 developed, separation between P2 and P3 became evident (Figs. 6, 8, 10, 11, 12); when N2 was large, P3 preserved its individuality but P2 became a minor indentation between N1 and N2 (Figs. 6, 8, 10). All delayed negative oscillations were included as N3 (since latencies and shapes were variable, this group

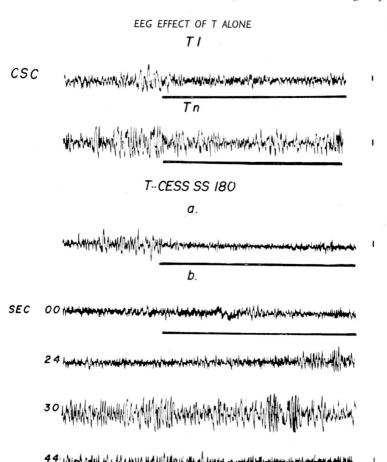

FIG. 4

EEG EFFECTS OF TONE APPLIED ALONE (without background SS). T1 (first application of T): 'desynchronization'. Tn (after numerous applications): T was no longer effective (habituation). T-CESS SS 180 (after 180 associations with cessation of SS): (a) if applied against a background 'relaxed' rhythm, T produced 'desynchronization'; (b) even when applied against an 'activated' background, T was followed (time 24 seconds) by reinforcement of slow rhythms and spindles lasting for about 20 seconds (up to time 34 seconds). CESS., cessation.

could be heterogeneous) (Figs. 6, 8, 10, 11) (Adrian, 1941; Bartley and Heinbecker, 1938; Bremer and Bonnet, 1950; Brookhart and Zanchetti, 1950; Buser and Albe Fessard, 1957; Dempsey and Morison, 1943; Dempsey, Morison and Morison, 1941; Eccles, 1951; Forbes and Morison, 1939; Li, Cullen and Jasper, 1956; etc.).

In each animal, responses exhibited marked 'spontaneous' variations that, as noticed by earlier investigators, predominantly involved the slower, later phenomena (waves N2, P3, N3 and, to a lesser extent, N1) (Adrian, 1941; Dempsey and Morison, 1941; 1943; Eccles, 1951; Forbes

EFFECT OF T ON POT. EV. BY SS ON CSC

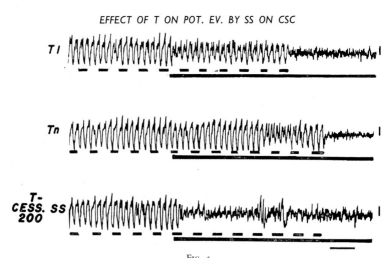

FIG. 5

EFFECT OF TONE ON POTENTIALS EVOKED BY SS ON CONTRALATERAL SENSORY CORTEX. T1 (first application): T produced a drop in amplitude and duration of slow waves induced by each peripheral shock. Tn (habituation): T produced little effects if any. T-CESS. 200 (after being followed 200 times by cessation of SS): T produced notorious 'masking' effects. EV., evoked. POT., potentials.

and Morison, 1939). These more variable waves were also the most susceptible to T effects (see below). It is necessary to point out that modifications induced in evoked potentials by effective agents (including tones) occurred always within the range of possible 'spontaneous' oscillations. Relative heights and duration of individual waves differed also from one preparation to another.

(B) *SS interruption*. When SS was cut off, cats reacted in a variable manner; the list of movements appearing at this instant was limited, however, and included head elevation or rotation, ear movements, eye opening or blinking, body straightening (or general shift) and interruption of certain previous activities as mewing, paw jerks and licking, etc. As was the case with SS application, response movements evoked by SS interruption were usually combined by each animal into a short number of typical patterns. The two cats that responded consistently to SS initiation by adopting a 'tense' attitude, reacted to SS interruption by reverting to the normal 'relaxed' attitude in an also stereotyped fashion (raising head, elevating ears, opening eyes, straightening body) (Fig. 2).

When SS ceased, evoked potentials naturally disappeared leaving low-voltage, fast activity.

(II) EFFECTS OF TONE (T). When the first T was applied alone an investigation reflex with EEG 'desynchronization' occurred (Fig. 4 — T1). When presented against a background SS, the preparation usually did not respond behaviourally; late waves of evoked potentials tended to be reduced in amplitude and duration (Fig. 6 — novel T). Behavioural and EEG effects diminished and disappeared in the course of Stage I; finally, tones produced little or no effect, either when applied alone or when presented against a background SS (Fig. 4 — Tn; 5 — Tn).

Thereafter (Stage II), T initiation was consistently followed by cessation of SS (Fig. 1 — C). During this period, animals came to react rapidly (before interruption of SS) to T: percentage of positive responses increased gradually and, in 3-10 sessions, reached and later remained at (or close to) 100 per cent (Fig. 7). From a behavioural standpoint, the same general comments mentioned in reference to SS application and interruption were applicable to T. (i) Responses to T were variable but the list was limited to: head elevation or rotation, ear movements, eye opening or blinking, body straightening (or general shift) and interruption of previous activities (mewing, licking).[1] This list was identical to that of SS interruption. (ii) Each cat associated individual movements into a short number of responses that characterized that preparation (but could vary from one animal to another). These compound responses to T coincided with those provoked by SS interruption. (iii) In the two cats that reacted in a uniform manner to SS application or substraction, T (when presented during SS) also gave a stereotyped pattern that consisted in head elevation or rotation, ear elevation, eye opening or blinking, body straightening (Figs. 2; 7 — lower graph). This pattern was identical to that produced by SS interruption (Fig. 2).

Tone initiation became capable also of modifying potentials (EP) evoked by SS on contralateral sensory cortex. Effects consisted in reduction

---

[1] As far as exclusively (and obviously insufficient) visual observation is concerned, limb jerks were not modified by T.

EFFECTS ON POT. EV. BY SS ON CSC

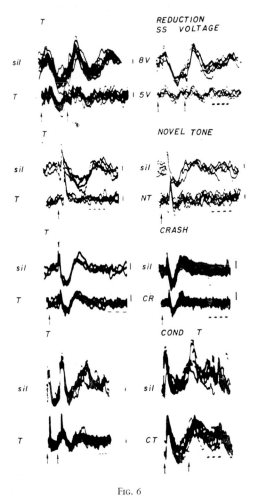

Fig. 6

COMPARISON OF MODIFICATIONS PRODUCED IN EVOKED POTEN-
TIALS BY DIFFERENT EEG 'AROUSAL' INDUCING INFLUENCES (I).
'Masking' effects of T were comparable in each instance to
those of SS voltage reduction (from 8 to 5 volts, top line),
first application of tone (NOVEL TONE NT, second line)
and application of intense sound (CRASH CR, third line);
a conditioned tone (COND. T. CT, fourth line) was less
effective.

of amplitude and duration (or even complete suppression) of cortical response waves (Figs. 2, 5, 6, 8). Susceptibility was different for each peak. P1 was resistant to the acquired influence of T (Fig. 6 — left column — second line). N1 was insensitive in certain preparations (Figs. 8; 9 —

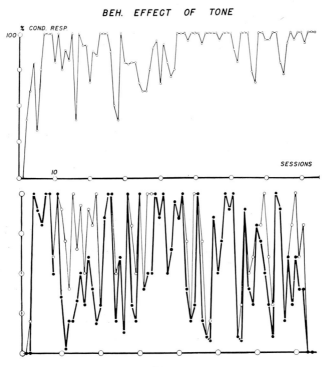

FIG. 7

LEARNING CURVE. On abscissae, number of training sessions; on ordinates, percentage of tones giving behavioural responses. Curve with narrow line and open circles, percentage of all responses; curve with broad line and black circles, percentage of 'typical', stereotyped response (see text). Top graph: cat exhibiting frequent but variable reactions to T (head raising or turning to right or left, blinking, etc.). Bottom graph: cat exhibiting a frequent 'typical' stereotyped response. BEH., behavioural; RESP., response.

left column; 10; 11) but responsive in others (Figs. 6 — left column — third line; 9 — II). The P2- N2- P3 complex was modified by T initiation: effects upon P3 were notorious (Figs. 6 — left column; 8; 9; 10 — I; 11; 12); N2 frequently responded well (Figs. 6 — left column — fourth line; 8 — IV; 10 — I), but, occasionally, was not affected by or even became

T

more clear-cut after T (Fig. 6 — left column — first line; 8 — I-II-III; 9 — I; 11 — I-II); P2 variations appeared to be a consequence of modifications in N1 and N2 (Figs. 6 — left column — first and fourth lines; 8 — III,

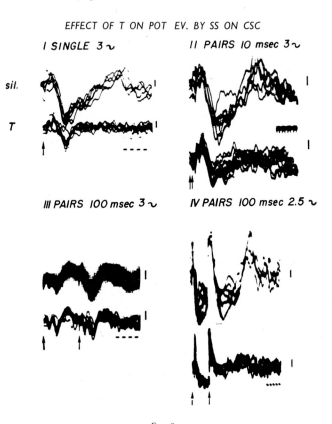

EFFECT OF T ON POT EV. BY SS ON CSC

I SINGLE 3 ᳝   II PAIRS 10 msec 3 ᳝

sil.

T

III PAIRS 100 msec 3 ᳝   IV PAIRS 100 msec 2.5 ᳝

FIG. 8

EFFECT OF TONE UPON POTENTIALS EVOKED BY SUBCUTANEOUS STIMULI. ADVANTAGES OF PAIRED SHOCKS. I, Single shocks at 3 c.p.s.: slow, labile phenomena are obvious and respond to T. II, pairs (10 msec. interval) at 3 c.p.s.; III, pairs (100 msec.) at 3 c.p.s.; IV, pairs (100 msec.) at 2.5 c.p.s.; application of second shock facilitated development of late, slow waves affected preferentially by T application; contrastingly, responses to first shocks are either small or suffered little modification.

IV; 11 — I). When present in control responses, N3 was markedly reduced or abolished by T (Figs. 6 — left column; 8; 13 — I; 10 — I; 11).

Paired shocks (at 1-100 msec. intervals) or different stimulation frequencies (2.5-8 c.p.s.) were used to enhance slow phenomena and thus provide a more susceptible background, upon which T effects if any would become more notorious (Figs. 6 — left column — first, fourth line; 8 — II, III, IV; 9; 10 — I). Figs. 6 — first line, 8 — III and 9 — I illustrate specially well the advantages of double stimuli showing instances in which T markedly modified potentials evoked by second shock.

Efficacy of T was critically related with two issues. (i) Voltage of SS background stimulation: responses (behavioural and EEG) to values producing reduced or intermediate conduct effects were susceptible; lability decreased and disappeared if stronger stimuli were used. (ii) Control responses (evoked by SS prior to T): if T was presented against background EP exhibiting important slow components, electrographic T effects were clear-cut; as control potentials became smaller, EEG effects became less obvious in a parallel fashion (behavioural effects occurred no matter the type of background potentials).

When SS was not discontinued after T, cats eventually (10-30 seconds) readopted behavioural and electrographic patterns exhibited prior to sound application. If applied during SS, intense intercurrent stimuli (e.g. loud crash) provoked effects described below: if T were presented a few seconds later, animals usually did not respond to it ('external inhibition').

Under Flaxedil, T provoked modifications of EP similar to those seen, in the same trained preparation, when freely mobile (Fig. 9): hence, electrographic alterations were not a consequence of concomitant performance. Pupillary dilatation occurred in flaxedilized animals upon application of T.[1]

Electrographically T effects resembled results of reducing SS voltage. In Fig. 6 — upper line, T (left column) a passage from 8 volts excitation to 5 volts (right column) reduced waves N2 and N3 (after second shock) and P3 (after both shocks) (P1 was larger with 8 volts during T than with 5 volts). Observed with ink-writer, T application induced a shift similar to that occurring in SS interruption (specially when spike P1 was not prominent) (Fig. 2). With oscilloscope (showing potentials more clearly), resemblance was not complete unless voltages used were threshold for EP: in these circumstances, responses were effaced by T and so obscured by 'spontaneous' rhythms that patterns became comparable to those obtained without peripheral excitation.

Changes in configuration of cortical evoked potentials are known to be

---

[1] Apart from this one, other learned EEG responses were found to subsist in preparations immobilized with Flaxedil (Galeano, Roig, Segundo and Sommer-Smith, 1959; Segundo, Sommer-Smith, Galeano and Roig, 1959).

associated with EEG 'arousal' (Gauthier, Parma and Zanchetti, 1956): therefore, T effect was compared with changes resulting from application of certain EEG 'activating' agents. (i) MRF stimulation (contralateral to SS) reduced amplitude and duration of N3, P3, N2, and, to a lesser extent,

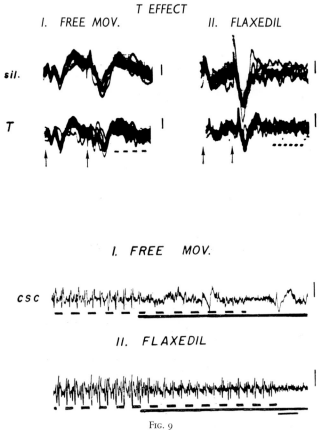

FIG. 9

PERSISTENCE OF TONE EFFECTS IN FLAXEDILIZED PREPARATION. I, T effects in freely moving, unanaesthetized cat; II, same cat under Flaxedil: electrographic effects were comparable.

N1; intensity of effects could be graded by variations in central excitation voltages: as far as morphological mutations are concerned, MRF excitation and T effects were indeed comparable (Fig. 10). (ii) Tones that after training provoked results described above had induced similar (though usually less noticeable) effects when novel (on first application) (Figs. 5 —

T1; 6 — second line). (iii) Effects of loud crashing noises resembled those of T (Fig. 6 — third line). (iv) In two cats training involved use of different frequency tones, one (conditioned tone CT) indicating SS initiation and

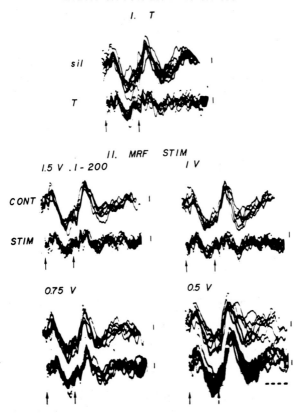

EFFECTS ON POT. EV. BY SS ON CSC

I. T

sil

T

II. MRF STIM

1.5 V .1 - 200   1 V

CONT

STIM

0.75 V   0.5 V

FIG. 10

COMPARISON OF MODIFICATIONS PRODUCED IN EVOKED POTENTIALS: I, TONE; II, MESENCEPHALIC RETICULAR FORMATION STIMULATION (pulse duration, 0.1 msec.; frequency, 200 c.p.s.). Modifications induced on evoked potentials by T or by 0.75-1.5 volts were comparable; stimulation with 0.5 was ineffectual. CONT., control.

the other (T) signalling SS cessation (Fig. 1D): the latter T acquired an intense capacity to affect behaviour and evoked potentials (when applied during SS). The former became conditioned in the current sense producing behavioural and EEG effects (startle, leg retraction, 'activation', etc.)

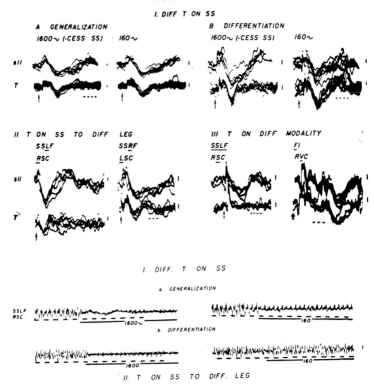

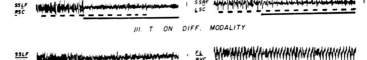

FIG. 11

SPECIFICITY OF TONE EFFECTS. I. Specificity for T frequency (DIFF. T ON SS). a (or A) GENERALIZATION stage: both 'reinforced' (1600 c.p.s. –CESS SS) and non-'reinforced' (160 c.p.s.) tones affected responses. b (or B) DIFFERENTIATION stage: only 1600 c.p.s. tones were effective. II. Specificity for localization (T ON SS TO DIFF. LEG). No differentiation was established: T affected both types of response, those on right sensory cortex (RSC) after left foreleg stimuli (SSLF) (currently cut off after T) and those on left sensory cortex (LSC) after right foreleg stimuli (SSRF) (currently not cut off after T). III. Specificity for modality (T ON DIFF. MODALITY). Differentiation was established: T affected responses on right sensory cortex after left foreleg stimuli occurring on right visual cortex (RVC) after repetitive flashes (FL.) (currently not cut off after T). DIFF., different; FL., flashes; LSC, left somatic sensory cortex; RSC, right sensory cortex; RVC, right visual cortex; SSLF, subcutaneous stimulus to left foreleg; SSRF, subcutaneous stimulus to right foreleg.

but, in spite of having clear-cut 'desynchronizing' abilities (when applied alone) was incapable (when applied during SS) of affecting evoked potentials in a manner comparable to that of T (Fig. 6 — fourth line). Resemblance of effects of T on the one hand and of EEG 'arousal' — inducing influences on the other, did not go beyond the electrographic sphere. Separation could be established in the behavioural field: MRF excitation was inoperant (sub-threshold); novel T and intense sounds were either ineffective or produced 'surprise' effects (investigation reflex, startle): conditioned tones (CT) produced slight or no changes when applied during SS.

'OPPOSITE' EFFECTS OF DIFFERENTIATED TONES

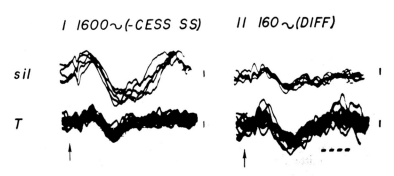

FIG. 12

'OPPOSITE' EFFECTS OF DIFFERENTIATED TONES. A tone of 1600 c.p.s. (but not one of 160 c.p.s.) was reinforced by cessation of SS. Eventually, differentiation ensued (see text and Fig. 11). Reinforced tones (1600 — CESS. SS) masked large control evoked potentials; non-reinforced tones (160 DIFF.) augmented small control potentials.

Specificity of effects described above was explored from different points of view.

1. *Frequency specificity.* When a cat had been trained to respond to a tone of a given frequency (e.g. 1.600 c.p.s.) habitually 'reinforced' by cessation of SS, the first applications of a different frequency (e.g. 160 c.p.s.) provoked a similar effect (generalization) (Fig. 11 — I, and A). After a number of sessions in which one tone (1600 c.p.s.) but not the other (160 c.p.s.) was reinforced by substraction of SS, three cats out of four, reached a point in which effects were produced consistently by 1600 c.p.s. and exceptionally by 160 c.p.s. (differentiation) (Fig. 11 — I-b, B). In this situation, it occurred frequently that small cortical responses (not modified by the 'positive' tone) were augmented by application of the 'negative' tone (Fig. 12).

2. *Localization specificity*. After establishment of learned responses to T by the usual practice of associating T with cessation of SS (to left foreleg), routine was changed in three cats. Thereafter, SS were applied separately to right and left forelegs: presentation of T during SS to left foreleg was followed (as before) by substraction of shocks; presentation of T during SS to right foreleg was not followed by change in shocks. Cats reacted to this procedure as follows: (i) in two preparations, efficacy of T during left SS was not modified and, in addition, application of T during SS to right foreleg led, from the beginning, to identical behavioural and EEG effects (that, since SS continued, were transitory) (generalization) (Fig. 11 − II); (ii) in the remaining animal and after a brief initial phase of generalization, responses to T (during excitation of either leg) became unpredictable. Therefore, 'differentation' could not be established in the sense of restricting T influence to effects of SS applied to one single foreleg.

(3) *Modality specificity*. A repetitive flash (Fl.) was used as non-somatic excitation. Flicker did not cause behavioural responses (except for initial orienting reflexes): hence, considerations refer exclusively to the electrographic sphere. In a first effort (*a*) SS and Fl. were applied separately, T being followed by cessation of SS but not of Fl.: no differentiation occurred (T continued to mask somatic and visual potentials). In a second effort (*b*) Fl. was presented continuously during the entire session; SS was applied intermittently and interrupted following T in the usual way. With this technique successful 'differentiation' took place: T application modified potentials evoked in somatic sensory cortex by SS but did not usually alter responses elicited at the same time in visual area by flashes (Fig. 11 − III).[1]

Concomitantly with observation of behaviour and with sampling of activity from sensory cortex (contralateral to SS), EEG records were taken from different regions of the central nervous system comprising (in the entire series) sensory cortex (homo-lateral to SS) HSC, acoustic cortex, visual cortex, NMDT, MRF and MCG. If activity in these areas exhibited relatively large voltage, slow waves and/or spindles during silence, application of T (producing typical effects in contralateral sensory cortex (CSC) could be followed by shift to low voltage, fast patterns (EEG 'arousal'). This was particularly consistent in HSC (three cats) and NMDT (one cat): EP masking was never encountered without 'desynchronization' appearing in HSC or NMDT. This was not always the case with

[1] Effort (*b*) succeeded in producing 'modality' specificity whereas effort (*a*) did not. Failure to establish localization specificity (see above) may have been due to application of a routine similar to that of (*a*) to a problem that might have been solved by a routine similar to that of (*b*).

other structures (acoustic cortex, visual cortex, MRF and MCG): in frequent instances, typical effects occurred on CSC and little or no alteration took place in the other regions.

Tones reinforced by cessation of SS and capable of provoking EEG and behavioural effects described above when applied against a background SS were usually also effective when presented alone. Though behaviourally responses were poor (minor shifts, investigation movements), tones consistently produced EEG 'arousal' generalized or localized to CSC (Fig. 4 – TCESS 180, a). Another characteristic EEG effect was a relatively delayed (initiation 10-30 seconds after T) and prolonged (10-30 seconds) discharge of large voltage and slow (4-14 c.p.s.) waves and spindles that followed initial 'desynchronization': this effect was noticeable even if T was presented against a background 'desynchronized' tracing (Fig. 4 – T-CESS SS 180 b).

When habituated, T initiation had no obvious consequences; after training (and against relatively slow background EEG) it elicited an evoked potential, specially noticeable on CSC, MRF and MCG.

In two animals, T was applied (with no previous SS) during natural sleep (behavioural and EEG). Responses were either absent or confined to slight and transient EEG 'desynchronization'. Hence tones associated with shock cessation lacked arousing potentialities of sounds reinforced by other absolute stimuli (e.g. SS initiation, brain stem excitation) (Rowland Segundo, Roig and Sommer-Smith, 1959).

DISCUSSION

Chronological relationship is critical when 'neutral' and 'biologically significant' stimuli are paired with the purpose of establishing a learned response. Efficacy of certain temporal sequences (tone initiation – feeding or pain initiation; tone cessation – pain initiation) has been widely confirmed (Pavlov, 1941; Rowland, 1954; Segundo, Roig, Sommer-Smith, 1959; Zeleny cited by Pavlov, 1941, etc.). Contrastingly, usefulness of other alliances (e.g. feeding – tone initiation, backward conditioning, etc.) has been less convincing (Zbrozyna, 1958). Conceivably, application of yet other possible patterns (e.g. tone initiation – cessation of absolute stimulus) might also develop novel (learned) responses to previously indifferent stimuli (Konorski, 1948). Experimental observations have supported this assumption: if each time a sound was applied food was withdrawn forcibly from an eating dog, animals eventually stopped eating on presentation of the auditory stimulus in spite of continued availability of aliment (Zbrozyna, 1958); in backward conditioning (rats) indifferent stimuli could signal cessation of unconditioned excitation (Barlow, 1956); in the present experiments, a cat came to react to a formerly ineffectual tone after the latter was followed, in a regular fashion by substraction of prolonged painful stimuli. Accordingly, 'signal reactions' may indeed be created as suggested by Konorski when absolute 'stimuli' are provided by interruption of biologically significant excitations — feeding, pain (Konorski, 1948);[1] this is not altogether surprising since suppression of pain (feeding) constitutes a biologically important reward (punishment), probably associated with central nervous readjustments as great as those accompanying their application.

Behavioural effects of SS cessation (when not preceded by T) and of T initiation (during application of SS) were variable. Nevertheless, affinity between consequences of both phenomena could be established, both as a group and individually. In the first place, variability though wide was not unlimited and lists of single movements and of combined responses provoked by SS substraction and by T presentation were coincident. In the second place, observation of cats answering to SS cessation with one predominant behaviour pattern indicated that this same performance constituted their most frequent response to T. Therefore, when T was applied cats behaved in an anticipatory fashion as if SS had been interrupted (even though excitation were sustained).

Tones used in this training routine also acquired the ability to modify potentials evoked in sensory cortex by SS excitation; effects consisting essentially in masking or cancelling of peaks N_3, P_3, N_2 and, commonly, P_2 and N_1; analysis of electrographic changes may serve to clarify problems posed by this type of learning. Similar blocking influences act upon cortical sensory evoked potentials as a result of: (i) physiological stimuli (e.g. blowing air into nostrils); (ii) central nervous stimuli (e.g. of MRF); (iii) anti-cholinesterase administration (Bremer and Stoupel, 1959; Desmedt and La Grutta, 1957; Gauthier, Parma and Zanchetti, 1958; etc.). Agents (i), (ii) and (iii) exhibit the second common feature, of provoking EEG 'desynchronization'. It is possible that T applied during SS also exerted an EEG 'desynchronizing' influence. This contingency was supported by the following observations: (a) such an effect was observed frequently as a generalized or localized (to somatic sensory cortices) phenomenon when T was presented alone;[2] (b) on T

---

[1] One cannot discard the possibility that new links could be established if indifferent tones were associated with cessation of relatively 'non-significant' stimuli (e.g. repetitive flash).

[2] When T was applied during SS, 'desynchronization' on sensory cortex was, strictly speaking, difficult to appreciate. Subsequent tracings added little because cessation of SS itself (preceded or not by T) was followed always by low-voltage, fast activity.

application and simultaneously with the potential drop in CSC, other areas frequently showed EEG 'arousal'.

Therefore, T probably operated by way of a process inducing EEG 'activation' and acting predominantly upon the somatic sensory cortices. All EEG 'activating' influences of this type are not necessarily identical, however, and may perhaps be separated on the basis of other criteria as intensity and distribution of EEG 'arousal', types of concomitant modifications in cortical evoked potentials and behaviour, etc. In these experiments, effects of tones reinforced by cessation of painful stimuli were compared with consequences of other EEG 'arousing' agents, applied in similar circumstances and, if various criteria were taken into account, global responses were indeed different. Firstly, dissimilar behaviour resulted from causes affecting evoked potentials in a similar manner: novel tones produced minor investigation reflexes; intense sounds, startle patterns; tones conditioned to SS initiation were inoperant during SS; MRF excitation was sub-threshold for visible effects; T produced 'anticipatory' effects described above. Secondly, ability to produce EEG 'arousal' and capacity to affect EP were not exhibited in a quantitatively parallel fashion by various agents: evoked potentials responded little or irregularly to novel tones, 'conditioned' tones or intense sounds that determined clear-cut 'activation'; they reacted markedly to T or to MRF excitation.[1] Finally, influences compared here differed in regional selectivity, either provoking generalized (MRF excitation; novel tone; intense sound; conditioned tone) or localized (conditioned tone) effects. T itself was not consistent in this respect: an important fact, however, was that masking of potentials (in contralateral sensory cortex) definitely could be associated with restricted EEG 'arousal' (present in CSC, HSC and NMDT; absent in acoustic and visual cortices, MRF and MCG). Further signs of topographical specificity issued from comparison of somatic sensory and visual effects of T: modification of subcutaneously induced responses (somatic sensory cortex) could take place without concomitant alteration of photically evoked potentials (visual cortex).

In short, and to summarize, the electrographic ability acquired by T (through association with substraction of SS) consisted in a capacity to mask somatic sensory cortical evoked potentials in an intense and frequently restricted fashion; such blocking seemed associated with a simultaneous and similarly distributed EEG 'activating' influence. Localized

---

[1] Blocking of cortical potentials during EEG 'arousal' has been known for some years; augmentatory effects have been reported recently (Bremer and Stoupel, 1959; Dumont and Dell, 1958; Gauthier, Parma and Zanchetti, 1956; Segundo, Sommer-Smith, Galeano and Roig, 1959).

'activating' influences have been shown to operate in rostral cortical areas upon repetitive excitation of ventralis posterior, centre median (rostral pole) or meso-ventral intralaminar nuclei of thalamus in acute experiments (Jasper, Naquet and King, 1955; Starzl, Taylor and Magoun, 1951). It is reasonable to advance the working hypothesis that the same nuclei participated in similar responses acquired by chronic preparations. A mechanism similar (in terms of general structures and influences involved) to that surmised above was presumed to intervene in the establishment of current conditioned reactions (Gastaut, 1959). No information is available as to the manner whereby T eventually became capable of selectively energizing these structures and specifically triggering these patterns.

Most features (method, similarity of absolute and learned effects, inhibitions, EEG manifestations, etc.) of typical conditioning were present in the learning process described here: if one considers that substraction of pain (and not pain itself) acted as absolute stimulus, this learned reaction may be incorporated to the conditioned reflexes group (Konorski, 1946; Zbrozyna, 1958). Terms 'excitatory' and 'inhibitory' are vague unless referred to precise effects: in this respect, T influence was not homogeneous, appearing either inhibitory (in the sense that it revoked posture and movements induced by SS) and excitatory (in the sense that it provoked 'desynchronization').

SS produced behavioural manifestations of pain and elicited potentials on contralateral sensory cortex; on application of T, performance and electrographic signs were altered. Before entering into the final considerations, the unavoidable questionability of the following points should be stressed. (i) The afflictive consequences of similar excitation in man plus behavioural manifestations exhibited by cats when receiving SS favoured the assumption that stimuli were basically painful subjectively; though heavily significant, this evidence was not totally decisive. (ii) Participation of cerebral cortex in pain perception is accepted currently in experimental and clinical literature and it is therefore possible that at least part of the evoked potentials was due to activation of pain-conducting afferent fibres (Anguelergues and Hècaen, 1958; Melzack and Haugen, 1957); this must be demonstrated conclusively, however. (iii) Tones reduced evoked potentials and this could in fact mean that their application blocked afferent volleys on their way to or at the cortex; the possibility subsists, however, that cortical waves were obliterated by way of some other type of influence (that, for instance, modified the temporal pattern of and the relationship between individual discharges). (iv) Finally and even if SS were painful and cortical responses were dependent (in part or *in toto*) on pain-producing centripetal volleys, it should be kept in mind that any effort to establish the behavioural (and, we may add, subjective) correlates to cerebral action potentials is ' ... bound to be tentative' (Morison, Dempsey and Morison, 1941). Therefore, experiments described in this presentation cannot be construed as evidence that, after training, T application blocked afferent volleys initiated by SS and, consequently, cats experienced less pain and relaxed; discussion of this possibility would be entirely conjectural.

In spite of the previous cautious remarks, two main conclusions may justifiably be drawn from these experiments. In the first place, that within certain limits, conduct and electrographic changes induced by sub-cutaneous, presumably painful stimuli are subject to variations, 'spon-taneous' or provoked. In the second place, that learned issues established through adequate training are significant in the determination of induced oscillations. Similar deductions may issue from experiments in which painful excitation became the conditioned signal for feeding and, con-comitantly, discomfort-suggesting manifestations were lessened (Pavlov, 1941).

Suggestion and hypnosis have been used for centuries by physicians and the laity to alleviate pain and its consequences: it is perhaps within this labile range confirmed experimentally and by way of mechanisms related to those mobilized in chronically implanted cats, that pain effects are vulnerable to such poorly understood but frequently effective measures.

SUMMARY

Experiments were performed on cats with chronically implanted electrodes in which application and substraction of prolonged subcutan-eous stimuli (SS) induced variable but characteristic electrographic (in somatic sensory cortex) and behavioural patterns. During training stage I, a tone (T) was presented repeatedly until rendered inoperant (habituation). During stage II, SS was consistently interrupted 2-5 seconds after T initia-tion.

A learning process was established by this 'reinforcement' of indifferent T with interruption of pain and cats eventually came to react to T in a consistent fashion. Behavioural responses to T initiation (during SS) resembled those to SS substraction (without previous T) and consisted in head, eye and/or limb movements, frequently carrying from a 'tense' to a 'relaxed, natural' position.

Electrographically (and even under Flaxedil) T masked potentials evoked by SS on contralateral sensory cortex; amplitude and duration of individual waves were reduced markedly (initial spike was resistant). T effects were compared electrographically as to quality, intensity and distribution with results induced by application of other agents known to reduce cortical evoked potentials (e.g. SS voltage reduction; EEG 'activating' influence as brain stem stimulation or presentation of novel, intense or conditioned sounds). T effects exhibited specificity: non-reinforced tones of different frequency become ineffectual; T influence could be restricted to the somatic sensory areas.

T application was followed by EEG 'activation', generalized or localized (to sensory cortices and to nucleus medialis dorsalis of thalamus); delayed and transitory reinforcement of slow rhythms also occurred.

Experiments indicated that changes (behavioural, EEG) induced by painful stimuli are subject to variations 'spontaneous' and provoked; they indicated, moreover, that learned issues established through adequate training are significant.

GROUP DISCUSSION

GERARD. In less careful terms than you used, how long can you fool the cat into thinking that it does not hurt?

SEGUNDO. For a period of 10–30 seconds; after that and if shocks were continued, cats reassumed the characteristic attitude and potentials returned to their initial amplitude.

GERARD. Is the sound effect extinguished?

SEGUNDO. Tone effects will be extinguished if sounds are repeated without their usual 'reinforcement' by shock interruption.

MYERS. I found it very exciting to hear, Dr Segundo, that the animals in your experiment did not differentiate between opposing extremities in responding to the conditioning stimuli. Such a result closely resembles the findings of Anrep and others working with tactile conditioning in the dog. Specifically, they found that after a positive conditioned salivary response had long been established to tactile stimulation of a given skin area on one leg, first stimulation of the homologous locus of the opposite leg also gave profuse salivary flow, whereas stimulation of nearby loci on either side gave little if any salivary response. Furthermore, it was not found possible to establish separate conflicting reflexes to tactile stimulation of the separate homologous skin loci. Rather, as the response to tactile stimulation of one locus changed character, that of its homologous locus tended always also to change 'spontaneously' in the same direction, the change in the homologous locus occurring without direct conditioning through its own receptor field. Thus was demonstrated a remarkable mirroring or symmetry of development of tactile 'gnosis' over both sides of the body surface subsequent to one-sided conditioning. Bykov subsequently found that section of the corpus callosum disrupted this symmetrical development of tactile conditioned reflexes, and further, that in corpus callosum sectioned dogs one could for the first time establish conflicting conditioned responses to tactile stimulation of the separate homologous skin loci. I wonder if you have considered carrying out your series of experiments, Dr Segundo, in corpus callosum sectioned animals to see if your results with regard to generalization between the extremities might not be different in such animals.

SEGUNDO. I was not aware of Anrep's or Bykov's results and they interest me very much. Before proceeding further, however, we would like to perform other experiments to be sure of the impossibility of 'differentiating between paws'.

NAQUET. Have you placed some electrodes in the afferent pathway?

SEGUNDO. With ink writer we explored potentials evoked by shocks in sensory-motor cortex, visual cortex, acoustic cortex, nucleus medialis dorsalis of thalamus, centre median of thalamus, mesencephalic reticular formation and central grey; with oscilloscope in primary cortical receiving area exclusively.

NAQUET. If I remember your slides you do not find any reduction of the first part of the evoked potential during desynchronization, only the last two were cut. Is that right?

SEGUNDO. Yes, when applied during subcutaneous shocks, tones blocked or reduced sensory potentials evoked by same in somatic cortex: late waves were susceptible, but the early spike was resistant. Waves evoked elsewhere (e.g. on visual cortex by flashes) were sometimes left unaffected. Tones frequently produced localized EEG 'desynchronization' but capacity to produce this effect was not parallel with ability to 'block' sensory cortical evoked potentials.

JOUVET. In your last slides, during subcutaneous stimulation, it looked as if you get slow waves on the cortical area, or at least the EEG is not desynchronized. Did you get any slow waves in the reticular formation during subcutaneous stimulation?

SEGUNDO. During shock application we occasionally observed cortical and sub-cortical spindles.

JOUVET. Because I wondered if this late component has not got something to do with supra-liminal inhibition in Pavlovian terms.

ASRATYAN. If I am not mistaken about the conditions of your experimentation you have elaborated a backward conditioning.

SEGUNDO. The tone preceded the cessation of a prolonged subcutaneous stimulus.

ASRATYAN. But the electrical stimulation precedes the tone by many minutes. And in these cases tone became a conditioned stimulus and produced the same effect as electrical stimulation. It seems to me that this is an expression of Reverse connection from tone to electrical stimulation. Have you some signs that you have also some direct conditioned connection? That is that the application of the electrical stimulus alone, after such a combination, is able to produce some change characteristic of the application of tone alone.

SEGUNDO. We believe shock 'interruption' and not shock 'application' acted as absolute stimulus. Substraction of environmental agents may produce positive effects within the central nervous system as, for instance, in the case of auditory units that react to tone interruption (Galambos, 1952). On the other hand, it is true that shocks preceded tones and therefore possible that they could acquire some behavioural or electrographic feature corresponding to the latter. In the behavioural sphere, we started off with tones to which cats had been habituated and therefore were inoperant; it would thus be difficult to define an absolute tone effect. In the EEG sphere, I am afraid we did not search for possible effects of somatic stimuli in auditory regions.

MAGOUN. Did your conditioned reduction of potentials occur in the thalamus as in the cortex?

SEGUNDO. Thalamic potentials were not studied.

GERARD. I would have assumed that you have evidence against any serious decrease in the input from the fact that your early waves often did not change at all. Is that unsound?

SEGUNDO. The classical interpretation of somatic sensory evoked potentials considers that the early wave of the cortical response is due to afferent volleys and late waves to intracortical processes. I find it difficult to admit, however, that no afferent activity at all reaches the cortex during those delayed oscillations.

MAGOUN. My interest in subcortical potentials is related to the question of whether activity evoked in the sensory cortex is to be correlated with pain perception. Might some feature of the evoked cortical potential later than the early spike or some activity which never reached the cortex at all, be of importance here? The reduction or block of pain perception might not be correlated with what you are recording in the sensory cortex. Conceivably you might find potentials subcortically that would be more directly related to the perception of pain. Could you give us your impression of what potentials are evoked in the CNS by a peripheral pain stimulus?

SEGUNDO. Various potentials were evoked by subcutaneous stimuli in our 'chronic' cats: though we did not explore extensively, it was obvious that, in these animals as in certain 'acute' preparations, subcutaneous stimuli evoked at least 'cortical primary', 'cortical associative' and 'reticular' responses. A number of dubious issues is involved, however, in the question of which electrographic phenomenon was correlated with perception of pain: correlation of pain probably experienced by our cats on the one hand, with potentials evoked in different areas or individual waves on the other is extremely hazardous (see Discussion in text).

LUNDBERG. I would like to ask to what extent you think it is likely that some of the evoked potentials are due not to stimulation of pain fibres but to stimulation of touch fibres. If so, these evoked potentials may not have any relation to the nociceptive behaviour of the animal.

SEGUNDO. As mentioned above, we cannot correlate individual waves pertaining to cortical evoked potential with cat behaviour or pain sensations. Other types of peripheral fibres were probably activated as well and we do not know to what extent each type participated in determination of each wave.

BUSER. I would like to ask whether in Dr Segundo's opinion, the cat felt pain during the period it submitted to sound; in trying to correlate the amplitude of an evoked potential to the 'conscious perception' of the corresponding stimulus, we are used to the fact that a higher level of wakefulness may correspond to a smaller amplitude of the cortical response (at least with peripheral stimuli); in the case of Dr Segundo's experiments, could it not be the opposite?

GERARD. I think you are talking about the differences between sensing something and attending to the sensation. We know morphine does not raise the threshold to pain stimulation, it just makes the person not worry about it so much; and frontal lobe operations do the same thing. I was wondering, along the same lines, whether perhaps your two separate waves represent the arrival of the initial peripheral stimulus and the secondary attending to it.

SEGUNDO. I think there are two main points in Dr Buser's comment. As regards the first, we cannot know for certain what the cat felt. As to the second, it is indeed true that EEG 'arousal' is associated usually with decreased cortical potentials. I would like to mention, however, recent experiments by Bremer and Stoupel and Dumont and Dell, in which stimulation of mesencephalic reticular formation produced EEG 'arousal' and simultaneously 'facilitation' of responses in primary receiving cortices (Bremer and Stoupel, 1959; Dumont and Dell, 1959). Hence 'desynchronization' is not associated necessarily with reduction of sensory cortical potentials.

OLDS. I think it relevant to the problem of whether pain is reduced is the question of whether you ever get adaptation to this subcutaneous stimulus by itself. How long is the series of shocks before the tone is introduced? And I would like also to ask: Is there ever any change in responding during the course, either recruitment or readaptation?

SEGUNDO. We stimulated between seconds and hours and an average of 3-4 minutes was used currently. There were marked spontaneous variations of evoked potentials: for instance, and since you mentioned 'recruitment', in certain cats 8 per second stimulation produced an effect that was entirely comparable to 'augmentation'.

HERNÁNDEZ-PEÓN. I would like to remind Dr Segundo of the experiments of Bremer and Stoupel. Electrical stimulation of the mesencephalic reticular formation produces striking facilitations of the cortical potentials evoked by electric shocks applied to the optic nerve. But when they used a flash of light instead (which I think is more physiological than an electric shock applied to the optic nerve) they observed a striking reduction of the evoked potential. With reference to Dr Magoun's question about subcortical changes in the somatic afferent pathways, specially where pain is concerned, I can say that we have recorded evoked potentials both at the spinal sensory nucleus in the bulb and in the lateral column of the spinal cord in conscious cats. Experiments have shown at both levels that the potentials evoked by nociceptive stimuli are reduced when the cat focuses its attention upon some other stimulus of greater significance. Of course, this reduction is more difficult to obtain on the potentials evoked by nociceptive stimuli than on the potentials evoked by tactile stimuli.

SEGUNDO. A priori, one would tend to think that also for sensory control, the nervous system has two types of mechanisms, one facilitatory and another inhibitory: in terms of unit responses this is true. When evoked potentials have been controlled, facilitation has not been frequent but we must remain receptive to the idea that under certain conditions, sensory evoked potentials may be facilitated.

NEUROHUMORAL FACTORS IN THE CONTROL OF ANIMAL BEHAVIOUR

K. Lissák and E. Endröczi

The homeostasis of the organism is regulated by two factors, neural and endocrine, which, by complex interaction, have influenced each other throughout the course of evolution.

Higher nervous activity and conditioned reflexes are also manifestations of the adaptability of the organism. Without wishing to disregard the basic role played by neocortical structures in the development of higher nervous processes, we regard it as necessary to analyse the role of sub-cortical systems in the organization of conditioned reflex connections and basic emotional behaviour.

After the discovery of the role of the diffuse activating system in the maintenance of the waking state of the cortex, a whole series of communications has appeared in recent years. All show that the neural network, described by Cajal sixty years ago, and termed reticular formation today, can be influenced not only by neural but also humorally. Therefore, when the mechanisms of the brain stem are considered, the neural organization of the mesencephalon and diencephalon must be regarded as an integrating system at a complex neurohumoral level.

During the past decade one of the subjects investigated in our Institute has been the interrelationship between complex neuroendocrine processes and behaviour. The problem which, first of all, concerns the neuro-endocrine control of the conditioned reflex and basic emotional behaviour in higher animals, is enormously complicated by the fact that interference with neural organization also affects endocrine regulation, the changes of which react on the nervous system and influence behaviour.

In our earlier investigations (Endröczi, Lissák and Telegdy, 1958) it was observed that during lactation the domesticated mother rat would attack and kill a frog put in her cage. This maternal aggressivity can be observed only during the period of lactation. The administration of oestrone for a few days (300-400 IU/100 g.b.w.) will abolish it completely without interfering with the care of the offspring. The interesting point in this experiment was that in the prevention of this folliculine action hydro-cortisone was more effective than progesterone. At the same time it was also observed that hydrocortisone not only abolished the inhibitory influence of oestrone but also elicited it in animals in which it had not been present previously. The phenomenon is based on the antagonistic action of two endocrine factors influencing the central nervous system. The point of attack has not been quite clarified as yet, although we have findings which suggest that certain subcortical systems play an important role in this mechanism. Thus electrolytic lesions of amygdale or of the area pyriformis and destruction of the septal region, will also abolish maternal aggressivity in the lactating rat. Another noteworthy observation of ours is that after removal of the amygdale and the hippocampal formation, the mouse-catching reaction of the cat is abolished for a longer period, although the animal feeds well and the somato-motor activities are satisfactory (Endröczi and Martin and Bata, 1958). These investigations show that the above-mentioned archicortical structures not only play a role in the organization of emotional behaviour but can also be influenced by endocrine factors.

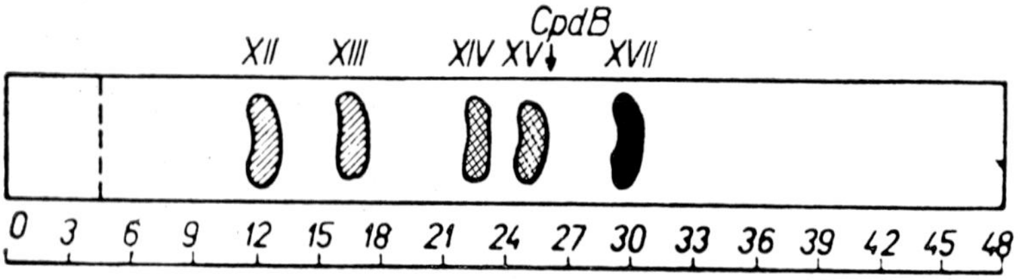

FIG. I
Paperchromatogram showing the difference of corticoid composition in the blood of the adrenal vein in wild and domesticated rats.
XII (Reichstein, S): the main component in the wild rat.
XIII and XIV: trace-components in wild and domesticated rats.
Cpd B (Corticosterone): the main components in the domesticated rat.
XVII: occasionally in the domesticated rat.

As is generally known, the hypophysial-adrenocortical system is important in keeping the endocrine system in a state of balance, to changes in which — as has been pointed out in previous detailed studies — the adrenal cortex will respond specifically by a change in the composition of its secretion. Not many investigators pay attention to the variations in the composition of the adrenocortical secretory products, which, according to our findings, are not only important in the control of vegetative and metabolic processes but also affect complex behavioural processes. Analysis of adrenocortical function is complicated by the fact that not only are there wide differences between species but that even within the same species, wide individual qualitative and quantitative variations may be observed. How wide the variations in the same species may be is illustrated by the difference between the corticoid contents of the adrenal venous blood in domesticated and wild rats respectively.

The corticoid spectrum of the blood in the adrenal vein is interesting not only in its quantitative aspect but also because, under certain conditions, the synthesis of such compounds may occur as will have an altered effect on central nervous organization. Considering all these aspects we

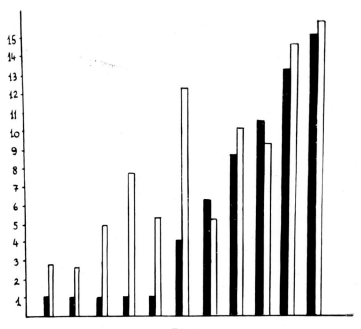

FIG. 2

Relationship between the inhibitory period of alimentary conditioned reflex caused by electric shock on the hind-leg and the corticoid content in the blood of the adrenal vein. Black columns: duration of inhibitory period in dogs. Blank columns: proportion of hydrocortisone and corticosterone.

should like to deal with certain data concerning the endocrine background of temporary connections or that of neuroses resulting from a break in those connections.

An alimentary conditioned reflex was established in dogs in the following manner: on the sound of the positive bell the animal pushed a swing-door to reach the food. Another bell sound served as negative acoustic stimulus. After sixteen daily trials at three-minute intervals, the conditioned reflex, free from intersignal reactions, was established after 300 associations. This was followed by the establishment of the neurosis. Simultaneously with the positive bell sound, on three subsequent occasions, a strong painful electric shock was administered to a hind-leg of the animal and it was observed how many days after the break the normal conditioned reflex would reappear. When the conditioned reflex had been fully re-established, the corticoid composition of the blood in the adrenal vein was examined.

Although the break of the conditioned reflex was brought about under identical conditions, the figure shows considerable variations in the duration of the inhibitory period. A long inhibitory period showed a close relationship to the adrenal secretion, or rather to the ratio of hydrocortisone and corticosterone. In the case of short periods of inhibition the hydrocortisone-corticosterone ratio was low, in prolonged inhibition, however, a high ratio was observed.

The question of whether or not adrenocortical secretion and duration of inhibition can be brought into a direct causal relationship was answered by our next experiment. In those animals which, prior to the break in the temporary connection had been treated with hydrocortisone for a week, not only was the inhibitory period several times longer than that observed in the animals many months before this treatment, but it was also accompanied by marked neurotic signs which were not observed in the untreated animals.

Those experiments would seem to indicate that the neurotic status caused by the break in the conditioned reflex is influenced by the ratio of the two main components secreted by the adrenal cortex, i.e. hydrocortisone and corticosterone. The qualitative difference in the effect of these two compounds on the nervous system has already been pointed out by Woodbury and his co-workers (1949-54). According to their observations hydrocortisone lowers considerably, while corticosterone does not influence, the convulsant threshold of the central nervous system; moreover, corticosterone counteracts the effect of hydrocortisone in this respect. The ratio of the two compounds varies with the individual, and this, according to our investigations, is of importance in the development of the neurotic state. Our experiments on the rat resulted in the same findings, on the basis of which the strain examined by us could be divided into four groups with different inhibitory periods. In each group the adrenocortical activity was found uniform and, what is more, could also be well distinguished quantitatively (Endröczi, Lissák, Telegdy, 1957).

On the basis of those experiments the effect of the adrenocortical hormones with high polarity was interpreted to increase the intensity of the inhibitory processes. After the administration of ACTH, Mirsky, Miller and Stein (1953), observed facilitation of the avoiding conditioned reflex, which would seem to indicate that hypophysial-adrenocortical activity supports the neural adaptation of the defensive mechanism. In later experiments, however, it was observed that ACTH and the corti-coids not only influence exteroceptive inhibitory and neurotic pheno-

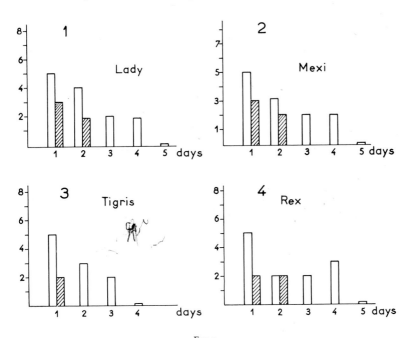

FIG. 3

Fig. 3 shows that in certain cases the administration of ACTH increases inner inhibition considerably. Development of inner inhibition on dogs. The ordinate corresponds to the trials for each day. Blank columns: without treatment with ACTH; Black columns: after administration ACTH for 4 days (2, IU/kg. Zn-Cortrophine, Organon).

mena but also increase the inner inhibition which develops after a positive stimulus administered without reinforcement every day until the conditioned reaction disappeared. On the following days this extinction was repeated until the conditioned stimulus elicited no response. In view of the fact that the times of extinction observed after an interval of several months were practically identical in the same animals, it was possible to check the effect of the treatment with adrenocortical hormones. The figure shows that in certain cases the administration of ACTH increases the inner inhibition considerably (Lissák, Medgyesi, Tényi, Zörényi, 1958).

Several examples illustrate that the conditioned reflex method enables us to study the effect of humoral factors on behaviour under objective conditions. Naturally, within those limits it is not possible to analyse the immediate effect of endocrine factors on the central nervous system. In our experiments we started from the assumption that the brain stem and the subcortical mechanisms — which play a fundamental role in the

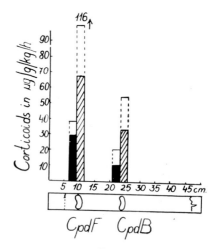

FIG. 4
Effect of brain stem stimulation upon the corticoid level and composition of the blood in the
adrenal vein of cats. The figure shows marked
elevation of hydrocortisone and corticosterone
secretion as a result of 15 minutes' stimulation.

moulding of emotional behaviour — are concerned in the integration of conditioned reflex connections and also in the organization of endocrine mechanisms. There are several data to indicate that humoral factors also influence these structures. Experiments with chronically implanted electrodes and electrocoagulation carried out with a stereotaxic instrument on dogs, cats, rabbits and rats revealed a complex circuit of neural processes, which play an important role in the regulation of endocrine mechanisms.

Without going into the details of the large number of observations I wish to deal only with the main points of our results. It has been observed in experiments with depth electrodes that stimulation of mesencephalic reticular formation, posterior hypothalamus including the mamillary bodies and the intralaminar nuclei of the thalamus activates the pituitary-adrenocortical system. This can be checked directly by estimating the corticoid content of the blood in the adrenal vein.

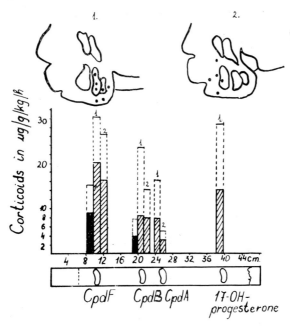

FIG. 5

Effect of stimulation of amygdale and pyriform cortex on dogs. The figure shows appearance of 17-hydroxy-progesterone following repeated stimulation (15 minutes daily for 5-6 days) of medial part of amygdale-pyriform cortex. Stimulation of lateral areas elicited only marked elevation of resting corticoid secretion without the appearance of new secretory product or sexual hyperactivity.

Step-like changes in the behaviour of animals were observed during the stimulation of the above-mentioned structures as a consequence of rising intensity of stimuli. Marked orientation elicited by threshold stimuli was followed by emotional reactions (fear, avoiding-reaction), and further elevation of stimulus intensity induced extreme furious behaviour (O, 5-5, O V, 60-90 H, 3 msec.). After cessation of stimulation the original behaviour returned without delay.

In addition to these short direct activating pathways influencing the pituitary-adrenocortical axis, there is a long circuit, which, with regard to its controlling effect, is of a modifying and inhibitory nature. Repeated stimulation of the medial nuclei of amygdale and pyriform cortex resulted in a change of composition of adrenal secretory products, whose endocrine manifestations were coupled with marked sexual hyperactivity in the post-stimulatory period (lordosis, copulative activity in females and copulative activity, priapism in male cats and dogs).

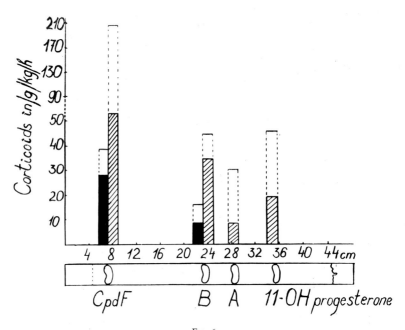

FIG. 6

Shows the appearance of 11-hydroxyprogesterone in the blood of the adrenal vein after stimulation of medial part of amygdale and pyriform cortex of cats.

In female ovariectomized cats we were not able to elicit the above-mentioned endocrine and behavioural changes which permit an insight into the complex mechanism induced by stimulation of area pyriformis.

In contrast to the stimulation of archistriatum (amygdale) which can modify adrenocortical activity and somatic behaviour through the pituitary-gonadal system, we found an inhibitory influence of hippocampal stimulation on the stress mechanism and in some extent on somatic behaviour. Stimulation of the hippocampus in various laboratory animals diminished the resting corticoid level in the blood of the adrenal vein and prevented the adrenocortical hyperactivity elicited by humoral or neurotropic stimuli (Endröczi and Lissák, 1959).

Except for a slight initial orientation-reaction no changes were observed during hippocampal stimulation. This is in agreement with the findings of other authors (Penfield and Jasper, 1953; Akert and Andy, 1953).

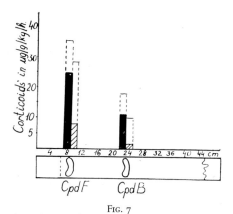

FIG. 7

The influence of hippocampal stimulation (through 15 minutes) on the corticoid content of blood in the adrenal vein of cats. Marked lowering of corticoid level was observed.

It may be asked in what pathways these neuroendocrine processes and behavioural changes are regulated by the archicortex and archistriatum. Without going into the details of relevant literary data we suppose that the chief ascending afferent pathways of archicortex and archistriatum pass through the septum and originate from the tegmental nuclei. Electro-coagulation destruction of the subcallosal area in the septum resulted in a spectrum of corticoids similar to that found after repeated stimulation of the medial part of the pyriform-amygdale complex. Other lesions of the septum touched only the subcallosal grey matter and elicited an opposing effect. In these animals a diminished content of corticoids in the blood of the adrenal vein was found 2-3 weeks after the operation. With regard to the varied localization of these lesions, we suppose it must be due to the chronic irritation of afferent connections related to the hippocampus. Complete destruction of these afferent pathways can abolish the hippo-campal inhibitory influence on the stress mechanism and the control of archistriatum influencing the pituitary-adrenocortical system then comes into prominence. It is an interesting fact that the animals electrocoagulated in the subcallosal area did not show sexual hyperactivity. The pituitary-adrenocortical activity, however, was in accordance with that of animals stimulated in the amygdale-pyriform complex. The lesion of these pathways resulted in a separation of behavioural and endocrine processes integrated by the telencephalon.

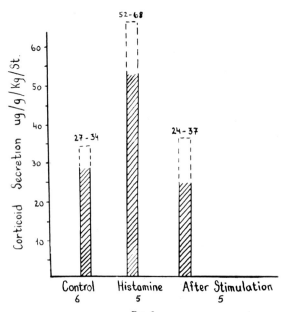

FIG. 8

Prevention of histamine induced adrenocortical hyperfunction, induced by hippocampal stimulation.

Summing up the above-mentioned results, we may say that common subcortical mechanisms take part in neuroendocrine control and in elaborating emotional or sexual behaviour. Naturally, for these complex integrating mechanisms we must take into account the feed-back action of the humoral system as we have demonstrated by the stimulation of area pyriformis (Endröczi, Lissák, Bohus and Kovács, 1959; Lissák, Endröczi, Bohus and Kovács, 1958; Endröczi, 1959).

It may be asked in what way those neuroendocrine controlling mechanisms are concerned with behavioural processes or the development of higher nervous activity. There is no doubt that in the subcortical organization of the conditioned reflex we must assume the participation of the same structures previously considered in connection with neuro-endocrine control. The action of the endocrine factors on the central nervous system cannot be regarded as the result of changes in the general

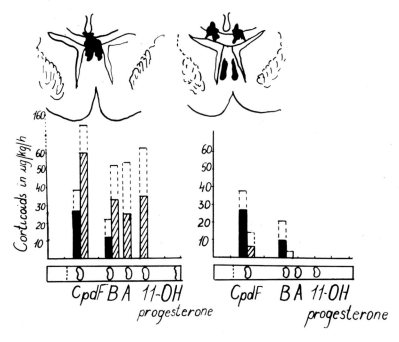

FIG. 9

Influence of septal lesions on the adrenocortical secretion of cats. Part 1 shows a marked elevation of resting corticoid level and appearance of gestagens in the blood of the adrenal vein. Part 2 shows the diminished corticoid level as a result of local irritation of septal pathways.

metabolic processes of the nervous tissue. Obviously, this is a more specific phenomenon. So, according to our observation on the dog, 2-3 minutes after an epileptic attack induced by the stimulation of the temporal lobe, the animal will respond to an alimentary conditioned stimulus in a normal manner, although at the same time a large number of post-convulsive metabolic changes are still taking place. On the basis of earlier experiments, according to which the development of a neurotic state is enhanced by adrenocortical hormones, it cannot be denied that the endocrine action is brought about by the inhibition of a specific temporary connection, which does not affect the whole series of conditioned reflex connections concerned in the shaping of behaviour. Effects of a similar character may be mentioned in connection with the action of sexual steroids, however, at a different level.

We should now like to pass on to some observations which show the influence of the environment on the development of conditioned reflex

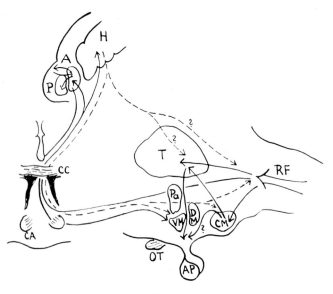

FIG. 10

Structural relationships between formatio reticularis, hypothalamus, septum, archicortex and pyriform area. Thick solid line shows the direct activating mechanism, thin lines correspond to the modifying pathways and dotted lines show the inhibitory pathways.

connections. In recent years we have been studying in conditioned reflex experiments the effect of the stimulation of the reticular formation of the tegmentum on alimentary conditioned reflex activity elaborated previously in the normal and the neurotic states. Experiments on dogs showed that stimulation of the reticular formation, more precisely of the grey matter round the aqueduct of Sylvius, induced a conditioned reflex, even though no positive sound stimulus was applied. This phenomenon resembles a finding by Grastyán and his co-workers (1956, 1959) at our

Institute in experiments on cats after diencephalic stimulation. Furthermore, it was interesting to see what changes in behaviour were elicited in the dogs by stimulation outside the conditioned reflex chamber. The experiments resulted in the surprising observation that in the new situation either a simple orientation reflex or a dominant conditioned reflex

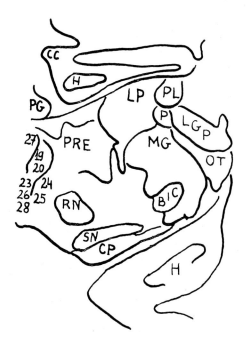

FIG. 11

Schematic illustration of cross-section of dog's brain at the mesencephalic level. Numbers show the points of stimulation eliciting positive conditioned reactions. (BIC: brachium of inferior colliculus; CC: corpus callosum; H: hippocampus; LGP: lateral geniculate body, pars post.; MG: Medial geniculate body; OT: optic tract; P: posterior nucleus and pyramid; PC: post. commissure; PL: pulvinar; PRE: pretectum; RN: red nucleus; SN: substantia nigra.)

corresponding to the new environment appeared. Thus, the animal lay down or sat down or gave its paw to the observer, which corresponded to a conditioned reflex learned before. An interesting result was obtained in the course of these observations by Lissák and Endröczi (1959) when stimulation was carried out in the neurotic state. In animals in which stimulation of the reticular formation elicited the conditioned reflex, a neurotic state was produced by the administration of a painful stimulus simultaneously with the positive sound stimulus. In this state all signs of neurosis (barking, defaecation, urination, escape reaction and fear) were elicited by the sound stimulus. When in this state stimulation was begun the animal calmed down and, as a result of stimulation, the conditioned reaction appeared. However, a few minutes after the cessation of stimulation the signs of neurosis were found to be dominant again. It should be mentioned that the conditioned reflex elicited by stimulation of the reticular formation appeared only if the parameters of stimulation exceeded a certain limit. If the intensity of the stimulus was increased emotional reactions (fear, escape reaction), appeared instead of the orientation or conditioned reflexes.

From the above-described experiments two conclusions may be drawn:

1. The conditioned reflex elicited by stimulation of the diffuse activating system depends on the environment which influences the animal through the specific projection system;

2. The neurotic state is due to a break in the temporary connection between the specific and diffuse projection systems.

From the foregoing it is obvious that, even in the elementary manifestations of behaviour, a whole series of neural and humoral processes are involved. Present-day data do not indicate what neural structures are responsible for the behavioural changes caused by a certain endocrine factor. However, they call attention to the fact that in the development of normal as well as neurotic states, humoral factors play an important role. The individual differences in the endocrine system will probably explain why the establishment and stability of temporary connections elaborated under similar condition as well as neurotic phenomena show those great individual variations.

GROUP DISCUSSION

MORRELL. I wonder if Dr Lissák has considered the role of diurnal variations in hormonal output in evaluating both electrical and behavioural signs of conditioning. One might expect that hormonal influences on behaviour and on conditioning would vary with the time of day at which the experiments were carried out. This might be another variable to be added to those determining individual differences with which much of Dr Lissák's previous work has been concerned.

The data on hypophysial adrenocortical influences are most interesting and bring to mind some unpublished observations from our laboratory which indicate that ACTH, hydrocortisone and progesterone have a marked normalizing effect on the EEG of animals with chronic experimental epilepsy.

LISSÁK. In our laboratory we are doing chronic experiments registering the electrical activity and introducing microcannules for recording the effects of different hormones or humoral factors parallel with the electrical activity.

COVIAN. We have been working for some years in hemidecorticate rats in which changes in the weight of the following glands were observed: adrenals, thyroids, thymus, hypophysis, ovaries and seminal vesicles — Regarding adrenals there was a sexual difference. Did you find any sexual difference by stimulating the hippocampus?

LISSÁK. No. We have not found any sexual difference. There was a complete inhibition of the adreno-cortical activity in both sexes.

GALAMBOS. Over what time duration have you studied the adrenal vein level of hormones? Drs Mason and Nauta at the Walter Reed Laboratories have been stimulating paleocortical structures in monkey and studying adrenal hormone levels in much the same way you have described. They find that stimulation in some structures leads to profound suppression of 17-hydroxycorticosteroid output for a period of days. Similarly if one stimulates a particular paleocortical structure he may find the expected response from stimulation of another structure to be different for many hours or days. Some of these events thus have an astonishingly long time scale. Over what time scale were your measurements made? Could it be that if you had delayed making your measurements for, say, 2 days you might have found even larger responses than you have observed?

LISSÁK. One of the chief difficulties of our present method of experimentation, is that we need to anaesthetize the animal, because we take the blood directly from the adrenal vein. Our experiments were done with stimulation times of between 5 to 40 l. We have not done experiments with such long stimulation. I hope that we can invert our method with the modified London-cannule, and then we will look for the result of longer stimulation on unanaesthetized animals.

PORTER. The initial studies indicating hippocampal inhibition of adrenocortical function were done using the eosinophil count as an index of the release of corticoids. In these experiments, there was no apparent effect of electrical stimulation of the hippocampus upon the level of circulating eosinophils in the blood. However, known stress-evoking stimuli applied during such hippocampal stimulation failed to induce their usual eosinophilic response. Subsequently Dr Mason showed that there is a marked fall in the level of circulating 17-hydroxycorticosterone following hippocampal stimulation which may persist for a day or two. This may be preceded by a slight rise in the level of corticoids, but it is small compared with the response obtained by hypothalamic or amygdala stimulation.

I should like to say how much I enjoyed hearing Dr Lissák's discussion of these rather complex neural-endocrine interrelationships. Considerable attention has been paid in the last few years to the control which the brain exerts over the endocrine system but much less has been directed towards the effects of circulating hormones upon the function of the central nervous system. Dr Feldman working in Dr Magoun's laboratory has shown that the adrenocortical hormones have a rather consistent effect upon the non-specific systems of the brain. Using evoked potential techniques he has found that the response in the reticular formation to sciatic nerve stimulation is greatly augmented after the administration of adrenocortical

X

hormones, whereas that in the classical sensory pathway was essentially unchanged. It seems likely then that the adrenal cortical hormones influence behaviour to a large extent through their effects upon the non-specific brain stem structures.

OLDS. Dr Lissák's work and ours have run parallel but different courses. He observes effects of stimulation on hormones; we observe the effects of hormones on stimulation; he has observed the effects of stimulation on preformed conditioned responses; we have observed the effect of stimulation reinforcement to form conditioned responses. But the same areas are always involved, indicating, I believe, reciprocal relations. For example in the hypothalamic amygdaloid system self-stimulation rate or, that is, the reinforcement of electrical stimulation is stopped by castration and renewed by replacement therapy, with electrodes in some places. With electrodes in quite different places of the same system, self stimulation is stopped by satiation and replaced by hunger. I believe that the places where he provokes sexual behaviour are the places where castration stops self stimulation. Similarly in the other studies of the posterior hypothalamus, the places where his stimulation evoked the preformed alimentary reactions our stimulus seems to us a positive reinforcement, related to food.

LISSÁK. Do you find a sexual difference, with amygdala stimulation between the male and female rats? I think that the main point is to find the structure in C.N.S. where the sexual difference can be made.

ASRATYAN. Though little is known at present may I refer to the question of structural and functional relationships between the reticular formation and automatic centres, especially the hypothalamic structures in the mid-brain. It seems to me that Dr Lissák's results show that a certain role is played by higher sympathetic structures in this region. The basis for such an assumption is that sympathetic structures innervate all endocrine glands and in addition exert a powerful immediate influence on the functions of different systems of the organism, particularly on the activity of the N.S. as was proved by Orbeli and his collaborators. I think that these data may be partially explained as follows: the structures stimulated in Dr Lissák's experiments also activate sympathetic structures of hypothalamus and therefore the changes in the activity of the brain cortex may be partially conditioned by this factor.

LISSÁK. In the tradition of Cannon our first line of investigations was directed to the sympatho-adrenal activity. The neuro-humoral factors in the control of animal behaviour and the manifestations of higher nervous activity in the adaptation of the organism constitute a very complicated mechanism in which sympathetic activity also plays a role.

CONSIDERATIONS ON THE HISTOLOGICAL BASES OF NEUROPHYSIOLOGY[1]

C. Estable

It might have been appropriate to begin this study with a critical evaluation of the three general conceptions of the structure of the nervous system held by different authors: (1) that of radical neuronism, (2) that of absolute reticularism, (3) that of neuronism modified by the assumption of anastomosis between the interstitial cells, this being accepted by the founder of the neuronal doctrine.

The remarkable summary made by Cajal in his last monograph, 'Neuronismo o reticularismo' (Cajal, 1933) and published in German under the title of *Die Neuronslehre*, in 1935, did not convince such supporters of the reticular theory as Boeke, Brauer, Stoer Jr. and others (Boecke, 1949; Bauer, 1953; Stoer, 1957).

Even Bielschowsky, who regards Cajal with reverence and calls him *Der grosse Altmeister*, finds that the basis of the neuronal doctrine and the criticism of the reticular theory made by the great neurohistologist are unconvincing (Bielchowsky, 1955). Gagel calls the said doctrine arrogant (stolzes Gabäude) but recognizes that, despite all the objections to neuronism, Cajal's law of axifugal conduction remains unshaken and intact.

In a report submitted to the International Neurological Congress in Brussels (Estable, 1957), we compared and studied the three conceptions and concluded that the doctrine best adapted to the facts revealed by the electron microscope and by experimental neurohistology is that of neuronism, but without the restriction of interstitial cells, for it is shown that those perceived in anastomosis with the aid of and within the field of the optical microscope are connective neuronoid cells and not actual neurones.

It is unnecessary to reconsider here problems we regard as already solved. It is our thesis that the neuronal doctrine is correct, *as long as it remains open to the possibilities of interneuronal influences that go beyond the laws of insulated conduction and dynamic polarization.*

Microscopic and submicroscopic observations prove that the nervous tissue is devoid of intercellular spaces through which a fluid internal

[1] Supported in part by grants from the Rockefeller Foundation (58122) and the U.S.A.F. Office of Scientific Research (Contract AF49 (638) (585)).

medium might move about. As neurones lack any direct contact with capillaries, except for the ones which they innervate, their nutrition is ensured by *angiogliocytes*. Furthermore, there are neither anastomosis nor

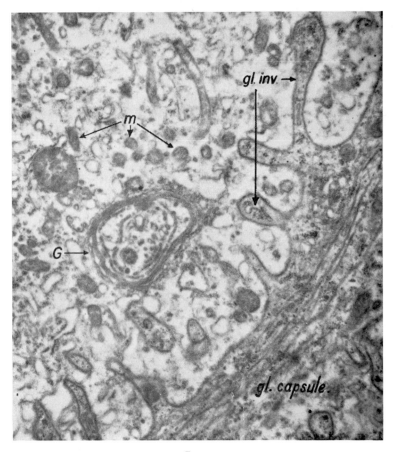

FIG. I

Insulation contact between neurone and glial cell. Electron-micrograph of a nerve cell belonging to a ganglion of *Xyleus fuscipennis* (Brunner) Gistel (orthoptera) gl. inv. shows finger-like processes of glia cells penetrating the perikaryon of a neurone and thus establishing a close 'insulating' contact with the neurone. No fusion or perforation of the cell membrane exists. G. = Golgi components; m = mitochondria; gl. = glial capsule.

loose ends in the nervous textures. All interactions occur by contact between membranes, with or without invaginations, the membranes being either of the same or of different nature. The first requirement, in an orderly and systematic review of the neurohistological bases of neuro-physiology, is to discriminate between the various types of contacts of a neurone. The second requirement must be the functional elucidation of such contacts.

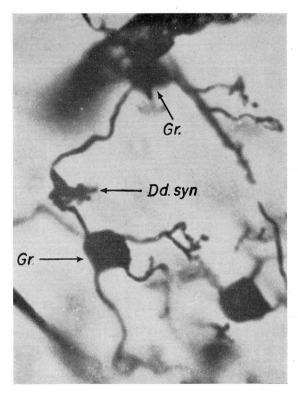

Fig. 2

Dendro-dendritic contact. Photo-micrograph of cerebellum of cat showing a typical dendro-dendritic synapse (Dd. syn.) between grains. Gr. = grains. (Golgi-Cajal method).

Each neurone has two kinds of contacts: (A) insulation and nutrition (neuroglial) contacts; (B) transmission contacts probably having either (1) one-way influence (dynamic polarization), or (2) mutual influence (reversibility), including trophic effects in it, independent of the glio-neuronal ones.

When the contact is neuroglial or neuroschwannian, whether with

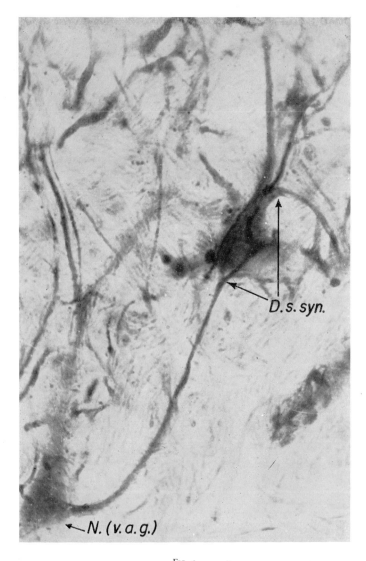

FIG. 3

Dendro-somatic contact. Photo-micrograph of acoustic ventral ganglion of adult cat showing a dendro-somatic synapse (D.s. Syn.). One dendrite of the neurone N. (v.a.g.) is seen ramifying around the body of the other neurone. (Cajal's silver method.)

or without myelin sheaths, it is an insulation contact (Fig. 1): it is not known whether it is possible for a neurone to act upon another neurone, through the slightest and thinnest glial sheaths. According to De Castro's theory, the synapse might comprise three elements, the affector, the effector and the glial layer (De Castro, 1947, 1951); our observations, reported in 1952 and 1953 (one of them in collaboration with Reissig and de Robertis) do not confirm the existence of the glial layer taken for granted by De Castro (Estable, Reissig and De Robertis, 1954).

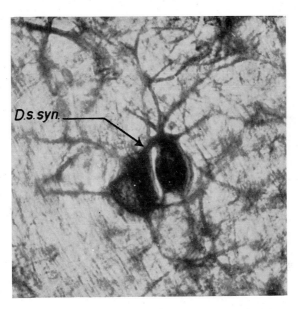

FIG. 4

Dendro-somatic contact. Photo-micrograph of two cells of the reticular formation of the human pons. D.s. syn. shows a dendro-somatic synapse which, because of closeness of contacts, appears as an anastomosis between neurones. (Cajal's silver method.)

Functional contacts occur either between neurones or between neurones and differentiated cells such as receptor cells (neuro-receptive contact), secretory cells or contractile units (neurone-effector contact). Since nerves and particularly axons have been studied with more attention and accuracy than dendrites and the perikaryon — except as to the trophic function of the latter — it is easy to realize why a certain axonism overshadows the doctrinary aspects of the general physiology of the nervous system. For the same reason, this axonism has been biased by the concept that the axon is the exclusive outlet for neuronal influence and acts only by way of its terminal portion, this being a generalization of what occurs at the level of better studied synapses, in the cord and neuromuscular junctions. Numerous electrophysiological facts and the discovery of specific chemical mediators released at the axon endings supported the thesis that neurones

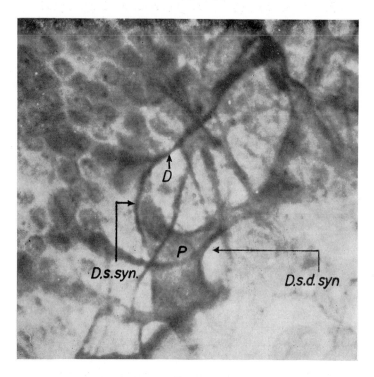

Fig. 5

Dendro-dendritic and dendro-somatic contacts. Photomicrographs of albino rabbit retina demonstrating dendro-dendritic and dendro-somatic synapses between horizontal neurones. D.s.d. syn. shows a dendrite establishing relationship with body and prolongations of neurone D; D.s. syn. is a synapse between the dendrite D. and the soma of neurone P. (Cajal's silver method.)

do act by these terminations. The statement that a neurone acts upon another through its axonic extremities cannot be gainsaid, but one should be careful not to infer that no other possible manner of interneuronal induction can exist.

Numerous investigations in recent years have shown the existence in the C.N.S. of Vertebrates and Invertebrates of the following contacts which are as intimate as the classical ones (axosomatic and axo-dendritic-synapse); contacts between one dendrite and another dendrite (*dendro-*

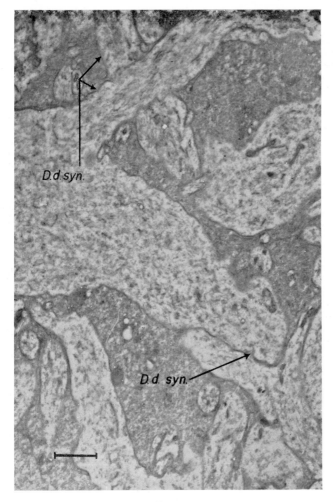

FIG. 6

Dendro-dendritic contact. Electron-micrograph of the albino rabbit retina where the dendro-dendritic contacts between horizontal neurones are shown. D.d. syn. × 15.600.

dendritic synapses) (Figs. 2, 5, 6), between dendrites and perikaryon (*dendro-somatic synapses*) (Fig. 3), between dendrites, soma and dendrites (*dendro-somato-dendritic synapses*) (Figs. 5, 8), between adjacent neuronal

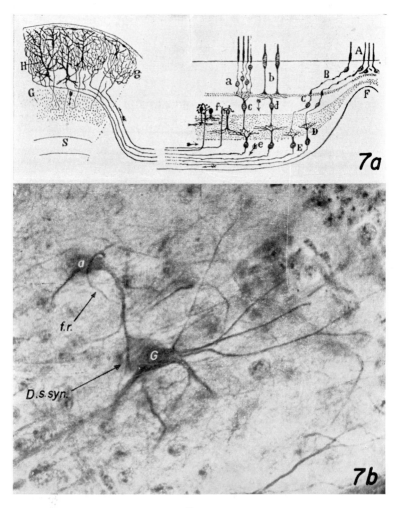

Dendro-somatic contact. (*a*) Schematic drawing reproduced from Fig. 23.4 of Cajal's *Textura del sistema nervioso del hombre y los vertebrados*. In this figure Cajal drew the ending of the retinipetal fibre on an amacrine cell and included a dendro-dendritic connection between amacrines and ganglionic cells. (*b*) This photomicrograph serves to demonstrate the relationship between amacrine cells and ganglionic neurones of retina, as well as the ending on the amacrine of one type of retinipetal fibres. The retinipetal fibre ends on the perikaryon of the amacrine and the dendrite D of this cell surrounds the ganglionic cell body G. The retinipetal amacrine synapse is of the currently accepted axo-somatic type; the amacrine-ganglionic synapse of the dendro-somatic type. (Cajal's silver method.)

bodies (*somato-somatic synapses*) (Fig. 12) and between axons (*axo-axonic synapses*). The latter kind includes three different types: (*a*) parallel contacts; (*b*) cross contacts; (*c*) axon endings on a non-terminal part of another axonic fibre. In the ganglia of Invertebrates, only axodendritic, axo-axonic and dendro-dendritic synapses exist.

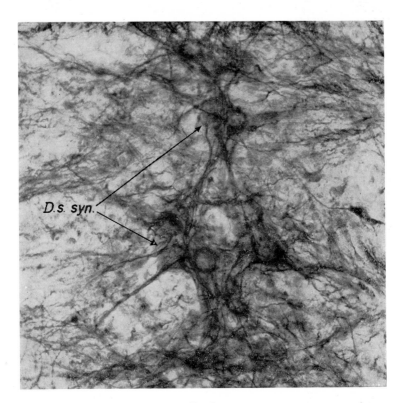

FIG. 8

Dendro-dendritic and dendro-somatic contacts. Micrograph of the human dorsal spinal cord (3 months old embryo); section perpendicular to the plane of symmetry. See disposition of dendrites in the interneuronal fascicles in which many dendro-somatic and dendro-dendritic contacts take place. (Cajal's silver method.)

Close dendro-dendritic, dendro-somatic, dendro-somato-dendritic and somato-somatic contacts having been brought to light in all nervous regions explored and, if at variance with the principle of polarization of the nervous influx, might well explain many until now unexplained physiological processes of the nervous system. Consequently, we find it necessary to complement the notion of synapse with a wider knowledge of interneuronal relations. A more adequate basic notion of *synapse* should not exclude any kind of *close contact between two membranes, of which at least one is of a nervous nature.* If this definition is accepted, different types of synapses can be described: their distinction into synaptic and non-synaptic contacts would be a matter of words rather than of facts.

If we remember that the physiological concept of synapse was worked out with a partial knowledge of the functional contacts between neurones,

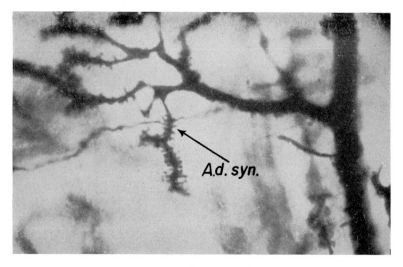

FIG. 9

Axo-dendritic cross contact in cerebellum (I). Photomicrograph of the cerebellum of cat. A.d. syn. shows a typical cross contact between a parallel fibre (horizontal in figure) and a dendrite of a Purkinje cell (vertical in figure) (see also Figs. 10 and 11). (Golgi chromo-argent c methods. Cajal's variance.)

we shall be more willing to admit, within the general theory of synaptic function, the existence of interneuronal influences which form a complement to, and do not contradict, the law of dynamic polarization, and we shall be even more willing to admit that the law of insulated conduction is complemented by a conduction which is neither insulated nor massive.

What the fundamental functional differences between neuronal substructures are is not known. Neither structures nor substructures, similar in all neurones, can account for notable physiological differences. *The synaptic spectrum* (afferent and efferent connections of one neurone) allows

us to obtain a better understanding of the functional specificity of neurones. This concept is clear so far as the afferent and efferent pathways and
their respective centres are concerned.

What are the functional differences and similarities existing among the
manifold contacts between membranes, one of which at least, is nervous?
Is it merely conventional to consider all of them synaptic, or some of

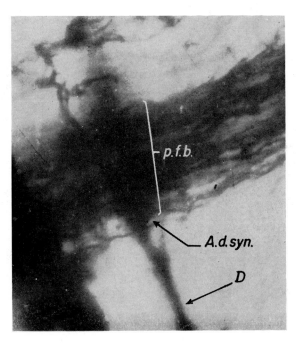

FIG. 10

Axo-dendritic cross contact in cerebellum (II). This figure shows a
tight fascicule of parallel fibres, each of which holds an intimate
cross contact (A.d. syn.) with a (D.) dendrite (as shown in Fig. 9).
The large amount of these axons (p.f.b.) in the plexiform layer is
clearly evident (see also Figs. 9 and 11).

them synaptic but not the others? Is there a factual or conceptual issue at
stake or is it simply a matter of words?

No structural characteristic (except contiguity and discontinuity) is
typical of synapses:

(a) The existence of mitochondria having been rediscovered in the
axonal terminal *pars* of certain synapses (in 1897 Held had pointed them
out in the cerebellar glomeruli under the name of neurosomes), the

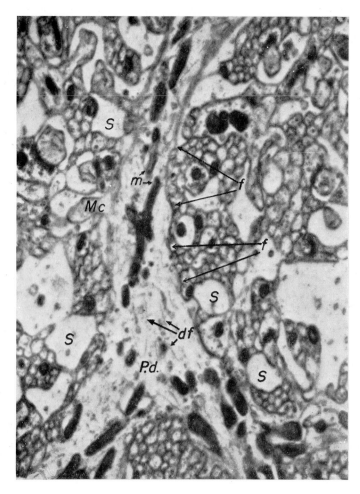

FIG. 11

Axo–dendritic cross contacts in cerebellum (III). Low magnification electron-
micrograph of rat cerebellum (molecular layer) showing the relationship of a
Purkinje dendrite — p d — with crossing fibres f. These are more or less of equal
diameter and are supposed to be parallel fibres. Palay interprets them as derivating
from Fañanas' cells (Palay, 1958). The clear spaces may correspond to glial fibres
— s. At Mc a micro–club or dendrite thorn can be depicted — M — Mitochondria,
d.f. dendrite filaments × 22.000. (See also Figs. 9 and 10.)

investigations of Bartelmez, Bartelmez and Hoerr Bodian (1937-40) led to the definition of a synapse as a contact between membranes with mitochondria subjacent in the pre-synaptic region (Bartelmez, 1915; Bartelmez and Hoerr, 1933; Bodian, 1937; Bodian, 1942; Held, 1897).

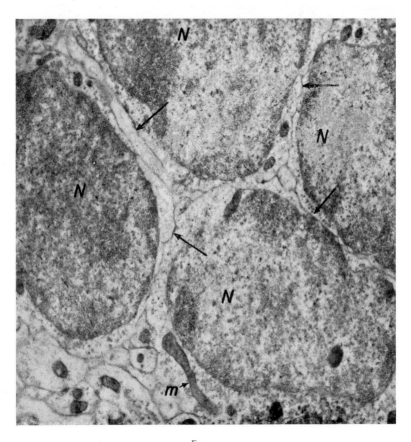

FIG. 12

Somato-somatic contacts. Low magnification electronmicrograph of the rat cerebellum granular layer showing the intimate somato-somatic relationship between grains. N. Nuclei, m = mitochondria × 16.000.

This definition, based on structure only, is not satisfactory, as it excludes incontrovertible synaptic types.

(b) The microvesicles having been discovered by Sjöestrand — and by him called 'granules' — in the synapse of cones and rods with the dendrites of bipolars, a series of investigations was initiated (De Robertis and Bennett, 1955; Palade, 1954; Palay, 1954; Palay, 1956; Palay, 1958; Robertson, 1956; Sjöestrand, 1954). with the purpose of determining whether the only and general characteristic of the synapse was the presence of the

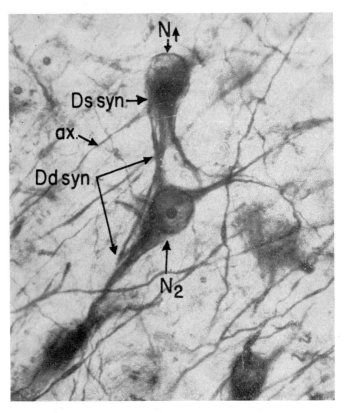

FIG. 13

Dendro-somatic and dendro-dendritic contacts. N_1 and N_2 neurones of the human common oculo-motor nucleus showing dendro-somatic synapses Ds. syn. and dendro-dendritic synapses Dd syn.; ax, axon which goes to form the common oculo-motor nerve. These are no intercalar neurones or recurrent axonic collaterals; the connections between the neurones of this nucleus are only dendro-somatic, dendro-dendritic and dendro-somato-dendritic.

above-mentioned microvesicles. Some neurophysiologists, such as Del Castillo and Katz, and more recently Eccles, have attempted to correlate the so-called synaptic microvesicles with certain physiological observations (Del Castillo and Katz, 1955; Del Castillo and Katz, 1956; Eccles, 1957):

in effect Del Castillo and Katz refer to the possibility of accounting for the miniature end-plate potentials which they discovered by regarding them as due to discharges of acetylcholine supposedly pre-existent in the

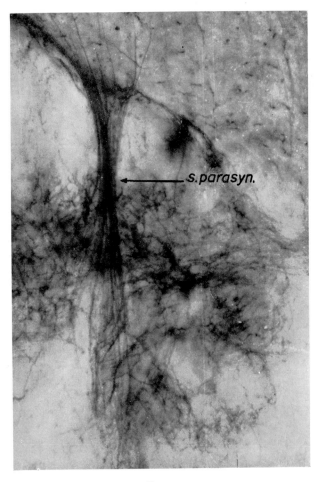

FIG. 14

Parasynapses (I) — Parasynapsis fibres — s. parasyn — in the cervical cord of an adult man. Tight bundle of closely placed axons.

microvesicles. However, there is no evidence that acetylcholine ions gather as microvesicles, and even less evidence that the microvesicles, which exist in certain synaptic types, are 'quanta' of the chemical mediator.

Y

The term 'synaptic microvesicles' does not imply more than calling the mitochondria of the motor plates and the synapses that contain them synaptic mitochondria. It must be borne in mind that these substructures do not exist at all synaptic levels and that, furthermore, there are synapses without special groupings of mitochondria or microvesicles.

It is our opinion that a synapse is characterized by *discontinuity* and by *contiguity*; the contact between membranes is very close, but lacks fusion,

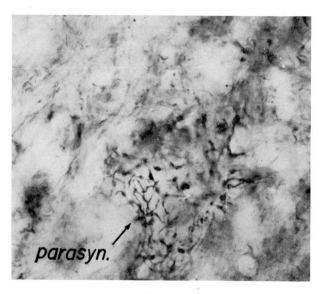

FIG. 15

Parasynapses (II) — Neurone of the cervical spinal cord of adult man showing the terminal fibres of the perisomatic axonic plexus contacting with each other.

the space between them being measured in Ångströms. Nevertheless, the contact of membranes alone is not a sufficient criterion of a synapse; the nature of those membranes must also be considered because one of them at least must be nervous; excluding neuroglial contacts which are probably insulation contacts only and therefore not synaptic.

Therefore, we propose the following concept: *A synapse is an anatomically close and functionally operant contact between membranes, one of them, at least, being of a nervous nature.*

Many questions remain unanswered: What is the functional difference between the synapses (*a*) with microvesicles and mitochondria only in the pre-synaptic *pars*; (*b*) with microvesicles and only mitochondria in the post-synaptic *pars*; (*c*) with microvesicles only in the pre-synaptic

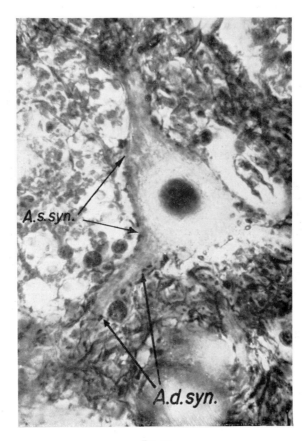

Fig. 16

Parasynapses (III) — Axo-somatic synapses — A.S. syn. — of a motor neurone of the cervical spinal cord. Adult man. This shows the terminations of fibres depicted in Figs. 14 and 15.

pars; (*d*) with microvesicles and mitochondria only in the pre-synaptic *pars*; (*e*) with only microvesicles in the post-synaptic *pars*; (*f*) without mitochondria or microvesicles, either in the pre-synaptic or in the post-synaptic *pars*?

In the ganglionic nervous system of Invertebrates, the rule is that the perikaryon *never takes part* in the synapses, as it is located in the periphery of the ganglion, so tightly enclosed in a glial capsule (Fig. 1) that it even shows deep membranous glial invaginations in the neurone. In addition, neither dendrites nor axons reach the cellular body; all these extensions, together with the glial ramifications towards the centre of the ganglion, constitute a dense, delicate and heterogeneous plexus improperly named 'neuropile'. In the nervous centre of Invertebrates there are only three synaptic types to be seen: (*a*) axo-dendritic; (*b*) axo-axonic and (*c*) dendro-dendritic synapses. In contrast, in the nervous system of vertebrates the perikaryon takes part in the synapse, with the only exception of the neurones of the sensitive ganglia along the neuraxis and the mesencephalic nucleus of the trigeminal nerve which, by the morphology of its neurones, is equivalent to a spinal ganglion.

In the nervous system of Vertebrates, intimate contacts occur in the three morphological regions of a neurone; perikaryon, dendrites and axon. These contacts are *homologous* or *heterologous* according to whether the membranes are in contact with the same or different morphological elements. The homologous contacts are (*a*) dendro-dendritic, (*b*) axo-axonic, (*c*) somato-somatic. The heterologous contacts are (*a*) axo-dendritic, (*b*) axo-somatic, (*c*) dendro-somatic, (*d*) dendro-somato-dendritic, those of neurones with sensory or receptor cells and of neurones with effectors, namely secretory cells (crinocytes), contractile fibres (myo-fibres), etc. The contact, either homologous or heterologous may be terminal, *de passage* ('de trayecto') or mixed.

In addition to the types of synapses described above we call para-synapses the axo-axonic, pre-terminal contacts between axons having different origins but converging upon a common post-synaptic element (Figs. 14, 15, 16). Parasynapses are as frequent as synapses; they enable a slender pre-terminal fibre to influence not only its own terminal synapse, but also the synapse of all the pre-terminal fibres with which it has a parasynaptic contact. Parasynapses may guarantee synaptic security.

In the next part of our study we wish to emphasize the importance of dendro-dendritic, somato-somatic, dendro-somatic, dendro-somato-dendritic and axo-dendritic cross synapses. The frequency of dendro-dendritic contacts in the cerebellar glomeruli, in the horizontal neurones of the retina, in the sympathetic ganglia, in the medulla, in the pons and in general in all the nervous centres explored is such that there is no place for the interpretation that these contacts are aberrant, exceptional or even physiologically meaningless.

Dendro-dendritic and dendro-somatic synapses can be described under many types: (1) with special modelling of the expansions in contact (glomeruli, Fig. 2; chalices, Fig. 3); (2) with dendrites not configuring a special articular contact splicing or connection device (Figs. 5, 6); (3) with an equivalent interchange of dendrites between the neurones united by the synapse (Fig. 4); (4) with an unequal participation of dendritic endings in the dendro-dendrito-somatic reciprocal synapses (Fig. 13); (5) with the dendritic participation of one neurone and the perikaryon and the dendrite of another neurone, that is, dendro-somato-dendritic synapse in one way and dendro-dendritic in the opposite way; (6) with the dendritic participation of a neurone and the perikaryon of another or other neurones (dendro-somatic synapse); (7) of parallel dendritic contacts; (8) of cross-dendritic contacts; (9) complex synapses, dendro and axo-dendritic at the same time.

Functionally there are two kinds of direct interneuronal relations: (a) one way, in which pre- and post-synaptic *pars* of different nature constitute polarized and irreversible synapses; (b) reciprocal, in which pre- and post-synaptic *pars* of similar nature constitute reversible synapses. The former are exclusively axo-somatic and axo-dendritic; in such cases, the neurone whose axon models the pre-synaptic *pars* controls the other. Prevalence of reciprocity may be suggested for the dendro-dendritic and dendro-somatic synapses and the somato-somatic and the axo-axonic contacts. Such useful reciprocity might be for isofunctional neurones of a same centre, which lack recurrent collaterals, to correlate themselves directly by means of dendro-dendritic, dendro-somatic and somato-somatic contacts (Figs. 2, 12). Thus the small neurones improperly called cerebellar grains, are reciprocally connected only by means of particularly modelled dendro-dendritic branches and close somatic contacts, but never interconnected through axonic collaterals. On the contrary, Purkinje neurones are reciprocally connected by means of double polarized pathways (axo-somatic and axo-dendritic synapses at the end of recurrent collaterals) never by means of dendritic interchange. The rule we have formulated does not exclude the co-existence, in certain centres, of the two kinds of neuronal connections of reciprocal action.

Cajal did not commit himself when considering the existence of dendro-dendritic synapses: dealing with the neuronal connections of the sympathetic ganglia (Cajal, 1891) he wisely and cautiously wrote: 'It is difficult to reject the possibility of the passage of a nervous impulse, either between non-medullated contiguous nerve fibres or between juxtapositional protoplasmic branches. To exclude this possibility would mean giving the theory of dynamic polarization too absolute a character' (Cajal, 1897). However, it happened that the synapses established by Cajal belonged to the polarization type; this explains why, a short time after, he stated the neuronal doctrine and formulated the law of dynamic polarization. Thus the Spanish author admitted the possibility of dendritic contacts and interinfluences, but later hesitated and disregarded them. However, he never denied their existence expressly or categorically (Cajal, 1891, Cajal, 1897; Cajal, 1897). Cajal's conviction was that, if dendro-dendritic connections existed at all, they were rare. He came to think that only occasionally did real dendritic interchanges exist. He therefore denied them an outstanding physiological significance as he believed them to be exceptional. In the second volume of his *Histologie du Systeme Nerveux*, when dealing with the sympathetic ganglia, there is a passage which, once more, shows his uncertainty (Cajal, 1911).

Our present aim is to emphasize the existence of neuronal interrelations through dendritic contacts, and their probable functional significance. Our observations, first upon the cerebellar dendritic glomeruli and retina and then upon many other centres, have shown the presence of (1) a certain closeness, not contact, of dendrites of two or more neurones which held contacts with axonal expansions (axo-dendritic synapses); (2) direct dendritic contact in closely grouped microglomeruli, formed exclusively by dendrites belonging to different neurones; (3) axo-dendro-dendritic glomeruli in which there exists a double type of close contacts; (a) axo-dendritic and (b) dendro-dendritic.

The cerebellar glomeruli are characterized by the diversity of their synapses: (1) according to the origin of the mossy fibres; (2) according to their composition, (a) axo-dendritic, with the exclusive participation of the mossy fibres, (b) with the exclusive participation of the slender collaterals of Golgi type II neurones, (c) with the double participation of rose-shaped endings of the mossy fibres and of the collaterals of the above-mentioned Golgi II neurones, plus glial fibres with a special terminal device, (d) with only the presence of dendrites of the grains; (3) according to quantitative variations besides qualitative ones; there are glomeruli of very different sizes, as well as glomeruli gathering in more or less numerous groups in which all the aforesaid synapses can be discovered, and also close somato-somatic contacts between grains (Fig. 12).

All cerebellar grains possess complex synaptic spectra: dendro-dendritic and somato-somatic in their connections with other grains; axo-dendritic in their connections with vestibular, spinal, bulbar, protuberantial and Golgi II neurones; axo-somatic in connection with this last neurone; in addition, the important cross synapses, with all the neurones whose dendrites are spread within the plexiform layer.

In an article, published in 1923, we called *mossy-cellular corticocerebellar system*, a complex of neurones directly and functionally linked, on the one hand, by means of axo-dendritic cross synapses, on the other hand, through synapses of the mossy fibres with the dendrites of the grains (glomeruli). The afferent *synaptic spectrum* of each Purkinje neurones is integrated by a small number of axo-somatic, axo-dendritic and axo-axonic synapses of pre-synaptic terminal *pars*, while the *cross axo-dendritic synapses are astonishingly numerous*, existing in the proportion of about *one million to each Purkinje neurone* (Estable, 1923).

In the spreading and beautiful dendritic arborescence, the slender axons of the grains, in parallel fibres, establish as many intimate contacts with Purkinje neurones as verticils are formed by the *microclubs* or *thorns* bristling on their surface (Figs. 9, 10).

It may be deemed fantastic to talk about *one million* cross synapses for each Purkinje neurone. There are, however, many techniques that confirm this figure. Furthermore, the axon of each single grain contacts *all* the Purkinje neurones in a cerebellar convolution, succeeding one another in the same direction.

Three more significant facts prove the importance of the axo-dendritic cross synapses: (1) they are not missing in any centre examined; (2) the said synaptic type is the only one in the afferent spectrum of Golgi short axon cerebellar neurones; (3) the cross synapses are remarkably prevalent over all the other synaptic types in the brain cortex. A single axon, among billions in the plexiform layer of the brain cortex, relates itself by means of cross synapses, with the neurones that, from the different layers, send their dendrites up to the pial surface.

In a re-examination of the neuro-histological bases of neuro-physiology, it is particularly important to study the *retina*.

Most heterogeneous ramifications occur in the outer-plexiform layer: (*a*) thin filaments branch off the feet of the cones and rods and in them no dendritic penetration has been noticed, as happens in the widest part of the feet; (*b*) dendrites of variable thickness, of two origins, from bipolar neurones and from horizontal neurones (there is no evidence that all the dendritic ramifications of the bipolar invaginate in the pedal widening of cones and rods); (*c*) axonic ramifications of the horizontal neurones and perhaps of the stellate neurones of the inner granular layer, besides certain ascending axons similar to the retinopetal fibres of the inner plexiform layer; (d) very slender transversal filaments rising from Müller's fibrocells. It is in this extremely dense plexus of heterogeneous nature that Dr Villegas (in her unpublished observations) has discovered the existence, in fish, of a sort of neuropile similar to that appearing in other centres (Villegas, personal communication); we have also observed it in the retina of mammals.

Dendro-dendritic, dendro-somatic and dendro-somato-dendritic synapses are most abundant in the retina and appear clearly in the horizontal neurones and in the amacrine cells, for instance. The synaptic spectrum of the horizontal neurones shows a prevalence of the dendro-dendritic, dendro-somatic and dendro-somato-dendritic synapses (Figs. 5, 6). However, not all horizontal neurones have the same synaptic spectrum.

The influence of some areas or foci over other areas or foci of the same retina has remained unexplained. However, we may take into account that there exist transversal contacts (a) of the filiform pedal expansions of cones and rods; (b) of the dendritic tufts of bipolars; of the dendrites of ganglionic neurones, whose axons very rarely give off collaterals.

Despite these connections, the intrinsic retinal associations are mainly due to dendritic connections of two kinds of neurones, the horizontal and the amacrine cells (Fig. 7a).

Cajal discovered the retinopetal fibres which form synapses with the body of the amacrine cells (Fig. 7b). Two more categories of retinopetal fibres are to be considered; those establishing direct synapses with the dendrites of ganglionic cells; others, more dispersed, with their collaterals spreading out, covering the field of the dendrites of these neurones and the amacrine cells (this last category was confirmed by Poliak (Poliak, 1941)).

According to Cajal, the centrifugal optic fibres are undivided in all their intra-retinal course, and end in a little bunch of short collaterals on the soma of an amacrine cell. *The above-mentioned retinopetal fibres would lack functional meaning (a) if the conduction in the dendrites of the amacrine cells were not 'antidromic', (b) if the dendro-dendritic contacts were not functional, or if the excitatory state did not propagate through it — in other words, if it did not constitute a real synapse.*

We have already mentioned three kinds of retinopetal fibres. There are fibres too, which, following the same course, end in the capillaries of the retina which may be taken for visual fibres if their vascular ending is not noticed.

As concerns the neuro-muscular junctions, let us mention a type of synapse in which the ending of the axon or its collaterals go into the myofibres, as far as the nucleus. We have given it the name of *axokaryo-lemmal synapse*.

By calling it axokaryolemmal we do not imply that the sarcolemma is not interposed between the axolemma and the karyolemma, but refer simply to the direction of the growth cone towards the nuclei of the motor plate and the apposition of the synaptic membranes to the nuclear membrane.

The question of the trophic function of the synapse may also be mentioned. When synapses are already modelled, the neuronal trophism depends so much on them, that the neurones may atrophy and die if the former are suppressed. When speaking of the polarization of the nervous impulse, no account is given, besides the new synaptic types we have described, of the trophic function of the synapse, whose direction is the same as the direction of the propagation of the excitatory state — oscillo-graphically registrable — or the reverse. By means of the trophic function of the synapse we might account for the existence, within it, of mito-chondria and perhaps microvesicles, and, as far as the neuromuscular synapse is concerned, for the abundance of nuclei in the sole.

To sum up our thesis:

It is unanimously recognized that in the normal activity of the neurones, the excitatory or inhibitory state starts from dendrites or somata, the excitation coming from a sensorial cell or another neurone. It is also known that the dendrite is *receptor* and *conductor*, while the axon is *trans-mitter* and *effector*, whether it ends on another neurone, on a myofibre or in a crinocyte.

The rigidity of our conceptions concerning inter-neuronal relationship contrasts with the functional plasticity of the nervous system, particularly well illustrated in the study of learning. The new contacts we have described extend this way of thinking. Dendrites, perikaryon and axon may normally fulfil the three mentioned functions; that of reception, conduction and effection. The axon would be receptor and conductor in the cone of origin (axon hillock) receptor, conductor and effector in the parasynapses; and effector in the axo-dendritic and axo-somatic synapses. The dendrites would be receptor, conductor and effector in the dendro-dendritic synapses (perhaps in the dendro-somatic synapses also), and only receptor and conductor in the axo-dendritic and axo-somatic synapses. The soma or perikaryon would be receptor, conductor and effector in the somato-somatic synapses (perhaps in the dendro-somatic synapses also).

SUMMARY

The purpose of this chapter is to insist upon the frequent presence, in many species and centres, of interneuronal contacts that (i) are as close as classically accepted synapses and (ii) exhibit the same variable submicroscopic structure. These contacts are *dendro-dendritic, dendro-somatic, somato-somatic* and *axo-axonic*. No valid morphological reason enables us to deny that these contacts are operant and, at the same time, to accept that regular axo-somatic or axo-dendritic contacts are functional. Two formulae sum up all the facts:

I. Pre- and post-synaptic *pars* of a different nature are functionally polarization synapses;

II. Pre- and post-synaptic *pars* of a similar nature are reversibility synapses, which means functional alternance between the receptor and the effector *pars*.

No submicroscopic entity (chondrioma, microvesicules, etc.) is typical of a functional contact. Only discontinuity and contiguity are always present.

GROUP DISCUSSION

Eccles. I am very interested, Professor Estable, in all that wealth of histological material that you have just shown us; it gives rise to a great many problems of a functional kind. There are certain physiological reactions which we have not yet fully understood and I think that some of these new kinds of synaptic contacts will be important in trying to develop explanations. I refer particularly to the dorsal root potential, where depolarization of the presynaptic fibres is conducted electronically out along the dorsal roots which may also carry the Toennies reflex discharge. The nervous system does not always work in the forward running direction, it can work backwards too and these synaptic contacts which you have mentioned give us possibilities of making explanations of such phenomena. But the point I want to make in a general way is that the electron-microscopists are showing us what a highly specific and very intimate structural relationship there is across the synaptic junction; yet I still feel that the essential criterion of a synapse is: does it work functionally? I believe that even a contact with 200 Å separation over a large area is insufficient to give any functional meaning or performance. There must be a process of specific chemical secretion on the one hand and specific chemical receptivity on the other, linking across that junction to give a functional performance to a synapse. I wonder whether we should define a synapse as a structure with a close histological relationship; or whether we should try to restrict the word to close relationships that do work functionally as far as the generation or inhibition of impulses is concerned.

Estable. Morphologically one must accept contiguity plus discontinuity as the basic criteria. Thereafter, we must be careful in discarding as non-functional contacts that are anatomically similar to those known to be functional. As mentioned in the text, we have indirect evidence that in some instances they do operate (e.g. in cerebellar cortex or retina, in invertebrate ganglia).

ECCLES. I readily agree that at the crossing of two fibres there can be a functional contact providing there is chemical secretion from one and chemical receptivity on the other.

ESTABLE. The electronmicroscope has not shown in cross-synapsis microvesicules or mitochondria. That does not necessarily mean that a chemical mediator is absent but, at the same time, it certainly does not suggest its presence: but, can we be too dogmatic as to the necessity of a chemical mediator for contacts to be operant?

GERARD. One of the main points in your summary was the relation of reciprocal or irreciprocal conduction to symmetrical or asymmetrical contacts. This is, of course, fully consistent with many physiological and model experiments and it may interest the group to recall first the experiments Lillie did with his iron wire model. He covered most of the wire with a glass tube, leaving two ends sticking out for different lengths. He excited the model by scratching one of these. The large one would cause the small one to respond, by currents through the wire and the medium; but the small one would not excite the large one. This is asymmetry in structure and in action. With equal sizes, this was always symmetrical activation.

A more direct biological experiment was done by compressing the parallel fibres at the middle of the sartorius muscle with a block of wood. If the muscle was squeezed symmetrically conduction block occurred from either end to the other; but if it was squeezed asymmetrically it was possible to get conduction in one direction but not in the other. Of course, this fits with the emergence of activity from the cell body into the axon and not always in the reverse direction, and many other experiments in the central nervous system at least seem to fit well with the kind of valve phenomena that have been demonstrated peripherally, such as the bouncing back of impulses from a cut cord. So that all in these cases Dr Estable's thesis is supported; and it seems to me it would be hard to justify any dogmatic statement that irreciprocal transmission can occur only when specific neurohumours are present; they could hardly be present in most of these instances.

ECCLES. I don't wish to be on record as dogmatically asserting that electrical transmission does not occur in the vertebrate nervous system, but I will go on record as saying that no experiments so far have shown that it does occur in an undamaged C.N.S. Possibly the dorsal root potential and the Toennies reflex of Vertebrates are due to electrical synaptic transmission. Elsewhere, when we have studied cells intracellularly and investigated them in detail, we would surely have recognized electrical transmission of the type described by Furshpan and Potter with some crustacean synapses. There is no evidence whatsoever that such electrical transmission does occur in the cells that have been investigated in this way.

FESSARD. I wish Dr Estable would clear up a point that has considerably troubled me. I mean his statement that the same neurone could send an axon branch to the radial fibres and another to the circular fibres of the iris; that is to say, it could elicit mydriasis and myosis at the same time. This sounds rather strange to me.

ESTABLE. Yes.

FESSARD. Have you good proof for that? It is certainly very disturbing.

ESTABLE. One can see in the iris of the penguin, whose iris is striated, axons which gives a collateral branch to the sphincter fibre and a collateral branch to radiatory fibres. I will provide you with the reprint of the paper I published on this subject.

ECCLES. I am very interested in the physiological significance of these histological findings. If the same nerve fibres do innervate these two different muscles of the iris they might still do it by the same chemical transmitter which could work in opposite ways on two muscles. It depends on the operation of the respective receptive sites on the muscles. For example we know that acetyl-choline can work on cardiac muscle inhibiting it and on skeletal muscle exciting it. We certainly need a functional and pharmacological investigation of neurones concerned in transmission to these iris muscles.

THE EFFECTS OF USE AND DISUSE ON SYNAPTIC FUNCTION

J. C. ECCLES

It must be an ultimate objective of both psychology and neurology to account for all the phenomena of learning and conditioning by the known properties of the patterned arrangements of nerve cells that occur in the central nervous system. We are still far from this goal; but I hope to show that the functional connections between nerve cells exhibit properties which correspond to the 'plasticity' that has long been the basis of one explanation of learning and conditioning, which may be called the trace theory of memory (cf. Gomulicki, 1953).

It is important at the outset to state that it will be assumed throughout that the synaptic connections between nerve cells are the only functional connections of any significance. These synapses are of two types, excitatory and inhibitory, the former type tending to make nerve cells discharge impulses, the other to suppress this discharge. There is now convincing evidence that in vertebrate synapses each type operates through specific chemical transmitter substances that in turn change the ionic permeability of the postsynaptic membrane and so bring about the excitatory or inhibitory action on the postsynaptic cell (Fatt, 1954; Eccles, 1957).

The alternative postulate is that, at least in part, interaction between neurones is caused by the flow of electric currents generated by active neurones. There is at present no experimental evidence that such interaction has any functional significance for the nervous system of vertebrates. With the ordinary random relationships of neuronal discharges the flow of electric currents between neurones is far too small to have any significant effect, and this is even the case for experiments using the unphysiological procedure of large synchronous volleys. For example Wall (1958) found that the large electrical fields generated by the antidromic activation of the motoneurones in the ventral horn caused no detectable change in the excitability of the afferent fibres synapsing on those motoneurones. However, under abnormal conditions of synchronization of large assemblages of nerve cells, the propagation of electrical waves suggests that there is direct electrical interaction between nerve cells (cf. Libet and Gerard, 1941) and Jasper has produced further evidence

335

that changes in excitability of neurones may be produced by the electrical fields generated by activity of adjacent neurones.

But even such conditions of electrical field interaction would merely have the effect of distorting the finely patterned influences that arise through synaptic action. There seems to be no alternative to the highly selective synaptic actions when attempting to account for the enormous wealth of information that is preserved during transmission through the central nervous system. It may be stated as a general rule, that the number of nerve fibres in any pathway is related to the wealth of information that has to be transmitted along that pathway. It seems inconceivable, for example, that all the fine grain of information transmitted by the optic nerve and tract could be dissipated in the mere generation of electric fields in the occipital cortex. In contrast it should be mentioned that some synapses in crustacea do operate by electrical transmission (Furshpan and Potter, 1959). But such a mechanism depends on special permeability and rectification properties of the apposed synaptic membranes, and is thus just as unique and localized in its action as is chemical synaptic transmission. Moreover such an electrical synaptic mechanism would have been detected if it were operative at any of the vertebrate central synapses that have been systematically investigated.

Two explanations, not mutually exclusive, have been proposed for the neurological basis of learning and conditioning (Hebb, 1949; Eccles, 1953; Young, 1951; Thorpe, 1956). According to one, learning is a dynamic process, due to continuously circulating patterns of impulses in closed neural chains (Rashevsky, 1938; Young, 1938; Hilgard and Marquis, 1940; Householder and Landahl, 1945). As a consequence, the reaction of the nervous system to any particular sensory input is changed in a unique way so long as this circulation of impulses continues. Conceivably, this explanation could apply at brief intervals — seconds or minutes — after some initial conditioning stimulus. It certainly cannot account for memories or conditioned behaviours that survive either a virtual suppression of all activity in the cerebral cortex — e.g. deep anaesthesia, concussion, coma, extreme cold, or even deep sleep — or the converse, convulsive seizures of the whole cortex. The alternative explanation is that activation of synapses increases their efficacy by some enduring change in their fine structure (Tanzi, 1893; Cajal, 1911; Hebb, 1949; Toennies, 1949; Eccles, 1953; Jung, 1953; McIntyre, 1953; Thorpe, 1956). We may assume that a given sensory input results in a uniquely patterned activation of central neurones, and, according to this explanation, a subsequent re-presentation of this input would tend to be channelled along the same pathways because of the increased efficacy of the synaptic actions exerted by all those neurones activated initially. There would thus be a further reinforcement of the synapses responsible for the unique pattern of activation and response, with consequently a more effective channelling; and so on, cumulatively, for each successive application of that sensory input. Necessarily, the postulated changes in synaptic efficacy must be of very long duration — days or weeks. There is no way in which relatively brief durations of synaptic change for each synapse of a serial arrangement can sum to give a more prolonged change.

In designing experiments to test for this postulated effect of use in causing a prolonged increase in synaptic efficacy, it was initially much simpler to test for the opposite effect — namely regression of synaptic function with disuse. The very recent investigations on excess use will be considered subsequently. Furthermore, the postulated effects of use in increasing synaptic efficacy and of disuse in depressing it can be investigated most rigorously with monosynaptic pathways, i.e. where there is only one synapse interpolated between the known input and the observed output.

The extreme complexity of neuronal connections in the higher levels of the central nervous system has, hitherto, prevented critical testing of the various hypotheses proposed for the neural mechanism of learning. As a consequence there has been an unrestricted growth of speculation, as may be seen by reference to Gomulicki's comprehensive review (1953). It is an initial postulate of the present investigation that synpases at spinal level share in some measure the synaptic property that is responsible for the phenomena of learning at higher levels of the nervous system.

The experiments have been restricted to the monosynaptic activation of motoneurones by impulses in the large afferent fibres from the annulo-spiral endings of muscle spindles. The advantage of this system is that the input is under precise control and the output can be measured as the size of the reflex spike response. This size is directly related to the number of motoneurones discharging, and hence to the efficacy of their mono-synaptic activation. As a routine procedure before all the monosynaptic testing described below, the spinal cord was transected in the upper lumbar or lower thoracic region so as to eliminate the possibility of reflex inequality caused by a tonic asymmetric discharge of suprasegmental origin. In addition to the investigation of the responses evoked by single afferent volleys, there has regularly been an investigation into the potentiation of these responses that follows a high frequency tetanus of the afferent pathway usually at about 400/sec., the so-called post-tetanic potentiation.

Post-tetanic potentiation will be specially considered later, when discussing the kind of enduring changes that can occur in synapses.

EFFECTS OF DISUSE ON SYNAPTIC FUNCTION

Prolonged and total disuse of monosynaptic reflex arcs has been secured by severing the dorsal roots just distal to their ganglia, thus retaining functional continuity between parent cell bodies and the central projections within the spinal cord of their silenced fibres (Eccles and McIntyre, 1953). Several weeks after this operation, the reflex responses evoked by stimulation of these disused dorsal roots have been compared with the control responses on the other side. Volleys in the disused dorsal roots were always much less effective in evoking monosynaptic reflexes into either flexor or extensor muscles. Post-tetanic potentiation was, however, effective in restoring much of the lost function, but it was still far below the potentiated control response (Fig. 1 A, B).

The question at once arises: to what extent can reflex deficiency on the operated side be attributed to changes in the presynaptic pathways other than those due to mere absence of the normal impulse barrage? Histological examination revealed two possible causes, but there was good evidence that only part of the discrepancy could be so explained. For example, there was in some experiments destruction of some dorsal root fibres either at the initial operation, or subsequently by scarring. Again, there was some shrinkage of the dorsal root fibres (about 10 per cent), which is probably attributable to diminished turgor consequent on the regenerative outgrowth from the ganglion cells into the peripheral stump (Gutmann and Sanders, 1943; Sanders and Whitteridge, 1946; Szentagothai and Rajkovits, 1955). It is not possible conclusively to refute the suggestion that the synaptic knobs shrink more than the main axonal shafts from which they spring, the large depression of their reflex excitatory power being thus explained.

However, subsequent to a prolonged repetitive stimulation these disused synapses exhibited a behaviour which was not simply explicable by depressed function and which indicated that the disused synapses had acquired special properties. In particular the post-tetanic potentiation of monosynaptic reflexes evoked from the disused roots ran an abnormal time course: maximum potentiation of the reflex occurred later than in the normal control; the decline from this maximum occurred several times more slowly; and, most significantly, the reflexes did not return to the initial size, as with normal post-tetanic potentiation, but exhibited a residual potentiation that persisted for hours (Eccles and McIntyre, 1953).

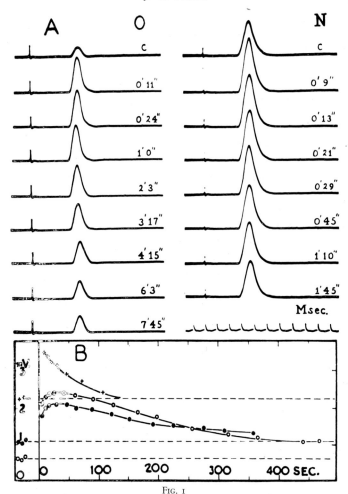

FIG. 1

A. Monosynaptic reflex discharges evoked by stimulating the appropriate dorsal roots and recorded in gastrocnemius nerves 40 days after extraganglionic operative section of the dorsal roots stimulated in the O records. The topmost record (C) of O and N series is the reflex response before any tetanic conditioning. The remaining series show potentiated responses after a conditioning tetanus of 6000 volleys at 400 a second. The figures above each response show the time, in minutes and seconds, at which it was elicited after cessation of the conditioning tetanus. Amplification same for O (operated) and N (normal) responses.

B. The crosses plot the N observations of Fig. 1A and the open circles the O observations partly shown in Fig. 1A. The vertical line marks the end of the conditioning tetanus, points plotted to left being preliminary controls (c of Fig. 1A). Horizontal broken lines give respective mean control heights of reflex spikes. The filled circles are also O responses some 2 hours later than the open circles. Note that initial control level is same as level of residual potentiation surviving at end of first potentiation (open circles to right). Abscissae, time after end of conditioning tetanus (Eccles and McIntyre (1953) with permission of the *Journal of Physiology*).

Further conditioning tetani led to additional, but smaller, residual potentiations, showing that a cumulative process was involved (Fig. 2). The gradual changes which unavoidably occur in the reflex excitability of a preparation (attributable for example to changes in anaesthesia and in

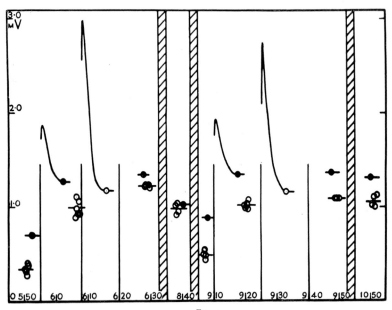

FIG. 2

Plotting of post-tetanic potentiation and residual potential as in Fig. 1B, but on a much reduced time-scale, note time-scale in hours and minutes on abscissae. Ordinates give sizes of monosynaptic reflex spike in millivolts. L_7 and S_1 dorsal roots severed extraganglionically 38 days previously. The open circles about 5.50 p.m. give reflex spikes in biceps-semitendinosus nerve in response to single volleys in the combined L_7 and S_1 dorsal roots, and the filled circle the mean control spike in gastrocnemius nerve, these same conventions being used throughout. The first tetanic conditioning (7500 volleys at 500 per second) is shown by vertical line at 5.55 p.m., and the five other tetanic conditionings (of similar severity) are likewise indicated. The post-tetanic potentiation curves are shown for gastrocnemius and biceps-semitendinosus after first and second conditioning respectively in each of the test series. As indicated by abscissae the vertical shaded columns mark lapses of 2 hours, 20 minutes and 55 minutes respectively, and during the second an injection of nembutal was given (Eccles and McIntyre, 1953, with permission of the *Journal of Physiology*).

circulation) prevented any precise determination of the time constant of decay of residual potentiation, but probably half decay takes at least 3 hours, which would make it about 160 times slower than the decay rate for the normal post-tetanic potentiation after a similar conditioning tetanus.

In addition to this investigation on the effect of dorsal root section on the monosynaptic activation of motoneurones, the monosynaptic action exerted by the same afferent fibres on the cells of Clarke's column has also been investigated (McIntyre, 1953). There, too, synaptic depression was observed, but it was less readily demonstrated, since that synaptic relay has such a high safety factor.

It has been concluded from these investigations on monosynaptic action that disuse had reduced synaptic efficacy and also rendered synapses more susceptible to the adjuvant effects of activity. In particular the very prolonged potentiation of disused synapses provided a response that appeared to be particularly relevant to the problem of the synaptic mechanism of learning (Eccles and McIntyre, 1953; Eccles, 1953; McIntyre 1953).

Comparable results have been obtained using intracellular recording of the excitatory postsynaptic potentials induced monosynaptically in motoneurones (Eccles, Krnjevic and Miledi, 1959). Total synaptic disuse was effected by severing the nerve to one muscle of a synergic group, the other one or more nerves serving to give control synaptic activation. This procedure also introduced the complications of chromatolysis of the dorsal root ganglion cells and shrinkage of the afferent fibres, though these effects would be much less than when the afferent fibres were severed just distal to the dorsal root ganglion cells. There was as well chromatolysis of those motoneurones with severed axons. However, there was the advantage of allowing a comparison to be made between the intracellularly recorded potentials (the excitatory postsynaptic potentials) evoked monosynaptically in the same motoneurone by normal afferent pathways and those changed by operation. No additional complication was introduced by the chromatolysis of motoneurones, for the responses of chromatolysed motoneurones to monosynaptic stimulation via normal and severed afferent pathways exhibited the same differences as were found with normal motoneurones. It was found that, relative to the control afferent path, the monosynaptic excitatory action of the disused path to the same motoneurone was reduced to about half after 2-4 weeks of the total inactivity. Furthermore, it was increased relatively much more by post-tetanic potentiation, so that the normal size was largely regained during the maximum potentiation that occurred a few seconds after an intense conditioning activation (Fig. 3). Thereafter, the synaptic potential progressively declined, but often a small residual potentiation occurred for as long as 20 minutes, while, after application of a similar conditioning stimulation to a control nerve, the post-tetanic potentiation usually passed over into a prolonged phase of depression (Fig. 4).

Besides thus confirming the earlier work in which synpatic function was tested by monosynaptic reflexes, this investigation of synaptic potentials allowed quantitative estimates to be made of the depression of synaptic function and established that this depression was restricted to the inactivated synapses on a motoneurone. It also revealed the time course

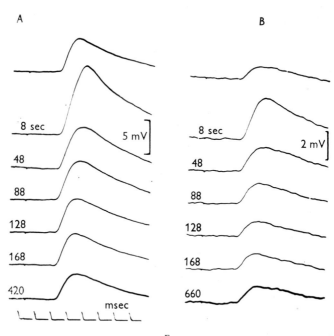

FIG. 3

Intracellular EPSPs evoked in a flexor hallucis longus motoneurone by maximum Group ia volleys in flexor hallucis longus nerve (A), and in flexor digitorum longus nerve (B) which had been severed 15 days previously. Top records in A and B were taken before the conditioning tetanus 400 c/s for 10 seconds, and the subsequent records at the indicated intervals after the tetanus. Same time scale throughout, but different voltage scales for the two series as indicated. (Eccles, Krnjevic and Miledi, 1959, with permission of the *Journal of Physiology*).

of the onset of depressed function; it was negligible at 6 days, but by 10 days after the nerve section the depression was already about half developed and by 13 days it was fully developed.

As we have seen, the operative procedures for inducing disuse by sectioning the afferent fibres have the disadvantage that a small shrinkage of the dorsal root fibres occurs (Eccles and McIntyre, 1953; Szentagothai and Rajkovits, 1955). Conceivably, this shrinkage may extend right to the synaptic terminals and account for at least part of the depressed synaptic efficacy. It is important, therefore, to attempt by other procedures to produce a profound diminution of the discharge of impulses from the annulospiral endings of the muscle spindles belonging to the muscles under test. Several experimental procedures, either alone or in suitable combination, have been tried (Westerman, unpublished). For example, tenotomy or splinting the limbs in plaster should considerably reduce the activation of the stretch receptors of a muscle, although it must be realized that annulospiral endings are extremely sensitive to mechanical stimuli and certainly could not be silenced by these procedures (Matthews,

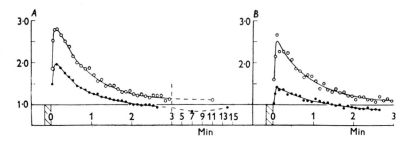

FIG. 4

Plots of the time courses of post-tetanic potentiations of EPSPs produced by a conditioning tetanus of 10 seconds at 400 c/s, as indicated by the hatched columns. Specimen records are shown in Fig. 3. In Fig. 4A the heights of the EPSPs are plotted relative to the control height, open circles being for the operatively severed pathway (FDL) and filled circles for the control pathway (FHL). Fig. 4B as for Fig. 4A, but for maximum slopes of the rising phases of the EPSPs. Note that in Fig. 4A the time scale is greatly shortened after 3 minutes (reproduced from Eccles, Krnjevic and Miledi (1959), with permission of the *Journal of Physiology*).

1933; Hunt and Kuffler, 1951; Kobayashi, Oshima and Tasaki, 1952; Granit, 1955). In attempting further to reduce their discharge, the appropriate ventral roots have been severed so as to suppress the activation of muscle spindles by impulses in the gamma efferent fibres (Leksell, 1945; Kuffler, Hunt and Quilliam, 1951; Hunt, 1951; Granit, 1955). In all these experiments, controls were provided by the symmetrical reflex paths of the other limb, where a suitable dummy operation had been performed; and, in addition, the degree of post-tetanic potentiation gave a sensitive measure of relatively small changes in synaptic efficacy. Finally tests for the symmetry of monosynaptic reflexes were made with afferent paths which were unrelated to those being investigated, e.g. the knee flexor pathways when the operative procedures were restricted to muscles acting on the ankle and digits.

No significant change has been observed in the reflexes from such relatively disused pathways, there being sometimes a small depression relative to the control, but more often an increase, as has been independently reported by Beranek and Hnik (1959); furthermore, no significant changes were observed in the post-tetanically potentiated reflexes. A possible interpretation of these negative results is that the various procedures were ineffective in silencing the discharges from annulospiral endings, there being sufficient residual activity to prevent the depression of function that occurs with the complete disuse of severed pathways. Alternatively, it could be maintained that disuse does not cause depression of synaptic function. The depression observed in the synaptic action of severed pathways (Eccles and McIntyre, 1953; Eccles *et al.*, 1959) would then be attributed entirely to the shrinkage of the primary afferent fibres as a consequence of the chromatolytic changes of the dorsal root ganglion cells. This dilemma can be resolved only if complete inactivity of monosynaptic synapses can be secured without severing the primary afferent fibres. An attempt to do this by a prolonged cold block of peripheral nerve has so far failed on account of technical difficulties. This indecisive situation for the disuse experiments makes the investigations of excess use of crucial significance. However, it must be remembered that, on posttetanic potentiation, the synapses belonging to severed afferent pathways exhibited a slower recovery and a residual potentiation, which has suggested that the depression arose specifically from disuse, rather than from a mere shrinkage due to chromatolysis (cf. Eccles and McIntyre, 1953; Eccles *et al.*, 1959).

EFFECTS OF EXCESSIVE USE ON SYNAPTIC FUNCTION

If, as seems likely, prolonged disuse has a deleterious effect on the potency of synapses, it follows that normal use has a sustaining function; and it is further likely that excess use leads to an enduring enhancement of synaptic function above the normal level, which provides of course the synaptic basis for the suggested explanation of learning. There is, however, in the literature very little experimental data on the effect of excess use. The most significant findings were the increased monosynaptic reflexes, relative to the control side, in the segment immediately rostral to those with severed dorsal roots (Eccles and McIntyre, 1953). This asymmetry may reasonably be attributed to the development of some compensatory reaction to the operative disability, particularly in extensor muscles that had been partly deafferented. The simplest explanation of this compensa-

tion is that the partial deafferentation had thrown more mechanical stress
on the remaining stretch-receptors of the weight-supporting extensors,
with the consequence that there was increased activity of their synapses,

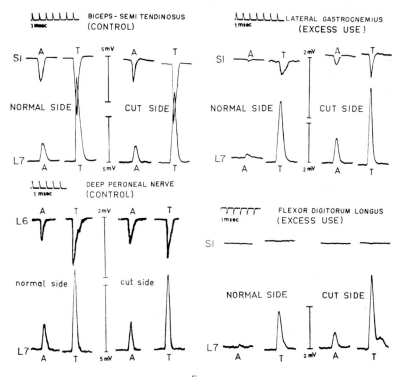

FIG. 5

Monosynaptic reflexes recorded in the L_6, L_7 or S_1 ventral roots in response to maximum
group Ia afferent volleys from the four muscles as specified. On the left side of the figure, the
biceps-semitendinosus and deep peroneal volleys served to control the symmetry of the
preparation, there being approximate equality of the reflexes into comparable ventral roots
on the two sides. Each of the reflexes is shown before (A) and during maximum post-tetanic
potentiation (T). On the right side of the figure the monosynaptic reflexes from the two other
muscles are similarly assembled, but each of these muscles on the cut side had been subjected
to excess use as described in the text. Note that, in response to a lateral gastrocnemius afferent
volley, both A and T reflexes are larger into the S_1 and L_7 ventral roots on the cut side. This is
also seen for the flexor digitorum longus reflex into L_7 (reproduced by permission of R. M.
Eccles and Westerman (1959) and of the Editors of *Nature*).

the excess use giving an enhanced function. Of less significance in relation
to learning is the finding that functionally over-loaded muscles have
hypertrophied nerve fibres (Edds, 1950).

In investigating further the effect of increased use, it was important to design experiments in which central synapses were subjected to an excessive discharge from annulospiral endings and in which adequate controls were available. For example, tenotomy or nerve section for all but one muscle of a synergic group was employed in order to place excessive stress on the remaining muscle, and as a consequence it was presumed that there was excess discharge from its stretch receptors. An appropriate dummy operation was performed on the other side. By having the animals walk in a treadmill for 20 to 30 minutes every day, it was ensured that there were ample opportunities for this muscle to be subjected to the excessive stress. After some weeks the monosynaptic reflex evoked by an afferent volley in this muscle nerve was always larger (Fig. 5), the main increase being 50 per cent or more in the fourteen animals so far investigated, than for the corresponding afferent volley on the other side (Eccles and Westerman, 1959). Control observations were made for reflexes from nerves to synergic groups of muscles with undisturbed innervation on both sides (Fig. 5). Since there was no significant asymmetry for such monosynaptic reflexes, it can be concluded that the excess use had resulted in enhanced function. A slightly smaller relative increase was also observed during post-tetanic potentiation of the reflexes evoked by afferent volleys from the stressed muscle and its symmetrical control. Thus we have here the most convincing demonstration yet provided that excess synaptic use over several weeks results in enhanced synaptic function. Experiments are in progress to test for the effects of excess synaptic use on other synaptic systems, e.g. for the activation of Renshaw cells from the ventral spinocerebellar tract by impulses from Golgi tendon organs.

DISCUSSION

It will be appreciated that these investigations are restricted to simple synaptic systems in the spinal cord. If, as now seems likely, excess activation gives a prolonged increase in synaptic efficacy, experimental investigation could be extended to the more complex polysynaptic reflex pathways and, finally, to pathways in the higher levels of the nervous system. Since investigations of learning and of conditioned reflexes have been carried out almost exclusively with these higher levels of the central nervous system, it has generally been thought that synapses at these levels had properties of 'plasticity' that were not shared by synapses in the spinal cord. Experimental evidence is now against any such qualitative distinction between the synapses of higher and lower levels of the central nervous system. However, there may be quantitative differences, the synapses at higher levels being more sensitive, relatively few impulses producing large and prolonged plastic changes.

On account of the very long time scale of the synaptic changes produced by use and disuse it would be extremely difficult to discover their nature by direct investigation. However, in many respects post-tetanic potentiation resembles the effect of excess usage, and it can be readily investigated.

With post-tetanic potentiation of neuromuscular transmission a highly significant finding is that the potentiation is paralleled by an increased frequency of the quantal emission of transmitter substance from the presynaptic endings (Brooks, 1956; Liley, 1956; Hubbard, 1959), as signalled by an increased frequency of the miniature endplate potentials (cf. Katz, 1958). Electron microscopy has revealed a dense assemblage of the so-called synaptic vesicles in the presynaptic terminal, and it is highly probable that the quantal emission of transmitter substance is due to the bursting of these vesicles into the synaptic cleft. Hence, an attractive explanation is available for post-tetanic potentiation: the repetitive presynaptic stimulation causes the mobilization of these synaptic vesicles close to the synaptic surface (cf. Palay, 1956), so that not only is their rate of spontaneous emission increased, but there is also an increase in the number emitted by a presynaptic impulse (cf. Eccles, 1957).

However, there is also good experimental support for an alternative explanation of post-tetanic potentiation: the repetitive presynaptic stimulation is followed by an increased membrane potential of the presynaptic terminals, with the consequence that the presynaptic impulse is increased in size and so synaptic transmission is potentiated (Lloyd, 1949; Eccles and Krnjevic, 1959 a, b).

Presumably both of these postulated processes are concerned in post-tetanic potentiation, but it seems most improbable that an increased membrane potential of presynaptic fibres could account for the very prolonged increase that excess use causes in synaptic efficacy, or even for the several hours of the residual potentiation displayed by disused synapses. On the other hand it seems a likely possibility that changes in the population or disposition of synaptic vesicles could account at least in part for very prolonged changes in synaptic efficacy.

Besides these physiological investigations into the effects of excess use, it is important to see whether electron microscopy reveals any structrual changes in the presynaptic terminals. Already it has been reported that, after several days of disuse brought about by complete darkness, there is diminution in the size of the synaptic vesicles at the synapses made by both rods and cones with the bipolar cells in the rabbit's retina (De Robertis and Franchi, 1956). A further observation was that, after 1 day of darkness, the synaptic vesicles tended to accumulate close to the presynaptic membrane (De Robertis and Franchi, 1956). It would be of interest to see whether, correspondingly, there is a phase of increased synaptic efficacy after comparable periods of disuse brought about by nerve section or by the other procedures outlined above.

The ultimate aim of these investigations on plasticity would be to correlate the observed structural and functional changes and to understand the way these changes are brought about by excess use and by disuse. Inevitably, such a programme involves questions relating to the control of the manufacture of transmitter substance and to its availability for release by the activated synapses. It would seem more probable that use gives increased function by enhancing the manufacture and availability of transmitter substance, although enlargement of synaptic knobs and even the sprouting of new knobs are alternative devices for securing an increased synaptic action (Konorski, 1948, 1949; Hebb, 1949; Young, 1951; Eccles, 1953). Evidently, further investigation by electron microscopy is of the greatest significance in providing evidence discriminating between these alternatives.

Perhaps the most unsatisfactory feature of the attempt to explain the phenomena of learning and conditioning by the demonstrated changes in synaptic efficacy is that long periods of excess use or disuse are required in order to produce a detectable synaptic change. In contrast, conditioned reflexes are established by relatively few presentations, and unique events may be remembered for a life time. A probable explanation is that prolonged reverberatory activity occurs in the neuronal network, so that a single event may activate each synaptic link in a spatio-temporal pattern thousands of times within a few seconds. Hebb (1949) makes a related postulate when he supposes that 'a reverberatory trace might co-operate with the structural change, and carry the memory until the growth change is made'. A similar suggestion has been made by Gerard (1949). Furthermore we may suppose that the plastic changes in synapses are susceptible to reinforcement by the replaying of the specific spatio-temporal patterns each time that the memory is recalled. It is also possible that synaptic plasticity may be much more highly developed in the cerebral cortex.

GROUP DISCUSSION

HEBB. Was I correct in understanding that the excessively used synapses were the ones that showed the most post-tetanic potentiation? Isn't this just the opposite of what one would expect? They are the ones which have been exposed the most to the PTP, in their use, and we would now expect them to react the least.

ECCLES. The figures I showed you did indicate something like that. But you must remember that these are reflexes in ventral roots and therefore quite unreliable as samples of relative synaptic potency. I would not place any reliance on these results with reflexes as measures of PTPs. Comparisons of relative sizes of PTPs should be made by excitatory post-synaptic potentials.

KONORSKI. The view put forward by Dr Eccles is that while excessive use of given synaptic connections increases their efficiency, the disuse produces opposite effects, namely regression of synaptic function. This would be the simplest physiological model of memorizing and forgetting. I held the same view several years ago (cf. Konorski, *Conditioned Reflexes and Neuron Organization*, Cambridge, 1948), in spite of the fact that a great body of evidence seemed to contradict it. Indeed, we know very well that firmly established conditioned reflexes, as well as our own memory traces remain intact even after many years of 'disuse'. But I couldn't conceive any other mechanism of the phenomenon of forgetting than the atrophy of long disused synaptic connections.

The realization of the great role played by dynamic memory traces in establishing conditioned connections allows me now to overcome this difficulty and to interpret the phenomenon of forgetting from quite a different point of view. As I pointed out in my paper the chief feature of recent memory traces, as contrasted with old memory traces, is that they are based on some dynamic mechanism consisting probably in the transient activation of reverberating chains of neurones. The ultimate fate of these traces depends on the effects they produce: either they give rise to appropriate morphological connections and are then transformed into stable memory traces, or in certain conditions, as shown in my paper, they have no chance to do so and are then totally obliterated. In such a case we have to do with the phenomenon of forgetting.

According to these considerations one is inclined to suppose that synaptic connections once formed, whether in ontogenesis or as a result of special training, do not atrophy by disuse, and that forgetting would probably concern only dynamic, but not stable, memory traces.

The recent results obtained by Dr Eccles seem to confirm my assumption. Excessive use of the given spinal pathways led in his experiments to the increase of efficacy of the synaptic connections involved, a fact analogous to the formation of stable memory traces. But the disuse of the given pathways did not lead to the deterioration of the reflex because of the stability of synaptic connections.

ECCLES. Now, of course, you cannot know what is going on in the dog's brain! He may not have been subjected to the experimental training procedures for long periods, but he may be 'reliving' them in some experiential way. I realize that the higher level synapses are probably quantitatively different from the lower ones, but we can show qualitatively that the lower ones have the kind of properties you would postulate as the basis of memory in the higher ones. I would not like to comment on these disuse experiments until we have done a further series of experiments. We must block the afferent pathways without cutting them, which is probably a matter of improving our technique of cold blockage.

GERARD. This is the same kind of answer I gave to Dr Grastyan's point, that one single stimulus could leave a trace. Secondly there are many experiments to show that memories mostly (not always) do not remain unchanged over time; pictures are recalled with directional distortions.

ESTABLE. I would like to make some comments: in the first place, the problems of learning are usually approached taking for granted that the neurone is static, that it is not modified during life. Neurones are like trees that modify their finer branches, for example, the neurones in the skin, which change the direction of their terminal branch when the cell they were ennervating dies and has peeled off. I wonder whether something like this might not occur in the C.N.S. and provide an explanation for the changes in its performance. In the second place, small changes in synapses may give large functional changes — for example in certain diseases and after some drugs — and in the embryo, where the synapses are identical to those of the adult but do not yet operate.

ECCLES. I do agree that there are all sorts of growth processes going on in synapses. Anyone who has seen the cine-photography of Pomerat in tissue culture will agree that the outgrowing nerve terminal is vividly alive. It is growing, retracting and moving all the time.

OLDS. Dr Eccles has shown us a good example of a long run adaptive change through use, and with such few examples of this type, it cannot be ignored. However, I wish to sound a word of warning to my fellow psychologists. What Dr Eccles has suggested is that by sending an impulse down an axon we cause more transmitters to be available in the terminal, and note that this is true whether or not the impulse 'crosses' the synapse. This data is often used by theorists to show how the successful synapse gains power at the expense of the unsuccessful synapse — and my impression is that both these synapses are equally reinforced and that makes this mechanism unusable for theories like those of Hebb, Konorski and Gerard.

ECCLES. I think Dr Olds had misunderstood the problem. I am not interested in whether a particular synapse generated an impulse or not. All I am interested in showing is that every time you activate synapses they become more efficacious. Every time a signal comes in from some receptor it fires more cells and thus operates along channels that become progressively more powerful with more impulses in parallel, more convergence on the next stage and so on ... Thus there is a progressively more effective channelling. Now this would only occur if the 'unsuccessful' synapses shared in the potentiation.

ASRATYAN. I want to congratulate Dr Eccles on his valuable new data which is a great contribution to neurophysiology. I want to draw attention to the extreme importance of new data provided by Dr Eccles concerning the stable results of excessive use and disuse of synaptic apparatus on their structural and functional properties. Recently we have obtained in our laboratory some facts which are in full accordance with this data, although it was not obtained under such precise conditions. We worked with dogs whose spinal cord has been transected at the level of the lower thoracic segments. If the animals are strictly limited in their mobility it leads to an evident muscular atrophy of these limbs and to a lessening of their reflex activity. If, however, these limbs are systematically treated by special training, or massage or mechanical and electrical stimulation, etc., this results in a good trophic state of the limbs and a very rich and lively reflex activity of the caudal part of the transected spinal cord. The precise data obtained by Dr Eccles has importance, not only in general neurophysiology, or in the problem of recovery of functions in injured organisms, but also in the problem of learning. It seems to me that although morphological and functional changes of synaptic apparatus as a result of their excessive use is a common property of all the nervous structures, nevertheless, these changes lead to an elaboration of conditioned reflex only in the neural structures of the higher parts of the nervous system, at least, in high developed organisms. I cannot agree with Shurrager and other authors that the spinal cord is also able to elaborate conditioned reflexes. In any case, Dr Eccles's data shows that achievements in general neurology are and will ever remain a source of investigations of brain processes and especially conditioned reflex research.

ECCLES. Thank you Dr Asratyan. We have very similar experiments going on in Canberra. Dr Kozak from Dr Konorski's laboratory is investigating the changed reflex pattern that occurs in spinalized kittens. There is here evidence that you have new patterns developing in the C.N.S. under changed conditions.

FESSARD. Would you consider that an inhibition at the synapse would produce the same effect as a long disuse?

ECCLES. If the cell does not fire impulses, the synapses that it makes with other cells would be disused.

FESSARD. Disuse obtained by inhibition would be produced in a more natural way than by section of the nerve. Would it be possible technically to make such an experiment?

ECCLES. I have thought about such a possibility but I do not know how to do it experimentally.

SEGUNDO. Dr Eccles, when you compared the 'used' side with the 'non-used' side, tetanic potentiation was greater in the latter (as measured in reference to a 100 per cent value of the initial monosynaptic response amplitude). How did you select stimulus intensity in order to make effects on both sides comparable

ECCLES. With all experiments there was maximum stimulation of group I fibres and in addition the series were repeated in alternate sequences many times.

HEBB. I would like to make a comment on a different track. There is some evidence which needs to be considered when you discuss learning over a long-range period. Chimpanzees put into darkness after being raised in light to the age of 6 months suffer complete forgetting of visual responses when brought out again. The clinical ophthalmologist tells us that if a child becomes blind before the age of 2 years he will be indistinguishable from the congenitally blind at maturity. If he becomes blind at the age of 4 years he will never be like the congenitally blind, he is like the person who has had vision until maturity. In other words there can be well established visual learning but it will not last if it is not maintained for 4 or 5 years. Once thoroughly established, it will last for good.

ANOKHIN. In our laboratory we are now doing experiments which have a direct correlation with yours. We have changed muscles from extensor or flexor position. For 3 or 5 weeks these cats presented abnormal movements — but after 1 year they moved in the normal fashion. The electromyographical analysis shows that the muscles performed their new function. But after spinalization these muscles reverted to their old function. Do you think this process occurs only at spinal levels or is capable of being produced by the whole nervous system?

ECCLES. I am very interested in the experiments of Dr Anokhin. We have done, too, transplantation of muscles but have tested only the monosynaptic pathways in the spinal animal. We find that the original pathways have been retained, and there has been little or no resculpturing of the spinal connections. McIntyre has done similar experiments. There is general agreement that at the spinal level there is little or no change of connections after muscle transplantation.

LA FACILITATION DE POST-ACTIVATION COMME FACTEUR DE PLASTICITÉ DANS L'ÉTABLISSEMENT DES LIAISONS TEMPORAIRES

A. Fessard et Th. Szabo

Quelle que soit la complexité d'organisation des structures nerveuses et des opérations qui sont impliquées dans tout comportement d'apprentissage, il est certain que la question se pose à tout esprit analytique de la nature des processus élémentaires impliqués dans ce comportement. Que se passe-t-il dans les neurones d'un cerveau qui modifie de façon durable ses potentialités réactionnelles sous l'influence d'actions extérieures appropriées, dont la plus simple est la répétition monotone d'un stimulus, dont une autre est l'association, plusieurs fois présentée, d'un stimulus avec un autre, comme dans la technique du conditionnement pavlovien? Que se passe-t-il enfin au niveau moléculaire, puisque, en fin de compte, cette modification durable de l'excitabilité neuronique doit avoir un support dans les ultra-structures actives de la cellule nerveuse?

Sans doute, ces questions étant supposées résolues, il ne s'ensuivrait pas que nous serions capables d'expliquer entièrement l'apparition d'un phénomène d' 'habituation', ou la formation de nouvelles liaisons fonctionnelles, car les caractéristiques de l'*organisation* des appareils de la vie de relation mis en jeu — centre nerveux, récepteurs et effecteurs — jouent évidemment un rôle essentiel dans la réalisation des manifestations globales du comportement d'apprentissage, comme de tout comportement. Il n'en reste pas moins vrai que les composantes primaires de ces manifestations doivent être recherchées au niveau du neurone d'abord et, dans la mesure où les techniques le permettent, au niveau moléculaire, pour tenter finalement d'établir les bases physico-chimiques de la conservation des traces d'activité.

Ces réflexions ne sont pas nouvelles, mais tandis qu'elles sont restées longtemps purement spéculatives, elles peuvent aujourd'hui par suite du progrès considérable des microtechniques, trouver des prolongements efficaces dans des approches expérimentales diverses: recherche à l'aide de la microscopie électronique de changements dans les ultra-structures dus à l'activité répétée, application des techniques cytochimiques modernes à la mise en évidence des modifications moléculaires d'origine métabolique, exploration de l'état électrique cellulaire à l'aide de microélectrodes ultra-fines. A vrai dire, ces techniques raffinées ont encore peu servi à l'étude des traces cellulaires durables d'activité. Mais ces techniques existant, et se perfectionnant sans cesse, on peut prévoir que des données nouvelles ne tarderont pas à étayer certaines hypothèses anciennes, à en faire écarter d'autres, et peut-être à suggérer des mécanismes encore insoupçonnés.

Parmi les hypothèses les plus anciennes, celle qui fait appel à la croissance de nouvelles terminaisons et à la formation de synapses *encore inexistantes* n'a conservé que peu de fidèles, faute de preuves; mais certains faits permettent aujourd'hui de penser qu'elle regagne des chances, et qu'il serait imprudent de la rejeter complètement. Elle rendrait compte, évidemment, des traces bien fixées, ou mémoires à long terme. Plus récemment suggérée, l'hypothèse d'une persévération dynamique des traces d'activité par l'intermédiaire de circulations d'influx dans des boucles fermées ('circuits réverbérants') soulève tant d'objections justifiées (voir notre article du Symposium 'Sensory Communications', Boston, 1959) que nous ne considérons ce mécanisme que comme au plus capable d'entretenir passagèrement une certaine dynamogénie, sans pouvoir préserver la structure de l'information qui l'a déclenché.

A l'échelle élémentaire, il ne reste de vraiment plausible parmi les idées anciennes, que celle d'une 'perméabilité' plus grande vis-à-vis de l'influx nerveux pour des synapses *déjà existantes* et qui ont longuement travaillé; c'est-à-dire, en langage moderne, d'un accroissement durable de leurs potentialités transmettrices, qu'il s'agisse d'excitation ou d'inhibition.

Si nous posons en principe qu'en l'état actuel de nos connaissances, très pauvre comme nous l'avons rappelé, il est sage de ne négliger aucun fait qui ressemble à la formation d'une trace, si peu durable soit-elle, nous sommes en droit de nous étonner que l'on n'ait pas encore exploité le phénomène, aujourd'hui reconnu général, de la 'potentiation post-tétanique' que nous appellerons ici *potentiation tétanique prolongée* pour lui conserver la même abréviation qu'en anglais, PTP (*post-tetanic potentiation*). Nous allons essayer de voir dans quelles conditions cette PTP pourrait être une des causes, peut-être la principale, de la conservation *à court terme* de traces d'activité et l'un des facteurs de l'amorce d'associations inter-centrales à plus long terme, de 'liaisons temporaires' au sens dynamique de la théorie des réflexes conditionnés.

Nous ne ferons pas un exposé préliminaire sur la PTP, le phénomène étant supposé bien connu. On se reportera au besoin à la Revue générale de J. R. Hughes (1958). Que ce phénomène ne cesse de susciter l'intérêt des neurophysiologistes est prouvé ici même, dans ce symposium (voir l'article de J. C. Eccles) et par les mémoires récents de Eccles et Krnjević (1959, *a* et *b*) et de Curtis et Eccles (1960). Il est bien établi que son siège est dans les terminaisons présynaptiques qui appartiennent aux fibres tétanisées et à celles-là seulement, qu'il se signale par une hyperpolarisation et par l'accroissement d'amplitude qui en résulte pour le potentiel d'action et son post-potentiel de dépolarisation; mais sa *cause* exacte reste matière à conjecture. Pour notre thème, le fait majeur est qu'il s'agit-là d'un processus de facilitation résiduelle qui s'étend sur plusieurs dizaines de secondes, ou même plusieurs minutes, ce qui représente un ordre de grandeur temporelle convenant bien pour tout un ensemble de phénomènes explicités par les techniques de conditionnement d'une part et correspondant d'autre part sur le plan psychologique, à ce qu'on appelle des rétentions mnémoniques à court terme. Une autre caractéristique favorable à notre conception est que ce processus, découvert d'abord en étudiant les transmissions mono-synaptiques ganglionnaires et spinales, s'est révélé très général, puisqu'on l'a retrouvé au niveau des relais visuels, auditifs et olfactifs. Cette généralité a suscité la réflexion suivante de Granit (1956): ' ... un phénomène fonctionnel aussi commun, puissant et frappant que la facilitation résiduelle post-tétanique doit jouer un rôle majeur dans la physiologie du système nerveux central'. Et pourtant, on n'a guère cherché jusqu'ici à attribuer un rôle fonctionnel précis à ce phénomène. Nous n'avons trouvé que Kupalov (1956), pour qui l'accroissement des réflexes absolus (dans certaines condi-tions) doit être basé 'sur ce mécanisme d'intensification des réponses réflexes qui a été étudié sous le nom de potentiation post-tétanique ... ' Nous pensons qu'il est possible d'aller plus loin et d'envisager pour la PTP un rôle dans l'établissement des liaisons temporaires. Mais, avant d'entreprendre notre démonstration, nous devons réfuter certaines objec-tions, celles que sans doute beaucoup de neurophysiologistes ont dans l'esprit, et qui expliquent la note décourageante de Ström (1951) déclarant: 'La potentiation post-tétanique semble avoir peu d'importance, si même elle en a une, pour les formes physiologiques de la transmission réflexe'. Quelles sont donc ces objections? Elles sont de deux sortes:

La première est que la PTP ne se manifeste nettement, en général, dans les expériences classiques, que pour des tétanisations d'assez longue durée (plusieurs secondes ou dizaines de secondes) à fréquence relativement élevée (plusieurs centaines par seconde) c'est-à-dire dans des conditions expérimentales assez rarement rencontrées dans la réalité naturelle.

La seconde met l'accent sur le fait que cette facilitation ne profite qu'à

AA

l'afférence tétanisée, et nullement aux voisines qui convergent sur des neurones communs: ce caractère 'privé' du processus intime de la PTP n'interdit-il pas de le considérer comme un agent possible d'un transfert de facilitation d'une voie activée efficace à une voie d'abord inefficace?

Ces objections sont légitimes si l'on s'en tient aux observations classiques, généralement tirées de l'étude des propriétés du réflexe monosynaptique spinal chez l'animal anesthésié. Le test de la PTP est alors la capacité de réponse du motoneurone, mesurée soit statistiquement par l'accroissement d'amplitude d'un potentiel d'action multi-fibres, soit unitairement, par l'augmentation de la probabilité de décharge du motoneurone étudié. C'est déjà l'indication qu'un relais synaptique simple qui a beaucoup fonctionné se trouve de ce fait facilité pendant un certain temps, nettement plus long que les durées auxquelles l'électrophysiologiste du neurone est généralement habitué. Mais la liaison de ce fait avec les phénomènes macroscopiques de l'apprentissage n'est pas claire. On ne voit pas bien à première vue comment il peut être la cause d'associations intercentrales; et il est somme toute à l'opposé de ce qu'on observe le plus souvent en considérant la réaction d'un organisme à des stimulations répétées: déclin des réponses, ou 'habituation', phénomène que l'on sait dépendre de processus d'inhibition. Finalement, il apparaît que vu à l'échelle du neurone, tout phénomène d'apprentissage doit se résoudre en interactions associatives d'une certaine 'durée de vie', comportant donc au minimum deux termes, même lorsqu'il s'agit de l'apprentissage négatif que représente une habituation à un stimulus uniforme (ou 'accoutumance', pour employer un terme que la langue française accepterait plus volontiers); car dans ce cas il y a interaction entre une catégorie d'afférences excitatrices avec celles que déclenche progressivement une contre-réaction négative. Les neurones intéressés doivent donc être dans tous les cas des neurones à afférences multiples et hétérogènes, c'est-à-dire appartenir à des architectonies du type polyneuronique et réticulaire. L'expérimentation classique, électrophysiologique et opératoire, sur animaux soumis à des conditionnements, a confirmé à cet égard les propositions de la logique: pour s'associer, les messages hétérogènes doivent d'abord se rencontrer, et ils ne peuvent le faire que dans les structures non-spécifiques de l'organisation cérébrale. D'où l'importance de mieux en mieux reconnue, pour l'établissement de nouvelles liaisons fonctionnelles, du rôle des noyaux intégrateurs du mésencéphale et du diencéphale, et, bien entendu, des aires 'associatives' du cortex cérébral. (Cf. Fessard et Gastaut, 1958, *Symposium de Strasbourg*, 1956).

Le problème devient donc, pour nous, de comprendre comment la

PTP pourrait modifier, pendant le temps de sa persistance, les propriétés transmissives et intégratrices de ces structures polysynaptiques. A première vue, encore une fois, la perspective n'est pas encourageante. Processus de localisation pré-synaptique, dont l'influence n'a été constatée qu'à propos de transmissions monosynaptiques (voir cependant V. J. Wilson, 1955) la PTP semble représenter un phénomène de trace de caractère strictement privé, non capable de diffusion latérale ou caténaire, donc peu faite pour imprimer une marque, même temporaire, dans une structure centrale de type réticulaire.

Il y a cependant une clef qui ouvre à ce processus l'accès à une conquête efficace des réseaux polyneuroniques, c'est celle qui fait jouer la propriété de beaucoup de neurones des parties supérieures du névraxe de se trouver, chez l'animal non-anesthésié, en état d'activité permanente. Ce fait, que l'exploration systématique par microélectrodes des structures corticales et sous-corticales a bien mis en évidence chez l'animal éveillé, n'a pourtant pas été, en général, considéré à sa juste importance. Il est vrai que les études de microphysiologie, chez l'animal éveillé, ont été jusqu'ici relativement peu nombreuses; et d'autre part, l'autorythmicité neuronique, si facile à déclencher artificiellement par des lésions, est souvent suspectée de n'être qu'un artefact provoqué par le traumatisme qu'engendre la microélectrode. Si cela est parfois vrai, on ne peut plus douter aujourd'hui que ces *décharges répétitives autogéniques*, comme nous les appellerons de préférence au terme ambigu d'activité 'spontanée', soient un des phénomènes élémentaires fondamentaux de l'activité nerveuse centrale normale.

Qu'apportent donc de particulier pour notre problème ces décharges répétitives autogéniques?

Tout d'abord, on saisit immédiatement qu'elles entretiennent dans toutes les extrêmités d'axone appartenant aux neurones qui les engendrent un certain état d'activation terminale, fonction de la fréquence moyenne des décharges cellulifuges, et marqué par un niveau de polarisation membranaire supérieur à ce qu'il serait en l'absence de toute autoactivité. De ce niveau dépend l'efficacité des transmissions, comme les recherches sur la PTP nous l'ont appris. En effet, il est évident que leurs résultats sont applicables, non seulement à ce qui se passe *après*, mais aussi *pendant* la tétanisation. L'autoactivité d'un neurone réalise en somme de façon naturelle une tétanisation quasi continue des terminaisons plus ou moins profuses qui ramifient son axone et elle y crée un degré plus ou moins élevé d'efficacité transmettrice que nous nommerons simplement 'potentiation tétanique' ou PT. Lorsque, par le fait des variations de fréquence qui sont la modalité ordinaire de travail de ces neurones la polarisation et l'efficacité transmettrice des terminaisons se modifient, cette modification ne disparaît pas immédiatement avec sa cause. Si par exemple celle-ci est un bref accroissement de la fréquence du pace-maker neuronique, soit $\triangle F$, il en résultera un accroissement $\triangle PT$ qui sera lui-même prolongé, car il mettra plusieurs secondes, ou même plusieurs minutes à se dissiper.

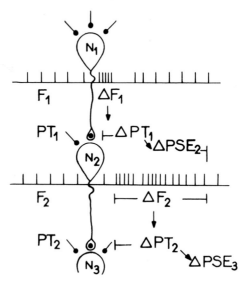

Fig. 1

Schéma figurant une partie d'une chaîne de neurones autoactifs, de fréquences F_1, F_2 ..., transmettant les effets d'une brève accélération initiale de fréquence $\triangle F_1$ par l'intermédiaire des accroissements $\triangle PT_1$, $\triangle PT_2$, de la potentiation tétanique et de l'augmentation correspondante des potentiels synaptiques, $\triangle PSE_2$, $\triangle PSE_3$ ... On a symbolisé la région du pacemaker par une forme sinueuse et la modification présynaptique corrélative de la potentiation par un contour soulignant les boutons. Noter l'allongement de $\triangle F_2$ par rapport à $\triangle F_1$.

Introduisons cette opération dans une structure caténaire d'abord, puis dans une structure en réseau, et voyons ce qui peut arriver.

Dans une chaîne de neurones autoactifs, il convient de se préoccuper, pour chaque élément, de la cause de son $\triangle F$ et de l'effet de son $\triangle PT$. Aidons-nous d'un schéma simple réduit à deux neurones N_1 et N_2 (Fig. 1) et donnons-nous pour commencer $\triangle F_1$, en laissant de côté la question de sa cause que nous supposerons quelconque. $\triangle F_1$ va donc produire aux extrêmités axonales un $\triangle PT_1$, qui survivra un certain temps à sa cause. Si le neurone N_1 n'était pas autocatif, cette potentiation serait à la lettre une potentiation post-tétanique, attendant pour être révélée les choc-tests appliqués par l'expérimentateur. Ici, c'est le nerf lui-même qui fournit les décharges répétitives: elles jouent le rôle des chocs-tests. Ceux-ci actualisent périodiquement la potentiation, produisant en N_2 pour chaque 'spike' afférent un potentiel synaptique d'excitation (PSE_2) plus ample qu'avant la stimulation (Fig. 2) (Fessard et Tauc, 1958; Curtis et Eccles, 1960). Si N_2 n'était pas autocatif, rien d'autre ne se passerait tant que PSE_2

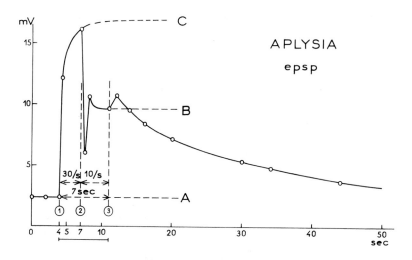

FIG. 2

Variations d'amplitude du potentiel synaptique d'excitation d'un neurone ganglionnaire d'Aplysie, soumis à une excitation orthodromique répétée, d'abord à basse fréquence (1/sec), puis, de 1 à 2, à 30/sec, et de 2 à 3, à 10/sec. A partir de 3, on revient au régime de 1/sec. A chaque régime correspond une amplitude d'équilibre, A, B ou C, vers laquelle on tend après chaque transition (D'après FESSARD et TAUC non publié).

n'aurait pas fourni un taux de dépolarisation capable de faire atteindre au neurone son niveau critique de décharge; mais si l'on a encore affaire à un neurone autocatif, le moindre accroissement de PSE_2 n'aura pas été produit en vain, et le pace-maker de N_2 accélerera son rythme en conséquence. Il le maintiendra plus élevé que sa valeur primitive tant que la potentiation supplémentaire $\triangle PT_1$ créée par $\triangle F_1$ n'aura pas été dissipée. Si le même processus se reproduit plusieurs fois, au niveau des synapses et des pace-makers d'une succession de neurones N_3, N_4, etc. ..., la trace active laissée par une brève surexcitation initiale $\triangle F_1$ pourra atteindre, en principe, une durée bien supérieure au temps de dissipation d'une simple PTP. En fait, le mécanisme d'ensemble doit être bien plus complexe, à cause de l'intervention certaine de processus d'inhibition. On sait que les processus synaptiques de l'inhibition directe sont également soumis aux normes de la PTP (Lloyd, 1949). Seulement, la cinétique de l'induction en chaîne des phénomènes de désactivation par inhibition n'est probablement pas la même que celle des phénomènes d'activation et de leur persévération. C'est là un point à étudier, expérimentalement et théoriquement.

Peu après la présentation de ces idées au Symposium de Montevideo, de nouvelles observations microphysiologiques ont été faites sur le ganglion viscéral de l'Aplysie par Fessard et Tauc (1960). Il a semblé intéressant de les rapporter succinctement

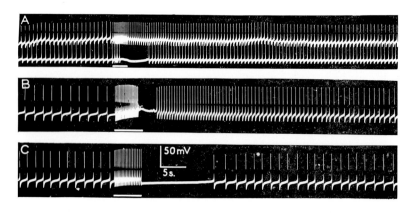

FIG. 3

Décharges de neurones autoactifs du ganglion d'Aplysie. En A, tracés pris simultanément dans deux cellules du même ganglion. Action durable d'un bref tétanos de la voie orthodromique sur la fréquence des décharges. En B, autre exemple. En C, le tétanos a été appliqué directement à la cellule de B (microélectrode anodique interne).

ici. On stimule une voie afférente par un train de chocs d'une durée limitée, et on observe l'effet produit sur la rythmicité autogénique d'une cellule autoactive pourvue d'une microélectrode interne. On constate souvent (mais non toujours) que l'accélération de fréquence $\triangle$F persiste après la cessation du stimulus (Fig. 3) parfois pendant plusieurs dizaines de secondes (une courte pause précède souvent le départ du régime accéléré). Une stimulation directe de la cellule pendant un temps analogue ne produit que l'accélération concomitante et la pause consécutive, sans aucune persistance d'accélération (Fig. 2 C).

La persistance de $\triangle$F observée après la stimulation par voie synaptique peut s'expliquer comme une conséquence d'un processus de PTP, à condition que la stimulation ait en même temps activé les pace-makers de neurones autoactifs connectés à celui que nous interrogeons, qu'il s'agisse de neurones intercalaires, ou bien de neurones de même catégorie pourvus de collatérales intercurrentes (schémas de la Fig. 4). Nous sommes alors ramenés au cas précédent, l'élément interrogé apparaissant comme une unité du deuxième ordre lorsqu'on l'atteint par ce détour. Le bombardement qu'il subit de la part des neurones autoactifs actualise sur les surfaces post-synaptiques correspondantes la potentiation $\triangle$PT de ces neurones et accélère le rythme de son pace-maker pendant le temps de la persistance.

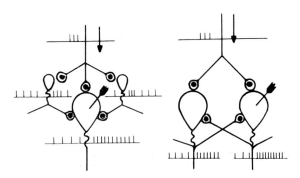

FIG. 4
Deux types communs de connexions grâce auxquelles, si les neurones sont autoactifs, tout bref train d'influx incident doit avoir un effet prolongé sur la fréquence du neurone principal.

Cependant, nous avons souvent échoué à mettre en évidence un tel bombardement (ce qui ne prouve pas son inexistence). Peut-être existe-t-il, du côté post-synaptique cette fois, un autre processus de conservation de traces, co-opérant avec celui que manifeste la PTP. Dans une structure caténaire, il contribuerait à allonger considérablement la durée de persévération des variations de fréquence.

De ce qui précède, nous avons tiré la notion que le phénomène de trace représenté par une facilitation latente localisée pré-synaptiquement, la PTP, peut s'actualiser, se prolonger et se répandre dans les structures polyneuroniques, à condition que leurs éléments soient des neurones auto-actifs. A cet égard, on peut dire que dans chacun de ces neurones l'information contenue dans une tranche d'activité répétitive modulée dépend davantage du passé que du présent. La mission 'intérieure' des trains d'influx engendrés par le pace-maker d'un neurone est d'informer ses terminaisons d'axone, généralement divergentes et profuses, sur les traces d'activité antérieure qui subsistent dans les terminaisons du neurone qui le précède, opération qui exige l'autoactivité de ce dernier. Pareillement, ces influx auront à leur tour une mission 'extérieure', celle d'actualiser pour les neurones de l'ordre suivant les 'souvenirs' d'hyper- (ou d'hypo-) activité que les terminaisons d'axone auront retenus.

Remarquons aussitôt que l'absence d'autoactivité dans un des éléments d'une chaîne linéaire de neurones interrompt fatalement ce processus de conquête des structures polyneuroniques par des messages informatifs marqués par un passé récent. Or, l'exploration microphysiologique des territoires associatifs chez l'animal éveillé révèle qu'une assez grande proportion de neurones sont non seulement inactifs mais inactivables par un stimulus simple. Il est tentant d'émettre l'hypothèse qu'un des premiers effets de l'apprentissage pourrait être de *réveiller* les 'pace-makers' d'un certain nombre de neurones silencieux et de permettre ainsi à des vestiges présynaptiques d'un passé récent de se faire connaître à une plus grande masse de tissu nerveux. Inversement, les processus d'oubli commenceraient par le simple évanouissement des traces élémentaires au niveau des terminaisons nerveuses, et auraient pour conséquence immédiate un 'désamorçage' de l'autoactivité d'un certain nombre de neurones, d'où restriction progressive du champ des neurones impliqués dans les activités résiduelles. On doit admettre en outre que les processus d'habituation, d'extinction et de différenciation comportent de telles opérations de désamorçage, avec le concours actif de connexions inhibitrices.

Les processus de conservation des traces d'activité ne sont qu'un des aspects de l'apprentissage, plus précisément une de ses conditions nécessaires. Envisageons maintenant l'opération élémentaire capitale, qui est évidemment la formation de nouvelles liaisons stimulus-réponse. Si, laissant de côté ici les questions relatives à la participation des grandes structures nerveuses centrales aux mécanismes de conditionnement nous nous limitons à considérer ce qui peut se dérouler au niveau des réseaux neuroniques, nous avons à nous demander si l'introduction de l'opération élémentaire $\triangle F \rightarrow \triangle PT$, définie plus haut, dans une structure de neurones autoactifs disposés en réseau, peut nous fournir des éléments pour placer à ce niveau un mécanisme d'association.

Aidons-nous pour cela d'un schéma aussi simple que possible (Fig. 5), figurant la maille élémentaire d'un réseau polyneuronique, et limitant à deux seulement le nombre des afférences reçues par le neurone central (*a* et *b*) et à deux aussi le nombre de ses rameaux divergents (notés *ab*). Cela suffit pour les déductions essentielles. La question est alors de savoir si la facilitation de post-activation laissée par une activité de *a* pourra profiter à un message ultérieur arrivant par *b*. Pour simplifier encore, supposons que *a* et *b* transportent uniquement des messages d'activation phasique, sans assurer aucun bombardement tonique (d'autres afférences, non représentées, peuvent jouer ce rôle). Les neurones en présence seront notés, selon leur ordre, N_A et N_B, (1er ordre), N_{AB} (2ème ordre), N_{ABC} et

au BA suivant, et en offrant à ces traces, qui peuvent être au début très discrètes, la possibilité de s'accumuler.

Jusqu'ici, nous avons raisonné par déduction, en partant de faits dont la réalité est bien établie, mais dont l'enchaînement, tel que nous nous le représentons, reste à soumettre à l'épreuve de l'expérience. Nous avons réservé pour la fin de cet exposé la présentation des quelques évidences expérimentales déjà obtenues par nous et qui démontrent la possibilité du

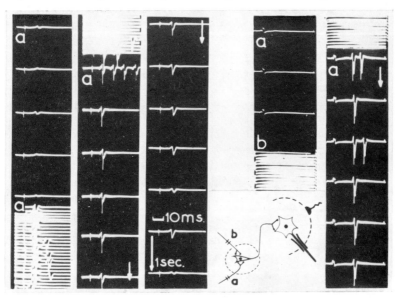

Fig. 6

Enregistrements des réponses globales d'un lobe électrique de Torpille (centre nerveux qui commande les organes électriques) lorsqu'on stimule l'une ou l'autre de deux voies afférentes, a ou b.

A gauche, les trois colonnes de tracés se suivent. Ils sont pris chaque seconde sauf pendant la tétanisation de a (à 12/sec). Noter la potentiation post-tétanique.

A droite, c'est l'afférence b qui est tétanisée. Le bénéfice de la potentiation est transféré de b à a. Noter qu'initialement la stimulation de a n'activait pas les neurones du lobe (mais provoquait certainement la décharge du neurone intermédiaire).

transfert de facilitation dont nous venons de parler. Ce sont des expériences d'électrophysiologie macroscopique, qui devront être prolongées par une étude plus fine, à l'échelle du neurone. Nous les avons déjà brièvement relatées dans des publications antérieures (Fessard et Szabo, 1959; Fessard, 1960a).

Nous nous sommes d'abord adressés au dispositif bulbaire de commande des organes électriques de la Torpille. Ce dispositif (schéma, Fig. 6) a l'avantage de présenter un arrangement neuronique particulièrement simple et de structure bien connue (Fessard et Szabo, 1953; Szabo, 1954). Il est le support d'un réflexe disynaptique, avec un noyau d'interneurones, récepteurs d'afférences convergentes. Enregistrant seulement la réponse efférente avec une macroélectrode posée sur un des lobes électriques, nous avons pu montrer que ce dispositif permet de transférer le bénéfice de la PTP d'un ensemble d'afférences *b* à un autre *a* (Fig. 6). C'est un cas où les deux afférences peuvent isolément, l'une comme l'autre, provoquer la décharge rythmique du noyau intermédiaire reconnu comme pacemaker de la décharge des organes électriques (Fessard et Szabo, 1954). Il n'est donc pas nécessaire ici que les cellules de ce noyau soient le siège d'une autoactivité permanente, propriété qu'en fait elles n'ont pas.

Nous avons également obtenu des transferts de potentiation dans le cerveau du Chat en prenant comme test la réponse des cellules pyramidales de l'Hippocampe à la stimulation d'afférences fornicales homolatérales. La stimulation tétanisante était appliquée à différentes voies connues pour converger sur les mêmes cellules, mais seulement après un ou plusieurs relais. La figure 7 est un exemple typique, dans lequel la potentiation était obtenue par tétanisation du groupe amygdalien médian. On remarquera que l'accroissement du potentiel évoqué porte sur la seconde onde, c'est-à-dire sur la réponse qui correspond à une liaison certainement polysynaptique. On voit aussi, sur les enregistrements-tests, quelques indices d'une activité 'spontanée' (points blancs) qui n'existait pas avant la tétanisation. Dans l'échantillon du milieu, 3ème colonne, l'onde spontanée, survenant par hasard juste avant une stimulation-test, a bloqué la grande réponse, mais non la petite.

Il est certain que seule une analyse microphysiologique des propriétés des structures polysynaptiques de type caténaire ou réticulaire permettrait de fonder la validité de nos hypothèses. Cette analyse reste à faire en ce qui concerne les mécanismes de l'apprentissage. Dans une certaine mesure cependant, on peut considérer que les données de microphysiologie cérébrale obtenues sur des animaux soumis à un conditionnement par Ricci, Doane et Jasper (1957) et par Morrell (1960) appuient partiellement nos idées, puisqu'elles ont montré qu'à l'échelle unitaire les progrès de l'apprentissage se marquent par des changements dans les rythmes autogéniques de la décharge des neurones étudiés.

Nous avons essayé d'aller plus loin théoriquement en spéculant sur les causes possibles de ces changements. Nous avons utilisé pour cela des données maintenant classiques: existence dans les structures cérébrales d'architectonies polyneuroniques en chaînes et en réseaux, importance longtemps insoupçonnée des champs de neurones multivalents, vers lesquels convergent des afférences hétérosensorielles, généralité de la rythmicité autogénique des neurones centraux chez l'animal non-anesthésié, et enfin existence d'une propriété générale de plasticité,

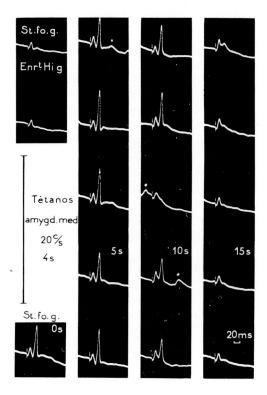

FIG. 7

Enregistrement d'une activité évoquée au niveau des cellules pyramidales de l'Hippocampe du Chat, par stimulation du fornix homolatéral (chocs-tests à 1 par sec). Après un tétanos de 4 sec à 20/sec appliqué au groupe amygdalien médian, il y a transfert de facilitation. Les points indiquent des activités autogènes.

représentée par cette rémanence des effets de l'activité nerveuse au niveau des synapses que l'on nomme 'potentiation post-tétanique'. Ces faits ont entre eux d'étroites relations. Il nous est apparu qu'en les considérant dans leur ensemble, sous l'angle du système dynamique qu'ils forment, ils pouvaient nous apporter des bases d'explication pour un certain nombre de phénomènes de comportement se rattachant aux thèmes de l'apprentissage.

RÉSUMÉ

1. Selon l'idée courante, le processus fondamental qui sous-tend tout comportement d'apprentissage au niveau du neurone semble être la persistance aux synapses d'effets facilitateurs ou inhibiteurs résultant de la présentation répétée du même stimulus ou celle du même ensemble de stimuli associés.

2. Le seul résidu facilitateur (ou inhibiteur) de post-activation qui ait été jusqu'ici découvert et soit maintenant reconnu comme processus présynaptique général est celui qu'on nomme 'potentiation post-tétanique'. C'est en fait plutôt une 'potentiation tétanique prolongée' (PTP).

3. Les études classiques sur la PTP la représentent comme un processus strictement localisé dans les terminaisons pré-synaptiques des fibres qui ont été impliquées dans une hyperactivation assez intense (stimulation à fréquence élevée). Si le bénéfice de la PTP ne peut être transféré d'une sorte d'afférences à une autre, s'il reste monosynaptique alors que les processus d'apprentissage nécessitent en fait la participation de structures polyneuroniques, comment pouvons-nous ici faire jouer un rôle à ce phénomène?

4. La clef semble être dans le fait maintenant bien établi que la plupart des neurones, dans le cerveau d'un animal en état de veille, fournissent continuellement des décharges répétitives autogéniques. Celles-ci maintiennent dans les terminaisons d'axone un certain niveau d'efficacité transmettrice que nous avons proposé d'appeler 'potentiation tétanique' (PT). Tout accroissement transitoire de fréquence $\triangle$F entraînera un accroissement $\triangle$PT qui survivra à sa cause pendant des secondes ou des minutes. Par suite, les potentiels post-synaptiques de tous les neurones recevant des afférences de ceux dans lesquels un $\triangle$F s'est produit seront augmentés en amplitude, aussi longtemps que l'incrément de potentiation persistera. Cet effet à son tour accroîtra la fréquence de décharge des neurones impliqués, et, parmi ceux auparavant muets, en induira quelques-uns à commencer à se décharger.

5. Il est facile de comprendre comment la même suite d'événements opérant plusieurs fois le long d'une structure polyneuronique en chaîne peut aboutir à un très important allongement de la trace finale laissée par une hyperactivité de durée brève à l'entrée. Des $\triangle$F négatifs dus à

une chute d'activité ou à l'intervention de processus inhibiteurs peuvent pareillement donner naissance à des traces durables d'inactivation.

6. Des caractéristiques de réseaux existent dans toutes les structures polyneuroniques du cerveau. Beaucoup de neurones y sont de ce fait connectés à des voies afférentes hétérogènes et peuvent ainsi être activés par des signaux de différentes qualités sensorielles. Un neurone multivalent de cette catégorie peut évidemment transférer à n'importe lequel de ses groupes d'afférences le bénéfice d'un $\triangle$PT résiduel causé par l'hyper-activité transitoire d'un autre groupe. Si le neurone commun est autoactif et que les influx afférents n'en provoquent pas la décharge, le transfert est néanmoins possible par l'intermédiaire du changement résultant $\triangle$F de la fréquence de son pace-maker.

Des influx afférents d'une catégorie ne produisant pas d'effet décelable à la sortie d'un réseau sont ainsi supposés pouvoir acquérir de l'efficacité s'ils arrivent pendant l'intervalle de dissipation des traces d'activité laissées par une activation plus forte amenée par une autre sorte d'influx afférents.

7. Des séquences de paires de stimuli associés, comme on en applique dans les procédés de conditionnement classiques, opèrent probablement de le façon décrite ci-dessus lorsqu'elles établissent progressivement de nouveaux liens fonctionnels au sein du Système nerveux central.

8. Quelques preuves expérimentales étayant la validité des hypothèses précédentes ont été obtenues. Les cellules ganglionnaires autorythmiques de l'Aplysie ont été utilisées pour montrer les changements durables de fréquence du pace-maker qui survivent aux effets immédiats d'un bref tétanos appliqué à un tractus afférent. Un test satisfaisant du mécanisme de transfert de facilitation, tel que nous le suggérons dans notre théorie, a été appliqué au système disynaptique de neurones qui contrôle les décharges des organes électriques chez la Torpille. Nous avons prouvé aussi que les cellules pyramidales de l'Hippocampe peuvent révéler des transferts de potentiation, quand on les active à travers des voies diffé-rentes qui convergent sur les structures polysynaptiques intermédiaires qui y conduisent.

9. En concluant, on a d'abord insisté sur la nécessité de compléter notre évidence expérimentale avec des explorations microphysiologiques de structures de type réticulaire; et l'attention a été attirée vers le fait que notre conception a été entièrement tirée de données classiques, qui ont ici été considérées conjointement au lieu de l'être séparément: rythmicité cellulaire autogénique, potentiation post-tétanique, neurones multivalents et architectonies de type réticulaire.

SUMMARY

1. According to the generally accepted view, the basic process underlying any kind of learning behaviour at the neuronal level seems to be the persistence of synaptic facilitatory (or inhibitory) effects as a result of the repeated presentation of the same stimulus or of that of the same set of associated stimuli.

2. The only post-activation facilitatory (or inhibitory) residue that has so far been disclosed and is now recognized as a general pre-synaptic process is the so-called 'post-tetanic potentiation' (PTP). Actually it would be better termed a 'protracted tetanic potentiation'.

3. Classical studies of PTP represent it as a process strictly localized in the presynaptic terminals of the fibres that have been involved in a rather strong hyperactivation (stimulation at high frequency). If the benefit of the PTP cannot be transferred from one kind of afferents to another, if it remains monosynaptic while learning processes actually need the participation of polyneuronic structures, how can we here give a role to this phenomenon?

4. The key seems to be in the now well established fact that most neurones in the brain of an animal in the waking state are continuously delivering autogenic repetitive discharges. These maintain in the axon terminals a certain level of transmissive efficacy we propose to call 'tetanic potentiation' (PT). Any transient increase in frequency $\triangle F$ will result in an increase $\triangle PT$ that will outlast its cause by seconds or minutes. Consequently, the post-synaptic potentials of all neurones receiving afferents from those in which some $\triangle F$ has occurred will be enhanced in amplitude as long as the potentiation increment will persist. This effect in its turn will increase the firing frequency of the neurones involved, and, among those previously silent, will induce some of them to start firing.

5. It is easy to understand how the same sequence of events operating several times along a chain-like polyneuronic structure can result in a very important lengthening of the final trace left by a brief input hyperactivity. Negative $\triangle F$ due to a drop in activity or to the intervention of inhibitory processes can similarly give rise to long-lasting traces of inactivation.

6. Network-like characteristics are found in all polyneuronic structures of the brain. There many neurones are connected to heterogeneous afferent pathways and can thus be activated by signals of different sensory qualities. A multivalent neurone of that kind can obviously transfer to any of its group of afferences the benefit of a residual $\triangle PT$ caused by the

transient hyperactivity of another group. If the common neurone is an auto-active one and the afferent impulses have no firing effect upon it, the transfer is nevertheless possible through the resulting frequency change $\triangle F$ of its pace-maker.

Afferent impulses of one kind producing no detectable effect at the output of a network are thus assumed to be able to acquire efficacy if they arrive during the subsidence interval of the activity traces left by a stronger activation brought about by another kind of afferent impulses.

7. Sequential pairs of associated stimuli as are applied in classical conditioning procedures may operate in the way described above when progressively establishing new functional links within the central nervous system.

8. Some experimental proofs supporting the validity of the preceding assumptions have been obtained. Auto-rhythmic ganglion cells of Aplysia have been used to show the long-lasting frequency changes of the pace-maker that survive the immediate effects of a brief tetanus applied to an afferent tract. A satisfactory test of the facilitation transfer mechanism as suggested in our theory has been applied to the disynaptic system of neurones that control the discharges of electric organs in Torpedo. Pyramidal cells in Hippocampus have also been proved to be able to reveal potentiation transfers when activated through different pathways that converge on to the intermediate polysynaptic structures leading to them.

9. In concluding, the necessity of completing our experimental evidence with microphysiological explorations of network-like structures has first been emphasized and attention has been drawn towards the fact that our conception has been entirely derived from classical data, that have here been considered jointly instead of separately: autogenic cellular rhythmicity, post-tetanic potentiation, multivalent neurones and network-like architectonics.

GROUP DISCUSSION

Eccles: It is very important for the theory of learning that the stimulated line is the only one that increases in efficacy. But it is also important to show what Dr Fessard has shown — that interneurones which are common to both lines, fire and they increase the effectiveness of their synaptic action in turn. In other words, you are converging through an interneurone which both lines are firing but which is not powerful enough for one of the lines to transmit to the next stage of the synaptic relay. This has to be built in to any theory of learning or conditioning. I did set up a very provisional diagram — in 1953 — which did presuppose what Dr

BB

Fessard has found when I was attempting to give some picture of the neuronal mechanism of learning, at least at the simplest level.

FESSARD: I remember your diagrams.

GERARD: I hope this will be elaborated in the general discussion on Saturday. I remind you that in Lloyd's experiments with the monosynpatic reflex each afferent did not influence the response induced by any other afferent and Dr Fessard's results seem to be in conflict with that unless you take into account the existence of interneurones.

KONORSKI: Post-tetanic potentiation (P.T.P.) was first discovered many years ago in neuromuscular preparations. In curarized preparations the P.T.P. is very strong and long lasting. We did some of these investigations with Lubinska and found that the P.T.P. lasted for minutes. Do you think this is a different phenomenon from the P.T.P. found in C.N.S.?

FESSARD: I would say it is just the same.

KONORSKI: Dr Kozak and Dr Bruner have shown that the P.T.P. in neurosalivary preparations (where the effector is a salivary gland) is even more prolonged — from 10 minutes to half an hour. So we see that the P.T.P. phenomena are general and apply to the C.N.S. as well as to the peripheral nervous system.

FESSARD: As Dr Eccles just recalled, motoneurones may be taken as models of any others, but there may be strong quantitative differences.

MAGOUN: Is there any value in considering the alterations in the sensitization of enervation in this question. The increment of excitability in this case occurs at the receptor sites on the post-synaptic membrane rather than on the pre-synaptic membrane. As long as one is looking for all possible instances in which there is an enhancement of excitability persisting for a long time, I wonder if there would be any concepts to be applied from the field of sensitization of denervation.

ECCLES. There are important facts: for example, Axelsson and Thesleff have shown that when you cut the nerve to a mammalian muscle and it degenerates, the well-known hypersensitivity to acetyl-choline in fact is not a real hypersensitivity of the endplate region, but simply a spreading sensitivity at the same level throughout the whole length of the muscle fibre which effectively becomes a long, extended endplate. This has been tested by micro-injection techniques.

MAGOUN: What about the influences in the C.N.S. such as have been explored by Stan?

GERARD: Dr Luco commented on that. Would you like to add anything?

LUCO: Professor Canon did some experiments on sensitization. If you cut the nerve to the motor nerve cell, the sensitization is increased. I want to add one interesting thing. We cut the post-ganglionic fibres of the superior cervical ganglion which innervates the nictating membrane. We re-innervated the membrane with cholinergic fibres of the hypoglossal nerve, and the sensitivity to adrenaline was normalized after re-innervation with a very different nerve. In other words, the normal sensitivity which had been lost was regained with a different nerve which normally is not innervating the membrane.

GERARD: Let us not forget the plasticity or enduring effects of activity even at a simpler level than the synapse, in the nerve fibre itself. After brief activity there is a change in the magnitude and duration of the after-potentials which increases from milliseconds to minutes, and the heat or oxygen consumption increases for hours.

It is unthinkable to me that in the simpler animal one would get more enduring effects of activity than in the more complex animals. I remind you also that the spontaneous rhythms in the membrane potential or peripheral nerves fit the same story. Both in nerves and in spontaneous beat of frog brain neurones a chemical control to balance the potassium and sodium seems to me to fit in very nicely.

ECCLES: About Dr Luco's suggestion that we take post-denervation sensitization into account. That would tend to make the disused line more effective than it used to be and so would work against our results on the depression induced by disuse. Furthermore, we have already controlled this kind of effect in the experiment where we were recording intracellularly the synaptic potentials of the nerve cell and firing at it from two different paths, one disused, the other normal.

LUCO: The sensitization is normally increased when the membrane is denervated; the point is that another, different nerve is responsible for this return of sensitivity.

LASTING CHANGES IN SYNAPTIC ORGANIZATION PRODUCED BY CONTINUOUS NEURONAL BOMBARDMENT[1]

FRANK MORRELL

I should like to present some experimental observations which have led us to suggest an analogical model for cellular learning. The model is interesting in two respects. (1) Although the process is a pathological one, it is presumed to utilize the same neural pathways available to physiological stimulations. (2) Changes in synaptic organization, cellular excitability and cellular chemistry have been demonstrated on a time scale comparable to behavioural learning.

For the past few years our laboratory has been concerned with a study of chronic epileptogenic lesions produced in animals by local application of an ethyl chloride spray to a small (2 mm.) area of cortex (Morrell and Florenz, 1958; Morrell, 1959). Such animals develop paroxysmal electrographic discharges at the periphery of the lesion within a few hours. Within a few days a secondary focus of paroxysmal discharge may be recorded in the contralateral homologous cortex. Fig. 1 illustrates such a development. In the first 24 hours after application of the ethyl chloride (Fig. 1A), the electrical record disclosed paroxysmal activity limited to the area around the primary lesion. There was little or no evidence of abnormal discharge in an electrode (electrode 4) placed symmetrically over the cortical region opposite the lesion. Three days later, however, in the same animal, epileptiform spikes appeared quite prominently in the symmetrically placed contralateral electrode (Fig. 1B).

Such secondary foci have been observed in patients with convulsive disorders (Gastaut, 1959) and in animal preparations by Erickson (1940), Rosenblueth and Cannon (1942), Speransky (1935), Nims, Marshall and Nielsen (1941), Morrell (1959), Kopeloff et al. (1954, 1955), Pope, Morris, Jasper, Elliott and Penfield (1947) and Roger (1954). In the terminology of the electroencephalographer, the area of secondary discharge has been called the 'mirror' focus. In the early stages of its development, the secondary discharge represents a 'reflection' of the primary discharge. It is dependent upon activity in the primary lesion in the sense that it subsides

[1] This work was supported by the Teagle Foundation and by USPHS Grant 1185.

375

following ablation or neuronal isolation of the primary lesion. Electrographically, this *dependent* stage of homotopic discharge may be characterized by the fact that secondary spikes appear only at the time that spike discharges are evident in the primary region (and often only in response to the larger of the primary spikes) and have an appreciable latency following the primary discharge when measured with cathode ray oscillography (Fig. 2).

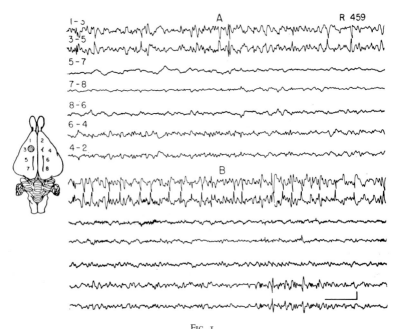

FIG. 1

Electroencephalogram of an unanaesthetized rabbit 24 hours (A) and 3 days (B) after production of an ethyl chloride lesion. The site and extent of the lesion is indicated by the cross hatched area on the diagram. Derivations are bipolar from implanted electrodes over the indicated regions. Calibration is 50 microvolts and 1 second.

After a given period of time (24 hours to 7 days in the rabbit, 4 weeks to 3 months in the cat; about 8 weeks in the monkey) the secondary contralateral focus becomes independent in that it does not disappear upon ablation or coagulation of the primary region of discharge. Electrographically, the *independent* stage of homotopic discharge is characterized by random spikes and paroxysmal bursts which bear no relation in time to the activity present in the primary lesion (Fig. 3).

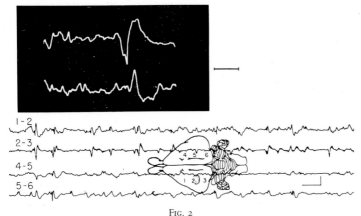

FIG. 2

Characteristics of the dependent mirror focus. In the ink-written tracing the upper two channels record the primary focus and the lower two channels the mirror focus. The ethyl chloride lesion is indicated by cross hatching. Calibration: 100 microvolts and 1 second. In the oscillographic tracing the upper channel records the primary region and the lower one the secondary region. Calibration: 100 msec.

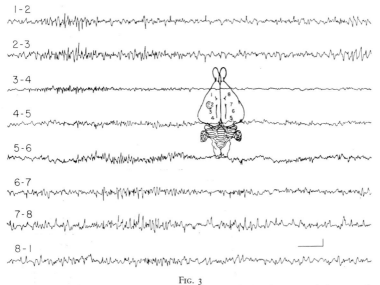

FIG. 3

Electrographic characteristics of the independent mirror focus. Electroencephalogram of an unanaesthetized rabbit taken 3 weeks after production of an ethyl chloride lesion in the area designated by cross hatching. Discharges originating in the primary lesion (electrode 2) and in the secondary region (electrode 7) are unrelated in time of occurrence. Note also that there is some depression of activity in electrodes just posterior to the primary lesion while this is not true of electrodes posterior to the mirror focus. Calibration: 50 microvolts and 1 second.

Once the independent stage of secondary discharge has been reached, local changes in cellular excitability may be demonstrated by alterations in evoked potentials. For example, one measure of excitability change is the amplitude of the direct cortical response (DCR) to the same electrical stimulus presented before, and 7 days after, development of the focus. Electrodes were implanted in various cortical regions of the hemisphere contralateral to the ethyl chloride lesion (Fig. 4) so that a bipolar stimulating electrode consisting of two 75 micron silver wires cemented to-

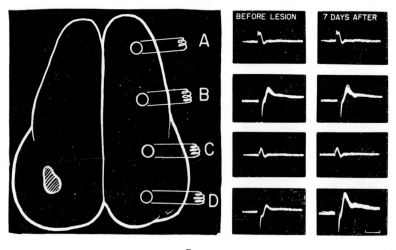

FIG. 4

Direct cortical response tested before, and 7 days after, production of an ethyl chloride lesion. The derivations are from implanted electrodes as indicated in the diagram. The area of the ethyl chloride lesion is cross hatched. Variations in duration and configuration of the evoked potentials are due to differences in inter-electrode distance and in orientation of the recording electrode with respect to the stimulating electrodes. Photographs consist of ten to forty superimposed sweeps. Calibration: 15 msec.

gether and exposed only at their tips rested approximately 2 mm. away from a monopolar steel needle used as a recording electrode. The reference electrode was a steel screw in the calvarium. Direct cortical responses were tested repeatedly at each of these sites before producing the ethyl chloride lesions. Responses obtained in each area are demonstrated in the first column of oscillograph tracings. These tracings were made by super-imposition of ten to forty responses and thus serve to indicate the stability and, therefore, reliability of amplitude measurements under these circumstances. An ethyl chloride lesion was then produced in the left visual cortex and the animal was again tested 7 days after development of the lesion (second column of tracings). The marked augmentation of the directly evoked response limited to the contralateral visual cortex is clearly apparent. A similar augmentation of the direct cortical response in areas contralateral to a cortical circumsection has been noted by Eidelberg Konigsmark and French (1959). These authors also attribute such augmentation to increased epileptogenic properties.

These data suggest that the secondary area of discharge may be described as a ganglionic network in which spontaneous and evoked activity have been chronically altered as a result of experimental alteration of its environmental input in the form of continuous epileptiform bombardment.

The sequence just described may be altered and the development of the mirror focus prevented by section of the corpus callosum either before production of the primary lesion or within 24 hours afterwards. A similar observation has been made by Erickson (1940) with respect to electrically induced after-discharges. Interestingly enough, the development of independent contralateral secondary discharge may also be prevented if the callosal connections remain intact but a subpial partial isolation of the contralateral cortex is carried out within the same time interval. Such an isolation deprives the cortex of all of its subcortical connections as well as those relating it to other cortical areas of the same hemisphere (Fig. 5A and B). This would suggest that the enduring changes in synaptic function which form the basis of the independent mirror focus require that at least two forms of input be available to the cortical region concerned.

We may now proceed to ask whether the change in excitability or irritability is dependent upon impulses circulating in closed chains of neurones or whether it is based upon structural alterations of cells within the network. As a first step, neuronal isolation of the region of primary discharge was carried out according to the technique of Kristiansen and Courtois (1949). Fig. 6A illustrates persistent, perhaps even augmented, activity in the mirror focus after isolation of the primary lesion. Note that the paroxysmal discharge in the primary lesion had ceased: (Compare with Fig. 3 on the same animal.) The mirror region may then be similarly isolated (Fig. 6B and C). Some residual spiking sometimes persists for several minutes in the isolated mirror region (Fig. 6B) but soon disappears to be replaced by electrical silence (Fig. 6C). After these isolations were performed, the calvarium was replaced and the animal returned to its cage for several months. Surface recording during that period indicated no return of paroxysmal discharge. At the time for the definitive experiment,

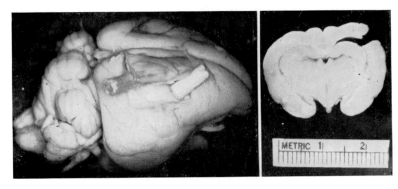

A

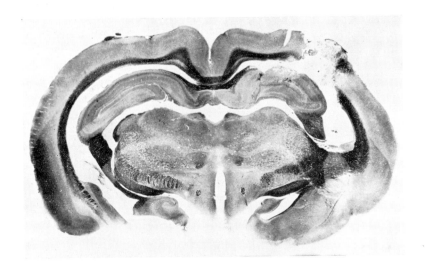

B

FIG. 5

Dissection of rabbit brain to illustrate features of the extra-callosal isolation. A slab of cerebral cortex in the hemisphere opposite the ethyl chloride lesion is dissected so that the cortex is separated from all subcortical connections and from the surrounding intracortical regions as well. The callosal pathway remains intact and is the only connection through which input is available to the dissected region (5A). In a Weil stained cross section (5B) the integrity of the callosal pathway may be visualized. For photography the cortex was lifted to demonstrate the underlying white matter but the operative procedure, of course, is done in such a way as to preserve the pial circulation to the cortical slab.

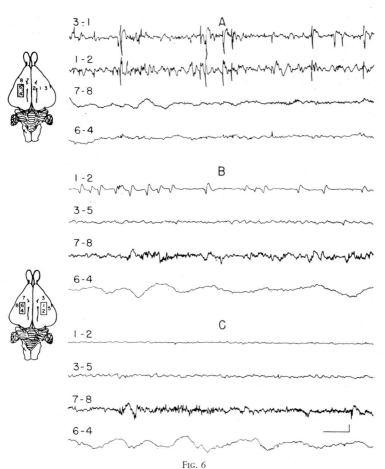

FIG. 6

Bilateral cortical isolation in an animal with well-developed independent mirror focus. This is the same animal shown in Fig. 3. Recordings were made with the animal under 40 mg. per kg. of nembutal anaesthesia. Derivations are from the electrodes indicated in the diagrams. Isolation of the primary lesion is first carried out (6A) and demonstrates loss of paroxysmal spike discharge in the primary region while the secondary area continues to discharge actively. Isolation of the secondary region was then undertaken (6B and C). For a few moments abnormal discharge persists in the isolated secondary region (B) but soon disappears (C) to be replaced by almost complete electrical silence. Note that the electrode positions have been changed in B and C. Calibration: 50 microvolts and 1 second.

a tracheotomy was performed under ether anaesthesia and the animal placed on flaxedil and artificial respiration. Local anaesthesia was used for the scalp incision, the hemispheres were widely exposed and the pia arachnoid covered with warm mineral oil. At the end of the experiment the isolated regions were serially sectioned to confirm the completeness of loss of neural continuity. The pial circulation was, of course, preserved intact in these preparations. The appearance of the whole brain at autopsy, as well as a cross section through the isolated region, are indicated in Fig. 7.

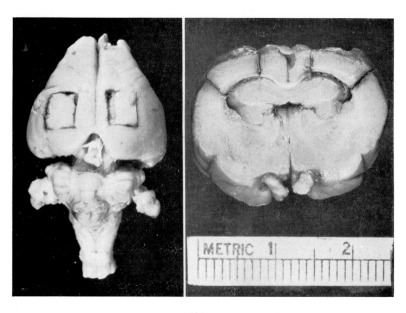

Fig. 7
Whole brain at autopsy and cross section through the isolated regions. The defect in the right frontal pole was produced in the course of removal of the brain at autopsy.

Gross electrodes were placed upon the surface of the isolated mirror region and adjacent surrounding cortex and one to four tungsten micro-electrodes (Hubel, 1957) were inserted into the isolated slab at a depth of 500 to 1000 micra. Search for spontaneously firing units was rarely successful so that one had to rely upon multiple placement at a depth where unit discharge might reasonably be expected in connection with surface electrographic paroxysms. A pledget of metrazol placed upon adjacent normal cortex elicited a seizure discharge which slowly spread across the neuronal gap into the isolated region (Fig. 8). Gross electrodes on the slab first recorded volume conducted potentials unaccompanied by unit discharge and then suddenly the slab burst into self-sustained activity which was associated with massive unit discharge. Since the high impedance of the microelectrode tip precludes recording at any distance, we must conclude that the discharge truly represents ephaptic activation of ganglionic elements within the isolated region. We do not have time here to discuss the physiological properties of isolated, non-epileptic cortex (see references Libet and Gerard, 1939; Bremer, 1941; Burns, 1949; Sloan and Jasper, 1950; Bremer and Desmedt, 1958; Torres, Ziegler and Wissof,

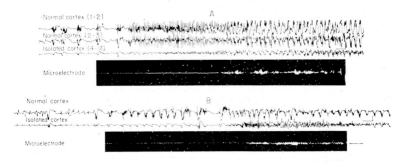

FIG. 8

Examples of propagation of abnormal discharges to isolated regions. A pledget of metrazol had been placed on the normal cortex 2 cm. distant from the isolated region. The electrographic discharge so induced spreads slowly across the cortex and after some delay was seen to invade the isolated region. Micro-electrode tracings are from tungsten electrodes as described in the text. Calibration is 50 microvolts and one second for the ink-writer tracings and 1 second for the oscillograph.

1958; Morrell and Torres, 1958; Marshall, 1959). In our own experience we have never been able unequivocally to demonstrate transmission of electrical discharge into completely neuronally isolated (but otherwise normal, i.e. non-epileptic) cortex. The ease with which such ephaptic transmission can be demonstrated in isolated epileptic cortex makes it clear that the increased excitability or irritability has persisted in the cellular elements of the mirror region despite the fact that the spontaneous manifestation of this irritability was abolished by the neuronal isolation. We believe this to be crucial observation because it demonstrates that the mirror focus is a region which has not only 'learned' to behave in terms of paroxysmal discharge, but which 'remembers' this behaviour even after months of inactivity. The isolation experiment has excluded reverberating impulses as the basis of the changed electrical behaviour and makes it it necessary to search for structural alterations.

The material presented thus far indicates that a region of chronic epileptiform discharge in one hemisphere can induce a similar pattern of neuronal activity in cells of the opposite hemisphere which were untouched by the initial experimental procedure and which are related to the primary region by massive commissural pathways. After a time these contralateral alterations become permanently fixed in local cellular organization and

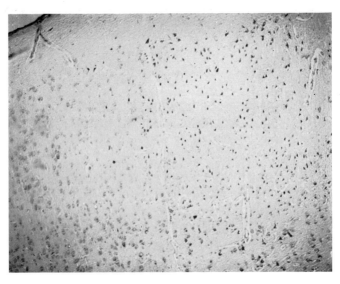

FIG. 9

Section through the region of the mirror focus. Note the collection of densely stained cells to the right of the photomicrograph compared with the characteristic staining of normal cortex to the left. Methyl green pyronin stain. Magnification × 75.

persist independently of the neural system which originally established them. In addition to the spontaneous behaviour of these cells, we have traced some measures of evoked activity which also indicate a reorganization of the synaptic properties within the altered population. Of special interest is the fact that these changes are long-lasting and that they survive the chronic neuronal isolation of the involved neurones, an isolation which prevents the spontaneous manifestation of the alteration which has taken place.

I should like to conclude by reporting some preliminary experiments which illustrate the use to which our model of neural learning may be put. The experiments involve the supposition that the molecular basis of memory might be found within the cells or cell systems of the mirror focus.

Among the most important known determinants of membrane responsiveness is the distribution of charge across the cell boundary. While the relative internal and external concentration of various ion species are known to produce radical alterations in membrane potential, these changes

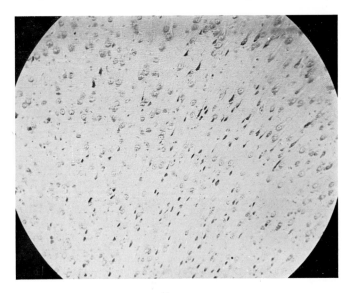

FIG. 10

Slightly higher power photomicrograph through region of mirror focus. The appearance of normal cortical cells with this method is seen in the lower right and upper left hand corners. Methyl green pyronin stain. Magnification × 85.

are transient and it seems unlikely that distribution of the relatively permeable free ions could account for lasting patterns in the intricate local distribution of membrane potential. A much more likely candidate for such permanent patterning is the configuration of potential set up in ordered sequences of amino acids or proteins. Yet these substances, too, are known to be in continual flux, in generation, breakdown and regeneration. One must postulate an organizer substance, a substance which in its synthesis, breakdown and resynthesis can perpetuate or regenerate the same pattern of polarized molecular configurations which were previously present. The search for an organizer substance leads one logically to the nucleic acids and, for events which are primarily cytoplasmic, to the ribonucleic acids.

Ribonucleic acid stains (methyl green pyronin method) have been done on sections through the region of the mirror focus in nine animals after preliminary electrical studies had clearly indicated the extent and distribution of both primary and secondary discharging areas. Control sections were taken from electrically uninvolved areas of brain and, in addition, every third section was treated with ribonuclease to insure that the sub-

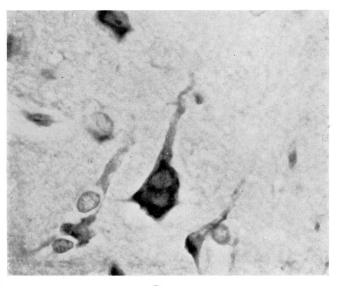

FIG. 11

Higher power photomicrograph demonstrating the characteristic concentration of pyronin positive material along the inner surface of the membrane. The stained material extends far into the dendrite. Note also the appearance of a bilobed nucleus. Methyl green pyronin stain. Magnification × 840.

stance stained was ribonucleic acid. Fig. 9 demonstrates a small nest of darkly stained cells surrounded by the more lightly coloured regions of normal cortex. Such densely stained cells were consistently found in areas coincident with the electrically defined mirror focus. A slightly higher power photomicrograph (Fig. 10) illustrates the penetration of the pyronin-positive material into the dendrite and also indicates the wedge-like distribution of the stained cell system. Pigmented cells extend throughout the depth of the cortex. At still higher magnification the extent of penetration into the dendrite is clearer (Fig. 11) and one may observe a concentration of the pyronin-positive material in a dense layer along the inner surface of the cell membrane. Not infrequently the cytoplasmic space between the membrane zone and the nucleus is considerably paler. Such a concentration might be expected for an arrangement of protein molecules capable of influencing the distribution of potential across the membrane. It is not the concentration pattern to be expected as a result of simple decrease in cell volume. Note also the suggestion of a bilobed nucleus. Andrew (1955) has considered the occurrence of bilobed nuclei in mouse Purkinje cells to indicate an abortive attempt at amitotic division in nerve cells subjected to certain forms of stress. The primary lesion (Fig. 12A) is surrounded by cells of a similar appearance. The contralateral homologous region of the same section (Fig. 12B) is less deeply stained than in sections slightly further away from the primary histological lesion, (compare Fig. 9). Similarly, the electrical records indicated that the most active discharge in the mirror region was not homotopic with the centre of the ethyl chloride lesion but rather with its periphery just as the primary electrical discharge is at the periphery rather than the centre of the primary lesion. Adjacent sections treated with ribonuclease show loss of almost all the tinctorial properties of these cells.

Although these are still preliminary observations, some controls have been introduced to insure that the histological changes are not artifactual. One might argue, for example, that such nests of deeply stained cells are occasionally (although rarely, in our experience, if the brain is properly fixed) found in normal brain. These may be due to random variations in penetration of dye, fixation of material, or even in the capacity of the cell to take the stain for reasons other than those suggested in our experimental procedure. One might also consider that such cells were damaged in the course of removal of the brain or in the fixation procedure and that the deep stain indicates nothing more than pyknosis. Most of these objections may be countered by the following evidence: (1) The densely staining cell aggregates were seen in different cortical zones in each of the experimental animals and consistently were related to the electrical focus rather than to any particular cortical zone. (2) Adjacent sections from the same animal indicated that stained areas could be superimposed, thus excluding random staining of the slide. (3) The brains were perfused with fixatives while the animals were under deep anaesthesia but still alive. This procedure minimized cell changes due to poor fixation. Moreover, it would seem unusual that fixation artifact would vary in location from animal to animal in a manner precisely concordant with variations in the site of electrical discharge. There remains the argument, which may be

CC

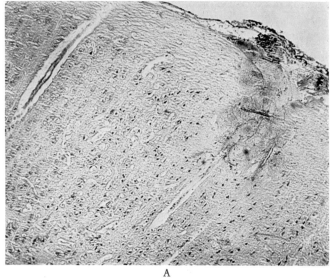

A

Fig. 12

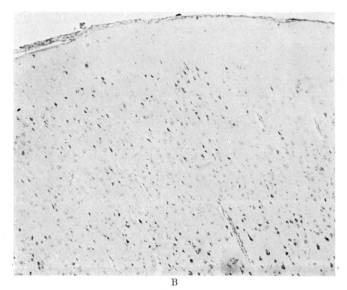

B

Fig. 12

Area of the primary histological lesion compared with the exactly homotopic
region in the same section. Small densely stained cells are seen around the
primary lesion while in the contralateral cortex fewer cells seem to take the
stain than in regions closer to the area of maximal electrical discharge. Methyl
green pyronin stain. Magnification × 75.

valid at least for the primary lesion, that the dark cells are simply partially chromatolysed neurones. Yet the same sort of cells are seen in the mirror focus, an area which has been untouched by the experimental procedure, the cortex remaining unexposed until the brain itself was removed. Neither can one account for these findings on the basis of retrograde degeneration for such histochemical changes are not seen contralateral to a simple cortical excision.

The observation that changes in ribonucleic acid occur in cell populations subjected to continuous synaptic bombardment is not in itself surprising. Hyden and co-workers, using much more elegant techniques (Hyden, 1943; Brattgard and Hyden, 1952) have already demonstrated increases in cellular RNA with various kinds of stimulation (Hamberger and Hyden, 1949). They have also demonstrated that such changes occur transneuronally (Hamberger and Hyden, 1949a). The intriguing question raised in the present investigation is not the relation of RNA to nerve activity or inactivity, but rather the relationship of RNA to the coding of that information necessary to effectuate permanent alteration of cellular excitability.

For the moment it seems reasonable to present the working hypothesis that the cells of the mirror focus undergo a structural alteration and that changes in distribution of RNA, perhaps linked with protein or phospholipids, form the chemical correlates of this alteration. Since the cells and cell systems of the mirror focus have been shown to have some of the attributes of learning and of memory, it is perhaps not too far fetched to consider that the complex of ribonucleic acid and protein represents an essential element in the molecular basis of memory.

ACKNOWLEDGMENT

I should like to express appreciation to Doctors Kenneth Osterberg and K. L. Chow for help with the histochemical material.

GROUP DISCUSSION

MAGOUN. I wonder if Dr Morrell plans to profit in his cytochemical studies from a simpler situation, where the sensitization of denervation can be detected in greater isolation than in the cortex, such as in a post-ganglionic relay in the peripheral autonomic system which Cannon and his associates studied for so many years. Study of the sensitization of a mirror focus in epileptic genesis in the cerebral cortex is one of which Dr French and others have been investigating at Los Angeles. Dr Morrell's results are similar to theirs and since he has made reference to their work I will not need to elaborate it here. Dr Doty in an earlier meeting was interested in the effect of mirror foci in the cerebral cortex, from the point of view of cerebral cortex in the establishment of intracortical conditioned reflexes. I wonder if he has now additional information?

DOTY. The conditions of our experiments would not have permitted the observation of such a focus.

CHOW. I would like to add a word of caution about the histological pictures Dr Morrell showed. The R.N.A. staining is a very tricky thing to study unless another stain is used to corroborate this result. Another point is that in the last few years Dr Riesen, Dr Rush and I studied the problem from another angle, that is we want to study the problem of disuse. We have reared cats, rats, monkeys and chimpanzees in darkness and studied the visual, behavioural and retinal structural effects. We have examined the retina of dark-reared animals with the conventional stain and the R.N.A. stain. In rats, cats and monkeys reared in darkness the retina appeared normal to the haematoxylin and eosin stain, but with the Azure B stain there was a reduction in the content of the R.N.A. of the rod and cones, bipolar and ganglion cells. In the chimpanzee we have observed in two cases, almost complete degeneration of the ganglion cell layer. In these eyes we did not stain the R.N.A. This is the first example we have had of possible structure changes in the visual system in higher animals due to disuse.

MORRELL. We have not proved that the histological changes observed are due to neuronal bombardment of these specific cells. Some of the negative observations are consistent with those of Dr Chow in that the area opposite the primary histological lesion is paler and shows a loss of R.N.A. I do not think that the electrical changes can be attributed to denervation sensitization since experiments on the partially isolated cortex in which the corpus callosum was intact do not show the characteristic electrical changes. The electrical as opposed to the histological changes in the mirror focus are, I think, a result of synaptic bombardment.

MYERS. I should like to suggest that the firing of some areas of cortex may be more effective than of others for the elicitation of contralateral effects of the nature under study by Dr Morrell. Since he and others have demonstrated the importance of the corpus callosum for the development of the mirror focus it would seem desirable that the areas chosen for the making of epileptogenic lesions have the most dense interhemispheric interconnections. Such a suggestion may be of more than academic importance inasmuch as there exists profound differences in density of corpus callosum projection from different areas over the cortical surface. The visual receptive area and the primary projection areas in general, including incidentally the somatomotor areas, have the least dense while the adjoining or so-called associative cortex tends to have the most dense projection through the corpus callosum.

The Pacella Kopeloff and Jasper group have carried out a number of early studies of the mirror focus and, as I recall, investigated the mirror focus using biochemical as well as electrographic techniques. I believe they found significant changes in the chemistry of the mirror focus as compared to normal tissue. I wonder if Dr Morrell recalls what these findings might have been in relation to the present discussion.

MORRELL. Although most of our lesions were placed in visual cortex a good number of them were in somatosensory and in motor cortex.

MYERS. Again, it seems that these three cortical areas have least to offer in terms of contralateral firing.

MORRELL. One of the reasons why most of our lesions have been made in sensory areas is that epileptogenic lesions of the motor cortex often produce clinical seizures. These may result in death of the animal or may require anticonvulsant treatment, and this of course complicates the experiment.

MYERS. Have you had the opportunity to study species variation in regard to the development of contralateral foci of independent firing?

MORRELL. I have not had time to delineate species variation in the development of secondary foci. However, we have done these experiments in rabbits, cats and monkeys and have been able to demonstrate differences in the time required for the establishment of mirror foci in each of these animals. In the cat and monkey it is much longer than in the rabbit. Penfield has made the statement that if a lesion has been present for approximately 2 years (monkey) ablation of the primary site does not lead to disappearance of the mirror focus.

MYERS. Was Penfield's data related to cortical areas other than the temporal tip.

MORRELL. In motor cortex.

NAQUET. You said that the isolated cortex in the normal animal has a higher threshold than in your preparation.

MORRELL. In preparations with well-developed secondary foci there is, of course, no normal side. The threshold to electrical stimulation of the non-epileptic isolated cortex is higher than that in the adjacent surrounding cortex.

NAQUET. I agree but I feel that we cannot compare what happens in the isolated cortex when you stimulate electrically to what happens spontaneously. I think we may ask Dr Garcia-Austt what he thinks about it.

MORRELL. There have, as you are all aware, been great disputes as to whether spontaneous rhythms are present in completely neuronally isolated cortical tissue. It is obviously impossible, even with serial sections, to be sure that no threads of tissue remain connecting the cortical slab to the surrounding brain. Nevertheless, in our experience, if good isolation is achieved there is no clearly demonstrable spontaneous paroxysmal epileptiform activity in the isolated region.

FESSARD. Sensitization of isolated slabs of cortex to acetyl-choline is a fact that has been carefully studied recently in monkeys by Dr Frank Echlin. His paper will come out soon in the EEG Journal. Have you heard of this work? It impressed me much when I visited Dr Echlin recently in New York.

MORRELL. We have not placed acetyl-choline directly on isolated cortical regions. With electrical stimulation the non-epileptic isolated slab has a higher threshold than normal cortex.

LISSÁK. Regarding Dr Fessard's question, some 10 years ago with my colleagues Dr Endroczi and Dr Hasznos we did some experiments on isolated cortex. We found an increased sensitivity to acetyl-choline and we determined the choline esterase activity too and we found that it was decreased not only in the isolated cortex but also to some degree in the contralateral mirror part of the cortex.

GARCIA-AUSTT. I would like to ask some questions. We also have been working with isolated cortical slabs. We think that the slabs have a greater capacity to respond with a seizure to stimulation and also to spontaneous seizure discharge. As to the threshold — we have not studied it as measured by the threshold voltage to give a seizure — but we found that post-discharge, if measured half an hour after isolation is more prolonged in the isolated cortex than in the cortex before isolation. On the other hand, if it is tested within the first half-hour, it is very hard to get. So the question is — what do you mean by threshold and when were these tested in relation to the isolation procedure? Also did the epileptical activity in the mirror cortex in some cases increase after isolation? Have you tested the sensitivity to metrazol given intravenously of the cortex from the other side?

MORRELL. Thresholds were determined by electrical stimulation measured in terms of the amount of current required to establish self-sustained afterdischarges. Excitability is usually depressed immediately after isolation, may be augmented a few hours later and is usually depressed again days or weeks later. We often did find that spontaneous electrical abnormality increased for a short period after isolation in some cases. In most cases it did not persist and gradually disappeared. It is interesting that the electrical abnormality of the mirror region frequently increased after isolation of the primary cortical lesion. We have administered systemic metrazol to most of these animals and found that the paroxysmal discharges usually did begin in the isolated epileptic regions. This is not surprising because I think it is a common observation that seizures induced by systemic metrazol start in any region where trauma to nerve cells has been produced.

GERARD. I am delighted with these findings, and with the demonstration of transmission of influence across a cut — one, incidentally, considerably more than 200 micra. This is very satisfactory. I do not know of another clear-cut case since our frog brain work. On the question of spontaneity of the isolated part, I suspect that we have been too easily assuming that all parts will be alike, I remind you that even with the frog's brain, where a fraction of a milligramme bit will give regular electrical beats, not any part of the brain will do. The olfactory bulb is particularly vigorous. A second point: have you to your own satisfaction excluded possible secondary effects through the pia, either neural or humoral — like the findings of Burn and the automatic activity described by Bach, where effects on the slab were induced indirectly and not electrically? Finally, on the R.N.A. story I would like to mention work done by Edith Maynard in our laboratory. She has followed spontaneous or evoked discharges in the isolated lobster cardiac ganglion. A ganglion soaked in the R.N.A.ase for 8 hours, and shown then to have no R.N.A. by histological tests, continues to show normal physiological activity. It is, however, possible that the R.N.A.ase is not destroyed by the fixation process and only enters the cell at the time of fixation; so that this observation requires further check. It is, however, most interesting, especially considering the evidence of Tobias that peripheral fibres soaked in proteolytic enzymes could practically dissolve without significant change in the action potentials, whereas with lipases conduction was quickly abolished with no evidence of histological change.

MORRELL. It is very difficult to exclude the effects which might be produced by substances carried through the pial vessels. One has to maintain the pial circulation intact in order to have a viable slab. I do not know any way of getting around this difficulty.

FUNCTIONAL ROLE OF SUBCORTICAL STRUCTURES IN HABITUATION AND CONDITIONING

R. HERNÁNDEZ-PEÓN AND H. BRUST-CARMONA

Until a few years ago it was generally assumed that at least in mammals the cortex was necessary for learning and that learning was therefore a cortical process. Furthermore, it was assumed that the neural association of stimuli during positive learning takes place intracortically by means of two-dimensional cortico-cortical connections. However, it has been established in dogs and cats that decorticated animals can learn and can retain some simple responses learned before decortication. Therefore, it is evident that subcortical structures play an important role in basic learning processes. In the present paper this role will be discussed on the basis of the experimental evidence obtained by the authors.

HABITUATION

If a non-significant stimulus is repeated even at intervals of hours or days, a decrement of response is observed which may last for hours, days and years. Recognized as having a nature different from fatigue and adaptation at the receptor (Griffith, 1924) this long-lasting decline of behavioural responses is usually referred to as habituation. As it has been rightly pointed out by Thorpe (1950), habituation represents the simplest type of learning. It involves stimulation of a single modality, and it is found through all the animal scale, from protozoa to man. Habituation in the latter can be observed both in effector responses (somatic and autonomic) as well as in sensory experiences. Because of the ubiquity of habituation in organisms of every grade of evolution, it seems warranted to conclude that learning derives from some fundamental property of living matter, and that, therefore, learning does not necessarily require special complex neuronal circuits. We consider it convenient to use the term *plasticity* proposed by Konorski (1948) in order to distinguish that property from another fundamental phenomenology of living cells, *excitability*, which is related to very transient changes produced by the stimulus. In animals with nervous systems in which 'all or none' signals are transmitted, plasticity permits the storage of information delivered by those signals, whereas excitability is concerned with their generation and transmission.

393

Habituation is not only the primary learning process, but seems to be a common and necessary denominator in the establishment of all other more complex types of learning. Indeed, the acquisition of any specific motor performance is accompanied by the elimination of a great number of originally present irrelevant responses. Therefore, when searching for the neurophysiological basis of learning, the importance of understanding the basic mechanisms of habituation becomes apparent.

Granting that through specialization of function, plasticity as well as excitability are more developed in certain elements of multicellular organisms, there is no doubt that the nervous system is endowed with the privilege of both properties. There are two fundamental questions about the mechanisms of plastic changes, and therefore of learning, (1) What is the ultimate nature of plasticity? (2) Where are the neurones in which these properties are more developed? Our total ignorance on the first question cannot be overemphasized. The reason for this, it must be admitted, is that the right method for obtaining direct evidence of plastic changes has not as yet been elaborated and applied to the study of the nervous system. More attention has been devoted to the second question concerning the locus of learning in the nervous system. The outstanding development of the cortical mantle in the human brain, and its upper anatomical location have impressed most scientists in the past who have granted the cerebral cortex the highest rank in the neural hierarchy. Very often, this contention has been upheld to the point of assuming that all the learning processes take place exclusively at the cortical level. There is much evidence, however, to indicate that many types of simple learned behavioural responses do not require the cerebral cortex. Lower vertebrates with no true cortex as well as invertebrates which do not even have a brain, are capable of learning. But although it is evident that habituation in lower vertebrates does not require phylogenetically new structures such as the cortex, it might be argued that in mammals the greatly developed cortical mantle has taken over the basic mechanisms of learning originally located in lower brain structures of other animals. With the aim of assessing the role and capacity of different levels of the mammalian neuraxis for the establishment of habituation the following experiments were performed.

Vestibular habituation in decorticated and decerebrated cats. Following a period of controversy, Griffith (1920) established that post-rotatory nystagmus in man decreases with repetition of rotation, and that such decline bears a striking resemblance to the traditional learning curve. The same author observed the cumulative and long-lasting effects of habituation in response to vestibular stimuli. In one case, habituation persisted 4 years after the last experiment during which the subject was rotated.

By means of electromyographic recordings from the extra-ocular muscles, we have confirmed in intact cats that repeated rotation leads to a decrease of the number and amplitude of ocular movements. As shown in

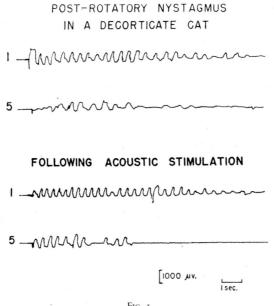

FIG. 1

Electromyographic recordings of post-rotatory nystagmus in a decorticate cat. Recording was initiated immediately after stopping rotation which lasted for 15 seconds. The rotations were repeated every minute. The uppermost tracings represent the initial control. The second shows the reduction of nystagmus (habituation) after five trials. A startling acoustic stimulus was applied and the nystagmus recorded after the next rotation showed recovery (dishabituation) but it was reduced again after five more trials (rehabituation).

Fig. 1, habituation of post-rotatory nystagmus was also present in cats with bilateral removal of the neocortex, and usually the number of rotational series needed to extinguish completely ocular movements was less in them than in the intact cats.

Since these experiments demonstrated that the neocortex is unnecessary for habituation to vestibular stimuli, the role of the diencephalon and rostral mesencephalon was tested by transecting the brain stem at the mid-collicular level. In these animals, a rapid decline of post-rotational ocular movements was also obtained (Fig. 2). Such results indicated that habituation of post-rotatory nystagmus does not require the thalamic station of the vestibular pathway either, and pointed to the lower brain stem as the

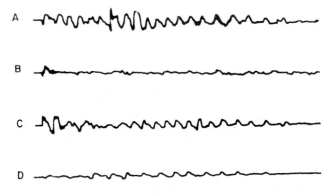

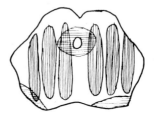

FIG. 2

Electromyographic recordings of post-rotatory nystagmus. (A) Nystagmus of the first experimental rotation. (B) After habituation had been established with thirty rotations an extensive electrolytic lesion which rendered the cat unconscious was made in the mesencephalic tegmentum. (C) The first rotation after the lesion elicited nystagmus which diminished at a faster rate than in the awake intact animal with successive trials. D represents the recording obtained after fifteen trials with the brain stem lesion.

probable source of inhibitory mechanisms which prevent the discharge of extra-ocular motoneurones after repeated vestibular stimulation. Subsequent experiments demonstrated that lesions in the mesencephalic reticular formation did not prevent habituation of post-rotatory nystagmus but that lesions placed in the pontine tegmentum prevented the habituatory process.

Tactile habituation at the spinal cord in intact cats. The participation of the various levels of the central nervous system (including the lowest one) in habituation can be demonstrated only by studying spinal afferent responses which might be modified by the spinal cord itself.

It is known that repetition of electrical stimuli applied to the skin results in a significant decrement of the corresponding sweat, respiratory and muscular responses (Seward and Seward, 1934). By local electromyographic recordings Hagbarth and Kugelberg (1958) have recently shown that the abdominal skin reflex also undergoes habituation by

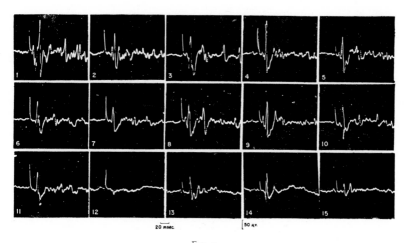

FIG. 3

Habituation of tactile evoked potentials recorded from the lateral column of the spinal cord in an awake freely moving cat. The tactile stimulus (single cutaneous shock) was regularly repeated at intervals of 10 seconds.

repetition of the corresponding stimuli. All these observations indicate that like other polysynaptic reflex responses, spinal reflexes induced by tactile stimulation can be diminished in the intact organism by a process of habituation.

Since previous studies have demonstrated that habituation can occur as far down as the cochlear nucleus (Hernández-Peón, Jouvet and Scherrer, 1957), the retina (Palestini, Davidovich and Hernández-Peón, 1959), the olfactory bulb (Hernández-Peón, Alcocer-Cuarón, Lavín and Santibañez 1957), and the spinal fifth sensory nucleus (Hernández-Peón, Miranda and Davidovich, 1959), it seemed likely that *afferent neuronal habituation* would also occur at the spinal level. With the purpose of testing this hypothesis,

bipolar electrodes were permanently implanted in the lateral column of
the upper thoracic segments of the spinal cord. In order to prevent dis-
placements of the spinal cord during movements of the vertebral column,
the vertebra to be perforated was tightly fixed to the adjacent vertebrae by
means of a vanadium plate. The electrode was made up of two insulated
stainless steel wires, the tips of which were bared and 1 mm. apart.
Single electrical square pulses of 0.1 msec. duration and of intensities
which produced only tactile sensations when applied to the experimenter's
skin, were delivered to the cat's skin. The cutaneous area whose stimulation evoked the potentials recorded by the spinal electrode was always
small and very localized.

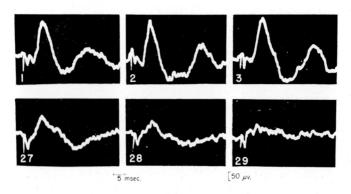

FIG. 4

Habituation of spinal potentials (recorded from the lateral column) evoked by
mild cutaneous shocks regularly repeated at intervals of 10 seconds in a freely
moving cat. Whereas the late waves were greatly reduced or abolished with
twenty-nine trials, the primary short-latency component remained unaffected.

Repetition of those tactile stimuli led to a progressive and oscillating
decline of the spinal evoked potentials (Fig. 3) which eventually could be
completely extinguished. As shown in Fig. 4, in contrast with the stability
of short latency components, the late waves of the evoked responses were
more susceptible to habituation. Usually the rate of repetition of stimuli
was one every 10 seconds, but decrement of response was also observed
with longer intervals between successive stimuli. Stimulation at faster
rates (once every 1 or 2 seconds) made the evoked potentials decline more
rapidly than at slower rates. As in afferent neuronal habituation in other
sensory pathways, great individual variation was observed in the number
of stimuli required to extinguish the spinal evoked potentials. That number
ranged between dozens and several hundreds.

Interruption of monotonous stimulation usually led to restoration of the diminished response (dishabituation). But successive series of stimuli elicited the same degree of response decrement with a lesser number of stimuli than was required for the first series. Dishabituation of the tactile

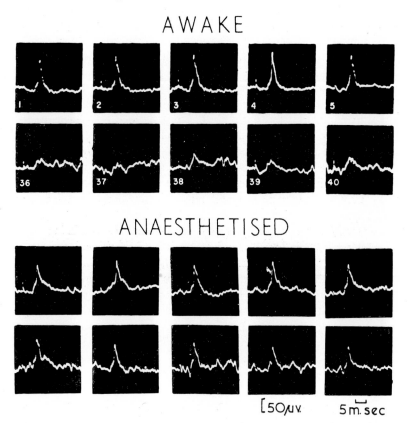

FIG. 5

Releasing effects of anaesthesia upon spinal tactile habituation. The upper two rows show the reduction of the evoked potentials obtained after forty repetitions of the tactile stimulus in the awake animal. Then the cat was anaesthetized with pentobarbital. The lower two rows show the great stability of the potentials evoked by the same number of stimuli.

spinal potentials was also observed by presenting an alerting acoustic stimulus, or by a transient increase of the intensity or frequency of the regular tactile stimuli. As has been observed in other sensory pathways, recovery of the extinguished responses was obtained by central anaesthesia. The spinal evoked potentials were not only restored to their original magnitude by sodium pentobarbital, but remained remarkably stable in this condition (Fig. 5).

Tactile habituation at the spinal cord in decorticated cats. After establishing that afferent neuronal habituation also occurs at spinal sensory neurones in intact cats, the possible participation of the cerebral cortex in this phenomenon was explored in cats whose neocortex had been totally removed 2 or 3 months before. In all of them, the spinal evoked potentials also declined, sometimes at a faster rate, with repetition of the tactile stimuli.

Tactile habituation at the spinal cord in decerebrated cats. It being evident that the neocortex is not necessary for the establishment of afferent neuronal habituation at the spinal cord, it was deemed convenient to test whether structures in the forebrain, temporal lobe or diencephalon might play a role in the demonstrated habituatory spinal sensory suppression. With this aim in view, the brain stem was severed at the mid-collicular level leaving intact all the mesencephalic tegmentum in the remaining brain stem. In these mesencephalic animals, habituation of tactile evoked responses at the spinal cord was readily observed (Fig. 6), and not infrequently the number of stimuli required for extinguishing those responses was again less than in intact animals. Dishabituation was also observed following a transient increase of the stimulus intensity.

From the results just presented it is obvious that tactile habituation at the spinal cord can take place in cats with only the sub-diencephalic portion of their central nervous system. If, according to the view proposed by one of us (Hernández-Peón, 1955, 1957, 1959), afferent neuronal habituation at second-order sensory neurones results from centrifugal inhibitory influences proceeding from the reticular system of the lower brain stem, the spinal responses extinguished by habituation in the mesencephalic preparation should be enhanced by interrupting the postulated descending inhibitory path to the spinal sensory neurones. This hypothesis was tested by performing a high transection of the spinal cord in those decerebrated cats which had already been habituated to repeated tactile stimuli.

Tactile habituation at the spinal cord in spinal cats. Shortly after severance of the spinal cord at C2, the tactile evoked potentials were remarkably enhanced. Very often, as illustrated in Fig. 6, not only did the evoked potentials recover the magnitude they showed before habituation, but the enhancement surpassed the original size. These results clearly indicate that a descending influence which acts upon spinal sensory neurones originates in the lower brain stem itself. Another conclusion to be drawn from the same results is that the electrophysiological correlates of afferent neuronal habituation at the spinal cord in mesencephalic cats depends on that descending influence.

From the preceding experiments it is evident that brain stem structures participate in spinal habituation. However, those experiments do not preclude the possibility that the isolated spinal cord might also be capable of performing that function. Whether the spinal cord is able to learn is a

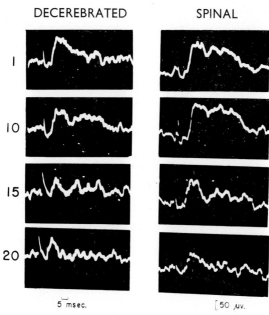

DECEREBRATED   SPINAL

1

10

15

20

5 msec.   [50 μv.

FIG. 6

Tactile evoked potentials recorded from the lateral column of the spinal cord. The left column shows the decrement observed in a decerebrate cat during a series of twenty cutaneous shocks delivered at a rate of 1/sec. The responses of the right column were obtained in the same animal immediately after transecting the spinal cord above the recording site.

question whose answer is of considerable importance to the conceptualization of integrative levels of the C.N.S. in learning processes.

Our spinal preparation permitted us to investigate this question. It was found that repetition of tactile stimuli in spinal cats also led to a progressive decline of the corresponding evoked potentials (Fig. 6). And, as happens in intact animals, a transient increase in the intensity of the stimulus caused the diminished responses to have a greater amplitude after the disrupting stimulus. Again, the effects of repetition of the tactile stimuli in the spinal cats were long lasting, and appeared to be cumulative.

These experiments indicate that plastic inhibition can develop in the isolated spinal cord and confirm the results obtained by Prosser and Hunter (1936) in the rat. By electromyographic and mechanical recordings they observed in the spinal rat fading of spinal flexor reflexes with repetition of the corresponding stimuli. Because of the features which prevent the identification of this diminution of responsiveness with fatigue and sensory adaptation, Prosser and Hunter, rightly interpreted the phenomenon as habituation and assumed that it involved spinal internuncial neurones rather than the first sensory elements or the final motoneurones.

From the foregoing considerations it is evident that in addition to the supraspinal influences acting upon sensory impulses there is an intraspinal mechanism which regulates the excitability of lower order sensory neurones, and consequently the entrance of afferent impulses into the spinal cord itself. Such a mechanism implies a local feed-back circuit in which spinal interneurones are likely to be involved. The interneurones are activated by collaterals from spino-thalamic fibres, and in turn they would inhibit the corresponding sensory neurones. This hypothetical sensory circuit would be comparable to the ventral horn circuit formed by the recurrent collaterals of motor axons and the Renshaw cells which have been found to inhibit the motoneurones (Eccles, 1957).

CONDITIONING

Conditioning results in the acquisition of a response (conditioned response) to a stimulus (conditional stimulus) which previously was not effective in eliciting that response. Conditioning may be considered to represent one of the simplest types of positive learning, just as habituation represents the simplest type of negative learning. From the neurophysiological point of view, conditioning must necessarily involve *plastic associative phenomena* which must take place in some central region of convergence of sensory impulses. Pavlov (Pavlov, 1928) used the term *temporary connections* to designate the process of neural association, but we prefer to call it simply *plastic association*, since its manifestations can be so permanent as to endure for the life of the individual.

In studying conditioning it must be borne in mind that the development of the conditioned behaviour involves the emergence of new responses to the conditional stimulus (*plastic association*), as well as the disappearance of inborn and acquired responses (*plastic inhibition*) (Hernández-Peón, 1957). Therefore, the total conditioned behaviour varies throughout the different stages of the experimental procedure. It should also be emphasized that the conditioned reaction is not a simple replica of the unconditioned response, but usually involves more complex behavioural changes revealed by the expectant attitude of the animal.

According to the Pavlovian traditional concept, all processes of plastic association and plastic inhibition occur at the cerebral cortex, in the absence of which conditioning is assumed to be impossible. There is plenty of evidence, however, to indicate that acquisition and retention of conditioned responses in dogs and cats do not require the neocortex (Bromiley, 1948; Culler and Mettler, 1934; Girden, Mettler, Finch and Culler, 1936; Ten Cate, 1938; Wing, 1946; Wing, 1947; Wing and Smith, 1942; Zelény and Kadykov, 1938).

Although conditioning in the decorticate animals provided clear evidence concerning the essential role of subcortical structures in plastic associative phenomena, the relative importance of each of them for the establishment of conditioning remained to be shown. By making subcortical lesions in cats, Hernández-Peón, *et al.* (Hernández-Peón, Brust-Carmona, Eckhaus, López-Mendoza and Alcocer-Cuarón, 1958) found that a nociceptive salivary conditioned response was eliminated only by lesions in the mesencephalic reticular formation. These lesions did not interfere with wakefulness, but produced striking behavioural changes to be described later on.

In so far as the mesencephalic tegmentum is a region of rich afferent convergence, and since the above-mentioned results pointed out its importance in basic associative phenomena, the following questions were raised: does a mesencephalic lesion equally impair conditioned responses to stimuli of different modalities? Does it affect to the same extent both classical alimentary and defensive conditioned responses? In an attempt to answer those questions the following experiments were performed using cats in which two different responses were conditioned: (1) alimentary responses to visual and olfactory stimuli and (2) defensive flexor responses to an acoustic stimulus.

Conditioned alimentary responses in intact cats. The unconditional stimulus consisted of a bit of fish. This was brought near the cat by means of a clamp attached to a thread which was introduced through a tube in the ceiling of the cage. The light of a lamp placed at the ceiling and the sight and smell of the fish were the conditional stimuli. Salivation was measured by counting the drops of saliva flowing through a poly-ethylene tube

DD

permanently implanted in the parotid duct. The light was turned on 4 seconds before presenting the food to the animal. A typical conditioned pattern of behaviour was established after ten to fifteen trials (Fig. 7). As soon as the light was turned on, the cat showed an orienting reaction directed towards the opening through which the food was delivered. Then the cat stared and approached the food-clamp upon its presentation. Very often, the cat tried to catch the food by rising on its hindlegs. During the presentation of the conditional visual stimuli, one or two drops of saliva flowed through the parotid catheter.

Conditioned flexor response in intact cats. After the establishment of alimentary conditioned responses, the cats were conditioned to acoustic and

FIG. 7

This figure illustrates the sequential behavioural response of a cat conditioned with visual stimuli (light and food-holder) and food. When the light was turned on, the cat oriented its head towards the lamp and when seeing the food-holder it rose on its feet and tried to catch the food.

nociceptive stimuli according to the following procedure: the animal was immobilized in a harness to which its legs were fastened. A buzzer was rung for 5 seconds and then a shock was delivered from a Grass Stimulator through electrodes attached to the left foreleg of the animal. The shock evoked a definite flexion of the limb and generalized struggling movements. The contraction of the flexor muscles of the left foreleg was recorded with bipolar intramuscular electrodes and an electromyograph. After six to ten buzzer-shock associations, the buzzer alone elicited the flexion of the limb and the struggling reaction.

Conditioned alimentary responses in decorticate cats. Salivation and the expectant attitude were easily conditioned to the light and to the fish odour in cats from which the neocortex had been bilaterally removed 2 to

6 months before (Fig. 8). But in contrast with the intact animals, these cats did not seem to recognize the fish-clamp nor could they reach the food easily.

Conditioned flexor response in decorticate cats. In decorticate cats the flexor response was readily conditioned to the buzzer. Usually the

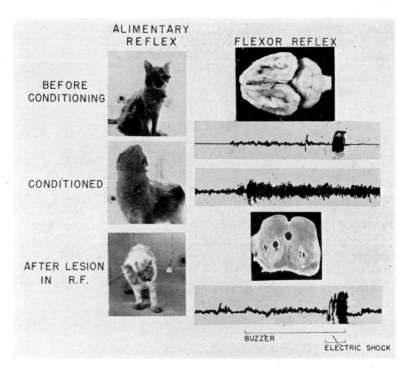

FIG. 8

Conditioned alimentary and flexor responses in a cat with the neocortex bilaterally removed. Then a lesion was made in the mesencephalic reticular formation and both kinds of responses disappeared.

number of associations required for establishing the conditioned response was not greater than in the intact cats.

Effects of mesencephalic lesions on the conditioned alimentary and flexor responses. Once the conditioned alimentary and flexor responses had been established, electrolytic lesions were made in the posterior part of the mesencephalic reticular formation (plane A-2 of the stereotaxic maps of the cat's brain). Usually the lesion did not yield unconsciousness, and the animals awoke when the anaesthetic wore off, although two animals remained unconscious for 2 days.

The cats were tested 1 to 3 days after the operation and when they were wide awake. All the alimentary responses conditioned to visual stimuli were absent. The orienting reaction and salivation were no longer elicited by turning the light on, nor by placing the fish-clamp with food within

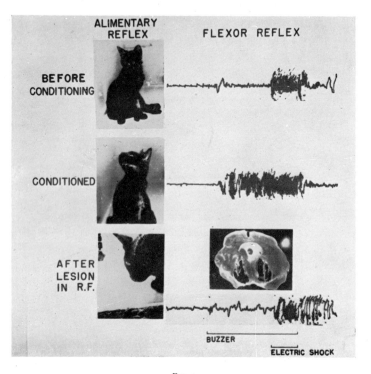

FIG. 9

This figure illustrates the disappearance of alimentary and flexor conditioned responses consecutive to a lesion in the mesencephalic tegmentum. Notice that the brain stem injured cat does not seem to perceive the food placed within its visual field.

the visual field of the animal at short distances from it, as illustrated in Fig. 9. Only when the food was put very near its nose did the cat begin to sniff and salivate, but it was unable to detect the location of the food. However, when the food was placed near its mouth, the cat eagerly ate it and salivated abundantly. Also in these cats the buzzer did not elicit the flexion of the limb nor the generalized struggle reaction (Fig. 9). And there were no indications that the conditioned motor response could be re-established by the buzzer-shock associations.

Moreover, the general behaviour of all these cats with such mesencephalic lesion was strikingly changed. The most notorious feature was impairment of their vision and pain reactions. When walking, they bumped into objects and the walls of the laboratory, i.e. they behaved as though they were completely blind. They were also unresponsive to painful stimuli which, both in the intact and in the decorticate cats, evoked crawling and aggressive behaviour.

From the foregoing results it is evident that whereas extensive cortical removals did not prevent conditioning, a small lesion in the mesencephalic reticular formation eliminated visual and acoustic conditioned responses. It must be emphasized that the mesencephalic lesion impaired various sensory discriminations to different degrees. While vision was most impaired, olfaction seemed to be the modality least affected. It is difficult to offer a satisfactory explanation for the surprising blindness produced by a lesion placed far behind the specific visual pathway. But the apparent difficulty may be disposed of, if one remembers (a) that the mesencephalic reticular formation receives photic impulses from the retina (French, Verzeano and Magoun, 1953) as well as from cortical visual areas (French, Hernández-Peón and Livingston, 1955), and (b) that electrical stimulation of the same area modifies the excitability of the retina (Granit, 1955; Hernández-Peón, Scherrer and Velasco, 1956), the lateral geniculate body (Hernández-Peón, Scherrer and Velasco, 1956), and the visual cortex (Bremer and Stoupel, 1959). The impairment of vision might be the result of an interference with the centrifugal mechanisms which regulate transmission along the specific visual pathway, and/or with the final integration of the photic impulses which result in conscious vision. This explanation falls in line with the view proposed by Penfield (Penfield, 1958, 1959) about the *highest level of sensory integration*. According to this author, the final integration of sensory impulses is not achieved at the cortical level but at the 'centrencephalon' where they are finally conveyed. The anatomical substratum of the 'centrencephalic system' is the higher brain stem which includes the diencephalon, the mesencephalon and probably the metencephalon. Our results indicate the important role played by the brain stem in the integration of sensory impulses which accompanies learning processes, and thus lend experimental support to Penfield's hypothesis.

The unavoidable conclusion that plastic association during conditioning takes place at subcortical levels does not preclude cortical participation in

certain aspects of conditioning and learning in general. The integrity of
the cortex for complex discriminations is as important as the integrity of
subcortical structures for some of the simplest types of learning (habituation
and earliest manifestations of conditioning). Therefore, all the levels of the
central nervous system appear to be endowed with plastic properties which
cannot be ascribed exclusively to any particular locus of the brain.

GROUP DISCUSSION

DOTY. I completely agree with Dr Hernández-Peón with regard to the exceptional importance of subcortical mechanisms in the establishment and performance
of conditioned responses.

We can offer some additional experimental support (Doty, Beck and Kooi,
1959) for his position. Fig. 1 shows extensive brain stem lesions totalling 100

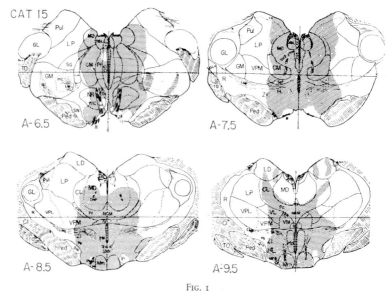

FIG. 1

Lesions in the central diencephalon, represented on plates from the stereotaxic atlas of Jasper
and Ajmone-Marsan (1954). See text. (From Doty, R. W., Beck, E. C. and Kooi, K. A.,
1959. Effect of brain stem lesions on conditioned responses of cats. *Experimental Neurology*,
1, 360).

mm.[3] anterior, however, to the mesencephalon. This animal gradually recovered
from a cataleptic stupor during the first two post-operative weeks, and Fig. 2
shows that the EEG ultimately returned to normal levels. The animal walked after
the third week and would blink to a visually presented threat. No other conditioned
reactions could be observed post-operatively. Prior to surgery this cat made
discrete, conditioned flexions of a leg 80 per cent of the time to a tonal CS and

conditioned respiratory responses 95 per cent of the time. During 1325 post-operative retraining trials in twenty-six sessions over a period of 37 days there was not even a suggestion of a conditioned response (e.g. Fig. 3).

On the other hand, in another animal an enormous lesion totalling 113 mm.[3] destroying most of the central mesencephalon (Fig. 4) and producing a profound catalepsy for the 21 days of survival did not preclude the appearance of conditioned reflexes. One could not claim the level of conditioned responsiveness was high in this cat, but neither had it been very good pre-operatively (see Doty, Beck and

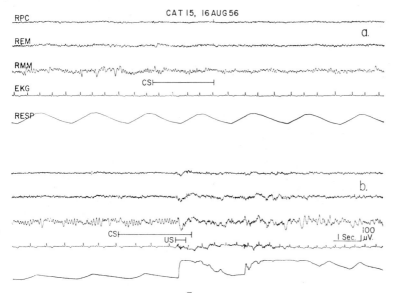

FIG. 2

EEG taken on the thirty-sixth post-operative day, of cat having lesions shown in Fig. D-6. (a) lack of response to presentation of CS alone after twenty-six CS-US pairings on this day which brought the total to 1253 pairings since surgery. (b) the forty-eighth pairing of the same day showing transition to low voltage, fast activity in marginal gyrus to the US but not the CS. (From Doty, R. W., Beck, E. C. and Kooi, K. A., 1959. Effect of brain stem lesions on conditioned responses of cats. *Experimental Neurology*, **1**, 360.)

Kooi, 1959) and it seems probable that a prolongation of life would have seen a more impressive recovery. The best performance was six flexion CRs in a session of forty-five trials and respiratory CRs were then present 25 per cent of the time. Equally interesting, in view of the importance of the mesencephalic reticular system is electrocortical 'arousal' reactions, in the return of low voltage, fast patterns for long periods in the EEG of this animal and the presence of an 'arousal' reaction accompanying conditioned responses (Fig. D-10).

Thus, we cannot support the idea that the mesencephalic reticular formation is of any extraordinary importance in this type of conditioning. I am certain that differences in period of survival and other details can account for this apparent contradiction between the experiments of Dr Hernández-Peón and ourselves.

HERNÁNDEZ-PEÓN. Were these animals unconscious after the lesion and how long did they remain unconscious?

DOTY. They were certainly unconscious for many days following surgery.

HERNÁNDEZ-PEÓN. The point is that the lesions we made did not impair consciousness. The animals awoke and were able to walk after the anaesthesia wore off. In cats with larger lesions producing unconsciousness, the long period of recovery probably involves several unknown processes which may mask completely the immediate effects of the lesion. In fact Dr Brust-Carmona reported in January of this year that in cats with small reticular lesions leg withdrawal can be conditioned

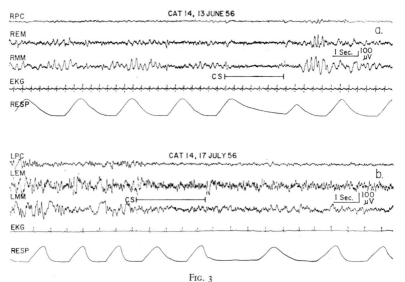

FIG. 3

EEG records from cat having lesions shown in Fig. D-8. (a) pre-operative record of conditioned respiratory response and electrocortical arousal reaction to the CS. (b) first CS presented on the sixth post-operative day produces an arousal reaction and a respiratory CR. Note that record b is at double the gain of a; hence the post-operative electrical activity is remarkably near normal. (From Doty, R. W., Beck, E. C. and Kooi, K. A., 1959. Effect of brain-stem lesions on conditioned responses of cats. *Experimental Neurology*, **I**, 360.)

1 month after the lesion was made, but that lesions in the subthalamic region (smaller than Doty's) definitely impaired this type of conditioning.

PALESTINI. It is interesting that different afferent systems may habituate because of participation of different structures placed at different levels of the reticular formation. I want to mention yet another possibility, based on Moruzzi's observations. Since, the 'cerveau isolé' also shows habituation we may infer that structures placed rostrally to the mesencephalon would also be capable of inducing this phenomenon.

BUSER. I already mentioned the observations made on the cat with an extensive lesion on the medial thalamus. Training to the routine motor alimentary conditioning (pressing lever for food at a given signal) was carried on post-operatively for 5 months without the least success: the animal revealed itself completely unable to perform the required task. In contrast, simpler associations were obtained very quickly (with an almost normal score): generalized movements then orientation towards the food tray at the signal.

This might indicate, if still necessary, that, depending upon the complexity of the training performance, the nervous structures to implicate as a site for the link may be different. It is perhaps significant that, in our observation, the mesencephalic reticular formation was apparently intact and that at the same time the ability for elementary conditioning, but not for a complex one, was preserved.

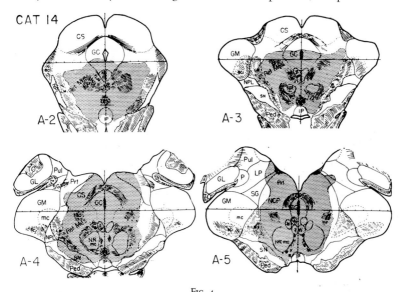

FIG. 4
Summary of lesions destroying the mesencephalic reticular system. (From Doty, R. W., Beck, E. C. and Kooi, K. A., 1959. Effect of brain stem lesions on conditioned responses of cats. *Experimental Neurology*, **1**, 360.)

SEGUNDO. Concerning lesion effects on conditioned responses, I would like to add observations made by our group. Small lesions in mesencephalic reticular formation or amygdaloid complex or large lesions in lateral nuclear complex of thalamus (involving lateral and medial geniculate and V.P.) did not produce marked perturbations in learned or learning abilities. A lesion that destroyed the centre-median provoked less of a response learned previously. A comparable loss was encountered after a large lesion of the head of the caudate nucleus in one cat but, contrastingly, another cat with a similar lesion was not perturbed: hence the caudate nucleus gave ambiguous results (as it did in the self-stimulating studies mentioned by Dr Olds) (Roig, Segundo, Sommer-Smith and Galeano, 1959; Segundo, Roig and Sommer-Smith, 1959).

When lesion effects upon conditioning are discussed, the learned effect should be identified since it is conceivable that one same lesion may affect different responses in different manners. Moreover, we must admit the possibility that an animal confronted with a certain training routine may have a 'choice' as to the neural structures it will utilize in that particular learning process: this could be one explanation for the apparently conflicting results of lesions.

HERNÁNDEZ-PEÓN. I think that different parts of the brain do have different roles in different types of learning and even for a given type of learning at different stages of learning. We must always point out the type of learning and the stage of learning and whether we are dealing with positive or negative learning. In other words, we have to take into consideration the effects produced by plastic association and by plastic inhibition, because certainly different parts of the brain have more importance for one or another type of learning.

ROSVOLD. I should like to emphasize the point already made. If comparisons are going to be made, the methods used must be the same. We found that very slight changes in the testing methods can elicit entirely different behaviour.

I should like also to say that in monkeys, at least, the effect of lesions in medialis dorsalis are not those one would expect from its connections in the frontal lobe. For example, one does not find any of the effects that one finds from frontal lobe lesions. On the contrary, one finds that lesions in the head of the caudate nucleus do give the effects found after frontal lobe lesions.

THORPE. I also would like to emphasize the importance of standardizing the circumstances in which these responses are obtained. Having in mind the biological importance of habituation, I like (see Thorpe, 1956) to distinguish it from various other types of response waning known to the ethologist and to regard it, from the biological point of view, as *long-term stimulus-specific waning*. It thus becomes very important to know the relation of the degree of habituation or dishabituation to the intensity of the stimulus. I was, therefore, particularly interested to know of Dr Segundo's results for it seems that information about the habituation effect of different tones may be a very important piece of evidence in understanding what is really going on. If in the case of spinal habituation we are uncovering something of the fundamental physiological mechanism of the habituation process, we might expect a very considerable difference in the detail of correlation between the intensity and the duration of the stimulus and of the response as between intact and decorticate animals. It is important that these should be standardized. It also bears on the similarity between habituation and internal inhibition. Pavlov, I think, at one time thought of internal inhibition as in some respect connected with the absence of the unconditioned stimulus. At other times he thought of it more as the result of some kind of competition. The first view seems much more natural to the biologist and that is why the ethologist thinks of habituation (*long-term stimulus-specific waning*) as characteristic of the absence of the consummatory act or consummatory stimulus situation. If this innately determined system is present we should expect the habituation to be reduced or absent. On the other hand, if some similar, but non-identical stimulus is present we should expect the habituation to be affected in corresponding degree. So again it becomes highly important, in experimental studies on habituation, to have specific information about the details of the stimulus employed and the relation between intensity of the stimulus and the intensity and duration of the effect.

FUNCTIONS OF BULBO-PONTINE RETICULAR FORMATION AND PLASTIC PHENOMENA IN THE CENTRAL NERVOUS SYSTEM

M. Palestini and W. Lifschitz

In investigations of the physiology of the Reticular Formation, the concept that this structure exerts a diffuse ascending and activating influence has predominated until a short time ago. Moreover, many experimental results are interpreted as deriving from the action of the reticular formation of the brain stem considered as a functional whole.

In this paper, our intention has been precisely to insist that the reticular formation of the brain stem has ascending influences which evoke contradictory phenomena. Thus, we shall see that this structure has not only its well-known desynchronizing action but also a synchronizing action, and that it can both exert an influence by facilitating the cortical potentials, evoked by sensory stimuli and by inhibiting them. We shall discuss these last functions in relation to their possible independence of the EEG pattern. Lastly, we shall refer to its participation in sleep and wakefulness, in habituation and attention.

Part of this report (paragraphs A, B, C) is concerned with experiments made in the midpontine pretrigeminal preparation (MPP) in the lines followed by Moruzzi's school. The following paragraph contains recent results obtained in our laboratory using the same preparation.

On this occasion, we shall omit the technical data, and summarize the findings of the studies which formed the basis for this paper. The reader will find further details in the articles that have already been published.

A. THE MIDPONTINE PRETRIGEMINAL PREPARATION AND THE SLEEP-WAKEFULNESS RHYTHM

EEG recordings in cats with electrolytic transsections at midpontine levels (Fig. 1) show a low voltage and high frequency activity that has generally been related to the waking state (Batini, Moruzzi, Palestini, Rossi and Zanchetti, 1958, 1959).

This desynchronized EEG pattern of the MPP predominates, and the periods of synchronized cortical activity observed are infrequent and short lived.

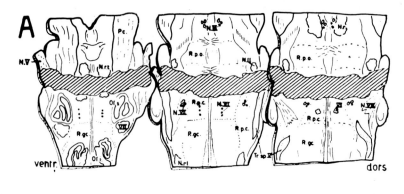

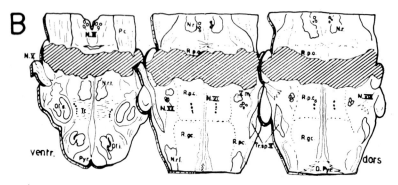

FIG. 1
EEG patterns following midpontine and rostropontine transsections
Drawings of horizontal sections of the cat's brain stem. Cross hatched areas indicate level and
extent of brain stem lesion in the midpontine (A) and rostropontine (B) pretrigeminal preparations. EEG patterns typical for each preparation, as recorded from right (F.d) and left (F.s)
frontal areas, are reproduced below each set of anatomical drawings. It can be noticed that
both types of transsection result in the complete interruption of ascending trigeminal influences. Anatomical abbreviations in the original. *Arch. ital. Biol.*, **97**, 1-12, 1959.

The EEG observations at hourly intervals for no less than 24 consecutive hours showed that cats suffering midpontine lesions present a desynchronized activity significantly more persistent than normal animals.

Such an experimental finding makes it necessary to verify some variables and only thus can an hypothesis about the probable mechanism underlying this lasting electrocortical desynchronization be postulated.

In fact, the desychronized EEG in the MPP could be due to an irritative action, while the low voltage pattern could be the result of a depressed cortical activity. Different controls effected in the animals during the postoperative survival time (1-9 days) made the first possibility unlikely while the second one was completely dismissed (Batini, Moruzzi, Palestini, Rossi and Zanchetti, 1959).

Some humoral factors are known to play a role in EEG activation. For instance, the effect of adrenaline on the cortical arousal is widely known. Nevertheless, it must be noted that adrenaline does not act directly on the cerebral cortex, but through the reticular formation. Its desynchronizing effect is not disclosed in the 'cerveau isolé' but is found in transsections similar to the midpontine (Bonvallet, Dell, Hiebel, 1953). On the other hand, there is some evidence of increased adrenaline secretion in decerebrated animals (Anderson, Bates, Hawthorne, Haymaker, Knowlton, Riosch, Spence, Wilson, 1957) which drops below normal levels in the spinal dogs. The above circumstances made it necessary to establish the role of adrenaline in the EEG activation of the MPP (Batini, Magni, Palestini, Rossi and Zanchetti, 1959).

Midpontine cats were observed for 24 hours following which a section at C_1 was performed in order to eliminate any brain stem influence on the adrenal gland. In these cases, the EEG remained desynchronized (Batini, Magni, Palestini, Rossi and Zanchetti, 1959).

The CO_2 blood increase must not be neglected either especially since the MPP sometimes presents periodic breathing. In a group of cats, the gaseous composition of the arterial blood was measured before and after the midpontine operation. This experiment demonstrated that the EEG activating pattern in the MPP does not depend on blood CO_2 pressure changes.

Summing up, the authors of these experiments stated: 'Irritative phenomena or humoral factors may occasionally contribute to, but are not likely to be responsible for the EEG activation' (Batini, Magni, Palestini, Rossi and Zanchetti, 1959).

All these experimental results support the hypothesis of a possible synchronizing structure, placed behind the midpontine section in the brain stem, whose exclusion would provoke an EEG activation. It is evident also, that the structures rostral to the midpontine lesion are indispensable for a desynchronized EEG since a little more rostral pontine transsection to the MPP (rostropontine preparation) produces EEG synchronization.

B. SENSORY DEAFFERENTATION IN THE MIDPONTINE PRETRIGEMINAL PREPARATION

Bremer (1935) observed that sensory afferences play an important role in the electric cortical activity of the 'encéphale isolé' and 'cerveau isolé' animals. Results obtained by Moruzzi and Magoun (1949) permitted a new interpretation of the influences that sensory afferences have upon cortical activity. They would act through their activating action on reticular formation.

Roger, Rossi and Zirondoli (1956) have thrown more light on the same experimental field. They established that the electrical activity of low voltage and high frequency of the 'encéphale isolé' is suddenly synchronized by the elimination of the trigeminal afferences.

The results observed in the MPP would seem to be at variance with the above-mentioned facts. Both experimental conditions eliminate the trigeminal afferences but, while Roger et al. (1956) maintain in their preparation the anatomical continuity of the brain stem, the MPP excludes the ascending influence of the medulla and the caudal pontine region.

Batini et al. (1959) repeated and confirmed the results obtained by Roger et al. (1956). It was thus possible to state that gasserectomy in 'encéphale isolé' cats determines EEG synchronization. But, if a midpontine transsection is performed in these animals, the EEG shows the characteristic MPP desynchronization.

These results permit us to establish another explanation of these facts and to insist, as we shall see later, on a possible ascending synchronizing influence coming from the bulbar reticular formation and from the caudal pontine region.

The MPP and its characteristic EEG pattern offers a more satisfactory way of studying the importance of sensory afferences on the electrical activity during wakefulness. Batini, Palestini, Rossi and Zanchetti (1959) eliminated on successive days the olfactory and visual afferences of animals submitted to pretrigeminal section. Destruction of the olfactory bulbs in the MPP did not modify the EEG. But if these animals suffered a lesion in their optic nerves, their cortical rhythms became synchronized.

However, one or two days after the completion of sensory deafferentation, the low voltage and fast EEG rhythms reappeared and persisted unmodified through the survival period.

To sum up, these facts show that the whole desynchronized EEG activity following MPP might be due either to the elimination of some ascending synchronizing influences, and/or to the exaltation of a tonic activity, rostral to the section. The latter would be able to sustain a cortical desynchronization when total deafferentation was done.

The hypothesis based on a 'synchronizing or possible sleep-inducing influences exerted by a structure present in the caudal brain stem' (Batini, Moruzzi, Palestini, Rossi and Zanchetti, 1958) has been strongly reinforced by recent experimental data.

Chronic midpontine hemisections show desynchronization in the hemisphere ipsilateral to the section, while the other hemisphere displays both synchronized and desynchronized periods of EEG activity (Cordeau and Mancia, 1959). These results can be explained by the presence of some ascending synchronizing influence on the cerebral cortex ipsilateral to the intact pontine region.

We want to mention another observation here. In an ingenious experiment performed in cats, the head circulation was split into two different circuits by a ligature of the basilar artery at pontine level, one of the circuits corresponding to the carotid arteries that irrigate the pontine rostral region, midbrain and cerebrum, and the other to the vertebral arteries for the medulla and the caudal pontine region. In these conditions, intravertebral administration of a low dose of Thiopental produced a general arousal reaction in a previous EEG spontaneously synchronized. These results can be interpreted as a functional and reversible inactivation by the drug of a synchronizing mechanism originating in the lower brain stem (Magni, Moruzzi, Rossi and Zanchetti, 1959). The experiments we have mentioned support the idea of the functional diversity of the reticular formation, to whose well-known desynchronizing influence is now added its synchronizing effect upon the cortex.

C. MIDPONTINE CATS AND WAKING BEHAVIOUR

The psychophysiological correlation between wakefulness and cortical desynchronization on one side and sleep and synchronization on the other has been recently discussed. Thus, EEG of normal cats during sleep shows periods of desynchronization (Dement, 1958). Observations made on human beings also show this type of EEG during normal sleep (Dement and Kleitman, 1957).

By means of an objective technique consisting of hypnotic induction, we have recently observed in humans that a synchronized EEG is recorded during the somnambulist phase of suggested sleep, showing theta and even delta rhythms. If a verbal contact is established with the hypnotized subject, it may be observed that he answers when his EEG pattern resembles those recorded during the waking state with closed eyes. Spontaneous post-hypnotic amnesia for the meaningful conversation is shown by the subject (Dittborn, Borlone and Palestini, 1959).

The desynchronized EEG patterns in MPP animals do not enable it to be inferred that they are in a waking state. But the fact that these animals have a normal pupil and can still make vertical eye movements, make it possible to study some behavioural reactions. In fact, they have shown the capacity to make an apparently directed or intentional movement with

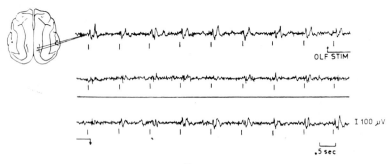

OLF STIM

I 100 μV

.5 sec

FIG. 2
Effect of heterosensory stimulation on visual potentials (MPP)
EEG record. Primary potentials decrease during olfactory extrastimulation.

their eyes to follow an object passing across their visual fields. Movements disappear as soon as synchronized EEG patterns are seen, while the pupil becomes myotic. A more important reaction is the pupil dilatation which appears in some cats with midpontine section when a more emotionally significant stimulus is presented to them (rat, dog).

In order to obtain further information about waking behaviour in the MPP we have been studying 'attention' in these animals (Palestini, Lifschitz and Armengol, 1959). In some, the cortical potentials evoked by a flash decreased when the MPP was submitted to a simultaneous hetero-sensory stimulation (olfactory). Of course, these results were obtained during a desynchronized pattern of activity which apparently was not modified during the process of attention (Fig. 2). This result, compared with controls, enabled us to conclude that the MPP would be able to develop an alert state resembling that of a normal animal.

In short, the midpontine animal develops a persistent desynchronized EEG, in correlation with seemingly wakeful behaviour. In no case can it be stated that the alert state is higher than the normal, as could be concluded from the EEG pattern.

Anatomical analysis of the midpontine section shows that it leaves the extreme anterior region of the reticular pontis oralis nucleus intact. This is considered to be one of the areas containing the largest number of cortico-reticular projections (Rossi and Brodal, 1956). The possible participation of these projections in the maintenance of wakefulness, after total de-afferentation, needs further experimental demonstration (Batini, Moruzzi, Palestini, Rossi and Zanchetti, 1959).

On the other hand, it is suggestive to remember that the lower brain stem, which would exert a synchronizing influence, is also the region where the long axon reticular neurones are located. These reticular neurones are connected with thalamic nuclei (Nauta and Kuypers, 1958) from which synchronizing and hypnogenic effects are obtained by electric stimulation. With regard to these anatomo-functional relationships hypothetical considerations have already been made (Batini, Magni, Palestini, Rossi and Zanchetti, 1959; Cordeau and Mancia, 1959). Finally, the possible anatomo-functional interrelations of structures posterior to the midpontine lesion also seem to be interesting. The fact that sleep is followed by a decrease in the muscular tone is well known. Therefore, the origin in the medulla of an ascending synchronizing influence and a descending inhibitory effect on reflex activity is a suggestive fact that needs to be studied.

D. HABITUATION IN THE MIDPONTINE PREPARATION

We have already remarked that the pretrigeminal cat is able to follow with vertical eye movements an object passing across its visual field. This is suggestive of the condition of 'purposeful attention' which together with the desynchronized EEG might indicate a possible vigilant state. Eye movements are maintained as long as the object is made to pass to and fro in the visual field, while a normal cat shows a rapid habituation.

The above observation led us to study habituation in the MPP (Palestini, Lifschitz and Armengol, 1959). Since in this preparation the animal has only two sensory afferences, visual and olfactory, we chose the visual cortex to analyse the behaviour of evoked potentials caused by repetitive stimulation from a flash given at a frequency of 1 per second. We have considered as habituation the decrease and even disappearance of an evoked potential produced in this way (Lifschitz, Palestini and Armengol, 1959) with the possibility of recuperation to the previous amplitude by some known dishabituating agents (extrastimulation, rest, changes in the characteristics of the stimuli, etc.).

EEG recordings of primary and secondary[1] visual responses were made before and after midpontine section. Each animal was its own control. The preliminary recording was made on unanaesthetized dark-adapted cats with permanently implanted bipolar electrodes in striate cortex and gyrus lateralis anterior. The pupil was dilated by homatropine and the head was maintained in the same position by means of a metal cone.

Midpontine section produced several changes in primary and secondary evoked photic potentials. In the first place, an increase in the amplitude of these potentials was recorded. This phenomenon will be discussed later. Secondly, a remarkable decrease in the speed of habituation of primary potentials was noticed. It was clear that it could be obtained only after a great number of stimuli and, in some cases, was not present during the whole test period (Fig. 3). Thirdly, the secondary potential had a time-course of habituation similar to that shown by the primary one (Fig. 4). This is quite different from that to be seen in normal animals. In a previous communication (Lifschitz, Palestini and Armengol, 1959) a description has been given of the rapid habituation of the secondary potential registered in the most anterior part of the gyrus lateralis, while habituation of the evoked potential in the striate area needed the application of hundreds and even thousands of stimuli to develop. There is a very striking difference between both potentials, for the secondary response practically disappears after the first twenty to thirty stimuli and even after only three to five stimuli (EGG recordings). Other authors have also described this prompt habituation of secondary responses (Jasper, Ricci and Doane, 1958) and have stressed their peculiar plasticity which has specially drawn our attention. The difference in habituation rates between primary and secondary potentials is altered in the MPP since, as we have already noted, both responses have a similar temporal course of habituation in this preparation.

So far, the mechanisms of attention and habituation have generally been attributed to inhibitory tonic influences originating in central regions of the brain stem. This hypothesis is based on experiments showing the blocking of sensory transmission at the level of gracilis nucleus (Hernández-Peón, Scherrer and Velasco, 1956), trigeminal nucleus (Hernández-Peón,

---

[1] We call photic secondary responses those recorded in the gyrus lateralis anterior and suprasylvian gyrus (Buser and Borenstein, 1959).

and Hagbarth, 1955), lateral geniculate body (Hernández-Peón, Scherrer and Velasco, 1956) and retina (Granit, 1955; Dodt, 1956). Experiments with anaesthetics (Hernández-Peón, Guzmán, Alcaraz and Fernández-Guar-

HABITUATION

NORMAL CAT
1ˢᵗ FLASHES

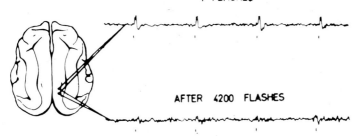

AFTER 4200 FLASHES

PRETRIGEMINAL CAT
1ˢᵗ FLASHES

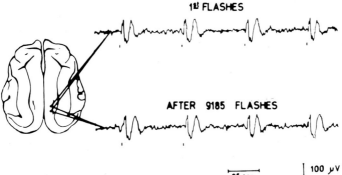

AFTER 9185 FLASHES

| 100 μV

05 sec

FIG. 3
Change in habituation rate by midpontine transsection
Control before the lesion in the same animal. Primary cortical photic potentials. Note lack of habituation and potentiation after lesion. EEG records. Time calibration 0.5 seconds.

diola, 1958) or mesencephalic lesions (Hernández-Peón, 1955) also showed the reticular mesencephalic mechanisms as responsible for these phenomena.

However, data obtained up to now show a possible difference between the mechanism of attention and habituation. The latter develops slowly at different levels of the specific pathway (Lifschitz, Palestini and Armengol, 1959), lasts for hours and even for days (Hernández-Peón, Guzmán, Alcaraz and Fernández-Guardiola, 1958) and is generally accompanied by

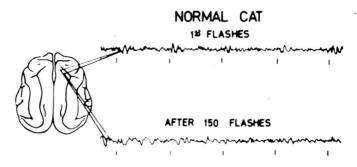

HABITUATION

NORMAL CAT

1ᴹ FLASHES

AFTER 150 FLASHES

PRETRIGEMINAL CAT

1ᴹ FLASHES

AFTER 2240 FLASHES

100 μV

05 sec

Fig. 4

Lack of habituation of secondary cortical photic potentials in midpontine pretrigeminal preparation
EEG record from gyrus lateralis anterior. Shows fast habituation in the normal cat and no habituation in the MPP. Time calibration 0.5 seconds.

a synchronized EEG record (Cavaggioni, Gianelli and Santibáñez, 1959). Attention, on the contrary, is accompanied by immediate reduction in the amplitude of the potential when the animal is suddenly submitted to an extra stimulation, it is a short-lived process and, finally, goes together with cortical arousal.

These facts, and especially the last mentioned, make us think of possible differences in the mechanisms responsible for these two plastic activities, for it is unlikely that the same mechanisms would account for such dissimilar characteristics. Attention combines the functional traits of a transitory influence which has at the same time an activating effect upon the EEG. Habituation, on the contrary, is the result of repeated stimulation, it appears slowly and is maintained for a longer period.

It has already been noted that state of attention can be provoked in the MPP when a heterosensory stimulus is applied. In this respect, the animal behaves normally, while habituation in pretrigeminal cats shows the above-mentioned alterations. In other words, this particular kind of brain stem transsection seems capable of dissociating both phenomena. This suggests that attention is a function of the mesencephalic reticular formation or of even more anterior regions. On the same basis, habituation of cortical potentials might be considered a function of caudal reticular mechanisms. Anyhow, we should point out that this is probably not the only habituating influence, since we have sometimes observed, in the MPP, a delayed decrease in the evoked potentials. It can be said that this part of the reticular formation acts as a habituation-facilitating mechanism.

When a more rostral pontine section is made, a synchronized EEG can be observed as a rule. This fact differentiates the rostropontine from the midpontine animal, but both preparations show the same slow type of habituation (Fig. 5). This points to the possible independence of synchronizing and habituating mechanisms.

Sharpless and Jasper (1956) remark that there is no strict correlation between the magnitude of the auditory evoked potentials in the cerebral cortex and habituation of the arousal reaction. Although this last is seen after twenty or thirty repetitions of the arousal stimulus, the evoked potentials remain of the same size or increase. These authors believe it necessary to distinguish between habituation of the arousal reaction and decrease of the evoked potentials as a consequence of the former. On the other hand, a detailed study of the zones of mesencephalic reticular formation that evoke the arousal reaction and those that inhibit responses in the dorsal cochlear nucleus (Jouvet and Desmedt, 1956) has induced these authors to assume that each of these functions has a different reticular organization.

Moreover, it is well known that stimulation of the reticular formation produces desynchronization of the EEG, while different authors have observed the facilitation or diminution of cortical evoked responses during stimulation of this structure (Rossi and Zanchetti, 1957). All these facts lead us to consider the possible existence of an independent control for these phenomena: size of potentials and EEG synchronization or desynchronization.

The results already described regarding the elementary plastic processes,

HABITUATION

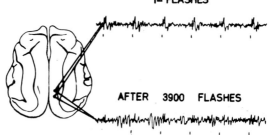

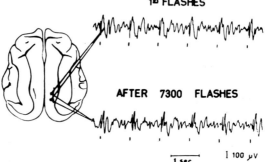

FIG. 5
Study of habituation associated to a synchronized EEG
Rostropontine cat. No habituation during stimulation period
almost twice as long as that of the normal cat.

attention and habituation, open a new line of research for studying the central mechanism of Pavlovian 'internal' and 'external inhibition' (Pavlov, 1928). The second concept corresponds to attention and the first to sensory discrimination and habituation. Habituation as negative learning has already been discussed (Hernández-Peón, Jouvet and Scherrer, 1957). It would seem useful to consider from this point of view the role of the low bulbo-pontine structures in the origin and development of the processes of internal inhibition, taking into account the Pavlovian view of the intimate relationship between the latter and sleep (Pavlov, 1928).

E. MIDPONTINE PRETRIGEMINAL PREPARATION AND CORTICAL POTENTIALS EVOKED BY PHOTIC STIMULATION

It is an accepted fact that the cortical potentials evoked by sensory stimuli diminish in amplitude during spontaneous desynchronization periods. Electrical stimulation of the reticular formation provokes an arousal reaction and reduces the cortical potentials evoked by physiological stimulation of the specific sensory pathways. On the other hand it has been observed that during EEG synchronization the evoked responses increase in amplitude (Bremer, 1953).

The midpontine animal, with its permanent state of wakefulness, and the rostropontine cat, with a synchronized EEG pattern, seemed to be two suitable preparations for studying these problems. In addition, we have assumed that inhibitory influences which facilitate habituation originate in the medulla. If this were so, midpontine section, separating this structure, might reveal a facilitation of the cortical evoked responses.

Cats with electrodes permanently implanted in the gyrus lateralis and gyrus lateralis anterior were used in these experiments. Primary and secondary photic cortical potentials were recorded (EEG and CRO) before and after midpontine lesion.

The secondary potentials recorded in normal cats showed an initial negative deflection. Latency, which was difficult to measure in such conditions, had an average value of 20 msec. and its amplitude was about 80 μV. Iterative photic stimulation with a frequency of 1 per second produced rapid habituation and the secondary response became masked by cortical activity.

The midpontine transsection performed in the same animals brought about some clear changes. Latency (20 msec.) became very regular and easy to measure and the amplitude increased notably, reaching sometimes 150 μV. or more. These results were obtained with a desynchronized EEG background (Figs. 4, 6). Similar changes to those described in the midpontine cat were also noticed in rostropontine lesions, accompanied in this case with cortical synchronization.

Pretrigeminal section performed in these animals also modified the primary responses. In Fig. 7 (CRO recording with bipolar electrodes) some of these modifications can be observed, i.e. a slight change in the first spike and a marked increase of amplitude in the following deflections which are precisely those which are most changed by habituation and conditioned learning (Guzmán, Alcaraz and Fernández-Guardiola, 1957; Hernández-Peón, Guzmán, Alcaraz and Fernández-Guardiola, 1958).

Studies made with monopolar electrodes demonstrated that the amplitude of the first positive deflection, currently designed wave 1, remained unmodified or increased slightly. Conversely, positive waves 3 and 4 and negative wave 5 showed a constant and appreciable increase. We wish to

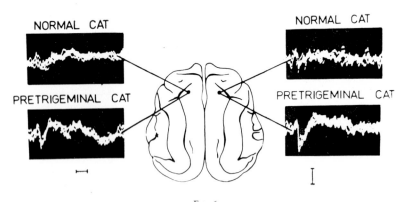

FIG. 6
Oscillographic recording of secondary cortical photic responses
Stimulus: flash 1/second. Monopolar record in the same cat before (normal) and after midpontine section. Five responses in each trace. Downward deflection negative. Time calibration 40 msec. Amplitude calibration 100 μV.

stress once again that these results were obtained with a desynchronized EEG pattern. In rostropontine animals exactly the same changes were seen, but cortical spindles interfered with the regularity observed in the midpontine cat.

Since the potentiation described was achieved after total transsection of the brain stem, we assume that it is the result of the elimination of a tonic inhibitory influence originated behind the lesion and as a consequence of the exaltation of facilitating influences situated above the level of the lesion.

Regarding the site of action of these ascending inhibitory influences of bulbar origin, nothing definite can be said at the present time. Nevertheless, on the basis of some anatomical and neurophysiological data, we may

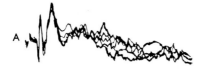

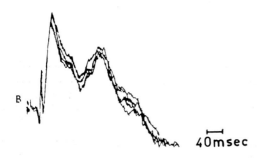

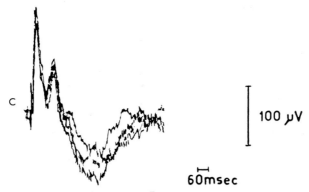

FIG. 7

Oscillographic recording of primary cortical photic responses
Stimulus: flash 1/sec. Bipolar electrodes. Five responses in each trace.
A. Cat unanaesthetized, chronically implanted and dark-adapted.
B. Same cat after midpontine section. Amplification and sweep rate
    as in A.
C. Same condition as in B, but sweep rate has been slowed to show
    the last deflection.

discuss *a priori* the possibility that these influences may act upon the non-specific systems.

Numerous axons have been recently described which originate in the medulla and are distributed across the midbrain tegmentum, grey periaqueductal matter, superior colliculus and pretectal area, non-specific thalamic nuclei and sub-thalamic region (Nauta and Kuypers, 1958).

From these diffused axonal projections those concerned with the non-specific nuclei seem worthy of special mention, since there is evidence that intralaminar stimulation facilitates specific visual responses in the 'cerveau isolé' animal (Jasper and Ajmone-Marsan, 1952; Jung, 1958).

We ascribe similar importance to periaqueductal and tegmental projections of the reticular formation. They might be the structural bases of functional antagonistic interrelations between different levels of the reticular formation of the brain stem according to inferences from the results discussed, although there is no direct demonstration.

It is also possible that these inhibitory influences may operate at a subcortical level of the specific pathway.

From data obtained by other authors, these inhibitory influences might be exerted on the retina by a centrifugal pathway (Granit, 1955; Dodt, 1956; Hernández-Peón, Guzmán, Alcaraz and Fernández-Guardiola, 1957; Palestini, Davidovich and Hernández-Peón, 1959), in the geniculate lateral nucleus (Hernández-Peón, Scherrer and Velasco, 1956).

Although we do not disregard these last possibilities, our findings lead us to consider them of less importance. In fact, as we pointed out before, potentiation of the primary response in the pretrigeminal animal has a marked and almost exclusive effect on waves 3, 4 and 5 which most authors believe to have an intracortical origin.

There is another point to which we should like to refer briefly. As we have noted, potentiation of the primary and secondary cortical photic responses was obtained either with a desynchronized (MPP) or synchronized EEG pattern (rostropontine animal). This observation induces us to consider that there may be no causal relationship between the facilitating and the synchronizing and desynchronizing influences.

To sum up, we can now say that the midpontine cat has the following characteristics:

1. A predominantly desynchronized EEG, generally correlated with a wakeful pattern, although we are not in a position to say that its alert state is greater than that of a normal animal.

2. Primary cortical potentials evoked by a flash do not show habitua-

tion or need a period at least three times longer than that required by the normal animal to show it. Much more evident, in this respect, are the results obtained on secondary cortical potentials, since they show rapid habituation in the normal cat.

3. A significant increase in the primary and secondary cortical potentials evoked by a luminous stimulus. Evidently the reactions described in points 2 and 3 only refer to photic cortical responses; this does not allow us to extend them to other sensory responses.

Aware of the oversimplification of our hypothesis and admitting that other structures of the nervous system also participate, we would ascribe different functions to two areas of the reticular formation. The influences originated rostral to the midpontine level would mainly participate in cortical desynchronization, in the facilitation of evoked potentials, in dishabituation and in attention, while those originated caudal to this level would synchronize the EEG, facilitate habituation and inhibit evoked cortical potentials. These three influences ascribed to the reticular formation of the medulla lead us to think that this structure should be regarded as an important part of a sleep system.

GROUP DISCUSSION

ADEY. I would like to discuss a few aspects of the study that Mr Lindsley and I have undertaken to assess the role of subthalamic areas in the maintenance of reticular excitability, and I think these findings bear very closely on the papers that have been presented this afternoon. These lesions are in chronic cats and monkeys and they involve the subthalamus, the dorsal part of the hypothalamus and frequently the ventro-medial part of the thalamus. These are chronic lesions and the cats were kept in good condition for 6 weeks to 2 months before they were used for subsequent acute or chronic experiments. It was found that, after such a lesion, when recording from the medial reticular formation of the rostral mesencephalon, many of the units which are normally present and respond to stimulation of sciatic nerve are no longer active, and in fact it is very difficult to find spontaneously firing units. When one is detected, it fires only slowly, and exhibits only a brief phasic rise in firing rate with each stimulus, in contrast to the tonic and sustained rise in firing rate induced in normal reticular units by repetitive sciatic stimulation in most cases. Since it is almost impossible to assess reticular function on the basis of such unit studies, we reverted to macro-electrode recordings in the rostral mid-brain reticular formation adjacent to the periaqueductal grey matter. After brief tetanization of the mid-brain recording electrodes for 2 or 3 seconds, there is a slight facilitation of the reticular response to sciatic stimulation as compared with the control records, lasting 5 to 10 minutes. After unilateral coagulation of the subthalamus there is slight reduction in the reticular responses, when compared with control records, but not very much. However, after bilateral coagulation the reticular response almost disappears. If one then briefly tetanizes the midbrain recording electrode the response returns almost to its original size and behaves in much the fashion of a post-betanic potentiation, with gradual decay to a low level over 10 to 15 minutes. This potentiation can be repeated indefinitely. These animals have certain curious behavioural alterations which may be classified as catatonic. They suffer a gross defect in avoidance behaviour, but in this respect tend to recover over a period of months, although they never revert to normal. They assume these curious postures even though they are apparently alert and in many cases do not feed spontaneously. Now on the basis of these findings, we would suggest that either arising in the subthalamus, or passing through it, there are certain tonic facilitatory influences which are mainly responsible for the normal accessibility of reticular units to input from the periphery. We also have evidence that there is a brief phasic inhibitory aspect to this activity, much as Huguelin and Bonvallet have described but the overall effect of subthalamic lesions of the type we have described is a loss of a tonic facilitation.

PALESTINI. We have postulated in this paper that EEG activation patterns and facilitation of visual cortical responses appear when bulbo-pontine structures are left out of action by the section. But we have also pointed to possible inhibitory and synchronizing influences originated in higher levels. In relation to facilitating mechanisms acting upon reticular formation and coming from upper segments we had only considered corticoreticular relationships. Now Dr Adey has presented us a new possibility of facilitating influences which seems quite important to us.

OLDS. I would like to address myself to Dr Adey's material, to ask whether there was any particular part of the reticular formation in which recording electrodes should be placed in order for this effect to be obtained. I would say that the area he describes as having his lesion is very similar to regions where we get very rapid self stimulation and I am just wondering if the part of the tegmentum used for recording is also the part that gives us very rapid self-stimulation which would be the ventro-lateral part of the tegmentum.

ADEY. First of all, the recordings were all made in the paramedian part of the dorsal reticular formation adjoining the peri-aqueductal grey-matter at the rostral mesencephalic level. As far as the subthalamic lesions goes, it is my impression that it is a region very heavily traversed by a rhinoncephalic descending flux which arises from the pyriform cortex, the amygdala. It is also the main descending area for fluxes through the corpus striatum and particularly from the globus pallidus. We have not looked specifically in the ventro-lateral tegmentum.

GALAMBOS. As Dr Adey has said, the main outflow region of the limbic system is to this midbrain reticular formation. I am not exactly clear where the pretrigeminal section cuts through the midbrain but wonder whether it might destroy the caudal part of the nucleus of Bechterew which is a specific midbrain terminus for the limbic outflow. As I understand Dr Palestini's view, he interprets the lack of habituation of the visual cortical response after the lesion to absence of impulses from regions caudal to the cut. Could it be that his lesion destroys a part of the nucleus of Bechterew and thus prevents inflow to the midbrain from the limbic structures more rostrally located?

PALESTINI. Pretrigeminal transection is made at a midpontine level and leaves intact the anterior part of the pons and midbrain structures. Previous research has given some data about the possible importance of nucleus pontis oralis in the maintenance of this permanent waking EEG rhythm, which is better observed when this nucleus is less destroyed.

LIFSCHITZ. I think it is interesting to compare results communicated by Dr Jouvet to this symposium to our own, because it appears that we are speaking in favour of two different inhibitory or synchronizing influences, one coming from the caudal part of the brain stem, and the other from higher structures. It is possible that both influences act in these processes, perhaps at different moments. During habituation an internal inhibition develops which is different from internal inhibition of inhibitory or negative conditioned reflexes. It is quite possible that one of these is acting in one type of internal inhibition and not in the other.

About Dr Galambo's remark, I think that the data we have from Moruzzi stating that the 'cerveau isolé' gets habituated is against the idea of an action coming from rhinencephalic structures. In this case pathways coming from the rhinencephalon to the midbrain have been also severed, but there is a different result in habituation.

CHANGES IN CORTICAL EVOKED POTENTIALS BY PREVIOUS RETICULAR STIMULATION

Miguel R. Covian, Cesar Timo-Iaria and Ricardo F. Marseillan

It is a well-established fact that the central nervous system possesses mechanisms by means of which the afferent inflow can be influenced, and that an important role in these mechanisms is played by the reticular formation of the brain stem. Reticular stimulation has been shown to affect the sensory discharge at various levels in the central nervous system. On the other hand on a background of continuous electrical activity there arises in the cortex on peripheral stimulation a primary response – only in the correspondent receptor areas – and a number of waves which follow it and spread to a somewhat wider area. The primary response is the one which has been studied in most detail; it occurs regularly on any kind of peripheral stimulation and is the most closely connected with the arousing of sensation.

The literature is contradictory regarding the interaction between those nerve elements which determine development of the primary responses and the central core of the brain stem which, receiving impulses coming from all sensory channels, is an adequate region for the integration of these different impulses.

In the present paper the influence of previous stimulation of the reticular formation upon the cortical evoked potential obtained by a tactile stimulus is studied in an attempt to understand the interaction between the specific and non-specific, diffuse projection systems.

METHODS

Experiments of this type were performed upon twenty-four cats. The animals were anaesthetized with initial (60 mg./kg.) and maintenance doses of chloralose given intravenously. The somatic sensory area of the left cortex was exposed by craniectomy and reflection of the dura and covered by mineral oil. A unipolar electrode connected to a Dumont double beam oscilloscope through a Grass AC pre-amplifier registered the electrical activity of the cortex with negativity upwards in all records. Photographic records of the evoked potentials were taken either in individual sweeps or

433

in three or five superimposed sweeps. One concentric electrode consisting of 32 gauge enamelled stainless steel wire enclosed within a 22 gauge stainless steel sheath was placed stereotaxically in the brain stem reticular formation. Bipolar stimulation was performed between the tip of the inner conductor and a bare collar of 0.5 mm. wide encircling the lower end of the insulated sheath. The distance between the tip and collar was approximately 1.0 mm. The electrical stimuli were short square waves of

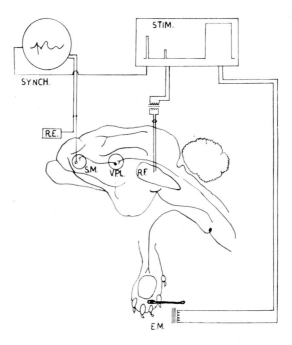

FIG. 1
Diagram showing the experimental arrangement.

0.2 msec. duration, 1/sec., voltage variable, delivered by a Grass stimulator through an isolation unit and preceding the skin stimulation at intervals of 100 and 50 msec. Tactile stimulation was applied to hair-covered areas of the right foreleg by a small camel's-hair brush mounted on a lever rigidly attached to the moving armature of an electromagnet device the coil of which was energized by a pulse of 4 msec. duration, 1/sec. by way of a Grass stimulator. The main features of the experimental arrangement are shown in Fig. 1. At the end of the experiment an electrolytic lesion was made in the brain stem reticular formation with a direct current of 2-3 mA during 15 sec. The animal's head was perfused with formalin through one carotid artery and electrode position was later determined from serial sections stained by Toluidine blue.

RESULTS

The stimulation of the right forepaw evoked (Fig. 2) the characteristic surface positive-negative primary responses in the corresponding area of the somatosensory cortex. With previous stimulation of the brain stem

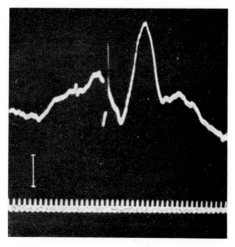

Fig. 2

Cortical evoked potential in somatosensory area by tactile stimulation. Time 200 cps. Calibration: 500 µV — same calibration for all other records.

reticular formation at 100 msec. interval and 1.5 volts, the negative component disappeared and a slight reduction of the positive one was observed (Fig. 3). In Figs. 4 and 5 the same phenomenon is presented when the stimulation was made at 50 msec. interval and 1.5 volts.

It can be seen in Fig. 6 in superimposed sweeps, in the lower record the evoked potential and in the upper one the effect of reticular formation stimulation, at 100 msec. interval and 4 volts.

FF

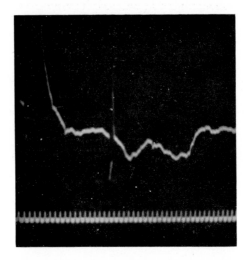

FIG. 3

Disappearance of the negative component of the cortical evoked potential by previous reticular stimulation (100 msec. interval, 2 volts). Time 200 cps.

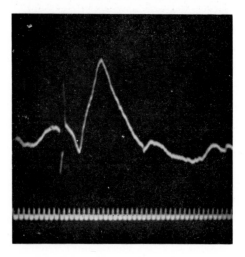

FIG. 4

Cortical evoked potential. Time 200 cps.

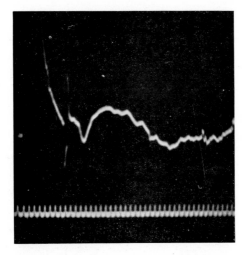

FIG. 5
Disappearance of the negative component by previous
reticular stimulation (50 msec. interval, 1.5 volts).
Time 200 cps.

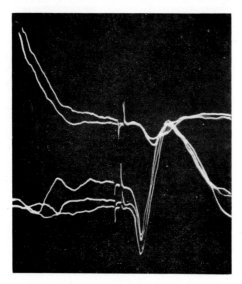

FIG. 6
Superimposed sweeps. Lower record: cortical evoked
potential. Upper record: cortical evoked potential
obtained 100 msec. after brain stem reticular stimulation.

VOLTAGE SERIES AT 100 MSEC. INTERVAL

One voltage series was made when the interval between stimuli was 100 msec. In Fig. 7 are represented the results obtained. It can be seen that at 2 volts there was no modification; at 3 volts the negative potential began to decrease and the positive one remained unchanged. At 4 and 5 volts the diminution of the negative potential was more marked and no change was observed on the positive potential.

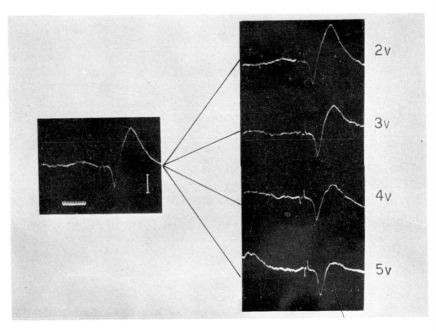

FIG. 7
Voltage series at 100 msec. interval. Time 200 cps. Calibration: 500 µV.

VOLTAGE SERIES AT 50 MSEC. INTERVAL

The same voltage series was repeated at 50 msec. interval between stimuli and the results are summarized in Fig. 8. It can be observed that at 2 volts there is already a decrease of the negative potential which is more marked at 3 and 5 volts. Regarding the positive wave a little increase was seen.

In all the previous experiments the negative wave underwent significant changes, while the positive wave remained almost unchanged. Only when very high voltage reticular stimulation (8 volts) was used did both waves disappear, as shown in Figs. 9 and 10 in superimposed sweeps at 100 and 50 msec. interval.

Control experiments. The possibility of spreading current to the medial lemniscus was ruled out by the following experiment: a concentric electrode was placed on the medial lemniscus at co-ordinates A5, L5, H3. Its stimulation determined an evoked potential in the cerebral cortex.

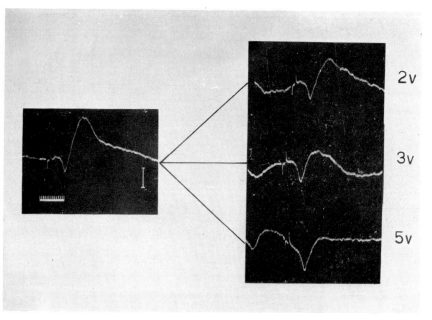

FIG. 8
Voltage series at 50 msec. interval. Time 200 cps. Calibration: 500 μV.

While the evoked potential in somatosensory area was being recorded by stimulation of the forepaw in the usual way, electrolytic lesions were made by a 5 mA direct current until the evoked potential disappeared. At this point the stimulation of the medial lemniscus did not evoke any potential in the cerebral cortex, but the stimulation of the brain stem reticular formation at co-ordinates A3, L2.5, H2 evoked a cortical potential as before. This evoked potential by single shock reticular stimulation was very similar to that obtained in the same conditions by Buser and Borenstein on the associative cortex. In Fig. 10 this type of response can be seen in superimposed sweeps.

On the other hand, after local destruction of the reticular formation, no

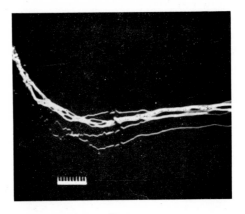

FIG. 9

Disappearance of the cortical evoked potential by previous reticular stimulation at 100 msec. interval and 8 volts.

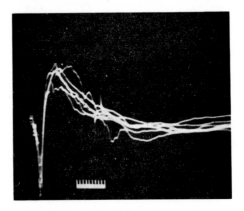

FIG. 10

Same as Fig. 9 but stimulation at 50 msec. interval and 8 volts.

evoked potential was obtained by its stimulation and of course the cortical evoked potential after tactile stimulus was not now influenced by the stimulation at that point of reticular brain stem.

COMMENTS

The activity in sensory systems is subject to modification by central regulatory mechanisms and background states, sufficiently pronounced to be capable of influencing perception and so to be of interest for psychology. Upon the arrival at the cortex, afferent discharge may show variation related to spontaneous cortical activity (Bishop, 1944), to cortical thalamic excitability cycles (Chang, 1950, 1951) or to influence of other afferent stimuli (Gellhorn et al., 1954). The possibility that not only spontaneous but also some electrical and chemically evoked cortical potentials can be abolished during electrocortical arousal has been pointed out by a number of investigators. Disappearance of recruiting potentials has been observed by Moruzzi and Magoun (1949) and later confirmed by other investigators (Jasper, Naquet and King, 1955) and it has been reported that local strychnine waves can be blocked during sensory arousal. It has also been demonstrated more recently that intermediary stages of afferent transmission are also subject to influence by regulatory mechanisms. Reticular inhibition of the medullary relays in sensory paths was shown by Hernández-Peón and Hagbarth (1955) and by Hernández-Peón and Scherrer (1955) in experiments on the trigeminal nucleus and by Hernández-Peón, Scherrer and Velazco on nucleus gracilis.

While some authors reported no interaction between the mechanisms that give origin to the primary cortical response and those which give rise to spontaneous periodic activity (Morison and Dempsey, 1942; Moruzzi and Magoun, 1949; Jasper, 1949) other investigators observed some kind of interaction (Jasper and Ajmone-Marsan, 1952; Bremer, 1954).

The present experiments support the findings that show that reticular formation is capable of exerting a clear influence upon cortical evoked potentials. The pathway used in this case by the stimulus of the reticular formation to reach the cortex seems to be the slower one as described by Adey, Segundo and Livingston (1957), which shows rapid fatigue, fails to follow repetition rates faster than 2-3 stimuli per second and which conducts exclusively or predominantly in an upward direction. The possibility of spreading current to the medial lemniscus is rejected by the results of the control experiments. The positive-negative evoked potential in the cortical forepaw projection areas is unequally affected by the previous reticular stimulation. There is a different susceptibility of the positive and negative components of the primary response, the negative being the more susceptible. Parma and Zanchetti (1956) observed a reticular blocking of cortical potentials evoked by thalamic stimulation.

In some conditions they obtained a reduction of the negative component whereas the positive potential remained completely unaffected. Gauthier, Parma and Zanchetti (1956) observed that the primary response elicited by peripheral stimulation is definitely decreased during cortical arousal but they did not give any detail regarding the influence upon the positive and negative component of the response. Appelberg, Kitchell and Landgren (1959) studying the reticular influence upon thalamic and cortical potentials evoked by electrical stimulation of the cat's tongue observed a considerable reduction of both components of the primary response. They did not mention any difference in the behaviour of the positive and negative components. This fact could be attributed to the different parameters of stimulation of the reticular formation used. Changes in two components of the primary response evoked by tactile stimulation were observed by Narikashvili (1957) related with the recruiting response: when the primary response preceded or coincided with the rising slope of a recruiting response potential, the negative spike of the evoked potential was increased (the positive was blocked); if the primary response arose when the potential of the recruiting response was fully developed, then its positive component was increased and the negative was blocked. He observed also that the EEG desynchronization had less effect on the primary response: it suppressed the negative component or had no effect.

Buser and Borenstein (1957) working in cats anaesthetized with chloralose report the existence of induced potentials in association cortex areas by single stimulation of the reticular formation and its inhibitory effects on the secondary response. The conflicting results obtained by different investigators regarding potentials evoked in the cerebral cortex by stimulation of the reticular formation could be attributed to the multisynaptic interneuronal organization of this system that makes it more susceptible to anaesthetic blockade, but this susceptibility varies with the different anaesthetics. Contrary to Buser and Borenstein, response to reticular stimulation in primary areas and inhibition of the primary response was obtained in the present work.

French, Verzeano and Magoun (1953) reported a different sensitivity of the waves of the primary response to anaesthetics. They observed that the initial event of the primary response was never diminished by anaesthesia (ether or nembutal); on the contrary it was sometimes augmented, while the second cortical deflection usually diminished in amplitude and finally disappeared. Feldberg, Malcolm and Smith (1957) observed that the intraventricular injection of small doses of tubocurarine in cats under chloralose caused definite changes in the primary response evoked by contralateral stimulation of the peroneal nerve. The evoked cortical response showed an accentuation of the positive and an attenuation or disappearance of the negative waves.

Purpura and Grundfest (1956) obtained similar depressing effects by intracarotid injection of tubocurarine. By topical application of gamma aminobutyric acid (GABA), Iwama and Jasper (1957) observed an immediate and reversible depression in the surface negative component of the primary evoked potential in somatosensory cortex of the cat in response to thalamic stimulation.

The positive and negative components of the primary response are post-synaptic events. The negative, which seems to signal the depolarization of the apical dendrites, appeared in the findings here reported most sensitive to the action of the reticular formation. It represents the activation of a larger number of neuronal units than the first one. This multisynaptic arrangement would be more susceptible to the action of the unspecific extralemniscal system than it is to the anaesthetics. The alternative of an interaction at a subcortical level has to be taken into account.

GROUP DISCUSSION

OLDS. We have material on chronic stimulation of the reticular formation and its effect on self-stimulation. It seems very interesting in the light of this inhibition of the negative component. We have an animal self-stimulating with electrodes in the medial forebrain bundle and we gradually turn up a stimulus in the dorsomedial reticular formation — the sine wave stimulus — up to 10 micro-amperes which is subthreshold for any effect which we could observe from this stimulus alone, self-stimulation comes to a complete halt. Going the other way, the situation is peculiarly just the reverse. If one now has the animal responding to escape from the tegmental stimulus and he now begins to augment stimulation in the medial forebrain bundle electrode just gradually raising the level, the rate of the escape response is increased. Just what this peculiar interaction may mean I have no idea but it seems interesting enough to put on the record at this time.

NAQUET. Did you try to stimulate the lemniscus? Some years ago, in 1954, working with Drs Magoun and Eve King, we obtained the same results as you, when we stimulated the sciatic nerve or the radial nerve. But when we stimulated the lemniscus, the stimulation of the reticular formation provoked sometimes a facilitation of the evoked potentials recorded after the thalamic relay. I think this facilitation was confirmed by Dumont and Dell (1958) and Bremer and Stoupel (1958). When they applied a shock on the optic nerve, the stimulation of the reticular formation gives some facilitation on the response record at the level of the cortex. When a flash is used, the stimulation of the same point of the reticular formation provokes a reverse effect or no effect.

HERNÁNDEZ-PEÓN. Perhaps the different results obtained concerning facilitation and depression of the sensory evoked potentials may be due to the placement of the stimulating electrodes. There is also a difference in the results obtained by an electric shock applied in the central sensory pathway or by using a physiological stimulus applied to the receptor. I would like to add that it was reported some time ago by Dr Purpura that dendritic potentials which are supposed to arise in the cortex are depressed during reticular stimulation or during arousal.

MAGOUN. Local cortical responses, along with other surface-negative phases of evoked cortical potentials, are most susceptible to EEG arousal by reticular stimulation or by natural alerting to attention. The conclusion that an inhibition of dendritic depolarization is the key feature of EEG arousal needs some qualification, however. Drs Eidelberg and Feldman tested this with thiosemicarbazide which blocks the formation of GABA to the point of generating seizure discharge in the nervous system. In this circumstance, surface-negative recruiting responses became very much augmented, as do negative phases of other evoked cortical potentials. However, these augmented surface-negative phases could still be abolished by reticular stimulation. This suggests that if an active inhibition is involved here, it is one that is independent of GABA biochemistry. Additionally, in this connection, when the surface-negative phase is blocked in EEG arousal, one does not see an inverted, surface-positive potential, as in the situations in which Drs Purpura and Grundfest proposed a hyperpolarizing potential to be unmasked.

ECCLES. The GABA is not just blocking an excitatory surface dendritic potential and leaving an inhibitory one. Grundfest has published records which show that a better interpretation is that GABA is simply eliminating surface excitatory potentials and leaving the excitatory potentials deeper down on the apical dendrites and somas, which of course would give rise to surface-positive potentials.

RECHERCHES SUR LES MÉCANISMES NEUROPHYSIO-LOGIQUES DU SOMMEIL ET DE L'APPRENTISSAGE NÉGATIF

MICHEL JOUVET[1&2]

INTRODUCTION

On peut distinguer de façon théorique deux grandes variétés d'inter-actions dialectiques entre l'organisme et le milieu extérieur: l'une d'ordre synchronique, l'autre d'ordre diachronique.

Elles peuvent s'illustrer par l'opposition des jeux de bridge et d'échecs — ... dans une partie d'échecs, n'importe quelle position donnée a pour caractère singulier d'être affranchie de ses antécédents ... celui qui a suivi toute la partie n'a pas le plus léger avantage sur le curieux qui vient inspecter la partie au moment critique ... (Pouillon, 1956).

Il en est ainsi de la grande majorité des réponses du système nerveux étudiées en cours d'expériences aiguës, sur des animaux anesthésiés ou même curarisés. Les fluctuations des réponses sont alors tenues pour aléatoires et ne dépendent point de l' 'histoire' de l'animal. Il en est également ainsi de l'étude de la plupart des réflexes absolus. La liaison entre l'organisme et le milieu extérieur est d'ordre synchronique.

Par contre, 'dans une partie de bridge, il est toujours capital de savoir ce qui s'est passé avant le coup à jouer ... on ne comprend pas pourquoi, à la dixième levée par exemple, le jeu se présente de telle manière si l'on n'a pas suivi les neufs levées précédentes ... ' (Pouillon, 1956). C'est exactement ce qui se passe au sein des liaisons diachroniques, lors de la confrontation, en expérimentation chronique, de l'organisme avec une quelconque variation du milieu extérieur.

Dans le cadre de ces liaisons diachroniques deux grandes variétés de réponses du système nerveux apparaissent:

L'une se traduit par l'*apparition* d'une réponse motrice ou végétative à un stimulus ontologiquement signifiant (la réaction d'attention ou d'orientation) ou à toute variation nouvelle du milieu extérieur (effet de nouveauté, de surprise). Cette réponse survient également lorsqu'un

1 Chargé de recherches au CNRS — Institut de Physiologie, Faculté de Médecine de Lyon.
2 Ce travail a bénéficié d'une subvention partielle de l'Office of Scientific Research and Development command, United States Air Force, attribuée par son Service Européen, sous contrat AF 61 (052) 109.

stimulus indifférent, par association répétée avec un stimulus absolu, devient historiquement signifiant, (lors du conditionnement classique de type pavlovien par exemple). C'est l'*apprentissage positif.*

L'autre modalité de réactivité nerveuse, au contraire, s'accompagne de la *disparition* d'une réponse motrice ou végétative. Il en est ainsi lors de l'extinction de la réaction d'attention ou d'investigation, lorsque sont répétés fréquemment à l'état de veille des stimuli 'indifférents', ou bien lorsque sont répétés au cours du sommeil des stimuli indifférents, capables au début d'entraîner un éveil (extinction de la réaction d'éveil).

Enfin cette modalité de réactivité caractérise également l'extinction du réflexe conditionné lorsque le signal conditionné est répété seul (inhibition interne par extinction).

Cette variété de liaison diachronique, plus élémentaire que l'apprentissage positif puisqu'il ne concerne en général qu'un seul récepteur, apparait bien ainsi comme l'une des formes les plus simples d'apprentissage, l'*apprentissage négatif* (dont nous ne considérons ici que les formes les plus simples).

L'usage tend actuellement à donner à cette variété de liaisons le terme d'*habituation* (Dodge, 1923; Humphrey, 1933; Thorpe, 1944; Konorski, 1948). Il recouvre ceux d'inhibition interne (Pavlov, 1929), d'extinction ou d'adaptation négative (Hilgard et Marquis, 1940).

Ces processus d'apprentissage négatif, dont l'importance est capitale, ont un caractère commun dont Pavlov, dans la quinzième des leçons sur l'Activité Nerveuse Supérieure, soulignat le premier la singularité: *leur relation étroite avec le sommeil.* On se rappelle l'expérience classique au cours de laquelle Pavlov décrivit l'endormissement d'un chien au cours de l'extinction d'un reflexe conditionné. L'étude de l'activité électrique cérébrale a révélé également la fréquence des phénomènes de sommeil électroencéphalographique qui accompagne ces processus d'Apprentissage négatif (Fessard et Gastaut, 1956).

Pour cette raison, l'étude des mécanismes de l'endormissement est capitale car elle peut nous donner des renseignements utiles concernant l'apprentissage négatif. C'est pourquoi nous exposerons, tout d'abord, les résultats de recherches concernant le sommeil.

I — OBSERVATIONS MONTRANT L'EXISTENCE DE DEUX SYSTEMES INHIBITEURS, TELENCEPHALIQUE ET RHOMBENCEPHALIQUE, ENTRANT EN JEU AU COURS DU SOMMEIL

Si l'on applique à l'étude des mécanismes du sommeil la méthode des sections étagées du névraxe, c'est au niveau de la partie du système nerveux en relation avec le milieu extérieur (par ses afférences et éfférences principales) que les fluctuations de l'activité électrique de l'encéphale doivent être mises en corrélation avec les signes somato-végétatifs du sommeil. Car l'endormissement traduit une forme de *comportement total* de l'organisme, et doit donc être jugé *par rapport à son environnement*.

On sait ainsi, depuis Goltz (1892) que le chien décortiqué est capable de sommeil. On sait également qu'un chat mésencéphalique chronique présente des fluctuations périodiques de vigilance (Bard et Macht, 1958; Rioch, 1954), celles-ci deviennent plus difficiles à percevoir dans le cas de préparations pontiques chroniques (Rioch, 1954). Enfin, l'observation d'une moëlle épinière isolée par une section sous-bulbaire, ne révèle aucune périodicité dans le sens d'un rythme nycthéméral (Magoun, 1954).

Ainsi, à chaque 'niveau d'intégration' du tronc cérébral, il devient possible d'observer des fluctuations de vigilance, en *terme ce comportement*. Notre but a été d'en étudier les corrélations électriques.

Les recherches, que nous rapportons brièvement, ont été effectuées sur trente chats chroniques étudiés plusieurs semaines et porteurs d'électrodes corticales, sous-corticales et intra-musculaires (Jouvet et Michel, 1958; Jouvet et col., 1959, b, c, d).

Certains animaux ont été totalement ou partiellement décortiqués, tandis que d'autres ont subi une section totale ou sub-totale du tronc, à la jonction mesodiencéphalique.

L'activité électrique cérébrale recueillie sur un appareil EEG. à plume a été mise en correlation avec les critères périphériques du sommeil: posutre de l'animal, pupilles et membranes nictitantes, température rectale, EKG, respiration, et surtout activité E.M.G. des muscles de la nuque qui nous a semblé être un des témoins les plus fidèles.

(1) *Chez le chat intact endormi* — On peut distinguer deux stades électriques bien différents. Le premier est bien connu (Rheinberger et Jasper, 1937; Hess et col., 1953).

A — *Endormissement et sommeil lent* (Figs. 1, II; 2, II) — L'endormissement est marqué par l'apparition de fuseaux envahissant d'abord le cortex et le diencéphale, puis la formation réticulée (F.R.) mésencéphalique.

Ensuite le sommeil lent est caractérisé par l'apparition, au niveau du cortex et des structures diencéphalomésencephaliques, d'ondes lentes de 2 à 4 cycle-seconde de grande amplitude, tandis que l'activité hippocampique ventrale présente des pointes très brèves et de haut voltage. L'activité pontique demeure rapide. Le seuil d'éveil par stimulation directe de la F.R. est pusl élevé lors de la présence d'ondes lentes que lors du stade des fuseaux.

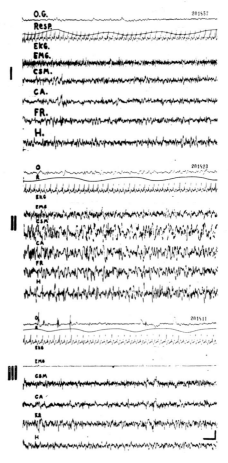

FIG. I

ANIMAL INTACT CHRONIQUE — I   Eveil
II   Phase télencépha-
lique
III Phase paradoxale.

Remarquer, au cours de la phase paradoxale, la supression totale du tonus musculaire des muscles de la nuque (E.M.G.), le ralentissement du rythme cardiaque (E.K.G.), les mouvements des yeux (O.G.) —(Jouvet, Michel et Courjon—C.R. Soc.Biol., 1959, sous presse). Calibrage: 1 seconde — 50µv. pour touts les figures.

Au cours de ce stade, l'animal s'est mis en posture de sommeil, les membranes nictitantes viennent recouvrir les pupilles qui sont en myosis — la nuque fléchit jusqu'à ce que repose la tête. Parallèlement, l'activité électrique des muscles de la nuque diminue progressivement jusqu'à un certain niveau de base alors qu'en général l'activité des autres groupes musculaires est nulle.

B — *La phase paradoxale* (Figs. I, III, 2, III) — Elle fait toujours suite à une phase de sommeil profond et n'apparait jamais d'emblée aprés un

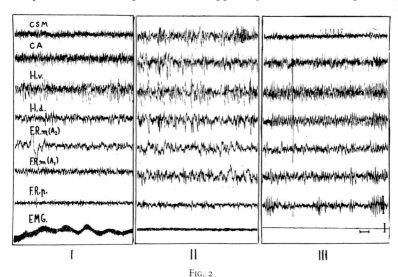

FIG. 2

ANIMAL INTACT, CHRONIQUE — I Eveil
                  II Phase télencéphalique du sommeil
                  III Phase paradoxale — apparition de fuseaux au niveau de la F.R. pontique (F.R.P.) et activité rythmique au niveau de l'hippocampe dorsale.
Hv, Hd: Hippocampe ventrale, dorsale.
F.R.m: F.R. mésencéphalique
Noter la vitesse réduite d'enregistrement.

tracé de veille. Elle débute soudainement et se caractérise par une activité cortico-mésodiencéphalique rapide et de bas voltage identique à celle de l'éveil. L'hippocampe ventral présente également une activité rapide. L'hippocampe dorsal peut présenter une activité rythmique lente identique à celle décrite par Green et Arduini (1954) au cours de l'éveil. En même temps, l'activité rhombencéphalique est le siège de fuseaux de 6 à 8 c/s, d'apparition synchrone avec l'activité rapide corticale. Cette phase s'accompagne immédiatement d'une disparition complète de l'activité

E.M.G. des muscles enregistrés. Elle dure en général 10 à 15 minutes. Soit spontanément, soit sous l'influence d'une stimulation extérieure, l'activité peut revenir au stade antérieur du sommeil avec réapparition de fuseaux ou d'ondes lentes mesodiencéphalo-corticales, disparition des fuseaux rhombencéphaliques et réapparition d'une légère activité musculaire, ou bien il peut y avoir un réveil généralisé de l'animal.

Au cours de la phase paradoxale, la posture de l'animal est celle du sommeil, il n'y a plus aucun tonus musculaire postural et — si la tête ou un membre de l'animal sont en surplomb — ils pendent alors, flasques, soumis uniquement à la pesanteur. Les membranes nictitantes recouvrent presque

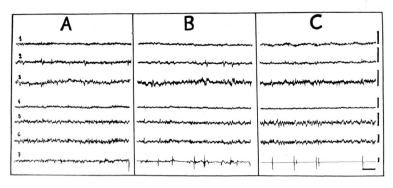

FIG. 3

ANIMAL DECORTIQUE CHRONIQUE — I   Eveil
                                  II   Endormissement
                                 III   Narcose au Nembutal (35 mg./kg.)

Remarquer l'absence totale de fuseaux ou d'ondes lentes au niveau des formations sous-corticales diencéphaliques (1-2), mésencéphaliques antérieures (3-4) ou postérieures (5-6). tandis que l'hippocampe (7) présente une activité caractéristique (Jouvet et Michel, 195 8)

entièrement les pupilles qui sont en myosis, tandis que les globes oculaires sont fréquemment animés de secousses rapides, ainsi que les vibrisses ; plus rarement, on peut constater de brèves secousses des machoires et de la queue. Le rythme respiratoire est plus ample et plus rapide, tandis que le rythme cardiaque se ralentit et que l'arythmie respiratoire se précise.

Le seuil d'éveil (en décibels) par une stimulation auditive augmente par rapport au stade d'ondes lentes. Il est de même pour le seuil d'éveil par stimulation directe de la F.R. mésencéphalique. Enfin, les réponses évoquées auditives, corticales ou réticulaires ont leur amplitude très diminuée par rapport au stade lent du sommeil.

Cette phase, que nous avons retrouvée chez chaque animal, se répète périodiquement, survenant en général à 3 ou 4 reprises au cours d'enregistrement continu de 2 heures de sommeil.

(2) *Chez un animal décortiqué total* (Figs. 3, 4) — Au cours de l'endormissement et du sommeil profond, les formations centrales rhombo-mesodiencéphaliques présentent continuellement une activité rapide, identique à celle observée au cours de l'état de veille; tandis qu'au niveau du rhinencéphale apparaissent des pointes brêves, l'activité E.M.G. est modérée

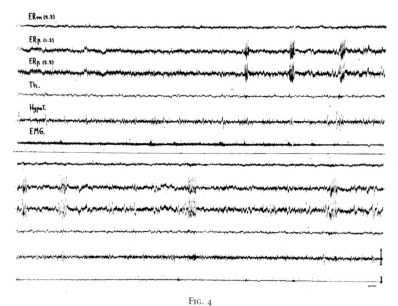

FIG. 4

— Phase paradoxale (rhombencéphalique) du sommeil chez un chat *décortiqué chronique*
Apparition de fuseaux au niveau du nucleus pontis caudalis (F.R.P.) et disparition du tonus musculaire (E.M.G.).
Le tracé inférieur fait suite au tracé supérieur.
Vitesse d'enregistrement 7 m, 5/sec.

(Fig. 3B). Cette activité rapide et de bas voltage persiste durant la période entière de survie de l'animal (jusqu'à 3 mois). La narcose profonde au Nembutal (35 mg./kg.) n'entraîne aucune variation du tracé sous-cortical, mais par contre provoque l'apparition d'une activité caractéristique au niveau de l'hippocampe (Fig. 3C). Cette absence de variation du tracé sous-corticale a été confirmée récemment par Sergio et Longo (1959) chez le lapin décortiqué.

Cette phase est suivie d'une '*phase paradoxale*', marquée par l'apparition

GG

de bouffées d'activité rythmiques de fuseaux à 6-8 c/s, de grande amplitude, se répétant de façon régulière au niveau de la formation réticulée
pontique (Fig. 4).

En même temps que s'installe cette activité, deux ordres de phénomènes apparaissent:

— d'une part, une activation rhinencéphalique (activité rapide), tandis
que les formations meso-diencéphaliques continuent à rester rapides;

— d'autre part, une disparition totale de toute activité tonique musculaire.

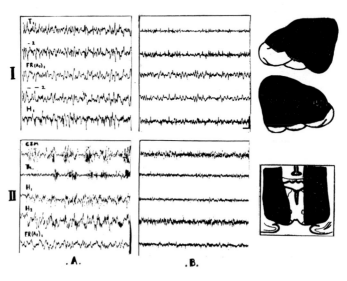

FIG. 5
Persistance d'ondes lentes au niveau réticulaire mésencéphalique (F.R.), lors de
la première phase du sommeil (A) chez un animal décortiqué subtotal (I) ou
porteur d'une section incomplète du tronc cérébral (II) — B: état de veille.

Animal décortiqué subtotal (Fig. 5) — Il suffit de respecter une surface très
minime du néocortex pour retrouver, au cours de la première phase du
sommeil, l'invasion des formations méso-diencéphaliques par des fuseaux
et des ondes lentes. Le 'stade paradoxal' s'objective de la même façon que
précedemment décrit: apparition de 'fuseaux' pontiques mais, cette fois,
les formations méso-diencéphaliques redeviennent rapides ainsi que la
surface corticale restante.

(3) *Animal mésencéphalique* (Fig. 6) — L'activité électrique des formations
corticales et diencéphaliques, situées en avant de la section, présentent

continuellement l'aspect classique décrit au niveau du 'cerveau isolé'
(Bremer, 1935), encore que de brèves et indiscutables phases d'activation
apparaissent au niveau du cortex lors de stimulations olfactives identiques
à celles décrites par Arduini et Moruzzi (1953).

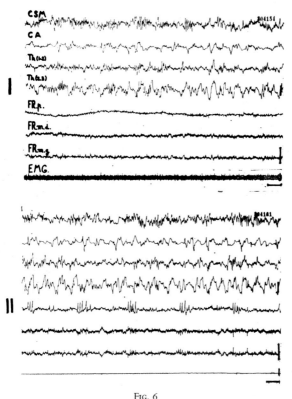

FIG. 6
ANIMAL MESENCEPHALIQUE CHRONIQUE —
En avant de la section, fuseaux et ondes lentes au niveau du cortex
(C.S.M. — CA) et du thalamus (Th) au cours de la veille (I) et de
l'archeo-sommeil (II). Par contre l'activité réticulaire mésencéphalique
reste rapide (F.R.m) tandis qu'une activité de fuseaux apparait au
niveau de la F.R. pontique (F.R.P.) au cours de la phase rhombencéphalique du sommeil (archeo-sommeil) (II), et que l'activité
E.M.G. disparait.

En arrière de la section, par contre, l'activité mésencéphalique reste
constamment rapide. Seule peut s'objectiver la phase 'paradoxale' qui
correspond, selon nous, à l'"archeo-sommeil' de l'animal mésencéphalique;
fuseaux pontiques, absence totale d'activité E.M.G. d'autant plus

remarquable qu'à l'état de veille le tonus musculaire est augmenté et se traduit par une riche activité E.M.G.

Si la section du tronc n'est pas totale et qu'il persiste une mince lame de tissu cérébral central reliant les étages meso et diencéphaliques, les deux premiers stades décrits sur l'animal normal se retrouvent et le stade paradoxal s'accompagne alors d'une activation meso-diencephalo-corticale et rhinencéphalique (Fig. 5).

Ces résultats conduisent donc à admettre deux niveaux de sommeil fort différents. Le premier 'niveau' concerne l'endormissement et le sommeil profond de l'animal normal. Il nécessite obligatoirement la présence, au moins partielle, du nécortex puisqu'il y a nue absence totale d'activité lente sous-corticale chez l'animal décortiqué total, ou en arrière d'une section du tronc cérébral. Cette activité lente traduit un phénomène d'inhibition puisque le seuil d'éveil par stimulation directe de la formation réticulée s'élève lors de ce stade. Il est donc légitime de parler de sommeil télencéphalique à propos de cette phase.

Le deuxième 'niveau' que traduit le *stade paradoxal* dépend d'un mécanisme totalement différent.

I — L'allure identique des 'fuseaux' rencontrés chez l'animal intact et chez les animaux décortiqués et mésencéphaliques chroniques, la même périodicité, les mêmes phénomènes musculaires permettent d'assimiler la 'phase paradoxale' de l'animal intact endormi à l' 'archeo-sommeil' de l'animal mésencéphalique ou décortiqué.

L'apparition d'une activité de 'fuseaux' au niveau du noyau réticularis pontis caudalis (R.P.C.) s'accompagne immédiatement, de façon absolue, d'une disparition totale de toute activité tonique musculaire, dont on connait la dépendance par rapport au système Gamma. Il est logique de supposer que le stade paradoxal représente la mise en jeu d'un mécanisme inhibiteur agissant caudalement sur le système Gamma. On sait qu'un tel contrôle supra spinal est possible au niveau de cette structure (Eldred et Col., 1953). La cause de l'apparition périodique d'un tel mécanisme reste encore inconnue, mais il semble qu'elle soit indépendante des variations du milieu extérieur.

II — Le déclanchement d'une activité rapide cérébrale en avant du rhomboencéphale, au cours de cette phase, pose de nombreux problèmes. La présence d'une activité rapide corticale au cours du sommeil a été signalée au niveau du scalp par Rimbaud, Passouant et Cadilhac (1955) et par Dement (1958) chez le chat, et Dement et Kleitman (1957) chez l'homme. Ces derniers auteurs décrivent également les mêmes mouvements rapides

des yeux et apportent de nombreux arguments qui permettent de supposer que cette activité rapide accompagne le rêve chez l'homme.

Pour ces auteurs, cette activité rapide représenterait un stade intermédiaire entre la veille et le sommeil. Nous pensons plutôt qu'il s'agit d'un stade de sommeil plus profond, étant donné l'élévation du seuil d'éveil et les phénomènes périphériques.

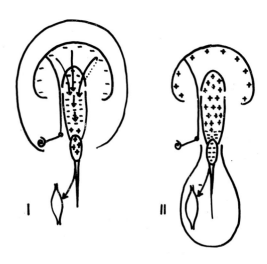

FIG. 7
Schéma des 2 systèmes inhibiteurs entrant en jeu au cours
du sommeil.
I — Le système inhibiteur télencéphalique agissant sur le
S.R.A.A.
II — Le système inhibiteur rhombencéphalique agissant sur
le système Gamma.

C'est pourquoi une telle activité rapide cérébrale, accompagnée de tous les phénomènes végétatifs et somatiques du sommeil profond, apparai bien *paradoxale*.

Ces données permettent ainsi d'admettre que deux mécanismes inhibiteurs différents entrent en jeu au cours du sommeil (Fig. 7) :

Le premier mécanisme représente le mise en jeu d'un système rostral inhibiteur, agissant sur le système réticulaire activateur ascendant (Moruzzi et Magoun, 1949). Au sein de ce système, le néo cortex représente un maillon essentiel, puisque sans lui les phénomènes de synchronisation ou les ondes lentes diencephalo-mésencéphaliques n'apparaissent plus.

Ce système entraîne un état d'inhibition des structures centrales du tronc, mais laisse cependant persister une certaine activité tonique musculaire périphérique.

Le deuxième mécanisme représente la mise en jeu d'un système cuadal inhibiteur agissant sur le système Gamma. Il se traduit par l'apparition d'une activité caractéristique au niveau de la F.R. pontique et traduit l'archeo sommeil périodique de l'animal décortiqué et mésencéphalique — Chez l'animal intact, il déclanche également l'apparition d'une activité paradoxalement rapide des structures rostrales du nevraxe. Il est probable que ce stade dépend du milieu intérieur. Enfin, il est possible qu'il soit le support de l'activité onirique.

Avec ces différents niveaux de sommeil, nous nous trouvons ainsi en possession d'un instrument de travail précieux puisque nous pouvons mettre en évidence, à chaque niveau d'intégration du S.N. les processus de base veille-sommeil qui se traduisent par des aspects électriques particuliers. C'est sur ces mécanismes de base qu'il est logique de tester les processus de base de l'apprentissage, en particulier les plus simples, ceux de l'apprentissage négatif, puisqu'il est fort probable qu'ils mettent en jeu des processus inhibiteurs.

II — L'HABITUATION DE LA REACTION D'EVEIL

Il est d'observation courante que nous nous habituons facilement à dormir dans un endroit bruyant; le passage de trains nocturnes, par exemple, qui nous reveille chaque fois les premières nuits, rapidement ne trouble plus notre sommeil. Les stimuli auditifs, qui excitent notre oreille, restent cependant les mêmes. A leur 'indifférence diachronique', à leur probabilité, notre système nerveux ne réagit plus par l'éveil.

Il reste à déterminer qu'il n'y réagisse plus ou qu'il y réagisse par de l'inhibition.

L'habituation de la réaction d'éveil apparait comme l'expression de la plasticité cérébrale au niveau des mécanismes de base, régulateurs de l'électrogènese.

La constance de ce phénomène chez de nombreuses espèces animales, la relative facilité de son étude électrique ont permis son étude dès l'avènement de l'électroencéphalographie (Ectors, 1936; Rheinberger et Jasper, 1937; Clark et Ward, 1945). Enfin récemment, ce sujet a fait l'objet d'une étude très complète par Sharpless (1954), Sharpless et Jasper (1956).

(A) *Les aspects E.E.G. de l'habituation de la réaction d'éveil*: Les résultats auxquels nous faisons brièvement allusion sont pour la plupart inédits (Jouvet et Michel, 1959 a). (L'habituation de la réaction d'éveil a été étudiée chez des préparations chroniques intactes, décortiquées ou mésencéphaliques qui ont servi à nos recherches sur le sommeil. Des stimuli auditifs étaient employés pour provoquer l'éveil).

Chez l'animal intact, la traduction E.E.G. de l'habituation ne permet pas d'élucider les mécanismes de bases de ce processus, mais elle montre

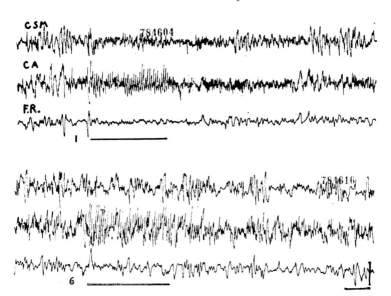

FIG. 8

Habituation de la réaction d'éveil —

— Eveil cortical (C.S.M. — CA) et réticulaire (F.R.) lors de la presentation au cours du sommei d'un train de clics à 12/sec.

— Absence de réveil lors de la 6ème présentation des stimuli acoustiques, augmentation des réponses corticales acoustiques.

cependant qu'il obéit aux lois de l'apprentissage et qu'il ne s'agit pas d'un phénomène de fatigue ou d'adaptation des récepteurs (Sharpless, 1954).

L'habituation est ainsi *spécifique* pour un stimulus donné — puisque la preuve même de ce phénomène est obtenue en induisant après habituation un réveil par un stimulus acoustique *différent*, mais moins intense, ce qui permet d'éliminer le facteur 'profondeur' du sommeil (Fig. 10) (voir aussi Sharpless et Jasper, 1956).

Cet apprentissage négatif peut persister d'un jour à l'autre, puisqu'il est plus rapide d'habituer l'éveil d'un animal à un stimulus le 2ème et le 3ème jour que le premier. Les courbes obtenues ainsi évoquent celles de tout apprentissage (Fig. 10, I).

Enfin, cet apprentissage négatif est également susceptible d'être intertompu: par le temps, par l'intervention d'un stimulus nouveau (Sharpless, 1954), et enfin et surtout par conditionnement (Fig. 10, II).

C'est ainsi qu'un animal qui s'habitue après six répétitions d'un son de 500 c/s. conservera ensuite longtemps une réaction d'éveil si ce son a été associé à des chocs douloureux.

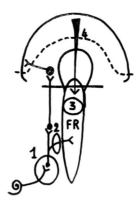

FIG. 9
Schéma des mécanismes possibles de l'habituation de la réaction d'éveil.
1 — Déafférentation spécifique.
2 — Déafférentation non spécifique au niveau des collatérales destinées au S.R.A.A.
3 — Processus inhibiteur primitivement réticulaire.
4 — Système inhibiteur extraréticulaire.

Tous ces caractères prouvent bien que nous sommes en présence d'un réel processus d'apprentissage négatif. L'analyse des activités électriques corticales et sous-corticales démontre que le processus survient en même temps aux étages corticaux et sous-corticaux.

(B) — *Observations montrant l'intervention d'un système inhibiteur télencéphalique au cours de l'habituation de la réaction d'éveil*: Depuis les travaux de Moruzzi et Magoun (1949) (Magoun, 1950), on sait que la condition nécessaire, sinon suffisante à un éveil du cortex (*arousal*) est l'activation du système réticulé activateur ascendant (S.R.A.A.). Le problème qui se pose devant l'habituation de la réaction d'éveil concerne donc les mécanismes responsables de l'absence d'activation réticulaire.

A priori, quatre mécanismes hypothétiques peuvent être mis en cause. Les deux premiers supposent une déafférentation spécifique ou non spécifique; les deux autres, l'intervention de processus d'inhibition active (Fig. 9).

(1) — Le premier mécanisme consisterait dans un 'blocage' des afférences sensorielles (déafférentation spécifique) responsables de l'éveil au niveau des premiers relais spécifiques (noyau cochléaire dans le cas des stimuli acoustiques): le système nerveux ne serait alors plus excité.

On sait qu'un tel contrôle des afférences est possible aussi bien dans des conditions expérimentales aigues (Habgarth et Kerr, 1954; Galambos, 1956) que chroniques (Hernández-Peón et Scherrer, 1955; Hernández-Peón, Scherrer et Jouvet, 1956).

Ce contrôle des afférences acoustiques suppose cependant un état élevé d'excitation centrale obtenu par stimulation d'aires corticales (Jouvet et col., 1956), des parties latérales du tegmentum (Jouvet, Desmedt, 1958) dans des conditions aigues. Dans des conditions chroniques, il s'accompagne d'une activation de l'écorce (Hernández-Peón et col., 1956).

Ce contrôle semble donc déjà, a priori, difficile sur un animal endormi. Un argument formel permet enfin d'éliminer définitivement l'intervention d'un tel mécanisme: la constatation de réponses soit cochléaires, soit corticales (d'amplitude augmentée par rapport à l'átat de veille) (Fig. 8), alors que l'animal ne se reveille plus à des stimuli acoustiques.

Il est ainsi établi que le processus décrit sous le nom d''habituation neuronale afférente' (Hernández-Peón, Jouvet et Scherrer, 1957) n'entre pas en jeu au cours de l'habituation de la réaction d'éveil.

(2) — Un deuxième mécanisme possible consisterait dans une 'déafférentation' du S.R.A.A. (déafférentation non spécifique) par l'intervention d'un mécanisme inhibiteur hypothétique agissant au niveau des collatérales issues des voies spécifiques et destinées au réseau réticulaire (Starzl, Taylor et Magoun, 1951; French, Verzeano et Magoun, 1953).

Ainsi, selon la suggestion de Sharpless (1954) '*This inhibition must be exerted on collateral pathways between specific auditory system and the final common pathway of the reticular activating system ...*'

Selon cette hypothèse, le S.R.A.A. ne serait plus mis en jeu au cours de l'habituation par les stimuli du monde extérieur, les afférences spécifiques — à elles seules — n'étant pas capables d'entraîner un éveil (Lindsley et col., 1950; French, Verzeano et Magoun, 1953; French et col., 1952)

La possibilité d'un tel mécanisme est infirmée par *la constatation de réponses évoquées réticulaires de grande amplitude au cours du sommeil physio-logique, durant l'habituation de la réaction d'éveil* (Fig. 11). Ces réponses peuvent cependant disparaitre lors de la narcose barbiturique (voir également Arduini et Arduini, 1954).

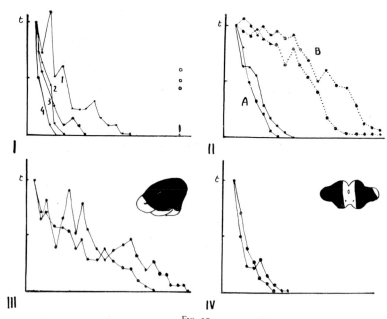

FIG. 10

I — Courbe d'habituation de la réaction d'éveil à des stimuli acoustiques chez le même animal au cours de 4 séances successives à un jour d'intervalle. Les points blancs repèrent la durée de l'Arousal provoque par un stimulus acoustique différent et moins fort après habituation.

II — A — Habituation à un son de 500 c/s.
B — Deshabituation, après que le son ait été associé 10 fois à des chocs douloureux sur la patte. Il persiste toujours une minime activation.

III — Habituation de la réaction d'éveil à un son de 2000 c/s chez un animal décortiqué subtotal et privé de ses aires acoustiques.

IV — Habituation de la réaction d'éveil à un son de 1000 c/s chez un animal aux voies spéci-fiques sectionnées au niveau du mésencéphale.

Il reste donc les deux autres hypothèses à examiner :

(3) — soit l'existence d'un mécanisme inhibiteur autochtone réticulaire, expression de la plasticité des neurones du S.R.A.A. responsables de l'éveil,

(4) — soit l'intervention d'un mécanisme inhibiteur extra réticulaire agissant sur le S.R.A.A.

L'existence de différents mécanismes de sommeil propres à chaque
niveau du tronc cérébral (voir chapitre précédent) permet de tester ces
deux dernières hypothèses.

Ainsi, au niveau du couple S.R.A.A. — système inhibiteur réticulaire
rhombencéphalique, l'étude de l'habituation de la réaction d'éveil (éveil

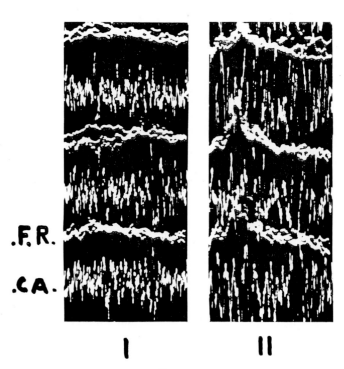

FIG. 11

Réponses évoquées réticulaires (F.R.) à des clics lors de l'éveil (I) et du
sommeil (II).
L'activité spontanée du cortex (C.A.) est également enregistrée à vitesse lente
de balayage (oscilloscope).

de l'archéo-sommeil) permet de tester l'activité autochtone des formations
réticulaires (en dehors de toute participation neocorticale).

Les résultats expérimentaux prouvent alors qu'il est impossible d'habitur
la réaction d'éveil chez l'animal mésencéphalique chronique ou décortiqué
chronique — l'animal se reveillant constamment, et pour un temps très
long, à chaque stimulus acoustique (Fig. 12).

Les mécanismes élémentaires de plasticité, responsables de l'habituation, ne semblent donc pas avoir un siège réticulaire mésencéphalique ou même thalamique.

Par contre, dès qu'apparaissent les signes E.E.G. d'intereaction S.R.A.A.

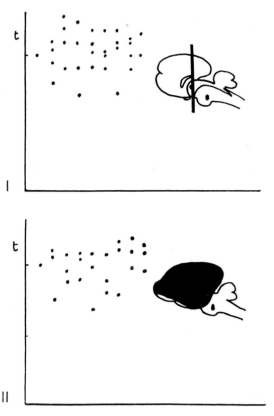

FIG. 12

Absence d'habituation chez un animal mésencéphalique chronique (I) et décortiqué (II).
Chaque point représente la durée du réveil, au cours de 4 séances successives pour I et 3 séances pour II.

— système diffus inhibiteur télencéphalique, — des courbes d'habituation peuvent être obtenues (animal intact, décortiqué subtotal, à section incomplète du tronc cérébral respectant les projections inhibitrices cortici-fuges (Fig. 10, III, IV). *C'est donc au Système Inhibiteur Télencéphalique qu'il revient d'inhiber le S.R.A.A. au cours de l'habituation de la réaction d'éveil.* Ce système n'est probablement pas l'apanage d'une aire déterminée de l'écorce, puisque l'habituation reste possible après ablation des aires spécifiques acoustiques (Sharpless, Jasper, 1956) (Fig. 10, III).

Le cortex frontal joue cependant un rôle important puisque l'habituation devient très lente après son ablation presque complète. (Ce phénomène est à rapprocher des constations de Konorski (1956) — qui remarque un ralentissement considérable de processus d'inhibition chez le chien après ablation des lobes frontaux).

Le système inhibiteur peut également être mis en jeu par des afférences non spécifiques puisque l'habituation est possible après section des voies acoustiques au niveau du tronc (Sharpless et Jasper, 1956) (Fig. 10, IV).

Ces afférences empruntent alors nécessairement le S.R.A.A. Il est possible qu'elles empruntent les voies décrites par Scheibel et Scheibel, 1957; Nauta et Kuypers, 1957, Brodal et Rossi, 1955, et qu'elles soient responsables ces différentes modalités de conduction au sein du S.R.A.A. qui ont été démontrées électrophysiologiquement (Adey et col., 1957).

Ainsi, l'habituation de la réaction d'éveil nécessite une part, même minime, d'écorce cérébrale. La délimitation de ce système inhibiteur agissant sur le S.R.A.A. est difficile dans le cas de l'habituation de la réaction d'éveil car l'aspect E.E.G. de sa mise en jeu est masqué par l'activité de sommeil. C'est pourquoi l'étude de ses modalités d'action au cours d'autres phénomènes d'apprentissage négatif est importante. Tel est le case de l'habituation de la réaction d'orientation.

III — L'HABITUATION DE LA REACTION D'ORIENTATION

L'habituation ou extinction de la réaction d'orientation, (ou reflexe d'investigation, ou reflexe de 'Qu-est-ce-que c'est que ça?' Pavlov, 1929) présente de très nombreuses analogies avec l'habituation de la réaction d'éveil. Cependant, dans le cas de la réaction d'orientation le 'gradient d'excitation' est moins important. Ce n'est plus le passage du sommeil profond à un réveil cortical mais le passage d'un état 'relaxé' de l'animal et de son tracé E.E.G. cortical à un état d'attention spécifique dont les composantes motrices, pupillaires, psycho-galvaniques, cardiaques, vasculaires, respiratoires, et enfin électroencéphalographiques ont fait l'objet de très nombreux travaux (Anokhin, 1956; Asratian, 1955; Berlyne, 1950; Pavlov, 1929; Rusinov, 1957; Sokolov, 1953). Un Congrès récent lui a été spécialement consacré (Moscou, 1957) (voir également Heissler, 1958).

Qu'elle soit induite par un stimulus nouveau (effet de nouveauté (Berlyne, 1950) ou par un signal ontologiquement ou historiquement signifiant (conditionnement), on peut admettre que la réaction d'orientation s'accompagne au niveau du système nerveux d'une augmentation d'amplitude du message spécifique, dès l'étape sous corticale, (Hernández-Peón, Scherrer et Jouvet, 1957; Galanbos, 1956) chez l'animal ou chez l'homme (Jouvet, 1957). Cette augmentation porte, avant tout, sur la

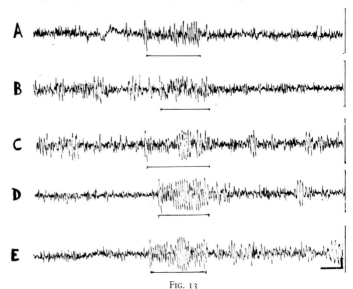

Fig. 13
Réponses du cortex acoustique à des clics.

A.B. — Lors de réaction d'orientation (arousal).
  C — Extinction de la réaction d'orientation (absences d'arousal).
    Augmentation des réponses.
D.E. — Inhibition supra-liminale — La présentation des clics induit des ondes lentes
    corticales (même si le tracé de base est rapide (comparer avec B).

phase rapide, surface positive de la réponse et certains résultats experimentaux permettent de supposer que la mise en jeu du S.R.A.A. pourrait jouer un rôle dans cette facilitation (Dumont et Dell, 1958; Bremer et Stoupel, 1958). Cette augmentation d'amplitude de la réponse s'accompagne également d'une répartiton plus étendue des réponses évoquées au niveau des structures sous-corticales (Galambos et col., 1956; Yoshii, 1956) ou du cortex (Jouvet et col., 1956, 1957) et d'une activation de l'écorce dont la durée est le meilleur index pour objectiver la diminution progressive de l'activation du S.R.A.A. au cours de l'extinction de la réaction d'orientation.

LES ASPECTS E.E.G. DE L'EXTINCTION DE LA RÉACTION D'ORIENTATION
(Fig. 13)

Deux phases distinctes caractérisent ce processus chez *l'animal intact* (Jouvet et col., 1956, 1957; Roitback, 1958; Marsallon, 1959).

(A) — Au cours de la première (Fig. 13 A, B, C) (Fig. 14, I), l'activation corticale induite par les stimuli (lumière suivie de train de clics) diminue progressivement et disparait. Parallèlement, les réponses corticales *aug*-

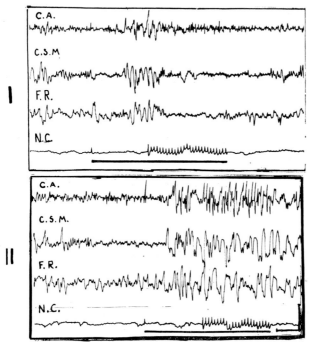

FIG. 14

I — Réaction d'orientation à la présentation d'une lumière et d'un train de clics à 8/sec.

II — Inhibition supra-liminale — la 6ème présentation des stimuli au cours de la 3ème séance induit des ondes lentes corticales (CA-CSM) et réticulaires(FR), augmentation importante des réponses corticales alors que les réponses du noyau cochléaire (N.C.) ne varient pas.

mentent d'amplitude aux dépens surtout de leur phase lente négative et secondaire positive. En même temps, toute réaction motrice de l'animal disparait.

(B) — Si la répétition des stimuli est poursuivie (une fois par minute environ), et si ceux-ci sont présentés sur un tracé cortical d'éveil, ils induisent alors des ondes lentes corticales et sous corticales (Fig. 13 D, E) (Fig. 14, II).

Ce phénomène aboutit enfin à un véritable endormissement (inhibition supra-liminale de répétition) de l'animal-objectivé sur l'E.E.G.

Chez l'animal décortiqué total, aucune variation des réponses sous-corticales n'apparait au cours de la répétition des stimuli. La réaction d'orientation ne peut s'habituer (Popov, 1911; Kvassov, 1956). Enfin, la répétition de stimuli 'indifférents' n'est pas capable d'induire de phénomènes d'archeosommeil E.E.G. aussi bien chez l'animal décortiqué que mésencéphalique.

Les structures centrales du tronc cérébral ne semblent donc pas *primitivement* responsables de l'installation du sommeil au cours de l'inhibition supra-liminale de répétition, comme l'hypothèse en a été soulevée récemment (Moruzzi, 1959; Gastaut, 1957). *L'intervention d'un système inhibiteur télencéphalique agissant sur le S.R.A.A. est donc également indispensable à l'extinction de la réaction d'orientation et à l'apparition de phénomène d'endormissement* (inhibition supra-maximale).

HYPOTHÈSES CONCERNANT LES MÉCANISMES NEUROPHYSIOLOGIQUES D'ACTION DU SYSTÈME INHIBITEUR TÉLENCÉPHALIQUE

L'apparition de variations électriques caractéristiques chez l'animal à cortex intact, au cours des processus d'apprentissage négatif, alors qu'aucune fluctuation ne s'observe chez les animaux décortiqués ou mésencéphaliques, conduit à abandonner l'hypothèse qui fait de l'habituation de la réaction d'orientation ou de la réaction d'éveil un processus primitivement réticulaire (Gastaut, 1957) car aucun mécanisme inhibiteur, capable d'apprentissage ne semble entrer en jeu au niveau des formations réticulées mésencéphaliques et thalamiques déconnectées du neocortex. (Dans le cas — il est vrai — d'apprentissage positif, certains résultats contradictoires de conditionnement obtenus chez des animaux décortiqués peuvent s'expliquer — selon nous — par le fait qu'une partie très minime de neocortex soit restée en place (Lebedinskaïa, 1935); d'autre part, il se peut que certaines lésions réticulaires qui empêchent l'établissement de liaisons diachroniques (Hernández-Peón et col., 1958) agissent par l'interruption des voies corticifuges).

Les données électrophysiologiques confirment donc l'hypothèse de Pavlov sur le rôle capital du cortex (La mise en jeu d'un freinage de l'écorce sur le S.R.A.A. a été mise en évidence récemment, en expérience aigue, au niveau du réflexe monosynaptique (Hugelin et Bonvallet, 1957, a, b). L'inhibition corticifuge serait alors mise en jeu par l'excitation de la formation réticulée et agirait en manière de 'feed back' immédiat. Une telle modalité opérationnelle semble incompatible avec les processus d'apprentissage négatif).

Chez l'animal à cortex intact, l'augmentation importante de la phase lente négative et positive de la réponse corticale aux stimuli apparait comme un processus important, puisqu'elle précède toujours l'extinction complète de l'*arousal* et l'apparition des ondes lentes réticulaires (dont on sait l'origine corticale).

De nombreux arguments permettent d'attribuer ces phases secondaires négative et positive à une réponse corticifuge, expression de l'activité d'interneurones corticaux (Bremer, 1934; von Euler, Magoun et Ricci, 1957), ou expression de *l'activité des dendrites* de l'écorce (Roitback, 1953, 1955; Purpura et Grundfest, 1956; Clare et Bishop, 1955) etc. *Quelle que soit son origine, cette phase secondaire semble representer la traduction d'une onde d'inhibition agissant sur le S.R.A.A.* Au cours de l'apprentissage négatif, tout se passe comme si les processus plastiques ou 'intégratifs' réticulaires (Fessard, 1954), dont certaines modalités ont été mises en évidence au cours du conditionnement (Buser, Hernández-Peón et Jouvet, 1958), étaient sous la dépendance d'influx inhibiteurs corticifuges, dont l'aspect au niveau de l'écorce est représenté par la phase secondaire de la réponse, les fuseaux et les ondes lentes.

Ainsi, sous l'influence de la répétition de stimuli 'indifférents' un changement d'excitabilité de l'écorce apparait selon un processus qui reste encore à être déterminé. L'intervention du rhinencéphale est possible puique l'on sait que sa stimulation est capable d'induire un ralentissement de l'activité corticale (Segundo et col., 1954); celle du 'système diffus thalamique' peut également être invoqueé puisque de nombreux arguments expérimentaux montrent qu'il est responsable des phénomènes de synchronisation et des potentiels négatifs observés au niveau de l'écorce (Jasper, 1949, 1954; Li et col., 1956).

Mais quel que soit le déterminisme de ce changement diachronique d'excitabilité corticale, une étape indispensable à tout phénomène d'apprentissage négatif est représentée par l'inhibition corticifuge diffuse agissant sur le S.R.A.A.

Elle a pour corollaire, au niveau de la formation réticulée, l'apparition d'ondes lentes, soit spontanées, soit accompagnant la réponse réticulaire (Fig. 15). La propagation de l'activité lente corticale au sein du S.R.A.A. semble s'effectuer *selon des processus originaux*, et se fait en général avec un certain délai par rapport au cortex car son installation est lente. Parmi toutes les hypothèses possibles pour expliquer l'influence inhibitrice de

HH

l'écorce sur le S.R.A.A., il se pourrait — selon la suggestion de Scheibel (1957) — que des effets électroniques induits par l'écorce puissent agir sur le S.R.A.A. afin de modifier la propagation des messages au niveau des voies pauci et multisynaptiques de la formation réticulée, selon des mécanismes semblables à ceux décrits par Barron et Matthews (1938) au niveau de la moelle.

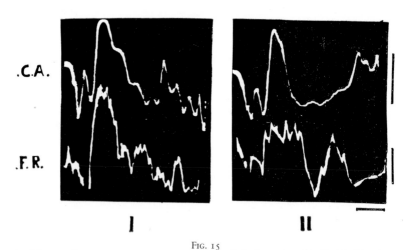

FIG. 15

I — Réponses du cortex acoustique monopolaire et de la formation réticulée bipolaire à un signal acoustique.
   1 — Lors du reflexe d'orientation.
   2 — Lors de l'extinction du reflexe.
Apparition d'une onde positive secondaire corticale et d'une réponse secondaire réticulaire.
Calibrage: 20:milli-secondes, 50 microvolts.

La première phase du sommeil, ou phase télencéphalique, semble mettre en jeu des processus analogues. *Cette phase acquise au cours de l'évolution et de la télencéphalisation traduirait ainsi la réponse de l'écorce aux stimuli indifférents que constitue notre environnement lorsque nous nous endormons.*

RÉSUMÉ

I — Les processus d'apprentissage négatif apparaissent comme l'une des formes les plus simples de liaisons diachroniques. Ils se traduisent par la diminution, puis la disparition d'une réponse du système nerveux à certains stimuli, lorsque ceux-ci sont longuement répétés sans effet nocif pour l'organisme.

Par ses rapports étroits avec l'endormissement et le sommeil, l'apprentissage négatif possède une singularité dynamique qui l'oppose à l'apprentissage positif; c'est pourquoi, l'étude des mécanismes du sommeil doit être abordée en premier.

II — Les corrélations E.E.G. des variations veille — sommeil ont ainsi été étudiées sur trois séries d'animaux chroniques (intacts, décortiqués et mésencéphaliques). Des arguments expérimentaux sont apportés en faveur de l'existence de deux systèmes inhibiteurs mis en jeu au cours du sommeil:

Le premier système nécessite le cortex. Son action inhibitrice se traduit par l'apparition de 'fuseaux' et d'ondes lentes au niveau du cortex, du diencéphale et de la F.R. mésencéphalique, alors que l'activité de la F.R. pontique demeure rapide et qu'il persiste un certain tonus musculaire. Les ondes lentes méso-diencéphaliques sont absentes chez l'animal décortiqué et n'apparaissent pas en arrière d'une section du tronc cérébral pratiquée à la limite postérieure du diencéphale.

Le deuxième système s'accompagne, chez toutes les préparations chroniques, de l'apparition de 'fuseaux' au niveau de la F.R. pontique en même temps que disparait totalement le tonus musculaire et qu'apparait une activité rapide généralisée aux structures rostrales du nevraxe (phase paradoxale du sommeil). C'est sur l'interaction de ces deux systèmes inhibiteurs, télencéphalique et rhombencéphalique, et du S.R.A.A. que les processus de base de l'apprentissage négatif ont été étudiés.

III — L'habituation de la réaction d'éveil ne peut s'expliquer par une déafférentation spécifique ou non spécifique puisque des réponses évoquées de grande amplitude continuent à être enregistrées au niveau des voies spécifiques ou de la F.R. au cours du sommeil.

Il ne s'agit pas non plus d'un processus inhibiteur primitivement réticulaire car on ne peut habituer la réaction d'éveil auxdépens de la phase paradoxale du sommeil chez l'animal décortiqué ou mésencéphalique.

Des arguments en faveur de l'intervention du système inhibiteur télencéphalique sont exposés.

IV — L'habituation de la réaction d'orientation subit les mêmes lois que celles de la réaction d'éveil. Elle ne peut être obtenue chez l'animal décortiqué chronique. Chez l'animal intact, ce processus s'accompagne de corrélations E.E.G. qui objectivent la mise en jeu du système inhibiteur télencéphalique (ondes lentes corticales et réticulaires).

V — Des hypothèses sont enfin émises pour expliquer le mode d'action du système inhibiteur télencéphalique au niveau du S.R.A.A., et le rôle probable des dendrites de l'écorce est évoqué à ce sujet.

Research on the Neurophysiological Mechanisms of Sleep and on Some Types of Negative Learning

SUMMARY

Negative learning (habituation, extinction of the orientating reflex) is one of the simplest types of learning since it involves usually excitation from only one receptor. It may be defined, after Thorpe, as an activity of the central nervous system whereby innate responses to certain stimuli wane as the stimuli are repeated for long periods without unfavourable result. It has been shown that habituation cannot be explained by fatigue or 'adaptation' at the receptor level and, since Pavlov, the relationship between habituation, extinction, 'internal inhibition' and sleep are well known.

Since the problem of falling asleep is intimately related with negative learning, we shall consider first some experimental facts which suggest that two different mechanisms at least act during sleep. Then, we shall describe some evidence concerning the intervention of one of these mechanisms during two types of negative learning: the habituation of the arousal reaction and the habituation of the orientation reaction.

I. OBSERVATIONS POSTULATING THE EXISTENCE OF TWO INHIBITORY SYSTEMS, TELENCEPHALIC AND RHOMBENCEPHALIC, ACTING DURING PHYSIOLOGICAL SLEEP

Since sleep involves the total behaviour of the organism, its mechanism has to be studied in relation to environment. Thus, in brain transsection techniques, we must mainly analyse that part of the nervous system which is in relation with the external world through its main afferent and efferent pathways.

It is well known that a neodecorticated animal can sleep. A sleep-waking rhythm has also been shown to occur in chronic mesencephalic cats, but there is no such periodicity at the isolated spinal level.

We recorded the electrical correlates of such sleep-waking rhythm in three types of chronic preparations: normal, neodecorticated and mesencephalic cats bearing chronically implanted multipolar electrodes in various cortical and subcortical locations.

The electrical activity of the brain was recorded and correlated with a number of somatic signs of sleep: sleep posture, aspect of pupils and nictitating membranes, rectal temperature, respiratory rhythms, E.K.G. We found that one of the best signs of sleep was the E.M.G. of the nucchal muscles.

1. *Normal Cats* (Figs. 1-2). Two opposite E.E.G. patterns were observed during physiological sleep:

A. *The first stage* is well known (drowsiness and sleep). Spindles and slow waves were recorded at the cortical, diencephalic and, later, at the mesencephalic reticular level. The ventral hippocampus may show a 'spike-like' activity. In contrast, the electrical activity at the pontine reticular level remained fast. During this stage, the E.M.G. of nucchal muscles decreased but did not disappear. The threshold of arousal by stimulation of the mesencephalic reticular formation was found to be higher during the slow wave activity than during spindle activity.

B. *The second stage or 'paradoxical stage'* (Fig. 1, III, 2, III): It begins suddenly (always after the first stage) and is characterized by a low voltage fast electrical activity at the cortico-diencephalo-mesencephalic level comparable with the arousal pattern. But the pontine reticular formation usually presents a spindle activity.

Behaviourally, the cat was soundly asleep and there was a total disappearance of any E.M.G. activity. Some very rapid jerks of the vibrissae and movements of the eyes were frequently seen. Spontaneously, or induced by any stimulus, the cat may go back to the first stage of sleep or awaken.

During the paradoxical stage, the threshold of arousal (by direct stimulation of the R.F.) was higher than during the slow wave stage.

2. *Neodecorticated Cat* (Figs. 3-4). In such preparations, the mesodiencephalic activity remained constantly fast with a low voltage. Neither spindles nor slow wave could be recorded, week after week, during the wake-sleeping cycle, even after injection of narcotic doses of Nembutal.

During the paradoxical stage, a 'spindling activity' was recorded at the pontine reticular formation level. Concomitantly the hippocampus showed an arousal type of activity.

The same behavioural phenomena as are found in normal cats occurred during this last stage.

Subtotally neodecorticated cats (Fig. 5): If a very small part of frontal or temporal cortex was left intact during the decortication, the patterns of electrical activity during the two stages of sleep were the same as in intact animals.

Mesencephalic cats (Fig. 6): *Rostrally* (i.e. in front of the transsection), the cortex and the diencephalon had the 'cerveau isolé' type of electrical activity with monotonous spindles and slow waves which might persist for several days.

Caudally (behind the transsection), the mesencephalic reticular formation presented continuous fast activity and no slow wave or spindle could be recorded. Only the paradoxical stage was present: rhythmic 'spindles' at the rhombencephalic level during which the cat had a behavioural sleep posture with complete atonia. This stage would thus appear as an 'archeo-sleep' for a preparation which possessed only an archeo-encephalon related to the external world.

If the transsection of the brain stem was not total, slow waves were recorded at the mesencephalic reticular formation and the patterns of electrical activity during the two stages of sleep were usually similar to those of the intact animal (Fig. 5). These facts lead to the following conclusions (Fig. 7):

Stage 1 of sleep:

Since the threshold of arousal was raised during the slow wave activity in the reticular formation, this slow activity must be inhibitory. Since no slow activity could be recorded at the mesencephalic level in a totally neodecorticated cat, or behind a total transsection of the brain stem, one may conclude that the inhibitory slow waves are a descending activity and that they require, at least, the integrity of a small part of the cortex. Thus, the first stage of sleep would appear to be the result of the activity of some telencephalic inhibitory system acting upon the ascending activating reticular system.

Stage 2 or paradoxical stage:

(*a*) Since the behavioural aspects of the paradoxical stage are the same in intact, decorticated and mesencephalic cats, and since during this phase a peculiar activity appears at the pontine reticular formation level, one may conclude that this rhombencephalic region is directly related to this stage. This structure appears to act caudally and suppresses totally the tonic muscular activity. It is suggested that this effect could be mediated through the supra spinal control of the Gamma system.

(*b*) The appearance of a fast activity, at the mesodiencephalic and cortical levels during this stage is paradoxical since the level of sleep is deeper than in the first stage and not intermediary between sleep and waking. Such a cortical activity has already been found in cats and human beings (Dement-Kleitman) and some arguments suggest that it could reflect a dream activity.

Since negative learning is concerned with the occurrence of sleep, its aspects (habituation of the arousal in sleeping cats, and habituation of the orientation reflex in awake cats) were studied in relation to the telencephalic inhibitory slow waves (stage 1) and the rhombencephalic spindle activity (stage 2).

II. THE HABITUATION OF THE AROUSAL

Repetition of a specific tone which initially produces long lasting arousal of a sleeping cat, fails to do so after several trials. A study of the effects of variations of the stimulus and of the effects of total neodecortication and transsection of the brain stem upon this habituation phenomenon has led to the following conclusions (Fig. 9):

(1) Habituation of the arousal does not depend on changes (i.e. 'blockage', 'inhibition') occurring in the specific auditory pathways or in the non-specific ascending pathways (mesencephalic reticular formation) since cochlear, reticular (Fig. 11) and cortical auditory potentials (Fig. 8) of great amplitude were recorded during complete habituation of the arousal.

(2) Habituation of the arousal does not depend on some intrinsic inhibitory reticular mechanism since it is not possible to obtain habituation of arousal (as judged on the arousal from stage 2 of sleep) in chronic mesencephalic or neodecorticated cats (Fig. 12).

(3) Habituation of the arousal may be obtained in cats with subtotal transsection of the brain stem or in subtotally decorticated cats. The smaller the cortical surface left intact, the longer is the process of habituation (Fig. 10).

(4) These results suggest that the habituation of the arousal reaction depends on the entry in action of a rostral inhibitory system (in which the neocortex is an essential relay) which acts downwards upon the ascending activating system.

III. HABITUATION OF THE ORIENTATING REFLEX

Novel indifferent stimuli (light and intermittent tone) evoke an orientating reflex in an awake cat. They rapidly failed to do so if repeated (habituation of the orientating reflex). If these stimuli were repeated still further, a stage of behavioural sleep may be obtained (Pavlovian internal inhibition).

(1) During the habituation of the orientating reflex in intact cats, a marked enhancement of the secondary negative and positive phase of the cortical (Figs. 13-15) evoked potentials of the indifferent stimuli was observed, and a similar enhancement of a secondary wave could be recorded at the reticular level (Fig. 15). This phenomenon precedes the appearance of induced bursts of spindles and slow waves at the cortical, diencephalic and finally at the reticular level, and it leads to the appearance of stage 1 of sleep (Figs. 13-14).

(2) Habituation of the orientating reflex did not occur, or at least was irregular, in neodecorticated cats. Repetition of stimuli did not induce changes of the subcortical evoked potentials and did not induce sleep.

(3) Repetition of indifferent stimuli failed to induce the 'archeo-sleep' in a mesencephalic cat.

(4) It is suggested that, during habituation of the orientating reflex, indifferent stimuli may trigger the inhibitory telencephalic system which acts upon the reticular activating system.

CONCLUSION

(1) There exists a rostral inhibitory system (in which the neocortex plays a foremost role) which acts upon the reticular activating system during the first stage of sleep. Its electrical manifestation is the appearance of spindles and slow waves first at the corticodiencephalic and later at the mesencephalic levels. This system is plastic and can be triggered by repetition of indifferent stimuli during habituation of the arousal and of the orientating reflex.

It is suggested that the late component of the cortical evoked response and the triggered slow waves which are recorded during habituation (and which may represent a cortical dendritic activity) are the electrical manifestation of the corticofugal inhibitory influence.

(2) There exists also a caudal inhibitory system (in which the reticular formation of the pons plays a major role) which is responsible for the second stage of sleep (paradoxical stage). This system acts caudally on the motor outflow, inhibiting the muscular tone and triggering an 'arousal-like' activity in the structures rostral to the pons. When this system is active, a 'spindling' activity is recorded at the pontine reticular level in intact, decorticated and mesencephalic cats (in which this activity may represent the entry in action of some archeo-sleep mechanism). This activity cannot be induced by repetition of stimuli and there is no evidence

that this caudal inhibitory system could be responsible for any negative learning in mesencephalic and neodecorticated cats.

(3) Habituation of the arousal reaction and of the orientating reflex necessitates the intervention of an active telencephalic inhibitory system.

GROUP DISCUSSION

MAGOUN. I wonder if Dr Jouvet's findings resemble those of Hugelin and Bonvallet, who have proposed the existence of a negative feedback from the cortex to the lower brain which checks the latter's facilitating effects upon motor activity.

They proposed that EEG arousal, evoked by reticulo-cortical stimulation, induced a recurrent inhibition of brain stem activity. Can the inability of your decorticate animal to display slow waves in the thalamus in sleep, be attributed to elimination of such corticifugal inhibition? Have you, or have the group in Pisa, in studies of the slow wave activity of the 'cerveau isolé', ever stimulated the cortex to see whether it is possible to block slow wave activity in the thalamus? Can reduction of spindle activity in the thalamus of the 'cerveau isolé' be used to test the corticifugal inhibition of brain stem activity proposed by Hugelin and Bonvallet?

JOUVET. I am aware of the experiments of Hugelin and Bonvallet and of their hypothetic negative feed back. But I consider, for the following reasons, that the mechanism which would act during the first stage of sleep is quite different:

(1) The time course of these two inhibitory mechanisms is very different.

In Hugelin and Bonvallet's experiments the inhibitory action of the cortex takes place in a very short time (several milliseconds). In our chronic experiments, recording directly at the reticular level, we could usually observe the appearance of the slow waves many minutes after the beginning of slow activity at the cortical level.

(2) But the main objection is this: according to Hugelin and Bonvallet, one may get inhibition of the reticular formation by stimulation of the reticular formation itself (negative feed back). In our cases, when we stimulated the reticular formation at the beginning or during sleep, we always got arousal, as is well known. If the inhibitory action of the cortex was driven by the reticular formation (as suggested by Hugelin and Bonvallet) we would have expected an augmentation of slow waves.

I cannot answer you, concerning the stimulation of the cortex in the 'cerveau isolé' preparation, because we have not done it.

NAQUET. This winter while doing some experiments on anoxia in the decerebrate cat with Fernández-Guardiola I found during the recovery period after anoxia some spindles on the anterior lobe of the cerebellum.

JOUVET. I also recorded on the cerebellum and I found this spindle activity, but with much lower voltage.

NAQUET. Don't you think they come from the cerebellum?

JOUVET. I don't think so, but I have no definite proof up to now.

NAQUET. Have you tried to explore the habituation for click stimuli in the cochlear nucleus in your mesencephalic cat?

JOUVET. I could never obtain, even in a series of intact animals, a consistent decrease of acoustic evoked potentials at the cochlear nucleus level by repetition of clicks (afferent neuronal habituation). So I considered that this phenomenon was not a good index to objectivate negative learning in other types of preparation, such as decorticated or chronic mesencephalic cats.

PALESTINI. I would like to mention experimental data strongly suggesting the presence of a hypnogenic structure in the caudal brain stem. I want to point out also that slides showing the mesencephalic lesions done by Dr Jouvet suggested that the connections with cerebellum and hippocampus are not severed and it is possible that they may be in the brain stem reticular formation. Lastly, the increase in the positive wave has been found in conditioning and also after pre-trigeminal section in cats.

JOUVET. If I understood the work of the Moruzzi school, these authors postulate the existence of both a group of tonically ascending excitatory cells in the upper pons and an ascending synchronizing mechanism in the lower pons or behind.

From our results, it seems that a lower pontine mechanism acts mostly caudally (on the motor outflow) because we observe a striking absence of EMG activity during the 'paradoxal stage' of sleep. There must be some relationship between the fact activity we observe during this stage of sleep and the rather continuous fast activity shown by the MPP cat. Did someone record at the pontine level in this type of preparation?

BUSER. How long after the decortication did you make your recording and observe the absence of slow waves? Could there not be any secondary effect (degeneration) which actually would be responsible for the disappearance of thalamic slow patterns after decortication.

JOUVET. There have been some papers about EEG in decorticate animals, mainly those of Morison and Bassett (1945), and Kennard (1943). These papers were concerned with acute experiments. In such conditions these authors could record spindles at the thalamic level immediately after the decortication. In our chronically decorticate cats we could not get any spindles or slow waves when we began to record (usually 6 to 12 hours after the decortication). This fact has been recently confirmed by Sergio and Longo in Rome, working on chronic rabbits.

In some cats, at the subcortical level, we could record slow waves and spindles during sleep, but a careful anatomical and histological control shows us cortical cells left in place. This fact eliminates, in part, the possibility of some degeneration or hypersensitization effects.

SEGUNDO. The following observations illustrate the participation, as demonstrated by the possibility of either 'habituating' or 'conditioning' the response, of learned issues in the determination of arousal.

(A) *Habituation*. Habituation of arousal from sleep was described by Sharpless and Jasper and similar attenuation was shown recently to involve recovery from animal 'hypnosis', a condition that behaviourally and electrographically resembles natural sleep (Sharpless and Jasper, 1956; Silva, Estable and Segundo, 1959). Further studies by Apelbaum and collaborators on EEG 'arousal' habituation have shown that, if a cat was primarily 'habituated' to a 'basic' tone of 200 c.p.s. and then series of other tones (202–500 c.p.s.) were presented, the responsiveness of the animal to the latter was modified in a characteristic manner. Initially, tones close to 200 (e.g. 202, 205, 210, 220 c.p.s.) did not induce EEG 'arousal', whereas tones removed from 200 (230–500 c.p.s.) did. As more series were applied to each cat, the remaining tones gradually became inoperant following a succession in which tones closer to the 'basic' frequency lost efficacy earlier. Finally, all 'test' tones were inoperant. These observations confirmed that specificity of habituation of EEG 'arousal' is not absolute, involving a certain degree of 'generalization' (5-20 c.p.s. in 200 c.p.s.). Secondly, the biased progress of habituation to 'test' tones indicated that after having learned not to respond to one pitch, learning not to respond to similar frequencies was facilitated. Obviously, the process determining habituation of EEG 'arousal' to a given pitch affects also mechanisms subserving 'activation' to other tones, in a manner related strictly to the frequency arrangement upon the pitch continuum (Apelbaum, Silva, and Frick 1959) Apelbaum, Silva, Frick and Segundo, *in preparation*).

(B) *Conditioning*. Tones reinforced (during wakefulness) by various absolute stimuli have been presented to naturally sleeping cats. The following conclusions could be drawn.

(i) The effectiveness of each sound in provoking arousal (EEG and behavioural) depended on the absolute excitation currently associated with it: reinforcement with centre median or mesencephalic reticular stimulation conferred marked arousing potency (Segundo, Roig and Sommer-Smith, 1959); reinforcement with painful subcutaneous stimulation, less so (Galeano, Roig, Segundo and Sommer-Smith, 1959); reinforcement with cessation of painful subcutaneous stimulation or with application of amygdaloid or caudate stimulation, little or no efficiency (Roig, Segundo, Sommer-Smith and Galeano, 1959; Segundo, Galeano, Sommer-Smith and Roig, *this volume*).

(ii) Certain discriminatory capabilities subsist during natural sleep and enable the animal to differentiate positive (usually reinforced) from negative (usually non-reinforced) stimuli; awakening takes place on presentation of the former but does not occur after the latter. A degree of generalization exists, however, and is greater for the EEG 'arousal' response than for the behavioural reaction; namely, if 200 c.p.s. are reinforced (and 210, 225 and 250 are not reinforced) EEG 'arousal' will be produced by 200, 210, 225 and 250 c.p.s. tones; behavioural arousal on the other hand only by 200 and 210 c.p.s. (Segundo, Roig and Sommer-Smith, 1959).

(iii) Conditioned inhibitory stimuli tend to have 'hypnogenic' qualities. Fig. 1 illustrates this 'depressant' influence of 'negative' excitations contrasting with the arousing potency of the 'positive' stimulus (tone) (Segundo, Roig and Sommer-Smith, 1959).

Consequently, and confirming observations from everyday life, learned issues participate in determination of awakening.

HERNÁNDEZ-PEÓN. Drs George Bach-y-Rita and H. Brust-Carmona in my laboratory have done some experiments on mesencephalic cats recording from the cochlear nucleus and they observed a significant reduction of the auditory potentials by repeating the same acoustic stimulus which has similarities to the same kind of habituation observed in the intact cat. We think that it is possible to obtain habituation in the mesencephalic cat. Dr Jouvet showed desynchronized tracings in the mesencephalic reticular formation both in the intact cat during deep sleep and in the mesencephalic cat which he believes to be permanently awake. How does he decide when the desynchronized tracing represents sleep and when wakefulness?

JOUVET. We use many indexes of behavioural sleep, including the classical posture of the cat, the aspect of the pupils, the nictitating membranes, the rhythm of respiration, the heart rate, the drop of rectal temperature. But we think that the

EFFECT OF COND. INH. STIM.

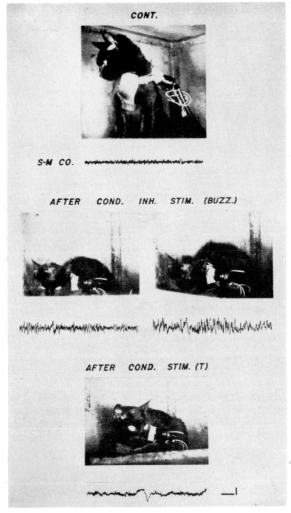

FIG. 1

Contrasting effects of 'negative' and 'positive' stimuli. During training the following stimuli were presented to this animal: (1) Absolute direct electrical excitation of ... (effects not depicted in this figure). (2) Conditioned or 'positive': a 1600 c.p.s. tone (currently reinforced by 1). (3) Conditioned inhibitory or 'negative': a buzzer (when tone was preceded by buzzer, the former was never reinforced). EEG from sensory motor cortex. Upper line: control. Middle line: repeated application of buzzer ('negative' excitation) produced a condition that behaviourally and electrographically resembled sleep; two successive stages are shown (left, right). Lower line: application of tone ('positive' excitation) provoked immediate arousal. Abbreviations: BUZZ., Buzzer; COND., Conditioned; CONT., Control; INH., Inhibitory; STIM., Stimulus; T., Tone.

Calibration: 100 u v 1 sec. (unpublished figure from work by Segundo, Roig and Sommer-Smith, 1959).

best index, just as in man, would be the muscle tone. In cats, the best place to record it, is the nucchal muscles. We never use the EEG alone to decide if the animal is sleeping, but we correlate the EEG and these indexes. That is the advantage of the polygraphic recording.

GRASTYÁN. Fast activity, during sleep was first described by Kleitman and Dement who found it to be characteristic of dreaming. Dement has also found it in cats. It was surprising to find at the same time that a continuous slow activity in the hippocampus existed, in this stage of the sleep. We have never seen so continuous and marked slow waves in an aroused animal. We have tried to influence and artificially elicit this activity and found that in deep sleep, stimulation of the reticular formation by a mild electrical stimulus has provoked this dream-like activity, without any sign of a behavioural arousal. We observed as you did, that the cat loses his tone, but I cannot agree with you that this stage represents a deeper stage of sleep than that of the slow activity. The first evidence is that stimulation of the reticular formation could induce this activity. If we stimulated with strong stimuli we got a full arousal. I think that the fast activity observed on the neocortex sleep is a partially aroused state of the nervous system, a stage between the deepest sleep and full arousal.

JOUVET. As far as I know, it was first reported in 1955 by Rimbaud, Passouant and Cadilhac that it is possible to record fast activity during behavioural sleep in cats. The problem of the level of sleep is difficult. If we use, as a measure of this level, the threshold of behavioural arousal by stimulation of the reticular forma-tion, we found a higher threshold during the paradoxal stage than during the first stage of sleep. We don't know what is the behavioural interpretation of this paradoxal stage. We are faced with a very peculiar pattern of nervous activity. There is some evidence which permits us to think that this activity represents dreams. But dreams are perhaps a routine activity of the brain during sleep, the function of which is unknown

REFERENCE

Apelbaum, J., Silva, E. E. and Frick, O.: Frequency discrimination and 'arousal' reaction. 18. XXI International Congress of Physiological Sciences. Buenos Aires, August 9-15, 1959. Abstracts of Communications.

CORPUS CALLOSUM AND VISUAL GNOSIS

RONALD E. MYERS

A full account of brain mechanisms in learning must be concerned at the same time with definition of structure and function. Yet, an essential lack of knowledge of both the anatomy and physiology of learning needs at once to be confessed, clarification of these problems having up to now been approached only in their more gross, macro context.

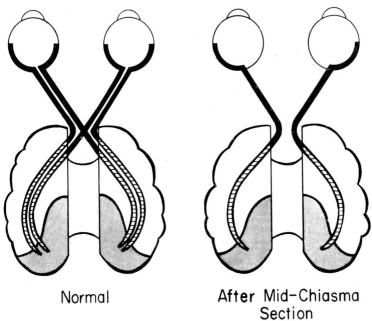

Normal

After Mid-Chiasma Section

FIG. 1
Optic chiasma-section results in unilateral restriction of retinal afferent stimulation.

The present discussion will unfortunately carry us only a short step closer to our goal of understanding. We shall be concerned with a side issue — that of characterizing the mechanism of exchange of information between the two brain-halves and this only as it involves visual learning.

Cats were used as subjects in the experiments to be described. All of these cats were first subjected to mid-sagittal transection of the crossing retinal fibres at the optic chiasma. This altered the retino-central relations such that excitations from each eye were conducted in an afferent sense only to the brain-half on the same side, as illustrated in Fig. 1. Thereafter,

Fig. 2

Chiasma-sectioned cat with one eye masked. A shifting of the mask from one eye to the other results in a shift of retinal afferent stimulation from one brain-half to the other.

by occluding one or the other eye it was possible in these cats to determine which of the two brain-halves was to receive afferent visual stimulation during any given visual experience. A simple rubber mask was used as shown in Fig. 2 to be applied only during periods of training or testing.

The chiasma-sectioned cats were taught visual pattern discrimination responses through one eye. In this procedure, the food-deprived and monocularly masked animals were placed in an enclosed darkened training box (see Fig. 3). The box presented at one end two transilluminated translucent visual patterns held in separate, swinging doors situated side by side. The different sets of paired patterns used in the experiments are

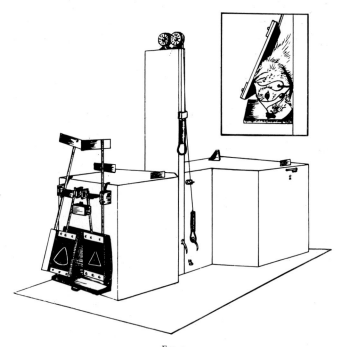

FIG. 3

Training box used for establishment of pattern discrimination responses. A cat is introduced into starting chamber at the right end of the box. Lifting of doors contained in the mid-panel admits the cat to the choice chamber to the left. The animal chooses by pushing on the swinging doors containing the patterns. Correct choice is rewarded by a morsel of food (see insert).

portrayed in Fig. 4. A push on the door containing one pattern of a pair was arbitrarily and consistently rewarded by the hungry animal finding food beyond; a push on the door containing the second pattern of the pair was punished by the door not opening, an annoying buzzer sounding, and sometimes a verbal reprimand being given. Following each such choice occurrence, the animals were trained to return to the opposite end of the box and were removed from the choice situation by intervening panels

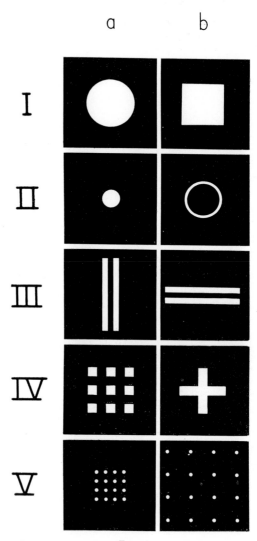

FIG. 4

Pairs of test patterns used. In describing a discrimination
taught to an animal the positive pattern is listed first. For
example, in discrimination I-ab, the positive, rewarded
pattern is a circular flat patch of white against a black background while the negative pattern is a similar square patch.

being lowered. The choice situation was then programmed for the next response by the patterns being exchanged or not exchanged between the doors according to a predetermined chance sequence; the appropriate stimulus door being baited; and the intervening panels again lifted allowing access to the choice chamber. The cats were subjected, in general, to 40 such training experiences or 'trials' each day. After a period of such training, usually from a few days to a few weeks according to the difficulty of the response, the animals achieved the criterion of learning on a given discrimination, choosing the 'correct' pattern 34 or more times in 40 trials. After the animals had learned the discriminations they were overtrained usually up to 400 additional trials to stabilize performance.

A successful or high level performance by the animal, assuming adequate control for undesired, non-visual clues, may be interpreted to mean that the animal can see, that he perceives a difference between the two discriminanda, and that his response to the stimuli is in keeping with antecedent experience or conditioning in the training situation. This latter capacity of specifying objects in relation to prior experience may be defined as *gnosis* from the Greek word meaning *knowledge*, and implies contribution from intact memory mechanisms. The specification of objects in terms of *gnosis* must be set off from their specification in terms of *dimensions*, *location* or *movement* or in terms of *colour*, *brightness* or the like. Our primary interest in this paper will be with *visual gnosis*.

PROBLEM I. IS THERE A SYSTEM OF GNOSTIC INTERCOMMUNICATION BETWEEN THE BRAIN-HALVES?

Nine chiasma-sectioned cats were used in this first experiment. Four were taught only a single discrimination through one eye (see Table I). Cat *Mmm* may be described as illustrative of this group. *Mmm* was taught and overtrained on discrimination I-ab while using the right eye. Final performance through this eye was 39 correct in 40 trials. Did this cat know using the left eye the pattern discrimination he had been taught using the right eye? First performance through the right eye was 38 correct in 40 trails. This initial performance through the untrained eye compared very favourably with the final performance through the trained eye.

The remaining five of the chiasma-sectioned cats were taught two or more separate discriminations, usually one through each eye. Cat *Bgw* may be taken as generally illustrative of all these animals. *Bgw* was taught pattern discrimination III-ab while using his left eye. After criterion of learning had been reached and he had been overtrained 80 trials on this response the mask was reversed and *Bgw* was taught a second discrimination, II-ab, while using the right eye. After this second response had been similarly established and overtrained 80 trials, the cat received further blocks of overtraining using alternately the left and right eyes. In the end *Bgw* experienced 400 overtraining trials through each eye, each on its own respective discrimination. Final overtraining performance with

TABLE I

INTEROCULAR TRANSFER IN CATS WITH OPTIC CHIASMA SECTIONED

Cat	Eye trained	Discrimination	Number correct on final 40 trials with trained eye	Number correct on first 40 test trials with untrained eye
Mmm	R	I-ab	39	38
Bgw	L	III-ab	40	39
	R	II-ab	38	37
Css	L	II-ab	39	33
	R	III-ab	40	39
Bsh	L	III-ab	40	39
	R	IV-ab	40	27
	R	II-ab	36	34
Sll	R	III-ba	40	34
	L	V-ab	40	39
Brn	R	III-ab	40	38
	L	IV-ab	39	30
Kns	R	IV-ab	39	21
Pll	R	II-ab	38	34
Hrl	R	IV-ab	38	35

discrimination III-ab was 40 correct in 40 and with discrimination II-ab, 38 correct in 40.

On tests of cross-availability of knowledge run through the 'untrained' eyes *Bgw* chose the correct pattern 39 times out of 40 on transfer testing with discrimination III-ab and 37 times out of 40 on testing with discrimination II-ab. The few errors made were scattered throughout the test session and were not necessarily made during the first trials.

Examination of Table I reveals that in all instances but three the performance using the untrained eye compares favourably with that using the trained eye. The three exceptional cases (*Bsh*, *Brn*, and *Kns*) will be discussed later (under Problem V) as examples of figural equivalence effects affecting level of interocular transfer.

From the above study it was concluded that there exists a well-ordered system of intercommunication between the brain-halves exhibiting a competence sufficient to handle experiential or gnostic information.

PROBLEM II. WHAT IS THE NEURAL BASIS FOR THE VISUAL GNOSTIC INTER-COMMUNICATION PROCESS?

The corpus callosum seemed a most likely structure subserving such a function because of its very large size and its relation as commissural linkage *par excellence* between the cerebral hemispheres. Conversely, it was difficult to delineate any other well-defined commissural system that would likely be capable of such differentiated and complex contribution as would seem necessary for the gnostic transfer activity. None the less, review of the relatively few carefully controlled studies of corpus callosum function yielded surprisingly few hints of defects following its total destruction or absence in man or animal.

Despite this disappointingly negative story derived from the literature, interocular transfer tests were extended to cats having section of both the optic chiasma and the corpus callosum. Cat *Mmm*, described above as having demonstrated high level transfer of discrimination I-ab from the right eye to the left eye, was one of six cats used in the present study and may serve as an illustrative case.

Following section of corpus callosum[1] and a post-operative recovery period of 21 days, *Mmm* was taught discrimination III-ba while using the right eye and II-ab while using the left eye. He was then given 400 over-training trials on each of these responses through the respective 'trained' eyes. Final performance during overtraining was 40 correct in 40 with discrimination III-ba and 38 correct in 40 with discrimination II-ab. On tests of transfer to the 'untrained' eyes performance on discrimination III-ba was 20 correct in 40 trials and on discrimination II-ab 19 correct in 40 trials. Performance was seen to drop from the consistent high level obtained through the trained eye to a chance level through the untrained eye. This remarkable result was similarly observed on tests run with the other animals in this series in all instances but three (see Table II).

In one of these exceptional instances, performance was significantly

---

[1] Along with section of the fibres of the corpus callosum there was always, in this study, concomitant section of a contingent of fibres of the psalterium because of the latter's close apposition to the inferior surface of the corpus callosum in its posterior extent.

poorer than chance, and in the other two it was significantly better than chance. The first cat, *Brd*, was taught discrimination I-ab through the right eye and III-ba through the left eye. Performance on transfer tests of discrimination I-ab through the left eye was only 13 correct in 40. This below chance performance indicated not only lack of transfer but revealed also a definite preference for the negative, I-b pattern. Inspection of the patterns of the two responses made it seem likely that the preference for I-b, while using the left eye was due to its resemblance to the positive pattern of discrimination III-ba already established through this eye.

TABLE II

INTEROCULAR TRANSFER IN CATS WITH OPTIC CHIASMA AND CORPUS CALLOSUM SECTIONED

Cat	Eye trained	Discrimination	Number correct on final 40 trials with trained eye	Number correct on first 40 trials with untrained eye
Slv	R	I-ab	40	20
Mmm*	R	III-ba	40	20
	L	II-ab	38	19
Brd	R	I-ab	40	13
	L	III-ba	40	20
Knt	R	II-ab	35	19
	L	III-ab	40	20
Bgw*	L	V-ab	40	34
Hnr	R	V-ab	40	28
	L	III-ab	40	20

* Prior training experience (see Table I).

Bgw appeared to recall discrimination V-ab on tests through the untrained right eye. This cat had earlier been taught discrimination II-ab through this same eye (see *Bgw*, Table I). The preference for pattern V-a expressed during the transfer testing may have been due to a previously unsuspected similarity between this pattern and positive pattern II-a of discrimination II-ab. This interpretation was strongly supported when subsequent work with a normal cat showed a near 100 per cent generalization from discrimination II-ab to discrimination V-ab. In such a generalization the cats presumably responded to some general feature of the two sets of patterns such as smallness versus largeness or concentration versus diffuseness (see Fig. 4).

Hnr failed to show any evidence of transfer of discrimination III-ab from the left eye to the right; however, tests of transfer of discrimination V-ab from the right eye to the left showed a performance better than chance (28/40). Figural equivalence effects may again have accounted for the partial transfer although these figures have not been tested in this respect. That the apparent transfer was due to effects other than a central neural intercommunication was strongly indicated, however, by the great ease with which *Hnr* was thereafter taught the inverse discrimination V-ba with the untrained left eye. Cat *Mmm* has also evidenced no cross interference after corpus callosum section when the two eyes were separately taught inverse discriminations (III-ab and III-ba).

The considerations just described led to the conclusion that the apparent transfer of the learned responses between the eyes seen in the instances of *Bgw* and *Hnr* and the depression of performance below a chance level seen in the instance of *Brd* were related not to the contribution of a commissural linkage other than the corpus callosum between the brain halves but to figural generalization effects arising from similarities between patterns of the separate discriminations taught the separate eyes.

From the foregoing experiment it is clear that the cross-availability of information between the two hemispheres in regard to the significance of complex visual pattern stimulation occurs through the corpus callosum. In the absence of corpus callosum visual learning and recall may occur independently in the two hemispheres given independent sensory stimulation. One hemisphere, under the circumstances, may support learned visual responses conflicting completely with responses subsumed by the other hemisphere without cross-interference.

Subsequent work (Sperry, Stamm and Miner, 1956) has shown that cats with optic chiasma and corpus callosum sectioned must relearn anew with one eye pattern discriminations learned with the other eye, the curves of relearning through the 'untrained' eye tending to reduplicate even in detail the learning curves obtained during initial learning through the 'trained' eye. This latter experiment tends to further accentuate the interpretation that no information leaks across the mid-line relative to visual pattern discriminative learning in the absence of corpus callosum.

PROBLEM III. TO WHAT EXTENT DOES GNOSTIC INTERCOMMUNICATION RESULT IN CONTRALATERAL MEMORY TRACE ESTABLISHMENT?

During the monocular training in the chiasma-sectioned cat, a stable and lasting change is induced in the 'trained' hemisphere receiving the direct afferent stimulation. This change has been called the memory trace. Its stability is attested to by the uniformity of performance found day after day during the periods of overtraining of the learned responses. Its persistence is attested to by the fact of unaltered performance on testing after periods free of training of up to a year.

The effects of the monocular training on the 'untrained' hemisphere not receiving the relevant direct afferent excitations are not known. Is a trace system developed in this second hemisphere independent of that induced

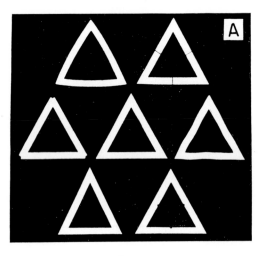

FIG. 5

The normal cat can consistently discriminate the positive central pattern (an equilateral triangle) from any of the closely similar surrounding patterns (Sperry, Miner and Myers, 1955). Compare this with the comparative coarseness of the discriminations depicted in Fig. 4 some of which begin to tax the discriminative capacity of the chiasma-sectioned cat.

in the first hemisphere receiving direct stimulation? If so, how do the two trace systems compare in terms of definition or capacity?

Explorations of these questions have been carried out in two ways: (1) by transfer testing of chiasma-sectioned animals who have had ablation of cortex from the 'trained' hemisphere subsequent to training, (2) by transfer testing of chiasma-sectioned animals who have had complete transection of corpus callosum subsequent to training. In this study two underlying assumptions have been made: (1) the memory trace system of pattern visual learning resides within or is dependent upon cortex, and (2) transection of corpus callosum completely removes one hemisphere from the sway of the other as regards aid and abetment in visual gnosis.

The consequence of 'trained' cortical ablation on contralateral mnemonics may be dealt with first. Fourteen chiasma-sectioned cats were monocularly taught one or both of the two discriminations, III-ab and II-ab. Discrimination III-ab is an 'easy' discrimination while discrimination II-ab is relatively much more 'difficult' as determined by the number of trials needed for the animals to learn, the general level of sustained per-

TABLE III

PERFORMANCE WITH UNTRAINED EYE ON DISCRIMINATION III-AB AFTER
DESTRUCTION OF CONTRALATERAL 'TRAINED' CORTEX

Cat	Eye tested	Lesion type	Test performance on successive days as number correct in sets of 40		
			1st	2nd	3rd
Msy	L	R; minimal	37	—	—
Msf	L	R; minimal	37	—	—
Grs	L	R; minimal	20	36	40
Fst	R	L; moderate	30	38	38
Pln	R	L; moderate	27	40	—
Crw	R	L; moderate	28	32	38
Spc	L	R; moderate	33	38	—
Csw	L	R; moderate	40	—	—
Sch	L	R; moderate	37	—	—
Chr	L	R; moderate	39	—	—
Nkm	R	L; extensive	7/10*	—	—
Kmn	R	L; extensive	37	—	—
Myn	L	R; extensive	27	37	40

* Nkm refused to run after 10 test trials, having erred in the last 3.

formance during overtraining, and the general behaviour of the animals in the training situation. It may be stated parenthetically that the visual capacity of the chiasma-sectioned cat as determined by the difficulty of discriminations that may be learned is vastly inferior to that of the normal cat (see Fig. 5).

After the monocularly trained discriminations had been established and stabilized by overtraining, cortex was surgically removed from the 'trained' hemisphere. The cortical removals were of three general types as illustrated in Fig. 6. The minimal type lesion comprised removal of cortex generally recognized as the striate or primary visual receptive cortex; the

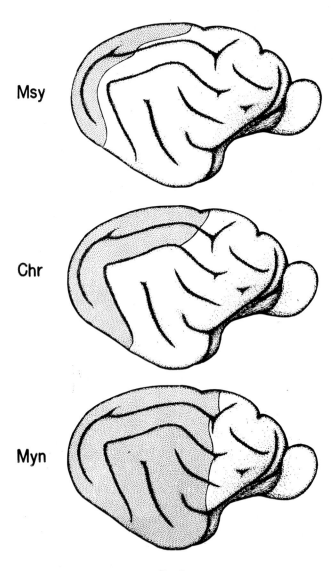

FIG. 6
Stylized diagrams depicting extent of cortical-removal from the 'trained' hemisphere in the three lesion-types. Variations in extent of lesion within a group were minor.

moderate type lesion, removal of the striate plus adjoining cortex generally believed to be visual in import; and the maximal type lesion, removal of all cortex exclusive of the anterior pole containing the sensorimotor cortex. The deep-lying ganglionic masses as well as piriform cortex were left undamaged by these procedures.

After a post-operative recovery period of at least 12 days, performance levels were tested for the first time through the opposite untrained eye. The results obtained with discrimination III-ab are given in Table III and with discrimination II-ab in Table IV. If the results of Table III are considered together regardless of lesion type represented, about half revealed high level performance on the first day of testing and the remainder a high level performance by the second day. Fig. 7 represents in graphic form performance of two of these cats showing greater (*Chr*) and lesser (*Myn*)

TABLE IV

PERFORMANCE WITH UNTRAINED EYE ON DISCRIMINATION II-AB AFTER
DESTRUCTION OF CONTRALATERAL 'TRAINED' CORTEX

Cat	Eye tested	Lesion type	Test performance on successive days as number correct in sets of 40			
			1st	*2nd*	*3rd*	*4th*
Chr	L	R; moderate	25	25	25	32
Myn	L	R; extensive	18	21	21	25
Bhf	L	R; extensive	23	—	—	—

degrees of interocular transfer. The general outcome bespeaks good recall on the tests through the untrained eye following cortical extirpation from the contralaterally lying 'trained' hemisphere. However, if this outcome is closely compared to that obtained on transfer testing after chiasma-section alone (without the superimposed cortical removal) it is clear that the cortical removal resulted in some decrement in contralateral recall (contrast discrimination III-ab, Table I with discrimination III-ab, Table III).

The numbers of cats included in this study trained on the more difficult discrimination II-ab have been few but results obtained have been consistent. Reference to Table IV shows that in all instances performance on the first day of testing did not differ greatly from chance and that through subsequent days, performances only gradually improved. Fig. 8 represents curves of *Chr* and *Myn* on discrimination II-ab depicting initial learning through one eye and relearning through the second eye post-operatively.

Four chiasma-sectioned cats were used to explore the induced gnostic capabilities of the 'untrained' hemisphere as tested following post-training

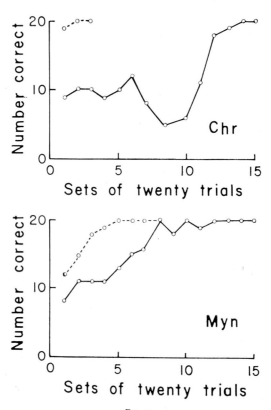

FIG. 7

Performance of *Chr* and *Myn* with discrimination III-ab. The solid line represents initial training with one eye, while the dashed line represents performances achieved through the second, untrained eye. *Chr* illustrates immediate recall through the untrained eye, while *Myn* gives evidence of considerable saving in relearning through the untrained eye.

corpus callosum section. Performance levels as post-operatively tested through both the trained and untrained eyes are given in Table V. *Krm* and *Bgw* may be taken as illustrative cases. *Krm* was taught and over-trained on discrimination III-ba and V-ba while using the left and right eyes respectively. *Krm* achieved perfect scores on final overtraining with both responses. The corpus callosum then was surgically divided in its entire antero-posterior extent through a left sided craniotomy. After a

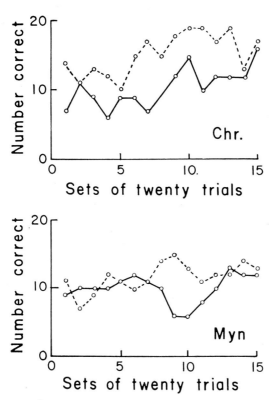

FIG. 8

Performance of *Chr* and *Myn* with discrimination II-ab on initial training through one eye (solid line) and on relearning through the second eye (dashed line). Training and testing procedures with this response were not strictly comparable owing to need for variable encouragements. Therefore, only the initial trials through each eye are represented. Neither cat shows definite indication of immediate recognition through the untrained eye. On the contrary, only slight saving is suggested in relearning in the case of *Chr* and no saving in the case of *Myn*.

post-operative recovery period of 22 days tests were carried out through first the trained and then the untrained eye on both responses. Performances through trained eyes on both discriminations yielded perfect scores.

Performances through untrained eyes were 28 correct in 40 on tests with discrimination III-ba and 20 correct in 40 on tests with discrimination V-ba.

In both of these latter instances of transfer testing a strongly perseverative mode of responding occurred in which the animal pushed always or nearly always on the door of one side regardless of which pattern it contained. Because such positional perseveration tends to continue and to obscure test results, *Krm* was next tested through the untrained eyes on both discriminations under conditions of 'polarity reversal' in which

TABLE V

PERFORMANCES THROUGH TRAINED AND UNTRAINED EYES IN CATS WITH POST-TRAINING SECTION
OF CORPUS CALLOSUM

Cat	Discrimination	Eye tested	Pre-operative performance (correct in 40)	Post-operative performance (correct in sets of 40)		
Krm	III-ba	Trained (L)	40	40	—	—
		Untrained (R)	—	20*	20/20†	—
	V-ba	Trained (R)	40	40	—	—
		Untrained (L)	—	28*	20/20†	36
Byr	III-ba	Trained (R)	40	39	—	—
		Untrained (L)	38	20*	40	—
Sll	III-ab	Trained (R)	39	40	—	—
		Untrained (L)	34	36	—	—
	V-ba	Trained (L)	40	40	—	—
		Untrained (R)	39	32	—	—
Bgw	III-ba	Trained (L)	40	38	40	—
		Untrained (R)	39	35	35	—
	II-ab	Trained (R)	38	39	36	—
		Untrained (L)	37	27	28	30

Left-sided craniotomy in all cases.
* Exhibited strong positional perseveration.
† Number correct in 20 trials run with polarity reversal.

reward-punishment values of the stimuli were reversed. Under these circumstances the animal chose the previously rewarded correct pattern 20 times in 20 in both instances despite its new association with punishment. This peculiar effect of polarity reversal on positional perseveration has also been clearly observed and described in work with interocular transfer in the pigeon (Levine, 1945). Subsequent to the polarity reversal testing *Krm* performed discrimination V-ba well through the untrained eye.

Bgw was similarly taught and overtrained on discriminations III-ab and II-ab while using the left and right eyes respectively. Prior to corpus callosum section this cat (as well as *Byr* and *Sll*) was tested for contralateral recognition of each discrimination using the untrained eye during which high level performances were obtained. Corpus callosum section was then carried out and subsequent retention tests were run through both the trained and untrained eyes. Again corpus callosum section caused no essential change in performance level through the trained eyes. However, on tests run through the untrained eyes a slight but definite lowering of performance was seen in the case of discrimination III-ba and a very large and sustained lowering in performance in the case of discrimination II-ab.

Several important points emerged from these studies. The good contra-lateral recall of the easier discrimination III-ab made it clear that the 'trained' hemisphere could induce lasting memory traces in the opposite hemisphere, traces that subsequently may have an existence of their own apart from transcallosal influences of the first hemisphere. Some lack of definition or relative incapacity in this secondary trace mechanism was hinted at, however, by the depression of initial recall of this easier response occasionally seen through the untrained eye. The near failure of recall of the more difficult discrimination II-ab through the untrained eye insists that when the differentiation handled is of greater subtlety the effects across the midline through the corpus callosum are not sufficient to induce a clearly defined secondary memory trace in the hemisphere not receiving the sensory stimulation. The degree of success or failure obtained in contralateral trace establishment seems, then, to depend in large part on the difficulty of the discrimination handled.

The impairment of recall through the untrained eye seen with lesions of the 'trained' cortex or with post-training section of the corpus callosum was not seen on similar tests run with these same discriminations in cats with chiasma-section alone (compare results of Tables III and IV with those of Table I, or compare pre- and post-operative transfer performances of cats *Bgw*, *Byr* and *Sll* of Table V). The removal of critical cortex from the initially trained hemisphere or the transection of corpus callosum subsequent to training apparently removes an influence which normally aids and abets performance through the untrained hemisphere at the time of testing. Two contributions of the trained hemisphere to mnemonics tested through the opposite untrained hemisphere must then be distin-guished. One must occur prior to the disruption of the influence of the trained hemisphere presumably at the time of initial training and results in the induction of the secondary, somewhat less well-defined memory mechanism. The second contribution appears to occur at the time of actual testing of the contralateral mnemonics and results in the facilitation of correct response above and beyond that sustained by the more or less incapable contralateral memory trace itself.

No gross differences were seen among the cortical lesion types in their effects on performance level through the opposite, 'untrained' neural apparatus, as may be seen from Tables III and IV. Differences in performances were far greater within than between lesion types, and greater deficits were not necessarily seen with greater lesions. This approximate equivalence of the lesion types would support the concept that neural tissue beyond the more restrictive removals contributes little towards the maintenance, and possibly also the development, of stable contralateral memory effects.

It may be noted from Table V that corpus callosum section subsequent to training did not affect performance on any discrimination on tests through the initially trained eye. This was true whether the eye (and hence the hemisphere) that underwent the tests was on the same side or the side opposite to that utilized in the surgical approach to the corpus callosum. From this it is apparent that the unilateral cerebral insult incident to the surgical approach to corpus callosum did not compromise the performance of either intrahemispheric mechanism for visual discriminative response. Furthermore, this lack of effect of corpus callosum section on the levels of learned performance through either hemisphere speaks for a bilateral competence in visual learning and recall speaking against the concept of unilateral cerebral dominance in visual learning for the cat.

PROBLEM IV. IS THE VISUAL GNOSTIC INTERCOMMUNICATION A GENERAL OR
LOCALIZED FUNCTION OF THE CORPUS CALLOSUM?

The question of functional localization of the visual gnostic intercommunication process was investigated by extending transfer tests to cats having varying extents of the anterior or posterior corpus callosum transected. The cats involved along with the number of millimetres of corpus callosum sectioned in each are given in Tables VI and VII. The percentage figures given in parentheses represent the part of the total antero-posterior extent of the corpus callosum included in each section. Each cat in the series following post-operative recovery was monocularly taught and standardly overtrained on discrimination III–ab. Final level of performance in all cases was 38 or more correct in 40. In the last column of the tables are given performances on the first consecutive days of transfer testing.

As may be seen from Table VI section of up to 75 per cent (12.0 of

16.0 mm.) of the corpus callosum anteriorly did not affect the level of transfer of simple discrimination III-ab. When, however, the section extended to section of the anterior 87 per cent (15.0 of 17.2 mm.) transfer

TABLE VI

INTEROCULAR TRANSFER IN CATS WITH OPTIC CHIASMA
AND ANTERIOR CORPUS CALLOSUM SECTIONED

Cat	Extent of section	Test performances through untrained eye (correct in 40)	
		Day 1	Day 2
Btt	12.3 mm. (70%)	32	38
Brd	11.4 mm. (75%)	39	40
Tll	11.7 mm. (77%)	37	38
Gry	15.0 mm. (87%)	24	13

was almost completely disrupted. On the other hand, Table VII shows that encroachments greater than about 45 per cent (6.2 of 14.0 mm.) posteriorly nearly completely abolished transfer while smaller posterior lesions tended in most instances to compromise somewhat the early transfer test performances.

TABLE VII

INTEROCULAR TRANSFER IN CATS WITH OPTIC CHIASMA
AND POSTERIOR CORPUS CALLOSUM SECTIONED

Cat	Extent of section	Test performances through untrained eye (correct in 40)	
		Day 1	Day 2
Cnt	4.8 mm. (26%)	33	38
Cto	5.3 mm. (37%)	35	39
Wld	7.3 mm. (42%)	33	38
Blk	6.2 mm. (44%)	22	20
Blc	9.0 mm. (53%)	23	28
Gbb	11.8 mm. (68%)	21	25

Fig. 9 illustrates graphically the rate of learning of the response through first one eye and then through the second eye in the case of the four cats having the maximal expanses of the corpus callosum sectioned. It may be
KK

seen that these cats with maximal lesions gave indication either of no saving or only slight saving in relearning through the second eye.

In summary, transection of broad expanses of corpus callosum anteriorly did not halt transfer while relatively much smaller lesions posteriorly interfered completely, speaking for a clear-cut posterior localization of the visual gnostic exchange activity. Further, a second important point emerges from a close consideration of these cases. Cat *Brd* transferred discrimination III-ab with only the posterior-most 4.0 mm. of the corpus

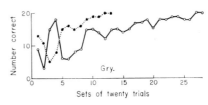
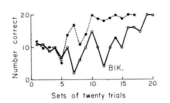
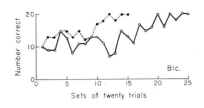

FIG. 9

Graphs comparing rates of learning through the two eyes on discrimination III-ab in four cats. Initial learning through the right eye is represented by the solid line and relearning through the left eye by the broken line. Extent of destruction of corpus callosum in each case may be seen by reference to Tables I and II. *Gbb* showed no saving in relearning with the untrained eye while some slight saving is suggested from the curves of *Gry*, *Blk*, and *Blc*. Cat *Gbb* was trained and tested by an individual different from the one handling *Gry*, *Blk* and *Blc*.

callosum preserved. Cat *Cto* transferred the same discrimination with the selfsame strand of posterior fibres severed but more anterior fibres preserved. These latter two cases taken together point up an equipotentiality or equivalence of function of different fibre strands within the broader posterior segment of the corpus callosum given over to the realm of visual gnostic intercommunication.

PROBLEM V. WHAT ROLE CAN ENVIRONMENTAL INFLUENCES PLAY IN DEFINING THE DEGREE OF INTEROCULAR TRANSFER IN THE CHIASMA-SECTIONED CAT?

Earlier, several exceptional instances were seen of depressed level of interocular transfer in the chiasma-sectioned cats. Examination of Table I shows that discrimination IV-ab was involved in all such instances. It was at first thought that the reduction in contralateral recall might be a reflection of some peculiarity in this discrimination such as a too close similarity between the two patterns of the pair resulting in an inordinate difficulty in their differentiation. This interpretation seemed unlikely, however, since no such difficulty was reflected in the initial learning curves of the cats trained on this response. Furthermore one cat, *Hrl*, was seen to transfer this response at a relatively high level. A second cat, *Kns*, who at first exhibited a strong positional perseveration on transfer testing, later revealed a good transfer performance on testing with polarity reversal. This latter case must, however, remain inconclusive. There remained for clarification the depressed transfer performances of cats *Bsh* and *Brn* on discrimination IV-ab.

Reference once again to Table I shows that both *Bsh* and *Brn* had earlier been taught discrimination III-ab through the same eye that had been used for the transfer testing of discrimination IV-ab. It seemed possible from inspection that the *depression* of transfer performance with discrimination IV-ab may have resulted from resemblances between its *negative* pattern, IV-b, and the *positive* pattern, III-a, of the antecedent discrimination III-ab. Thus was it first suggested that a degree of conflict in the experience of the two eyes of the chiasma-sectioned cat may result in interference with interocular transfer.

The final investigation to be reported was designed to test this hypothesis, and, if it be true, to determine the extent to which conflict may hinder transfer. Failure to resolve conflict between such monocularly-learned responses would indicate a definite limitation in corpus callosum function.

Patterns iii-a and iii-b were constructed such that iii-a closely resembled III-a and iii-b closely resembled III-b (see Fig. 10). Quite closely conflicting discriminations could then be created by making pattern III-a positive for one response and iii-b positive for the other. Three chiasma-sectioned cats were used in this study and were taught discriminaton III-ab through one eye, and, after 120 trials of overtraining, the closely conflicting discrimination iii-ba through the other eye. Such conditioning was alternated back and forth between the eyes until each eye immediately performed its own response correctly on each new presentation. These monocularly established responses were then further stabilized by the usual periods of overtraining (400 trials seen with each).

The patterns of the discrimination taught through one eye were then presented for the first time to the other eye for tests of interocular transfer;

the patterns of discrimination III-ab may serve as illustration. Ideally, one of two possibilities might have obtained on these transfer tests: the cat might have chosen pattern III-a preferentially because of the cross-

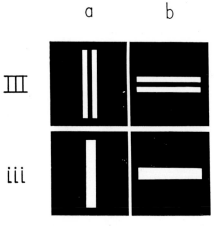

Fig. 10

The two pairs of test patterns used in conflict conditioning. The similarity between the two *a* and *b* patterns is easily seen.

availability of information through the corpus callosum tending to establish such a response tendency in the contralateral mechanism being tested; alternatively, the cat might have chosen pattern III-b because of its

TABLE VIII

INTEROCULAR TRANSFER FOLLOWING TRAINING OF CONFLICTING DISCRIMINA-
TIONS THROUGH THE SEPARATE EYES

Cat	*Wzz*		*Snz*		*Ptz*	
Eye tested	L	R	R	L	L	R
Discrimination tested	III-ab	iii-ba	III-ab	iii-ba	III-ab	iii-ba
Number correct in 40 test trials	1	0	0	9	7	—
Number correct in 40 test trials with polarity reversed	0	0	0	21	—	1

close resemblance to the positive, rewarded pattern of discrimination iii-ba which had just been taught through the eye being tested. Reference to Table VIII reveals that all cats tended very strongly to choose pattern

III-b, the pattern regularly punished during training through the opposite trained eye. Some cats chose this pattern 40 times in 40 trials despite its association with punishment. Tested through one eye they chose the one pattern; tested through the other eye they chose the second pattern. One hemisphere thus did not seem to benefit from the experience of the other under conditions of moderate conflict. Stated in other terms the inter-hemispheric communication process lacked the capacity of bringing about a differentiation of the two conflicting responses within a hemisphere. From the extreme degree of perseveration observed on the test trials of transfer it was concluded that the effects of direct sensory experience are a great deal more forceful in learning than the effects of information transmitted between the hemispheres through the corpus callosum.

ACKNOWLEDGMENTS

The investigations were carried out while the author was associated with the laboratory of R. W. Sperry. Support was received in turn from the Abbott Memorial Fund of The University of Chicago, Frank P. Hixon Fund of the California Institute of Technology, United States Public Health Service and National Science Foundation Grant #G-3880.

GROUP DISCUSSION

CHOW. Can you teach a cat these two discrimination problems, through the same eye?

MYERS. Yes, under certain circumstances cats can consistently be taught the conflicting discriminations through one eye. However, under other circumstances they seem never to differentiate between the two closely conflicting sets of patterns and have to be retaught each response with each reversal of the stimulus pairs.

ROSVOLD. I should like Dr Myers to mention some of his work on tactile discrimination in relation to visual discrimination since it gives a clearer picture of corpus callosum function.

MYERS. The question of whether corpus callosum functions in tactual as well as visual transfer is of great interest. The contribution of Bykov mentioned in the discussion of Dr Segundo's paper served as a first beautiful demonstration of the central importance of corpus callosum in the bilateral dissemination of information bearing on tactual learning. A second contribution in the area of touch was made by Stamm and Sperry who showed that the relatively slight degree of transfer of tactile discrimination learning that occurs from one paw to the other in the cat is interfered with by prior section of the corpus callosum (Stamm and Sperry, 1957). Dr Ebner, in our laboratory at Walter Reed, has found immediate high level transfer of tactile discrimination learning between the hands in normal monkeys and complete failure in corpus callosum-sectioned animals (Ebner and Myers, 1960). Similarly, a comparable interference with intermanual transfer of latch-box solving occurs after corpus callosum section in the chimpanzee (Myers, 1960). The accumulation of information thus far seems to indicate, rather definitely, a tactile gnostic intercommunicative function for the corpus callosum similar to that seen for visual gnosis.

ROSVOLD. Did you ever test for the locus of tactile functions in the corpus callosum?

MYERS. No.

ROSVOLD. Have you any inkling of what function the anterior corpus callosum may have. We have some suspicion that it enters into delayed response behaviour. In some animals with anterior section only, there seems to be an impairment of memory function.

MYERS. No, I have no information specifically related to anterior corpus callosum function.

SEGUNDO. Would Dr Myers comment on the publications of Akelaitis who, with the purpose of avoiding generalization of epileptic seizures, sectioned the corpus callosum in a number of patients (Akelaitis, 1941). Were those patients studied as to their discriminative capacities, and, if so, which were the results of this analysis?

MYERS. These patients were subjected to a host of examinations exploring their sensory, motor, and intellectual capacities both pre- and post-operatively. According to these tests the corpus callosum transection resulted in no clear-cut and consistent deficits. But I believe there is no conflict between these apparently negative human results and the results we have reported here. Akelaitis tested visual function in his patients by testing recognition of different visual objects in opposite homonymous fields of the same eye thus separately testing visual recognition through the separate hemispheres. Such recognition was found to be bilaterally undisturbed and he concluded that corpus callosum did not function in visual recognition. However, he failed to take into account the fact that past experience through each hemisphere's own afferent sensory systems could independently have established the basis for recognition of those common objects in each homonymous field apart from presence or absence of corpus callosum. Had we taught our chiasma-sectioned, callosum-sectioned cats, their visual response without a mask and later tested first through one and then through the other eye for recognition of the discriminanda I doubt whether the cats would have had difficulty in responding correctly through either eye. The central point to be made is that for cross recognition tests to be critical as tests of corpus callosum function the situation or experience to be tested must be, in some sense or other, novel or unfamiliar to the subject.

OLDS. About the last experiment, is it possible that the animal did not learn the discrimination you thought he learned — you assume he learned that when the vertical bar was solid it was positive and when it was split it was negative. It seems the animal might have learned that when the patch is on one eye vertical is positive and when the patch is on the other eye vertical is negative. Does that seem a possible interpretation?

MYERS. That must be considered a definite possibility against which no ultimate control can be conceived, bound as one is in this experiment to use two different receptive fields. However, the slight interference with transfer seen with mildly conflicting discriminations would be hard to explain on this basis. The configuration of results of later experiments not yet published also speak against the idea of the responses being contingent on the eye masked or the particular receptor stimulated.

GERARD. Downer reported in monkeys unilateral responses as far as pattern vision was concerned but I believe colour discriminations crossed over. Have you any information on this?

MYERS. Downer reported that interocular transfer of colour as well as of pattern discrimination was prevented by prior section of optic chiasma and corpus callosum in monkeys. He further maintained that after chiasma section alone the memory mechanism for colour discrimination learning achieved bilateral expression while that for pattern discrimination remained primarily of unilateral potential. He has published this work only as an abstract (Downer, 1958) and did not describe the basis for this conclusion. His interpretations seem to go in the same direction as ours to suggest that the more simple task finds more effective bilateral expression than more difficult. However, we found bilateral memory development for more simple pattern discrimination responses.

ANATOMICAL AND ELECTROGRAPHICAL ANALYSIS OF TEMPORAL NEOCORTEX IN RELATION TO VISUAL DISCRIMINATION LEARNING IN MONKEYS[1]

KAO LIANG CHOW

Our knowledge of brain functions relating to behaviour has advanced rapidly in recent years. One of the central issues in this area, that of the neural mechanisms of memory and learning, however, remains experimentally elusive. This problem may be approached from two directions. One is to use a simple preparation, such as a protozoan or a synaptic junction and to study any physico-chemical changes resulting from repeated excitation or exercise. The other is to use an animal with a well-developed brain in which learning can be defined behaviourally and to analyse at a gross level the neural structures involved. There are difficulties in both approaches. Thus, one wonders how to identify learning in the simple organism and how to extrapolate from any mechanisms detected there to a more complex brain. If one starts with the second type of system, on the other hand, there is only hope but no guarantee that such analysis will eventually reach the basic learning mechanisms at a neuronal or molecular level. Also, it is not clear whether there are one or more neural mechanisms underlying the various types of learning that are defined behaviourally.

The following material illustrates the second type of approach. The neural correlates of learning and retaining visual problems have been analysed at a gross level. In rhesus monkeys, the cortex of the middle and inferior temporal gyri have been shown to be concerned with visual discriminations (Chow and Hutt, 1953; Riopelle *et al.*, 1953; Pribram and Mishkin, 1955). After bilateral ablation of this cortical area, a monkey will learn to choose one from a pair of visual stimuli (such as, red or green colours, triangular or square patterns) in order to get food, but at a slower rate than normal, unoperated animals. Or, if a monkey has earlier learned to solve these problems the forgetting produced by the surgical ablation can be reversed by relearning. This detrimental effect is specific to the temporal cortex; lesions in other neocortical areas do not affect visual

[1] Studies reported in this paper were supported by research grant B-801 (C3) from the National Institute of Neurological Diseases and Blindness, National Institute of Health, and the Wallace C. and Clara M. Abbott Memorial Fund of the University of Chicago.

discriminations (Mishkin and Pribram, 1954; Pribram and Barry, 1956; Wilson and Mishkin, 1959). And this temporal lesion is specific to the visual tasks; it does not affect other learning problems, such as somesthetic discrimination (Wilson, 1957; Pasik, *et al.*, 1959). After establishing such a functional localization, i.e. visual discrimination to temporal cortex, the next step would be to analyse the neural mechanisms involved. Since one does not know what ultimate cellular or molecular mechanisms to look for, the studies conducted so far have dealt, at a gross level, with diverse aspects of the phenomenon, each designed to answer a particular question. For example, attempts to clarify the nature of the visual defect following temporal ablations have been reported (Mishkin and Hall, 1955; Chow and Orbach, 1957; Orbach and Fantz, 1958).

The experiments here reported were designed to investigate the anatomical pathways necessary for the retention of visual discriminations, and the function of isolated temporal and visual cortices in monkeys. Also, the effect of local epileptic after-discharges on learning and retention, as well as any consistent electroencephalographic (EEG) changes in the temporal and visual areas during learning, have been studied.

CORTICO-CORTICAL AND SUBCORTICO-CORTICAL PATHWAYS

The finding that the temporal cortex is implicated in visual learning and retention indicates the presence of more or less direct inter-communications between temporal and visual areas. In the monkey, the only known cortico-cortical pathways of the striate area are short axon fibres to and from the adjacent parastriate region (Mettler, 1935; Clark, 1941). From there, post-synaptic fibres secondarily transmit visual impulses to other cortical areas. Similarly, the anterior temporal cortex receives subcortical fibres from the n. pulvinaris medialis, and it sends fibres back to this nucleus (Chow, 1950; Whitlock and Nauta, 1956). Therefore, the temporal cortex may receive visual impulses or may exert influences on the visual area through either one of these two routes, or both. In earlier studies, I interrupted the cortico-cortical pathways by bilaterally ablating the parastriate cortex, and the subcortical pathways by bilaterally destroying the n. pulvinaris medialis (Chow, 1952, 1954). All these animals retained pre-operatively learned visual discriminations as did normal controls. In other words, these lesions did not duplicate the effect of bilateral removal of the temporal cortex. I have not been able to destroy completely in these animals the parastriate cortex or the pulvinar (it should be noted that only the posterior part of the n. pulvinaris medialis projects to the temporal region). It can be argued that a small remnant of tissue may be responsible for the lack of detrimental effects, thus illustrating the great plasticity of the system.

In order to remedy the inadequacy of the lesions described above, three other types of surgery were carried out in a series of monkeys. First, both the parastriate cortex and the pulvinar were ablated in two monkeys. This was done in the hope that these two lesions would overlap enough to prevent effective communication between the visual and temporal areas. Second, the temporal cortex was undercut parallel to the surface to

NO. 3

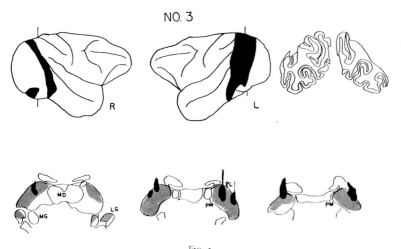

FIG. 1

Reconstruction of lesions of monkey No. 3 who had ablations of both the parastriate cortex and the posterior n. pulvinaris medialis. Solid black, area of destruction; hatching, surrounding degenerated zone; R, right; L, left; PM, n. pulvinaris medialis; PL, n. pulvinaris lateralis; MD, n. medialis dorsalis; LG, lateral geniculate body; MG, medial geniculate body.

eliminate all subcortical projection fibres in four animals. Third, in another four monkeys, the temporal cortex was cross-hatched to eliminate the intracortical and the arcuate fibres. This last operation was applied after failure to circumsect the temporal region. Two monkeys with ablation of the temporal cortex were included to serve as controls.

Pre-operatively all animals were adapted to the testing situation by applying a red and green discrimination. They were then trained on two, *simultaneous* visual pattern discriminations: black circle *v.* black square; and black and white vertical striations *v.* horizontal striations. The animals were required to choose the positive stimulus to receive a food reward, and to disregard the negative stimulus. The non-correction method was used. Thirty trials were given each day, until a criterion of 90 per cent correct responses in a one-day session was reached. The animals were then subjected to bilateral one-stage operation. Fourteen days later they were tested for retention of these visual discriminations.

The brains of all animals were examined histologically, and the lesions reconstructed. Fig. 1 is of the reconstruction of a brain with both parastriate and pulvinar ablations. The cortical lesion was not complete, but the posterior part of n. pulvinaris medialis was largely removed. A second monkey had similar lesions. The cortical regions subjected to the other

TABLE I

PRE– AND POST–OPERATIVE LEARNING SCORE OF MONKEYS WITH DIFFERENT
TYPES OF TEMPORAL NEOCORTICAL OPERATIONS. NUMBER OF TRIALS TO
CRITERION, EXCLUDING CRITERION TRIALS. NUMBERS IN ITALICS, LACK OF
POST–OPERATIVE RETENTION

Type of operation	Monkey no.	Visual Discrimination			
		Circle v. square		Vertical v. horizontal	
		Pre-op	Post-op	Pre-op	Post-op
Ablation	1	90	*120*	120	*120*
	2	180	*240*	50	*270*
Parastriate and pulvinar	3	120	*120*	180	120
	4	150	30	210	60
Cross-hatching	5	210	*240*	300	*420*
	6	150	*150*	240	*330*
	7	60	*90*	210	*270*
	8	120	*120*	150	120
Under-cutting	9	330	120	120	90
	10	300	120	150	90
	11	120	30	210	0
	12	180	30	240	60

three types of surgery (ablation, cross-hatching, undercutting) were all restricted to the middle and inferior temporal gyri rostral to the vein of Labbé. The locus and size of the lesion in individual monkeys showed minor variations. Retrograde degeneration appeared only in the posterior part of n. pulvinaris medialis. In general, the cortex above the plane of undercutting showed no damage. The subpial vertical hatching cut beyond the thickness of the cortex, invading to some extent the underlying white matter. The cortex between the cuts seemed to be normal in appearance.

Table I summarizes the results. The numbers of trials to criterion (excluding the criterion trials) in pre-operative learning and post-operative testing of all monkeys are included. The numbers in italics indicate that after operation the animal did not retain but relearned a specific discrimination. It is clear that, beside a few exceptional cases, only cross-hatching lesion produced an effect resembling that of ablating the temporal cortex. Animals with either the combined parastriate and pulvinar lesion or with the undercutting showed good retention; the degree of saving is comparable to that of normal animals (Chow, 1958). Thus, whatever the neural mechanisms are involved, the interchange of information between the visual and temporal areas for the discriminations used depends primarily on cortico-cortical pathways.

The present results may be compared with those of studies by Sperry. He found no motor defects after cross-hatching the sensorimotor cortex in monkeys when the cuts did not penetrate beyond the depth of the cortex (Sperry, 1947). Also, cats showed a normal rate of learning and good retention of visual discriminations after multiple subpial cuts of the visual area (Sperry, Minor and Myers, 1955). Different neural organizations between the primary projection areas and the association areas may be implicated to account for the different results.

ISOLATED TEMPORAL AND VISUAL CORTICES

One of the inherent weaknesses of using the ablation method is that one removes the structure to be studied. A more rational way of studying the function of a cortical area is to leave this region intact, but to remove all other cortex. To study the role of the temporal cortex in visual learning, one needs a decorticated monkey with sparing of only the temporal and visual areas. A series of behaviourally testable monkeys was prepared which more or less met this requirement. The animals were subjected to three separate operations with long recovery and training periods between. The first operative stage was used to cut one optic tract (left side), the corpus callosum, the hippocampal commissure, and to ablate one temporal cortex (left side). Extensive decortication of the contralateral (right) side, sparing the temporal and visual areas, was done during the second operation. The orbital and medial cortical tissue and the retrosplenial area were variably preserved. Monkeys after this second operation were suitable for studying the visual function of the temporal cortex in isolation. The third operation was performed to remove the remaining temporal cortex (right side). Such a monkey had by and large only one visual area to deal with visual tasks.

Six monkeys, four experimental and two control animals, were used. Three or 4 months after the first operation, they were adapted to the testing situation with the red and green discrimination. Because of the homonymous hemianopsia, many devices were needed to help the animals overcome this defect. The animals were then trained on the two visual pattern discriminations described in the preceding section. After they had acquired these two habits, the two controls were operated upon for the removal of the remaining temporal cortex. They forgot these two habits following this operation but relearned them. Thus, the effect of

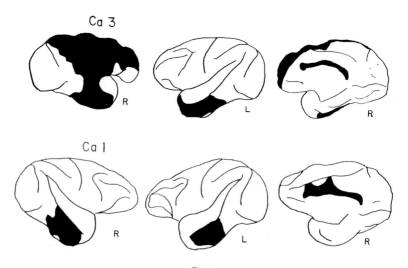

FIG. 2

Reconstruction of lesions (solid black) of one experimental monkey (Ca 3) and one control animal (Ca 1). R, right; L, left.

bilateral temporal lesions on retention of visual discriminations were not augmented by the additional interruption of one optic tract, the hippocampal commissure, and the corpus callosum. For the four monkeys in the experimental group, they retained the two discriminations after the extensive unilateral decortication of the second operation. They lost these habits after the third operation (temporal lesion), but reacquired the two problems with further training. Table II summarizes the results. Fig. 2 shows the reconstruction of lesions of one experimental and one control animal.

In addition, the four experimental monkeys were given a more complex task, the visual discrimination learning-set problem, to assess the capacity of the isolated temporal and visual areas. Two of the animals were trained on this problem after the first operation, retested after the second operation, and again after the third operation. The other two animals were given this problem only after the third operation.

TABLE II

POST-OPERATIVE LEARNING AND RETENTION OF VISUAL DISCRIMINATIONS. NUMBER OF TRIALS TO CRITERION, EXCLUDING CRITERION TRIALS. C . S, CIRCLE v. SQUARE; V . H, VERTICAL v. HORIZONTAL STRIATIONS; FIRST OPERATION, SECTION OF THE LEFT OPTIC TRACT, THE CORPUS CALLOSUM, AND ABLATION OF THE LEFT TEMPORAL CORTEX; SECOND OPERATION, DECORTICATION OF THE RIGHT HEMISPHERE SPARING THE TEMPORAL AND VISUAL AREAS; THIRD OPERATION, ABLATION OF THE RIGHT TEMPORAL CORTEX

Monkey no.	Test	1st operation	2nd operation	3rd operation
Ca 3	C . S	390	30	360
	V . H	390	90	480
Ca 4	C . S	210	30	180
	V . H	180	60	210
Ca 5	C . S	90	30	60
	V . H	180	0	210
Ca 6	C . S	180	30	210
	V . H	240	60	360
Ca 1	C . S	120	—	120
	V . H	120	—	150
Ca 2	C . S	330	—	300
	V . H	270	—	330

The learning-set problem involves a series of 467 two-choice, visual object discriminations. The preliminary sixty-seven problems were presented either fifty, or twenty-four, or six times per problem. Three trials per problem were given for the last 400 problems. After such a long series of problems a normal monkey would make a random choice on the first trial, but learn to choose correctly on the second trial (Harlow, 1949). The results of the four experimental animals are presented in Fig. 3. Both monkeys lost the previously established learning-set after the second operation. They reacquired the learning-set through re-training, but reached a final level lower than that achieved previously. The third operation which more or less left only one visual area intact, rendered all four monkeys incapable of learning or reacquiring the learning-set (Chow, 1954a). These animals, however, could still learn any one object discrimination to criterion within ninety trials.

These results add further evidence for the role of the temporal cortex of monkeys in vision. That this cortical area is not necessary for simple visual learning is also evident. The level of achievement on the learning-set problem is positively correlated with the level of phylogenetic development of the animal (Shell and Riopelle, 1958). The present finding indicates the indispensable role of the temporal cortex for such a complex task. Different neural mechanisms, at least at a gross level, must be sought in the two types of visual learning.

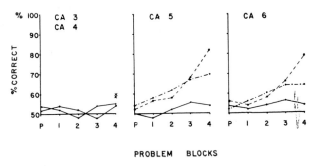

FIG. 3

Formation of learning-set. Percentages of correct responses on the second trial are plotted as a function of problem blocks. Monkeys Ca 3 and Ca 4 were trained after the third operation only. Monkeys Ca 5, Ca 6 were trained after the first operation (interrupted line), tested after the second operation (dash-dot line), and re-tested after the third operation (straight line). P, preliminary sixty-seven problems; 1 to 4, successive 100 problem blocks; cross, percentages correct responses on the third trials of the last one hundred problems.

EEG CHANGES IN VISUAL AND TEMPORAL CORTICES DURING LEARNING

Most of the studies on electroencephalographic changes of the brain during learning deal with the problem of functional localization (Gastaut, 1958; Rusinov and Rabinovich, 1958; Morrell, 1959; Galambos, 1959). As with the ablation method, such studies are a necessary first step. Once an electrographic change is localized to a neural structure, unless the genesis of the potentials is understood the mechanism of learning remains difficult of translation into neuronal terms. Furthermore, in order to establish such a correlation, the electrographic changes should follow the behavioural changes as expressed in learning curves. Except in a few cases, such a correlation has not been convincingly reported (Yoshii, 1956;

Beck, Doty and Kooi, 1958; Galambos, 1959). The present study emphasizes this point. The problem of functional localization is not of primary interest. The search here centres on detecting systematic EEG alterations in cortical areas known to be concerned with visual discrimination learning in the monkey.

Records have been obtained to date on six young monkeys. Each animal lived continuously in a monkey chair throughout the 5 to 6 months experimental period. The first 2 months were used to tame the animal which was held loosely in the chair so that it could turn around, scratch its head, lift the leg to scratch the back, etc. The animals continued to grow and remained in excellent health. They were adapted to the testing situation and trained to be quiet before each trial so that a relaxed, waking EEG baseline could be obtained. Eight pairs of bipolar electrodes made with 30 gauge nichrome wire, insulated except for the tip, were implanted in the temporal and visual areas. Additional placements of electrodes in the lateral geniculate body, the midbrain reticular formation, and the hippocampus will not be reported here. After the completion of the experiment, the brains were studied histologically. The electrodes were in the middle and inferior temporal gyrus, and the lateral surface of the visual areas. The electrode sites showed either slight cortical depression or some scarring of the tissue, caused by direct injury or by the repeated electric shocks (see next section).

The test situation is shown in Fig. 4. Either two or three *successive*, two-choice visual discriminations (red *v.* green; black triangle *v.* circle on grey background; black and grey vertical *v.* horizontal striations) were presented to the animals. The training was conducted in a darkroom with a specially constructed photic stimulator as the light source. The light was continuous between trials but changed to flashes (5–10 c.p.s.) before each trial. Thus, the animal saw the visual stimuli only through the flickering light, which may serve as a 'tracer stimulus' (Galambos, 1959, p. 334). Each trial consisted of presenting *one* visual stimulus. If it was a positive stimulus, the monkey was required to push open the door of the stimulus box to get a food reward within 5 seconds. For a trial with the negative stimulus, the door was locked and the animal was required not to push the door within 5 seconds. A piece of food was handed to the animal if it did not push the door when the negative stimulus was presented three times in succession. A trial was given in the following way: the opaque screen was in front of the monkey to conceal the stimulus box. The EEG machine was turned on, continuous light was changed to flashes, the opaque screen was removed and the stimulus was exposed

LL

outside the animal's reach for 2 seconds. The stimulus box was then pushed forward, and the animal was allowed to respond. Thirty trials (fifteen positive and fifteen negative trials) were executed each day until the animal reached a criterion of 90 per cent correct in a one-day session. The EEG was recorded for every trial with a Grass 4-channel model III machine.

The six monkeys learned a total of fourteen visual discriminations. The plot of percentage of correct responses in successive daily sessions showed

FIG. 4

Photograph to show the testing situation. A, monkey in chair, with the black screen around the chair removed to show the electrode wires; B, opaque screen moved to one side to expose the stimulus box; C, the flickering light passing through the box to illuminate the visual stimulus attached to the box frontal panel; D, the photic stimulator; all controls are operated manually.

the typical postively accelerated learning curves. The number of trials ranged from 90 to 180. EEG recordings of eleven discriminations were suitable for analysis.

The normal EEG of the visual area showed the fast, low voltage arousal pattern mixed with 4-5 per second relaxation waves. Occasionally there were some alpha-like waves. The temporal leads showed periodical (every 2-3 seconds) bursts of waves (100 µv. and 12-16 per second) superimposed on the arousal and relaxation record. These bursts were very regular and appeared in all records. When the training started, photic driving was prominent in the visual area. This driving habituated rapidly, usually within the first thirty trials. It very rarely appeared in the temporal tracings.

By inspection, the visual area EEG of each trial throughout the learning

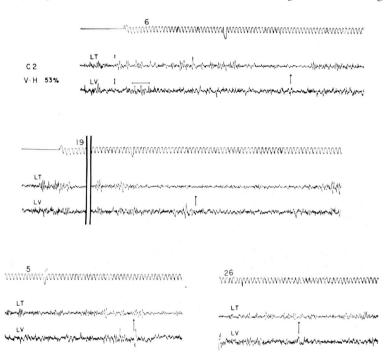

FIG. 5

EEG records of four negative trials taken from the second day of training. Monkey C2 made 53 per cent correct responses on vertical and horizontal striation discriminations on that day, but responded incorrectly to these four trials. Trials 6 and 19 show the decreased amplitude of temporal cortical EEG, and trials 19 and 5 show photic driving in the visual area tracings. The break in the upper tracings of light flashes indicates the presentation of the stimulus. The arrow shows the animal reaching the stimulus. LT, left temporal; LV, left visual; calibration, 50 μv. and 1 second.

process was judged as showing or not showing photic driving. For the temporal lobe, the disappearance of the periodical bursts accompanied by a decreased amplitude of the entire record was seen after exposure of the visual stimuli. No other EEG alterations were recognized. These changes, however, were not consistent, being present in one trial and absent in the next. Also, these changes occurred mostly during negative trials. Fig. 5

shows the EEG records of four negative trials taken from the second day of training of monkey C2. The EEG tracings show the four possible combinations of alterations (visual area: photic driving or not driving; temporal area: decreased amplitude or not decreased amplitude) in four trials. Fig. 6 was taken from another monkey, who responded correctly to the negative trials. Again, the four combinations appeared in the four

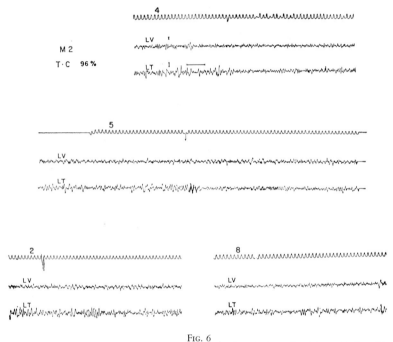

FIG. 6

EEG records of four negative trials taken from the fourth day of training. Monkey M2 reached criterion on triangle and circle discrimination on that day, and made correct responses (not reaching the stimulus) to these four trials. Trials 4 and 5 show the decreased amplitude of temporal EEG, and trials 5 and 2 show photic driving in the visual area tracings. The break in the upper tracing of light flashes indicates the presentation of the stimulus. LT, left temporal; LV, left visual; calibration, 50 μv. and 1 second.

trials. Similar examples could also be chosen from positive trials. Thus, it may be misleading to use sample records demonstrating EEG changes during learning. Some quantitative measurements are necessary to establish consistent trends. Fig. 7 presents such an analysis of two monkeys' EEG records on two visual discriminations. Tracings from the temporal and visual areas were plotted separately, with postive trials (vertical

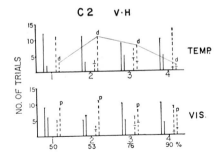

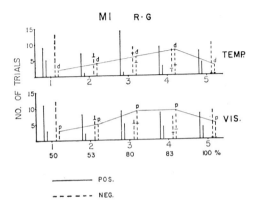

FIG. 7

Graphs of monkey C2 on vertical and horizontal striations discrimination and monkey M1 on red and green discrimination to indicate number of trials of temporal cortical EEG (TEMP) showing a decreased or no decreased amplitude, and of visual area tracings (VIS) showing photic driving or no photic driving. 1 to 5 refers to successive daily sessions of thirty trials each, with the corresponding percentages of correct responses indicated below. Each pair of vertical continuous bars are the fifteen daily positive trials, and each pair of vertical interrupted bars, the fifteen daily negative trials. The first bar of each pair indicates the number of trials of no decreased amplitude EEG (TEMP) or of no photic driving (VIS). The second bar of each pair indicates the number of trials that show decreased amplitude EEG (TEMP) or photic driving (VIS). A few trials are eliminated because of movement artifacts. The connected curves depict systematic EEG changes occurring only in negative trials. POS, positive trials; NEG, negative trials; d, decreased EEG amplitude; P, photic driving.

continuous bars) separated from the negative trials (vertical interrupted bars). In the graphs of temporal tracings, the first bar of each pair indicates the number of trials that showed no decreased amplitude, and the second bar, the number of trials that showed a decreased amplitude. For the visual area EEG, the first bar is the number of trials with no photic driving, the second bar, the number of trials with photic driving. The percentage of correct responses during the daily session was indicated at the bottom of the graph.

These graphs show that consistent changes occurred only in negative trials, but not in positive trials. This probably reflected the fact that the animals were initially trained to reach for the stimulus every time. The number of negative trials showing a depressed amplitude in the temporal EEG increased as the animal started to learn, but returned to the initial level when criterion was reached. Such transient changes occurred in eight out of eleven cases of discrimination learning. A similar change in the number of trials showing photic driving was illustrated in one of the graphs for the visual area. Such visual area EEG changes appeared, however, in only three out of eleven cases. Thus, it seems that the only significant electroencephalographic alterations in this study were confined to the temporal cortex which is known to be related to visual learning. The fact that the EEG change is transitory argues against it being a direct neural expression of the learning process. Rather, it probably represents some alerting or attention factor. When the animal began to be aware of the problem it had to concentrate not to respond to the negative stimulus. Once that was learned little effort was needed to respond appropriately.

LEARNING AND RETENTION DURING ELECTROGRAPHIC AFTER-DISCHARGES

The same six monkeys in the same testing situation described in the last section were used later to study the effect of local EEG after-discharges of the temporal cortex on learning and retention. Presumably, seizure after-discharges disrupt neuronal circuits. The present experiment was designed to show whether or not some such neuronal circuits are necessary for learning and memory processes.

The after-discharges were induced either unilaterally or bilaterally by bipolar electrical stimulation of the temporal cortex. A Grass stimulator was used to deliver monophasic square wave stimuli (3-5 ms. 50 c.p.s., 4-25 volts). Each trial was presented as follows: The EEG was turned on, the light was changed to flashes, the EEG was turned off, the electrical shock was turned on for 5 seconds. The EEG was turned on again and the opaque screen was removed to expose the stimulus for 2 seconds. If there were EEG after-discharges during the two-second period, the stimulus box was pushed forward for the animal to respond. If no after-discharges

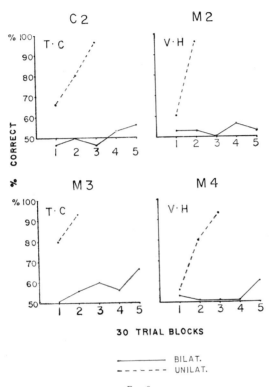

FIG. 8

Learning curves of four monkeys on four visual discriminations, first during bi-temporal seizure after-discharges (continuous line) and later during unilateral temporal seizure
(interrupted line). Percentages of correct responses are plotted
against successive two-day results (thirty trials). 1 to 5 refers
to thirty trial blocks. T.C., triangle *v.* circle; V.H., vertical *v.*
horizontal striations; BILAT, bilateral temporal after-discharges;
UNILAT, unilateral temporal after-discharges.

appeared, the stimulus box was not pushed forward and the trial was discounted (less than 10 per cent of the total trials). Fifteen shock trials were given every day with at least 5 minutes interval between trials. The seizure after-discharges in the temporal cortex were similar to those described by French, etc. (French, Gernaudt and Livingston, 1956; Konigsmark, Abdullah and French, 1958), and will not be detailed here. In the present study the stimulus strength was so adjusted that the after-discharges of about 60 per cent of the trials lasted 8-10 seconds. They were localized to the temporal cortex, and did not spread to visual areas. Following unilateral stimulation, the after-discharges appeared very rarely in the contra-lateral temporal cortex (less than 5 per cent of trials).

Four monkeys were trained on four discriminations. Fig. 8 shows the learning curves. The monkeys responded at a chance level in 150 trials when trained during bilateral temporal after-discharges, but learned the problem during unilateral EEG discharges. The animals reached for the stimulus in every trial during bi-temporal after-discharges. Their general behaviour during this period, however, appeared to be normal. They could pick up small pieces of food from among inedible objects. Some-times the animals seemed to be bewildered and glanced around, but this did not prevent them from reacting to the task.

TABLE III

RETENTION TEST RESULTS OBTAINED DURING EEG AFTER-DISCHARGES IN THE TEMPORAL CORTEX. PERCENTAGE OF CORRECT RESPONSES IN THIRTY TRIALS. (THE FIGURES IN ITALICS ARE BASED ON FIFTEEN TRIALS.) R.G, RED v. GREEN; T.C, TRIANGLE v. CIRCLE; V.H, VERTICAL v. HORIZONTAL STRIATIONS; S, SHOCK TRIALS; NS, NO SHOCK TRIALS; BILAT., BILATERAL; UNILAT., UNILATERAL

Monkey		C_1		C_2		M_1			M_2		M_3	M_4
Problem		R.G T.C V.H		R.G V.H		R.G T.C V.H			R.G T.C		V.H	R.G
Bilat.	S			53 50		60 53 43			57 60		67	60
	NS			97 97		97 97 93			97 97		93	93
Unilat.	S	97 93 93		*87* *93*		100 97			*100* *93*		*100*	
	NS	100 97 97		*87* *100*		100 97			*100* *100*		*93*	

The ability of the monkeys to perform the learned visual discrimina-tions during either bilateral temporal or unilateral temporal after-discharges was also tested. Each discrimination was tested in two days. Each daily session consisted of fifteen trials with electric shocks and fifteen trials without shocks presented in a balanced order. Each trial was given in the same manner described before. For no-shock trials, the animal merely waited for 5 seconds. The results are summarized in Table III. It is clear that the animals failed to retain the learned habits under the condition of bi-temporal after-discharges, but performed perfectly under uni-temporal after-discharges.

As a control, they were also tested either immediately after bilateral shocks to the visual areas, or during the shock period. Because of the difficulty of eliciting consistent seizure after-discharges in the visual areas (the EEG tracings usually flattened out for a short period after shocks to the visual areas), the latter procedure was used. The results were entirely negative. The animals performed the discriminations correctly under these conditions. Thus, electric shocks to the visual areas do not affect the monkey's retention of visual habits.

Several investigators have reported that electrical stimulation of sub-cortical structures rendered cats and rats incapable of learning (Buchwald and Ervin, 1957; Glickman, 1958; Ingram, 1958; Thompson, 1958). The data presented here show that only bilateral temporal EEG after-discharges prevent a monkey from learning or from retaining visual discriminations. Whatever neural circuits may be responsible for these discriminations, they are located in the two temporal lobes and can be temporarily disrupted by abnormal neuronal discharges. These results may be relevant to elucidating the effects of unilateral stimulation of the temporal cortex in conscious human patients. Such stimulations have been variously reported to elicit illusions, hallucinations, recall, and to cause transient amnesia (Penfield and Jasper, 1954; Bickford et al., 1958; Mullen and Penfield, 1959).

SUMMARY

Previous investigations have established that a restricted area of temporal neocortex in the monkey concerns with the learning and remembering of visual discriminations. This paper reports four studies illustrating how this problem is analysed at the present time. These studies are far from uncovering the mechanisms of learning and retention at a neuronal level, but they show what specific questions may be asked and answered experimentally. To ask meaningful questions about learning phenomena that can be identified behaviourally and tested empirically, constitutes one approach to the understanding of the neural mechanisms of learning.

GROUP DISCUSSION

GALAMBOS. Dr Chow has referred to 'brain-disorganization' experiments from which much, I feel, is to be learned. Besides his anatomical methods there are two physiological ways in which these disorganizations can be created. Shocks applied to the temporal lobes and elsewhere create after-discharges, highly abnormal electrical activity that presumably reflects a profound disorganization of the neurones under the electrodes. Besides this Bureš employs another method, the spreading depression technique, which yields an electrical record from the affected brain region that is entirely flat rather than abnormally active. Appropriate use of these physiological methods along with the anatomical ideas for disorganizing cortex Dr Chow referred to should give valuable additional information on the brain function in acquisition and retention of learned responses.

CHOW. I have talked about this with Dr Van Harreveld and he told me that in the monkey you cannot produce spreading depression very regularly.

ECCLES. I think Dr Chow is too hard on himself in interpreting this seeming inconsistency between the learning process and the EEG results. What I should like to think happens in the learning process is a simplification in the neural pathways. Originally a great deal of neural activity is concerned, a lot of it of no value to the learning but it is wandering through large areas, giving you this large depression of the EEG.

CHOW. This is very possible.

MORELL. From the standpoint of electrophysiology the behavioural learning curve must surely be considered a very coarse kind of measure. Even if these variously recorded electrical events are related to learning in some fundamental manner, I would not expect them to follow the same time-course as the learning curve.

ROSVOLD. We have evidence that can substantiate Dr Chow's point that the connections are cortico-cortical.

Will the monkey learn anything at all during the period of after-discharge? Dr Chow demonstrated clearly that he could not learn the visual discrimination problem. I am wondering whether the animal can learn anything at all.

What was your stimulation technique because we were not able to disturb the retention of the visual discrimination problem — by strong stimulation in the temporal lobes.

CHOW. I am using bipolar electrodes to stimulate the temporal cortex, and not recording with EEG. I only test them when the EEG shows after-discharge bilaterally. They are wire electrodes insulated except at the tip with 3 or 4 mm. separation between electrode tips. The stimulus is 3 ms. square waves 50 cycles per second, for 5 seconds.

With respect to whether this effect is specific to the task or not I have not looked into the problem. That is a question of functional localization, which is not the purpose of this study.

BUSER. I still believe in electrophysiology as an index of neuronal activity and neuronal activity is the basis of learning. Maybe the test you are using is not a good one or the process taking place is not uni-directional. Is it more complex than the total behavioural phenomenon you are observing? Did you happen to record evoked potentials to optic stimulation in the temporal region of the monkey, an observation which could be correlated with your results from ablation techniques?

CHOW. I did not make any recording of evoked potentials in the temporal or visual areas of the monkey.

As to your first question, I think one should pose meaningful questions to be answered by the EEG technique. Just implanting electrodes and recording the EEG to see what happens is not very satisfying.

ASRATYAN. I think that some of our data published in 1937 in Russia may be of interest to Dr Chow. That is why I want Dr Chow to become acquainted with these facts. We divided the brain cortex of the dog into three isolated parts, namely, the frontal, occipital and temporal parts, by surgical extirpation of ribbons of cortical tissue between main parts of brain cortex. Let me show the operation schematically on the blackboard. We cut only the cortex tissue, but as it was shown later by histological control degeneration of subcortical white tissue took place also. So, these cortical parts were fully isolated from each other and connected with each other only through subcortical structures. We were able to elaborate conditioned defensive motor reflexes to the visual as well as to the auditory stimulus. After repeated cortical operation during which we extirpated either the isolated occipital or temporal regions, the visual or auditory reflexes were correspondingly abolished.

CHOW (in answer to a question from Dr Naquet). In this experiment the only control I had was to stimulate the visual area either uni- or bilaterally or one electrode on each occipital area and to test on retention. I have not tested on learning. Whether you tested immediately after or during stimulation of the visual areas there is no detrimental effect on retention of the visual discriminations.

SEGUNDO. In support of Dr Buser's defence of the usefulness of electrographic recording in the study of learning, I would mention that, in our experience, the EEG provided more sensitive criteria than performance. First, EEG effects appeared earlier than behavioural effects during establishment and disappeared later during extinction of learned responses. Secondly, when studying very wild cats, animals gave little behavioural evidence of 'learning' but electrographically yielded obvious signs of conditioning.

OBSERVATIONS SUR LE CONDITIONNEMENT INSTRUMENTAL ALIMENTAIRE CHEZ LE CHAT[1]

P. Buser et A. Rougeul

Avec la collaboration de Melle D. Giraud[2]

Introduction

On s'interroge encore, et sans doute le problème ainsi posé n'a-t-il pas de solution simple, quant aux rôles respectifs du cortex cérébral — considéré partiellement ou dans sa totalité — et de diverses structures sous-corticales dans les mécanismes d'intégration sensorimotrice dont procèdent l'acquisition puis l'exécution d'un mouvement conditionné.

Au nombre des sources d'information dont on dispose, l'analyse électrophysiologique, telle qu'elle a été récemment étendue à ce domaine, apporte, il va de soi, un ensemble de renseignements essentiels sur les modifications globales ou localisées que l'on peut déceler au niveau des centres, et du cortex en particulier, dans les diverses situations d'un conditionnement moteur.

L'intérêt de cette méthode ne saurait toutefois en laisser ignorer d'autres, celle en particulier d'éliminations ou de destructions localisées du névraxe; classique, sans doute plus globale et moins analytique, elle reste néanmoins essentielle pour décider de l'importance d'une structure déterminée dans l'organisation fonctionnelle d'une certaine réaction motrice conditionnée.

Tel fut notre problème. Soumettant des chats à un type classique de conditionnement 'instrumental' — type 'reward training' de Hilgard et Marquis (1940) — nous nous sommes posé la question du rôle du cortex moteur dans l'enchaînement des processus qui conduisent l'animal à accomplir un mouvement 'volontaire' pour un signal déterminé. Certes, les documents électrophysiologiques sur le cortex moteur (modification de son tracé spontané, étude des réponses évoquées qui s'y développent,

[1] Le présent travail a bénéficié d'une subvention partielle de l' 'Office for Scientific Research of the Air Research and Development Command, U.S. Air Force', attribuée par son Service européen sous contrat AF 61 (052), 103.
[2] Nous tenons à remercier également Melle G. Giacobini et Mme S. Laplante, pour leur aide au cours des interventions, comme aussi dans la préparation des contrôles histologiques post-mortem.

modalités de mise en jeu, également, du tractus pyramidal) étaient précisément loin de faire défaut,[1] qu'il s'agisse de données recueillies sur animaux porteurs d'électrodes implantées (Chow, Dement et John, 1957; Beck, Doty et Kooi, 1958; Morrell, 1958; John et Killam, 1959; Segundo et col., 1959; Zuckermann, 1959; pour références antérieures, voir Buser et Roger, 1957; Fessard et Gastaut, 1958), ou d'autres obtenues sur préparations aiguës (voir Discussion).

Toutefois, la solution au problème ainsi posé n'était pas incluse; envisageant dès lors les résultats d'ablations, il nous apparut que, à l'exception de quelques travaux, dont ceux de l'école de Konorski (Konorski et col., 1952; Brutkowski et col., 1955, 1956; Stępień et Stępień, 1958, 1959, 1960) réalisés sur le chien dans des conditions comparables, mais non identiques aux nôtres, seul le comportement moteur spontané, tonus et locomotion, avait été analysé chez les carnivores, souvent d'ailleurs avec une grande précision, après de telles éliminations corticales (Olmsted et Logan, 1925; King, 1927; Langworthy, 1928; Laughton, 1928; McKibben, 1929, parmi d'autres).

Cette absence de documents dans le sens souhaité a dicté le présent travail.

TECHNIQUES

Les expériences portent actuellement sur 22 animaux, tous adultes; un certain nombre d'entre eux, normaux, ont servi de témoins; d'autres ont subi diverses ablations d'aires corticales.

Mode opératoire

Toutes les ablations ont été pratiquées aseptiquement, sous narcose au Nembutal, par aspiration ménagée, avec conservation des volets osseux; l'hémostase était réalisée au moyen d'éponge de gélatine (Spongel).

Les ablations d'aires motrices ont toujours été bilatérales et extensives. Elles portaient sur toute la région sensorimotrice péricruciée et l'aire somatique II, et débordaient sur les gyrus proreus, marginal, suprasylvien et ectosylvien selon des contours dont les détails seront indiqués ci-dessous. Elles s'étendaient sur une profondeur suffisante pour donner la certitude d'avoir éliminé la substance grise des sillons. Par ailleurs, les voies olfactives primaires (lobe olfactif en particulier) ont toujours été respectées.

[1] Un certain nombre de ces données, obtenues par notre groupe, et celles en particulier recueillies par nous-mêmes sur le chronique (Rougeul, 1958) ont été présentées au cours du Symposium. Il nous a paru préférable, pour l'homogénéité du sujet traité, de n'en pas faire état dans le cadre de cet article à objectif limité.

D'autres ablations ont été réalisées, destinées à servir de contrôle : soit destructions isolées, toujours bilatérales, de divers territoires (gyrus proreus, aires visuelles, aires auditives), soit élimination subtotale du néocortex, ne laissant subsister que les régions péricruciées et préfrontales.

Conditionnement

Tous les animaux et plus spécialement ceux porteurs d'ablations étaient maintenus dans des conditions aussi favorables que possible (semi-liberté), permettant d'observer à volonté leur comportement spontané.

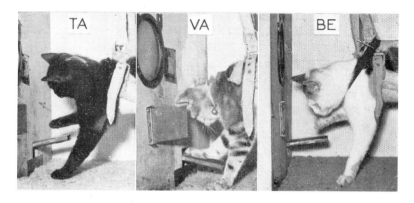

Fig. 1
Appuis conditionné normaux.
TA : chat normal; VA : animal à ablations frontale et péricruciée partielle; BE : animal à ablation du cortex temporal et de l'aire somatique II (voir Fig. 6).

Les épreuves d'apprentissage étaient effectuées quotidiennement à heure fixe, toutes précautions étant prises pour que les animaux se trouvent, d'une séance à l'autre, dans des états de faim pratiquement comparables. La durée de chaque séance n'a jamais dépassé 30 minutes (10 essais).

Le dispositif d'apprentissage 'instrumental' est d'un type relativement classique, s'apparentant plus particulièrement à celui récemment utilisé également pour le chat par Stamm et Sperry (1957) : le mouvement de bascule d'un levier déclenche automatiquement l'ouverture d'un volet, démasquant ainsi un plateau portant de la nourriture (Fig. 1); l'animal, qui est maintenu par un hamac dans une position déterminée, apprend à effectuer le geste d'appui à un signal donné; ce signal consiste en une succession de stimuli brefs acoustiques (pips à fréquence donnée) ou lumineux (éclairs) à la cadence de un, ou deux par seconde, selon les cas.

La stimulation est poursuivie à ce rythme jusqu'à l'accomplissement du mouvement; en cas d'absence d'appui, elle n'est pas prolongée au-delà de 20 secondes (pour les animaux normaux); elle le sera davantage pour des animaux porteurs de lésions.

L'expérience se fait en chambre relativement insonorisée, un fond sonore continu permettant en outre de masquer de manière satisfaisante d'éventuels bruits accidentels; cet aménagement, théoriquement insuffisant, s'est avéré néanmoins convenir, l'expérience nous ayant montré que dans de telles épreuves la susceptibilité des animaux à des effets d'inhibition externe est très réduite.

Evaluation des résultats

Au cours de chaque session, sur animal normal ou porteur de lésions, on procède à une évaluation aussi approchée que possible de la latence des réponses: temps qui sépare pour chaque essai le premier signal, du début de l'appui sur le levier. On relève également le nombre des appuis éventuellement effectués entre les essais ('appuis-erreurs').

A partir de ces données immédiates, on a procédé à d'autres estimations (moyennes de latences, etc....), qui seront détaillées ci-dessous. Enfin, l'on note toutes les manifestations de comportement anormal que l'on peut observer chez les animaux opérés au cours des séances de travail.

Contrôle port-mortem

Tous les animaux ont été maintenus pendant des périodes de 2 à 6 mois, les survies les plus longues étant celles d'animaux porteurs d'ablations et dont la récupération était régulièrement suivie. Avant le sacrifice, une analyse électrophysiologique des réponses en divers points du névraxe était effectuée, de préférence sous anesthésie au chloralose: exploration du cortex, précisant le nouvel aspect de la topographie des projections sensorielles après ablation; étude, également, par introduction d'une électrode au niveau pontique,[1] de la persistance – ou de la disparition – d'une activité pyramidale chez les animaux à ablation sensorimotrice. Ultérieurement, le cerveau était perfusé au sérum physiologique, puis au formol. Le cas échéant, une étude topographique de l'étendue de l'ablation était effectuée, d'abord macroscopiquement, puis sur coupes frontales, après coloration de Nissl.

---

[1] Selon une technique récemment utilisée pour l'exploration du tractus pyramidal sur la préparation aiguë (Ascher et Buser, 1958).

Résultats

On envisagera successivement quelques aspects de l'apprentissage chez les animaux normaux, pour ensuite considérer les effets des ablations.

I. MODALITÉS D'APPRENTISSAGE CHEZ LE CHAT NORMAL

Chez l'animal intact, le début du 'dressage' s'effectue, selon les cas, soit en amenant passivement la patte sur le levier pendant le signal, soit en procédant 'par imitation'.

La première méthode, par mouvement passif, dans laquelle on associe au signal une sensation complexe, à composante extéroceptive et probablement surtout proprioceptive, s'apparente directement au conditionnement du deuxième type. Nous lui avons assez vite préféré — sauf pour les sujets de contrôle aveugles — une technique impliquant une participation de l'animal peut — être plus en rapport avec l' 'intelligent behaviour' (Konorski, 1950); il suffit en effet d'appuyer avec la main sur le levier, pendant le signal, pour qu'au bout d'un certain temps, le chat, très attentif en général, tente de faire lui-même l'opération. Cet apprentissage par imitation réussit plus vite que le précédent et présente cet avantage que le sujet effectue d'emblée des mouvements efficaces, alors que le dressage par déplacement passif conduit fréquemment à des actes incomplets (soulèvements de la patte, sans appui réel sur le levier).

Le 'temps mort' qui s'écoule ainsi entre le début du dressage et les premiers mouvements conditionnés varie selon le sujet de 1 à 6 jours, à raison d'une session de 10 essais par jour.

L'animal, ayant appris à exécuter le mouvement, l'effectue certes fréquemment, surtout au début, en l'absence de stimulation conditionnante. Ces appuis-erreurs se raréfient au fur et à mesure que le sujet différencie les simples conditions ambiantes du moment de l'application des stimuli.

Evaluation et caractéristiques des performances obtenues pour un signal positif

On s'est d'autre part efforcé d'évaluer quantitativement les performances de l'animal en utilisant comme donnée aisément accessible la latence du mouvement, temps qui sépare l'appui franc du début de la série des signaux conditionnants. Ces valeurs sont notées pour chaque session et trois types de graphiques en seront déduits.[1]

[1] On ne tient compte dans la statistique ni des gestes inefficaces, ni des cas de performances accidentellement mauvaises liées à des causes identifiables (mauvais état passager de l'animal, oestrus chez les femelles, etc....)

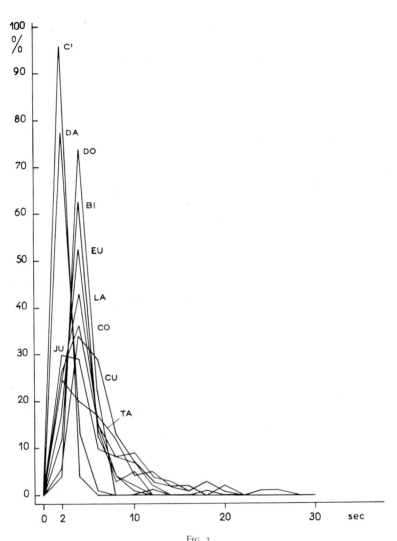

FIG. 2

Répartition statistique des latences d'appuis conditionnés correspondant à 10 sujets normaux. Pour chaque animal, le polygone correspond aux latences de 100 appuis, réalisés après stabilisation du conditionnement (voir texte).

(a) *Statistique des latences*

Une fois établi un conditionnement stable, c'est-à-dire lorsque les latences restent dans les mêmes limites et ne s'améliorent plus sensiblement, on considère la distribution de leurs valeurs pour 100 essais (soit 10 jours). Pour une présentation simple des résultats, on a choisi une fois pour toutes un intervalle de classes de 2 secondes, le temps 0 étant celui du premier signal conditionnant. Il ressort ainsi que (Fig. 2), pour l'ensemble des chats normaux, les latences sont relativement peu dispersées autour de la valeur modale qui se situe, selon le sujet, entre 1 et 4 secondes. Les polygones témoignent d'une bonne similitude d'un animal à l'autre; il est de plus apparu que, pour un sujet donné, à conditionnement stabilisé, cette distribution ne variait pas sensiblement au cours du temps. L'allure des polygones laisse finalement apparaître une rupture de pente du côté des latences élevées, telle qu'au-delà d'une certaine valeur se situe une zone de plus grande dispersion, mais où la fréquence ne dépasse jamais 5 pour-cent.

Dès lors, la plus grande latence correspondant à plus de 5 pour-cent des réponses pouvait, sans trop d'arbitraire, représenter pour chaque animal une *limite* supérieure caractérisant son domaine propre de latences courtes et peu dispersées. C'est cette valeur que nous avons considérée dans la construction des polygones d'évolution des latences.

(b) *Evolution des latences*

Une autre statistique a pu être établie, destinée cette fois à apprécier les modalités dynamiques de l'apprentissage pour chaque animal à partir du début des sessions.

Considérant les valeurs des latences obtenues au cours de chaque séance quotidienne de 10 essais, on retient:

— d'une part, le nombre des appuis effectivement obtenus dans la limite fixée comme durée maximale des stimulations, c'est-à-dire 20 secondes (Fig. 3, courbe grise);

— d'autre part, le nombre d'appuis à latence courte, c'est-à-dire réalisés dans des temps inférieurs à la limite qui aura été préalablement déterminée à partir de la répartition statistique (Fig. 3, courbe noire).

Les deux polygones ainsi tracés à partir des points caractéristiques de chaque session, résument assez concrètement l'évolution chronologique des performances: apprentissage brut, c'est-à-dire pourcentage des mouvements obtenus (courbe grise); proportion, d'autre part, des appuis à exécution rapide (courbe noire). On y remarque aisément l'existence d'un temps mort, très réduit pour certains animaux, et n'excédant pas 6 jours en général; l'ascension rapide de la courbe d'apprentissage brut, qui ordinairement se maintient telle tout au long des sessions n'impliquant aucune source particulière d'inhibition interne; la croissance également rapide, enfin, de la proportion des appuis précoces, mais, fait attendu, sa plus grande variabilité.

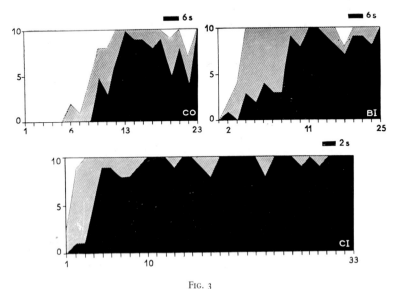

Fig. 3

Polygones d'évolution des latences chez 3 animaux normaux. Abscisses: jours de conditionnement successifs; ordonnées: nombres d'appuis réalisés au cours d'une séance quotidienne de 10 essais.

Contours gris et noirs: nombres d'appuis dont les latences sont respectivement inférieures à 20 secondes et inférieures à la 'latence limite', valeur indiquée pour chaque animal et déduite de la statistique des délais (voir texte).

(c) *Evaluation de la tendance aux 'appuis-erreurs'*

On a choisi de considérer, pour chaque session, le nombre d'intervalles entre deux essais, pour lesquels *un* appui-erreur *au moins* aura été effectué. Le polygone ainsi obtenu (Fig. 4) est alors comparé à celui des appuis de courte latence (courbe noire de l'évaluation b). Cette confrontation entre extrêmes — tendance à l'appui spontané et tendance au conditionnement optimal — fait assez nettement ressortir que, chez l'animal normal (Fig. 4, L, M, 1ère image), se développe toujours initialement, et quel que soit le mode d'apprentissage, une phase d'hyperactivité pendant laquelle les appuis-erreurs dominent nettement.

Malgré une raréfaction ultérieure, souvent assez brusque, les deux courbes conservent un certain parallélisme dans leur évolution, la tendance aux appuis à courte latence et celle à des appuis-erreurs étant sans doute conditionnées par le même mécanisme. La quasi impossibilité d'obtenir,

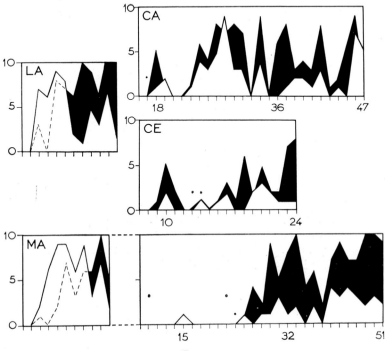

FIG. 4

Courbes d'appuis-erreurs correspondant à des animaux normaux (à gauche) et porteurs d'ablations sensorimotrices larges (à droite).
— abscisses : jours post-opératoires ; l'origine des graphiques coïncide avec le premier jour d'apprentissage.
— ordonnées ⎧ polygone noir : nombres d'appuis à latence égale ou inférieure à la latence
pour cha- ⎨ limite-polygone blanc : nombres d'intervalles au cours duquel un appui-
que jour ⎩ erreur au moins a été effectué (voir texte).
Les points signalent, en début d'apprentissage, le nombre d'appuis à latence longue (mais inférieure à 20 secondes).

chez le chat, une différenciation parfaite entre l'environnement et le signal conditionnant — fait d'ailleurs bien connu — est à mentionner une fois encore.

Ces diverses statistiques subissent, on le verra ci-dessous, des modifications significatives après ablations cortico-frontales.

II. RÉPERCUSSION DE L'ABLATION BILATÉRALE DU CORTEX SENSORIMOTEUR

Les dix chats de ce groupe se répartissent en trois catégories :

1er groupe : cinq ont subi l'élimination totale bilatérale du cortex sensori-moteur (PA, RA, ZA, BO, CA).

A l'examen électrophysiologique (sous anesthésie au chloralose) précédant le sacrifice, aucune activité typique des aires extirpées n'a pu être décelée pour une stimulation tactile, ni au voisinage des lésions corticales, ni au niveau correspondant au tractus pyramidal, où des réponses réverbérées sont normalement observées dans ces conditions (Adrian et Moruzzi, 1939; Ascher et Buser, 1958).

Le contrôle anatomique *post-mortem* a révélé des lésions comparables, incluant les territoires suivants (Fig. 5, I) : gyrus sigmoïde antérieur et postérieur, gyrus proreus, coronalis, avec empiètements à peu près équiva-lents dans tous les cas sur les circonvolutions latérale antérieure, supra-sylvienne antérieure, ectosylvienne antérieure et orbitaire.

En première approximation, ces animaux constituent donc un lot homogène privé à la fois des aires motrices pyramidales, somatiques I et somatiques II, ainsi que des lobes préfrontaux.

2ème groupe : chez trois animaux, une partie ou la totalité des aires soma-tiques II avait été épargnée (Fig. 5, II).

L'examen électrophysiologique a effectivement révélé la présence chez deux de ces sujets (MA, TA), de potentiels évoqués dans une zone très réduite, laissée intacte, du gyrus ectosylvien antérieur ; toutefois, l'explora-tion du tractus pyramidal n'a montré aucune réponse au stimulus tactile dans un cas (MA) et seulement des réponses très atypiques dans l'autre (TA). Le troisième sujet (CE), qui avait conservé la totalité des aires II, n'a accidentellement pas fait l'objet des contrôles *ante-mortem* habituels.

3ème groupe : *deux* chats n'ont subi que des ablations partielles. Chez l'un (CU), la lésion fut strictement limitée au cortex péricrucié superficiel. La région prémotrice (g. proreus), ainsi que le territoire de l'aire II furent laissés intacts (Fig. 6). Chez le second (VA), l'élimination a touché tout le pôle frontal (g. proreus et g. coronalis) et s'est étendue en surface jusqu'au sulcus cruciatus. Les aires somatique I, somatique II et la partie profonde de l'aire motrice furent conservées ; dans les deux cas, des réponses pyrami-dales normales, ainsi que des potentiels évoqués somesthésiques corticaux, furent observés au moment du contrôle électrophysiologique *ante-mortem*.

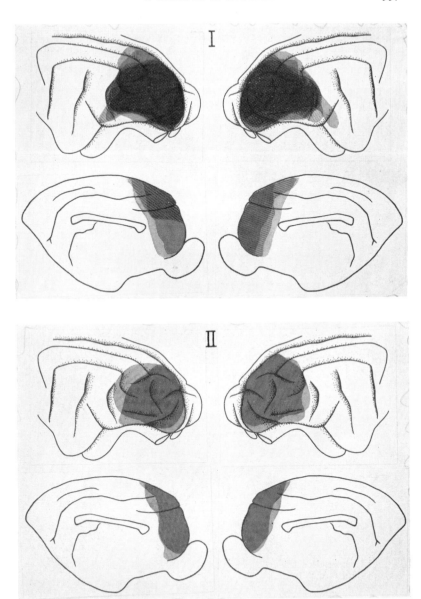

FIG. 5

Report, sur des schémas des faces latérales et médianes du cerveau du chat, du contour des ablations pratiquées dans les groupes I (5 chats) et II (2 chats).

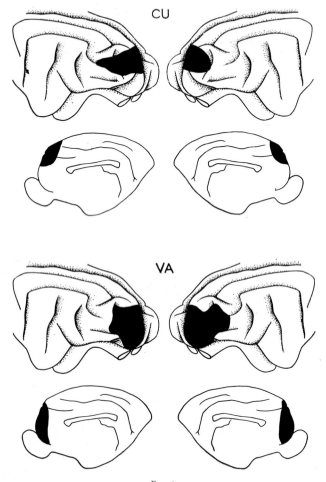

FIG. 6
Contours des ablations du groupe III (CU, VA) et des ablations contrôles
(UA, NA, BE).

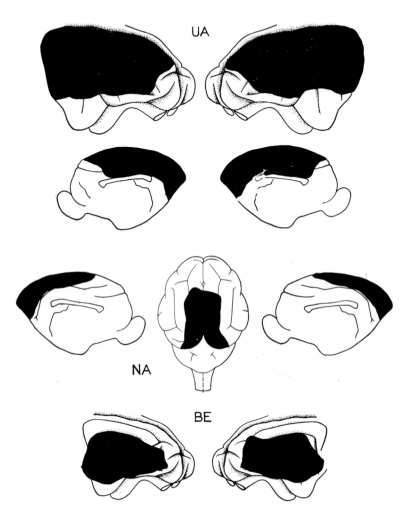

Fig. 6

Comportement spontané

Les cinq animaux du premier groupe présentaient tous le même ensemble d'anomalies, dont nous n'évoquerons ici que les traits essentiels, un certain nombre de travaux antérieurs relatifs à divers types d'ablation en ayant déjà détaillé les différents aspects (voir ci-dessous):

— Perte de vivacité, acquisition d'une certaine placidité et docilité; existence néanmoins d'une hyperactivité sans but (déplacements incessants mais lents);

— Troubles du tonus postural et des réflexes de redressement, hypertonie des extenseurs d'une part et perte de la réaction de placement tactile de l'autre. Ces altérations sont vraisemblablement à l'origine des troubles de la locomotion: circumduction des pattes postérieures, marche en ciseaux, marche sur les poignets fléchis, glissades, arrêts en position anormale, difficulté de marche sur une planche étroite.

— Troubles durables de la prise de nourriture: les animaux se montrent très voraces, mais ont une certaine difficulté à saisir les aliments dans leur gueule (morsure du bord du plat).

— Mouvements de léchage 'dans le vide' déterminés par toute stimulation tactile du corps (sauf de la tête).

Le deuxième groupe a présenté des tableaux du même type, mais incomplets, les anomalies effectivement présentées variant selon le sujet.

Les deux chats du troisième groupe se sont montrés apparemment normaux, mise à part une période transitoire de troubles toniques associés à une perte de placing chez l'un d'eux (CU).

Docilité, anomalies de l'alimentation et léchage dans le vide ont été analysés en détail chez le chat par Schaltenbrand et Cobb (1931), Bard et Rioch (1937), Bard et Mountcastle (1948), après ablation bilatérale de la totalité du néocortex; par Olmsted et Logan (1925), Magoun et Ranson (1938), après ablations frontales. Des troubles du tonus et de la locomotion, analogues à ceux que nous avons constatés, ont été reconnus après ablation soit des aires préfrontales (Olmsted et Logan, 1925; King, 1927; Langworthy, 1928), soit des aires motrices (Laughton, 1928; McKibben, 1929), soit après section des pyramides (Marshall, 1936; Liddell et Philips, 1944), soit enfin après ablation bilatérale isolée des aires somatiques I et II, chez le chien cette fois (Stępień et Stępień, 1958).

Conditionnement moteur alimentaire

Envisageant l'étude expérimentale des capacités d'apprentissage moteur chez les animaux porteurs d'ablations, le premier résultat global qui s'impose est que le conditionnement – ou le reconditionnement – s'est, avec le dispositif utilisé, montré possible dans tous les cas.

Ceci posé, l'intérêt se porte sur le fait que cet apprentissage des animaux opérés diffère de celui des normaux sous deux aspects concernant, l'un les caractéristiques chronologiques du conditionnement, l'autre la modalité même d'exécution du mouvement.

L'apprentissage pré-opératoire subi par deux de ces animaux n'ayant paru avoir aucune influence décisive ni sur l'évolution des performances ni sur les résultats finaux, nous ne ferons aucune distinction entre conditionnement et reconditionnement, dans le cadre de cet article.

1 – Aspect chronologique de l'apprentissage

(a) La plupart des animaux ont présenté un 'temps mort' d'obtention des premières performances se tenant dans les limites normales (1 à 5 jours, pour les groupes I, II et à fortiori III). Cependant, trois sujets (2 du groupe I, 1 du groupe II) ont nécessité des temps caractéristiquement plus longs (11 à 24 jours); aucune explication sûre ne nous semble pouvoir être proposée pour cette différence des durées de dressage. En effet, ni la présence ou l'absence des aires somatiques II, ni l'existence d'un apprentissage pré-opératoire ne paraissent influer sur cette durée. De même, il ne se dessine aucune corrélation entre la longueur du répit accordé après l'opération et ce 'temps mort'. Par contre, il semble que l'état fréquent d'hypotonie avec fatigabilité post-opératoire, variable en durée et en intensité selon le sujet, soit à prendre en considération: il est probable, en effet, que si, par le fait de cette fatigabilité, l'animal se trouve au début dans de mauvaises conditions de travail, il développe une inhibition interne retardatrice de l'apprentissage (fait signalé du reste par Konorski).

(b) L'examen des délais des mouvements conditionnés montre par contre un fait qui s'est révélé très général pour l'ensemble des animaux ayant subi l'ablation totale (groupe I) ou subtotale (groupe II) du cortex sensorimoteur.

La distribution des latences évaluée pour une période où les performances sont stabilisées (on considère ici comme stabilisé un conditionnement qui ne s'améliore plus après 6 semaines à 2 mois d'apprentissage) laisse en effet apparaître (Fig. 7) une dispersion très nettement supérieure à la normale (valeurs atteignant 40 secondes).

Tantôt on retrouve encore un groupement unimodal des latences courtes avec un mode qui ne correspond toutefois qu'à une proportion réduite d'appuis. Tantôt, au contraire, la répartition devient franchement plurimodale avec des sommets successifs.

La détermination de la *latence limite*, selon la méthode adoptée pour les normaux, si elle reste possible dans le premier cas, devient plus arbitraire dans le second; toutefois, si l'on fait intervenir ici encore une valeur déduite du premier groupement, celui des latences les plus brèves, on peut, malgré tout, dans cette seconde situation, évaluer les performances les meilleures de l'animal. Chez les sujets du groupe III, la statistique des latences revêt une allure normale.

(*c*) Les polygones de performances, tracés, comme pour les normaux, à partir des précédentes évaluations de latences, illustrent un aspect typique du conditionnement de ces animaux, c'est-à-dire sa grande irrégularité:

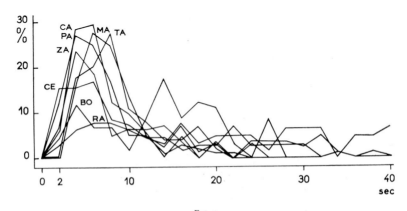

FIG. 7

Répartition statistique des latences d'appuis conditionnés correspondant à 7 chats porteurs de lésions bilatérales totales ou subtotales (groupes I et II) de l'aire sensorimotrice (comparer avec la Fig. 2).

plus encore que la répartition statistique globale des latences, l'allure générale des performances quotidiennes fluctue énormément d'un jour à l'autre, contrastant ainsi avec celle des normaux (Fig. 8). Ces fluctuations paraissent du reste refléter les altérations des modalités mêmes d'exécution du mouvement volontaire, dont il sera fait état ci-dessous.

(*d*) Les courbes d'appuis-erreurs, quoique assez différentes d'un animal à l'autre, ont toutes — pour les groupes I et II — une caractéristique commune qui est la rareté de ce type de mouvement en début d'apprentissage (Fig. 4, CA, CE, MA 2ème image); elles s'opposent ainsi nettement à celles relevées pendant la même période pour les animaux normaux, chez lesquels ces appuis-erreurs sont particulièrement fréquents. De plus, l'animal a, davantage qu'un normal, tendance à n'effectuer le mouvement que lors des stimulations et non en leur absence; ainsi ne peut-on guère attribuer

l'irrégularité du conditionnement à des troubles de l'attention, ni vraisemblablement à des troubles de la mémoire.

2 — *Modalités d'exécution du mouvement*[1]

L'observation des animaux des groupes I et II révèle qu'ils sont parfaitement susceptibles, au cours des essais, d'effectuer occasionnellement le
mouvement demandé d'une façon normale et dans un délai normal.

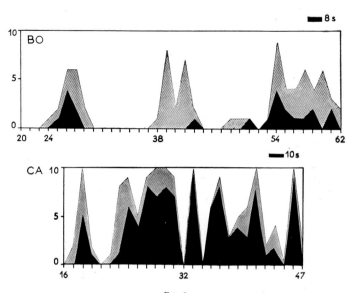

Fig. 8

Polygones d'évolution des latences chez des chats porteurs d'ablations et
appartenant au groupe I. Même signification des contours que pour la Fig. 3. Ici,
les chiffres portés en abscisses désignent les jours post-opératoires, le premier
chiffre correspondant au premier jour d'apprentissage.

Toutefois, la plupart du temps tous adoptent, sans exception, pendant les
séances de travail, un comportement qui leur est spécial, comportement
anormal qui consiste en deux types de conduites :
 — une hyperactivité automatique d'une part,
 — des phases de 'désorientation' de l'autre.
 (a) *L'activité automatique* se réduit du reste à une seule attitude, évoquant
celle du chat satisfait qui piétine sur place en ronronnant; cette activité
frappe ici, toutefois, par son exubérance et son caractère de persévération
(Fig. 9).

[1] Un film a été présenté, réalisé grâce au précieux concours du Docteur Verdeaux que nous
enons à remercier ici.

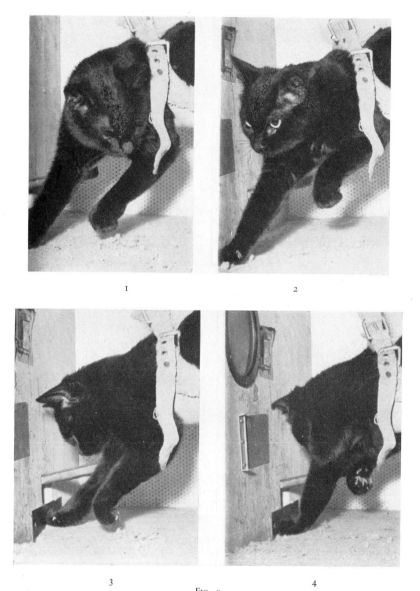

1   2

3   4

Fig. 9

Exemple individuel de réponse motrice d'un animal du groupe I.
Même sujet que sur la Fig. 1 (TA) 24 jours après ablation sensorimotrice bilatérale subtotale.
Images successives au cours des 30 premières secondes de stimulation. On devine le piétine-
ment répété accompagné de rotation progressive de l'animal vers le levier.

On s'interroge quant à la relation qui peut exister entre cette activité, apparemment automatique, et le mouvement conditionné d'appui sur le levier. Il ne semble pas que ces gestes répétés représentent simplement des tentatives d'appui inadéquates. En effet, si dans certains cas ils sont déclenchés par le signal, et par conséquent conditionnés, ils se développent tout autant dans la plupart des cas pendant de longues périodes, entre les stimulations, sans que l'animal n'appuie alors aucunement sur le levier (on a signalé ci-dessus la relative rareté des appuis-erreurs). D'autre part, si certains animaux semblent 'utiliser' ces piétinements pour finalement atteindre le levier et l'actionner, d'autres cessent brusquement de piétiner avant d'effectuer l'appui franc sur le levier. Dans ce dernier cas, on saisit nettement l'existence de deux mouvements distincts, se substituant l'un à l'autre et, le fait est possible, antagonistes.

(b) *Les phases de désorientation* se caractérisent ainsi: il survient fréquemment qu'après plusieurs réponses à latence convenable, l'animal paraisse, à l'essai suivant, brusquement et totalement désorienté: tout en manifestant son intérêt pour les signaux, il effectue des gestes d'appui dans le vide, et, semblant incapable d'utiliser le levier, présente une attitude de quête anxieuse dans toutes les directions. La cessation des signaux ramène le calme, mais le même comportement peut reparaître au cours de plusieurs essais successifs.

Parfois la phase de désorientation ne dure qu'un temps réduit au cours de l'essai, et le mouvement conditionné, nécessairement alors à longue latence, finira par être effectué.

Signalons que ces divers symptômes, très accusés dans le groupe I, ne sont que légèrement atténués dans le groupe II. Quant aux sujets du groupe III, ils ont manifesté de temps en temps une légère tendance à l'activité automatique.

Expériences de contrôle

Outre les deux animaux envisagés ci-dessus, constituant le groupe III (VA et CU), trois chats ont subi à titre de contrôle des ablations diverses, mais toujours bilatérales, de territoires corticaux (Fig. 6).

— BE: ablation des gyri suprasylvien, ectosylvien, y compris l'aire somatique II, avec en outre interruption des radiations optiques.

— UA: ablation de la quasi totalité du néocortex en arrière du sulcus cruciatus, y compris les aires somatiques I et II.

NA — ablation bilatérale et totale des aires visuelles.

L'apprentissage, ainsi que les modalités d'exécution du mouvement, se sont dans l'ensemble révélés normaux, à l'exception de certains troubles particuliers au type de lésion, qui ne reproduisent en aucun cas le tableau typique des ablations sensorimotrices totales ou subtotales. En fait, il n'y a guère à citer qu'un certain retard d'apprentissage chez les animaux aveugles non préalablement dressés (UA et BE) et dans le cas de l'ablation la plus étendue (UA) une tendance à des accès de rage probablement déclenchés par (Bard et Moutcastle, 1948) des lésions non néocorticales (ablation du gyrus cingulaire?).

DISCUSSION

Il est intéressant tout d'abord de chercher à dégager les traits les plus caractéristiques du comportement des animaux porteurs d'ablations sensorimotrices larges, dans les conditions d'expérimentation auxquelles ils furent soumis ici.

Deux constatations s'imposent: d'une part, la possibilité de principe, pour ces sujets, d'effectuer le mouvement appris — non point un geste quelconque de la patte, mais un appui précis à objectif déterminé — suivant le mode, qualitatif et chronologique, des normaux: d'autre part, l'existence d'un certain nombre de facteurs de perturbation qui sont à l'origine de la grande irrégularité des performances et sur la nature desquels on s'interroge.

A notre avis, deux causes paraissent essentiellement jouer: l'hyperactivité automatique d'une part, la tendance à la désorientation de l'autre.

On a souligné ci-dessus que l'hyperactivité ne s'exerçait pratiquement jamais sur le levier, ce qui correspond à la rareté des appuis-erreurs, mais apparaissait comme une suite de mouvements 'automatiques', apparemment distincts du geste appris.

Dans la mesure où se dessine ainsi, assez paradoxalement, une relative 'hypokinésie volontaire', on est tenté de conclure à une manière de conflit entre les deux groupes de mouvements — hypothétiquement d'ailleurs, leurs rapports précis ne nous apparaissant pas actuellement assez clairement —. Il ne fait pas de doute en tout cas, et la simple observation des animaux le montre, que le piétinement persistant représente une des raisons de l'irrégularité des latences.

Un second facteur perturbant paraît bien être la présence des phases de désorientation, qui surviennent et cessent de manière imprévisible. Ces états critiques ne semblent pas relever de troubles de la fonction mnésique; dans ce cas, en effet, on s'attendrait à observer les plus fortes perturbations en début de séance, les performances s'améliorant avec les essais suivants;

or, il n'en est rien. Non plus que de troubles de l'attention: le chat donne de nombreux indices de réaction à la stimulation-signal et son attitude traduit un comportement d'intense recherche, ce qui exclut enfin totalement l'hypothèse d'un état d'inhibition interne.

En fait, le tableau, décrit de façon analogue par Zubek (1952) rappelle beaucoup à notre sens celui de l'apraxie-agnosie chez l'homme,[1] à la fois par l'impossibilité d'accomplir 'sur ordre' une série de mouvements intentionnels et par la persévération caractéristique. On relève d'ailleurs des symptômes suggestifs d'une agnosie pure, telle par exemple l'incapacité momentanée pour l'animal de reconnaître la nourriture qu'il vient de se procurer par mouvement conditionné.

Finalement, on se heurte, dans cette tentative pour identifier le syndrome, à l'existence évidente de déficits purement sensoriels du domaine somesthésique, proprioceptif ou tactile, bien que ces déficits ne paraissent pas essentiels puisque l'animal est, on l'a vu, théoriquement capable d'apprendre et de réaliser le mouvement selon des modalités normales.

Si, d'autre part, on s'en tient aux données classiques sur les projections somesthésiques, il est essentiel de noter que quatre sujets étaient porteurs de lésions intéressant partiellement tout au moins les aires somatiques I et II (VA, UA, BE, CU); tous se sont comportés normalement vis-à-vis de la tâche imposée. Sous un autre angle, on ne peut d'ailleurs que rappeler les données récentes faisant état de la conservation d'un mouvement conditionné après déafférentation de la patte chez le chat (Gorska et Jankowska, 1959; Jankowska, 1959).

Ainsi que nous le rappelions en introduction, la plupart des ablations effectuées sur les carnivores et intéressant le cortex frontal avaient surtout conduit à des descriptions du comportement spontané et ne permettaient guère de prévoir les modalités selon lesquelles un animal pourrait, à un signal donné, accomplir un mouvement déterminé de caractère volitionnel. Parmi les quelques travaux qui cependant se rapportent plus directement aux problèmes d'apprentissage, certains ne concernent que la discrimination tactile après ablation du cortex somatique (Sperry, 1957, 1959), tandis que d'autres retiennent l'attention en ce qu'ils signalent des troubles plus généraux de l'élaboration motrice. C'est ainsi que Zubek (1952) décrit des phases de désorientation chez des chats dépourvus de cortex somatique, tandis que l'école de Konorski (Stępień et Stępień, 1958, 1959; Stępień, Stępień et Konorski, 1960) différencie les répercussions obtenues

---

[1] On est frappé en effet de l'analogie entre les signes rencontrés ici et les descriptions classiques en neurologie clinique; cf. en particulier Von Monakow et Mourgue (1928) et également Ajurriaguerra et Hecaen (1960).

NN

(chez le chien) selon que l'ablation intéresse le cortex proprement somes-thésique, ou moteur, ou enfin préfrontal. A ce titre d'ailleurs, les résultats cités dépassent en précision les nôtres. Il est vrai que les conditions d'analyse n'ont pas été identiques; il serait en particulier malaisé de saisir chez le chat des modifications fines de la faculté de différenciation (entre signal et simple ambiance) étant donné que celle-ci n'est jamais parfaite (ainsi qu'en témoigne la courbe des appuis-erreurs), au contraire du chien. Et de fait, l'ablation du cortex 'préfrontal' efficace chez ce dernier s'est avérée sans répercussion durable chez le chat (ablation du gyrus proreus).

Un certain nombre de points relatifs à l'aspect neurophysiologique de ces observations méritent d'autre part d'être examinés. Nous étant initialement proposé de connaître le rôle du cortex 'moteur', il nous apparaît maintenant qu'en raison sans doute de la contiguïté des aires somesthésique et motrice nos résultats ne permettent pas de résoudre avec sécurité la question d'un rôle plus particulier de l'un ou de l'autre terri-toire. A vrai dire, il semble, étant donné un certain nombre de résultats récents, que l'alternative ne saurait être posée dans le cadre des schémas classiques opposant strictement dans leur topographie corticale les affé-rences somesthésiques aux efférences pyramidales. Tout porte à penser que l'organisation du cortex sensorimoteur est plus complexe.

D'une part, il apparaît probable que chez le chat le cortex 'moteur' (gyrus sigmoïde antérieur et partie antérieure du gyrus sigmoïde postérieur) possède des projections somesthésiques indépendantes de l'aire proprement somatique (Oswaldo-Cruz et Tsouladzé, 1957; Buser et Ascher, 1960), en sorte que l'argument, développé ci-dessus, de la non-importance de l'aire somesthésique primaire, ne saurait en toute objectivité être considéré comme décidant de l'inutilité des informations tactiles ou proprioceptives dans l'apprentissage ou l'exécution du mouvement volontaire. De façon plus générale d'ailleurs, le rôle 'intégrateur' du cortex moteur, périsig-moïde, se dégage d'autre part d'expériences effectuées — toujours sur l'animal aigu — illustrant l'existence, à ce niveau, de convergences de projections sensorielles 'extra-primaires' visuelles, acoustiques, en même temps que somesthésiques (Feng et col., 1956; Buser et Imbert, 1959; Buser et Ascher, 1960); à cet égard, il est net que la zone périsigmoïde s'oppose à l'aire de projection purement somesthésique, à localisation plus postérieure.

Un autre point, corrélatif du précédent, est celui de la voie efférente responsable des effets observés. On évoque évidemment, par habitude et par tradition, l'intervention de la voie cortico-bulbo-spinale, 'pyrami-dale', d'autant que l'expérimentation aiguë nous a appris (Buser et

Ascher, 1960) qu'aux intégrations sensorielles réalisées au niveau de la zone périsigmoïde correspond la mise en jeu d'une réponse efférente réverbérée; l'intégration à ce niveau pourrait donc bien se ramener à l'élaboration d'une décharge corticifuge, pyramidale, vers le bulbe (noyaux crâniens ou formation réticulée bulbo-pontique) ou vers les motoneurones spinaux. Il est frappant, à ce titre, que les troubles observés ici ne l'aient été qu'après élimination totale — ou subtotale dans le cas du groupe II — du contour que l'expérimentation aiguë ou l'anatomie (Garol, 1942; Woolsey et Chang, 1948; Lance et Manning, 1954; Porter, 1955), délimitent comme aire de départ du tractus pyramidal. Mais, ici encore, le rôle exclusif des pyramides n'est pas démontré pour autant. Des interruptions du tractus pyramidal (Langworthy, 1928; Tower, 1935; Marshall, 1936; Liddell et Phillips, 1944), qui nous eussent peut-être permis de conclure, n'ont été effectuées, chez le chronique, que dans des buts distincts du nôtre. D'un autre côté, le tractus pyramidal n'est mani- festement pas l'unique système efférent issu de la zone sensorimotrice, puisqu'on connait l'intervention des voies cortico-réticulaires, particuliére- ment abondantes à ce niveau, dans le contrôle réflexe (Hugelin et Bon- vallet, 1957) ou dans la décharge motrice (Colle et Massion, 1958; Ascher et Gerschenfeld, 1960). D'autres observations devront toutefois dire dans ces conditions pourquoi les voies corticoréticulaires issues du cortex moteur ont, dans l'élaboration motrice, un rôle plus décisif que celles qui sont issues d'autres territoires tels le cortex visuel ou acoustique. A titre d'hypothèse, on pourrait suggérer que c'est l'élimination combinée des voies pyramidales et des projections corticoréticulaires — extrapyramidales par conséquent, et que seule réalise l'ablation du cortex moteur — qui pourrait décider de la gravité des troubles ainsi observés.

De façon générale donc, le problème de la participation du cortex moteur, nécessairement devenue celle du cortex sensorimoteur, à la motricité volontaire chez les carnivores ne paraît pas admettre de solution simple. D'une part, il est certain que ce niveau considéré dans son en- semble joue un rôle indubitablement plus important que d'autres aires corticales, ainsi qu'en témoignent en particulier les expériences de con- trôle. D'un autre côté, toutefois, l'obtention sporadique de mouvements pratiquement normaux pourrait évidemment laisser conclure à son 'inutilité', dans l'élaboration du geste conditionné. En somme, la question ne saurait être tranchée entre la nécessité ou non du niveau cortico-moteur dans le conditionnement étudié; il paraît bien davantage justifié de se demander comment s'accomplit l'intégration sensorimotrice soit en présence, soit en l'absence de ce niveau cortical, 'absence' qui d'ailleurs, par la mise en jeu probable de structures vicariantes, laisse une part d'incertitude aux déductions faites, point justement souligné par Semmes et Chow (1955). A cet égard, nos observations paraissent particulièrement bien concrétiser la conception plus souple, souvent proposée d'ailleurs, d'un rôle régulateur du niveau cortical, agissant sur des structures sous-jacentes, elles-mêmes susceptibles d'être le siège d'une élaboration sensori-motrice. Il est enfin probable que les conclusions déduites ici ne le sont que pour la catégoire envisagée de conditionnement, des tâches en particulier plus simples, telles que le réflexe positif de salivation, étant, on doit le penser, plus indépendantes encore de l'écorce (Hernández-Peón et col., 1958), alors que d'autres plus complexes, impliquant par exemple des opérations de discrimination, resteront sans doute plus directement liées à sa présence (voir par exemple Brutkowski, 1957).

Résumé

Cette étude concerne les répercussions de l'ablation du cortex sensori-moteur du chat sur l'apprentissage et l'exécution du mouvement dans une épreuve de conditionnement alimentaire-moteur.

1. L'ablation totale bilatérale du cortex sensorimoteur (avec ou sans persistance d'une fraction de l'aire somatique II) ne supprime pas entière-ment la possibilité, pour l'animal, d'effectuer le geste conditionné (appui sur un levier) selon les modalités et dans des délais correspondant à ceux des animaux normaux. Toutefois, de tels appuis sont rares, l'exécution du mouvement se trouvant définitivement perturbée à divers égards. On s'est efforcé d'analyser les composantes de ces perturbations dont n'existe pas l'équivalent chez des sujets porteurs d'ablations sensorimotrices partielles, ou de lésions étendues des zones préfrontales, postérieures ou latérales du néocortex et qui, à ce titre, constituent des contrôles.

2. L'évaluation statistique des latences d'appuis, effectuée pour chaque sujet, révèle une différence significative entre normaux (ou contrôles) et opérés; groupées, pour les premiers, elles sont notablement dispersées en cas d'élimination sensorimotrice. Ces latences varient d'autre part dans des limites considérables d'une séance de travail à la suivante, fait également en contraste avec le comportement des contrôles. Par contre, la fréquence des appuis spontanés qui surviennent en début d'apprentissage est plus réduite après ablation.

3. Les modalités mêmes d'exécution du mouvement chez ces sujets sont profondément troublées. On décrit deux groupes distincts d'ano-malies: des phases d'hyperactivité 'automatique' d'une part, qui paraissent

interférer avec l'élaboration volitionnelle; des périodes de désorientation, d'autre part, l'animal devenant transitoirement incapable d'exécuter le mouvement d'appui.

La signification de ces résultats est discutée, en particulier sous l'angle d'une confrontation avec les données neurophysiologiques relatives à la mise en jeu du cortex moteur, et d'un éventuel rôle de la voie pyramidale dans la régulation de l'activité volitionnelle chez le chat.

Summary

A study was performed on cats, of the effects of removing sensorimotor cortex (or other cortical areas) on learning and executing the lever-pressing movement to a signal stimulus, in an instrumental conditioning situation (alimentary motor).

After total bilateral removal of sensorimotor cortex (leaving or not a small part of somatic II), normal scores (pattern and latency of gesture) may still be obtained, but most of the observed movements are disturbed in several ways which have been analysed.

Evaluating latencies of pressing movement reveals a first group of significant differences between normal and sensorimotor deprived animals: statistical dispersion of latency values is much larger in the latter case; in time also, individual delays for deprived animals appear mostly variable in course of one session.

In contrast to this, spontaneous conditioned movement appear less frequent in ablated than in normal animals.

Two types of qualitative disturbances of movements are further described: 'automatic' hyperactivity on one side, which may interfere with volitional elaboration; desorientation phases, on the other, the animal becoming temporarily unable to execute the correct sequence of movements to obtain food — though remaining strongly motivated for food reward.

None of the previously described disturbances are definitely observed, following other cortical removals (visual area, temporo-occipital cortex, whole neocortex but sensorimotor area, prefrontal cortex).

These results are discussed in relation to neurophysiological data on afferent projections to and 'integrative' properties of the motor (perisigmoid) cortex in cat.

DISCUSSION

KONORSKI. Since our laboratory has been concerned in recent years with the study of the effects of sensori-motor lesions upon instrumental conditioned reflexes

(CRs) in dogs, and our results are in many respects similar to those obtained by Dr Buser, it would be relevant to summarize them at this point.

The general method of our experiments was such, that we trained the animals to perform a motor act consisting in lifting the right foreleg and putting it on the food-tray to given conditioned stimuli (CSs); each such movement performed to a CS was reinforced by food. After the motor CR was firmly established, particular parts of the sensori-motor cortex, or the whole of it, were removed and the effects of these lesions examined. I shall speak here only on the results of bilateral ablations.

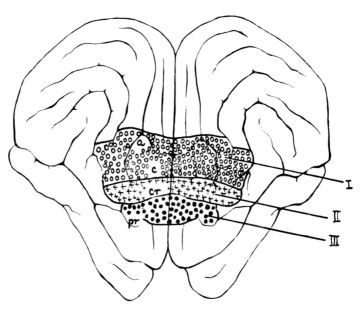

FIG. 1
The dorsal and lateral surface of the cerebral cortex of dog represented on the plan.
I, sensory cortex; II, motor cortex; III, pre-motor cortex. a, sulcus ansatus; c, sulcus centralis; cr, sulcus cruciatus; pr, sulcus presylvius.

In the course of our study it appeared to be useful to divide the sensori-motor cortex into three roughly parallel belts (Fig. 1): 1. 'sensory cortex', situated between the line of sulcus ansatus and of sulcus centralis and corresponding to the zone described recently by Hamuy, Bromiley and Woolsey; 2. 'motor cortex', situated between the line of sulcus centralis and of sulcus cruciatus; 3. 'premotor cortex', situated between sulcus cruciatus and its prolongation and sulcus presylvius.

After ablation of the first strip — sensory area — the instrumental CR is lost for several weeks, but the general behaviour of the animal is quite adequate, and he reacts correctly to CSs, although he seems unable to perform the trained movement. After some time the instrumental reaction returns without additional training (Stepień and Stepień, 1959).

After ablations of the motor cortex — second strip — the instrumental reflex is even less impaired than in the previous case, but the animals display a striking symptom of confusing legs, i.e. they perform the trained movement either with the right or with the left foreleg. This almost never occurs either before the operation or after any other cortical lesion. The animals also manifest hyperkinesis of the legs consisting in repeatedly lifting them to various heights — 'pedalling movements' — This symptom is best seen when the animal is lifted into the air (Stepień, Stepień and Konorski, 1960).

While after ablations of sensory or motor cortex the movements of the animal are more or less awkward and ataxic, after the removal of the third strip — premotor area — they are as skilful as before operation, but a striking disintegration of instrumental CRs takes place. The animal is able to perform the trained movement without any 'technical' difficulty, but he does not 'know' when to perform it. So the movements appear very often in the intervals, sometimes with great frequency, but they often fail to appear to the CS itself. Instead, the animals display either a strong orienting reaction towards the source of the stimulus, or a strong direct alimentary reaction to the bowl, or both. During the experiment the animal displays many irrelevant activities, so that his whole behaviour may be qualified as 'stupid' (Stepień, Stepień and Konorski, 1960).

To put it briefly one can say that after sensory lesions the animal is ataxic and paretic but his general behaviour is normal. After premotor lesions, on the contrary, the animal is quite skilful, but his general behaviour is 'senseless'. Lesions of the motor cortex produce intermediary symptoms. The ablation of the whole sensori-motor cortex makes the animal both strongly ataxic-paretic and 'stupid'.

BUSER. I was quite interested by Dr Konorski's remarks. As far as general behaviour is concerned it is true that cats and dogs behave in similar ways after total ablation of the whole sensorimotor cortex. But we were not led as yet, to consider that different divisions of this frontal cortex play different roles. The reason for these discrepancies may be due: (1) to phylogeny, the premotor cortex in cat being smaller and probably less important than in dogs. Actually, a cat deprived of premotor cortex almost behaves — in our pattern of testing — as a normal control animal; (2) to unequal capacity for differentiation between signal and environment, which is normally very clear cut in dogs, and never perfect in cats; thus a slight impairment in the latter case, could be considered as remaining within limits of normal variations.

DOTY[1]. I would like Dr Buser to tell us a little more about these very interesting units in the sensorimotor area, on which the auditory and visual systems also seem to converge. What are their firing patterns and latencies for the various sensory stimuli?

BUSER. In preparations under chloralose and in unanaesthetized but curarized preparations, exploration of the cat's motor cortex with macroelectrodes as well as microelectrodes reveals the existence of sensory responses to somatic stimulation. Average latencies are twice (or at most three times) the one on primary cortical fields; microelectrode recordings further show convergencies of all three modalities on the same neurones, finally, facilitation or occlusion occur at this level when two different sensory modalities are applied in combination.

[1] This and further questions refer to a chapter on electrophysiological recordings, which has been, for the sake of simplicity, omitted in this paper.

OLDS. Dr Buser mentioned that he could tell from the oscilloscope tracing that a response was abortive. I didn't see quite which was the characteristics of the tracing that indicated that a response was an abortive one.

BUSER: As recording evoked potentials to the signal stimulus from the motor cortex, it appeared to us that a normal lever pressing movement was preceded by an electrocortical activation as well as by an apparent 'suppression' of these frontal evoked responses. A further and rather surprising observation was that inefficient, or 'abortive' movements, though being also preceded by a slight desynchronization, were not, in most of the cases, accompanied by a suppression of motor evoked responses.

SEGUNDO. Dr Buser, various groups in the Institut Marey have explored the cortical and subcortical distribution of sensory volleys extensively. Could you give us an idea as to what pathways visual and acoustic impulses may follow to reach the motor cortex.

BUSER. The precise route for light and sound onto the motor cortex still remains a matter for discussion.

We have, until now, very little to add to opinions expressed by others, suggesting a role of the pretectal area (Wall et al., 1953) or reticular formation (Hunter and Ingvar, 1955). Nevertheless, some of our recent results seem to indicate that a small area in the posterior thalamus — close to both suprageniculate and magnocellular fraction of medial geniculate, as well as centre median could play an important role in transmission of light impulses to the motor cortex (Buser and Bruner, unpublished).

JOUVET. Did you record simultaneously in the visual cortex and the reticular formation?

BUSER. Not yet.

GARCIA-AUSTT. What differences exist, if any, between the latencies and shape of potentials evoked by visual stimuli on the motor cortex on one hand and on the visual cortex on the other?

BUSER. In brief, evoked responses to light, recorded from the sensory motor cortex, in chronic animals, show following characteristics: latency about three times that of the primary response, longer duration and smooth contours (no sharp surface positive component); smaller amplitude (one-half to one-third).

NON-SENSORY EFFECTS OF FRONTAL LESIONS ON DISCRIMINATION LEARNING AND PERFORMANCE

H. Enger Rosvold and Mortimer Mishkin

In his recent Salmon Lectures, Magoun (1958) has described how even the Ancients had formulated theories of brain-behaviour relationships. To them it appeared that sensory, associative and motor faculties were served by clearly separated parts of the brain each of which was uniquely organized for its specific function. Conceptions of brain organization have progressed through a variety of formulations, but at each stage there have been those who were ready to defend this ancient conception of a cerebral localization of function. Thus, at widely separated times, Ferrier (1875), Bianchi (1922) and Jacobsen (1935) have contended that the most anterior cerebral structure, the prefrontal lobes, was an 'association' area concerned with complex, non-sensory functions clearly distinguishable from the sensory functions served by posterior cortex. Recently, however, studies such as those of Woolsey (1958), Neff and Diamond (1958), Rose and Woolsey (1958) and Lilly (1958) have shown that the neural representation of sensory functions encroach upon 'association' cortex, suggesting that the prefrontal lobes may be involved in sensory processes after all. It is appropriate, therefore, to take a new look at the behavioural evidence related to this problem.

For the most part experimental studies concerned with frontal lobe function have emphasized the severe effects of damaging this structure on performance of delayed-response tests. Furthermore, the results have clearly supported the view that impairment on this type of problem is uniquely associated with frontal as opposed to posterior cortical lesions (Blum, Chow and Pribram, 1950; Meyer, Harlow and Settlage, 1951). Finally, and most important in connection with the present problem, in emphasizing the specific nature of this frontal-lobe deficit, investigators since Jacobsen (1935) have contrasted it sharply with the absence of deficit on sensory discrimination tasks. Impairment on discrimination tasks has, instead, been reserved for the effects of posterior lesions.

Unfortunately, however, this enthusiasm to dissociate delayed response and sensory discrimination functions has resulted in the neglect of important contradictory evidence. For example, Pribram, Mishkin, Rosvold and Kaplan (1952) did not deal with the fact shown in the right of Fig. 1 that

555

their frontal animals were significantly inferior to normals in retention of a visual discrimination habit.[1] They emphasized, instead, that their animals showed some savings in relearning the habit (the left of Fig. 1), and used these data to support the thesis put forth earlier by Jacobsen (1935) that frontal lesions leave discrimination functions unimpaired. In defending Jacobsen's thesis they were ignoring not only their own results, but also a number of other reports in the intervening 20 years which had clearly implicated frontal cortex in discrimination learning and retention. In

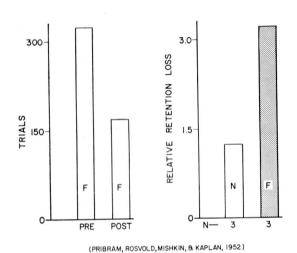

(PRIBRAM, ROSVOLD, MISHKIN, & KAPLAN, 1952)

FIG. 1

Effects of frontal lesions on visual discrimination retention.

1940, for example, Allen had demonstrated that dogs with prefrontal lobectomies were unable to learn to discriminate olfactory stimuli. In 1943, Harlow and Dagnon had shown that monkeys with prefrontal lobectomies were impaired in learning even simple discriminations in vision. And again in 1952, Blum had shown that prefrontal monkeys were deficient in auditory discrimination learning. Surely, such evidence demonstrating impairment after frontal lesions in all sensory

---

[1] This and the following figures are derived from the data appearing in the reports of the authors indicated. In all figures, operated and control groups of monkeys are denoted as follows: F — Frontal, N — Normal, P — Parietal, PT — Posterior Temporal, T — Temporal. A number below the bar graph denotes the number of monkeys in the group.

modalities can hardly go unchallenged if the theory that the frontal lobes are not concerned with sensory functions is to be maintained.

Until recently, however, even these disturbing results could be explained away. Few of the early studies contained operated controls and so it was possible to argue that a generalized impairment in all modalities simply reflected a non-specific post-operative disturbance which might be expected to result from any large cerebral lesion. Contrast this with the *specific* sensory-perceptual deficits which have been demonstrated after selective ablations of the *posterior* 'association' cortex. For example, Pribram and Barry (1956) and Wilson (1957) comparing directly the effects

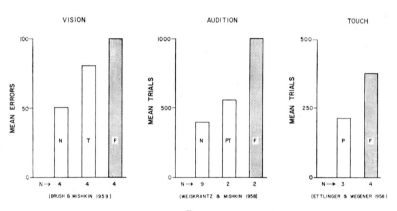

FIG. 2
Effects of frontal lesions on visual, auditory, and tactual discrimination learning.

of inferotemporal and posterior parietal lesions found a marked impairment in visual discrimination following the temporal but not the parietal lesion, and simultaneously, a marked impairment in tactual discrimination following the parietal but not the temporal lesion. In comparison with these specific deficits it seemed reasonable to argue, especially in view of the absence of evidence to the contrary, that frontal lesions were producing only relatively minor, non-specific impairment, which was unrelated to frontal-lobe function, *per se*.

As shown in Fig. 2, however, the contrary evidence has now been obtained. The discrimination impairment following frontal lesions may be non-specific as regards sensory modalities but it *is* specific to damage in the frontal area and it is certainly not minor. In fact, as these studies by

Brush and Mishkin (1959), Weiskrantz and Mishkin (1958) and Ettlinger and Wegener (1958) show, frontal lesions may, on occasion, produce deficits in discrimination learning which are even greater than those produced by lesions of the posterior area most closely associated with the modality in question. It can no longer be argued that a frontal lesion leaves discrimination learning unimpaired.

What then becomes of the notion that frontal cortex is unrelated to sensory discrimination functions? The answer appears to be that it is still correct, for a careful analysis reveals that it is, in fact, a non-sensory

VISUAL DISCRIMINATION LEARNING

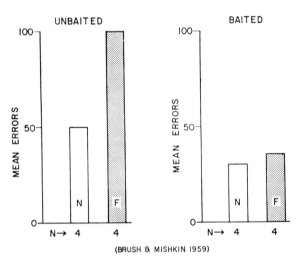

(BRUSH & MISHKIN 1959)

Fig. 3

Effects of frontal lesions on visual discrimination learning with two different training procedures.

deficit which underlies the frontal animals' discrimination impairment. This conclusion is based on experiments showing that manipulation of non-sensory variables determines whether or not the discrimination learning of frontal animals will be impaired .

In Fig. 3 for example, it may be seen that the identical animals, tested on the same visual discriminations, are deficient when trained in one way but not in the other. In both conditions there are a series of discriminations in which two objects are presented simultaneously for a few trials and the monkey must learn which of the pair is rewarded. The difference between the procedures is that in the 'unbaited' condition the choice on the first trial is never rewarded, and so on succeeding trials the animal must learn to choose the *other* cue. Conversely, in the 'baited' condition the choice on the first trial is always rewarded, and so on later trials the animal must learn to choose the *same* cue. It has been demonstrated that in this situation the monkey's initial response to each new pair of objects is frequently determined by its preference for one object over the other. Thus, for the animal, the difference between the two conditions is the difference between overcoming and persisting in an initial preference. Animals with

TACTUAL DISCRIMINATION LEARNING

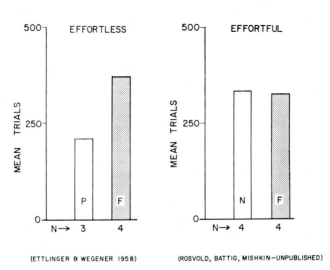

(ETTLINGER & WEGENER 1958)   (ROSVOLD, BATTIG, MISHKIN—UNPUBLISHED)

FIG. 4
Effects of frontal lesions on tactual discrimination learning with two different training procedures.

frontal lesions do find it difficult to reverse their preference, as shown by their poor performance in the 'unbaited' condition. They do not have difficulty, however, in discriminating the objects, since their performance in the other condition equals that of the normals. The evidence here is clearly against ascribing to frontal animals a visual perceptual loss.[1]

It is possible to show that the same pattern of results can be obtained in a tactual discrimination by manipulating another non-sensory variable. In Fig. 4 it may be seen that when frontal monkeys are trained on tactual discrimination with one procedure, they are impaired; with another

[1] It is perhaps worth indicating that such a loss can be assigned to animals with temporal lesions, since they have been found to be equally impaired in both conditions.

procedure they are not. Here the difference between the two procedures is that in the 'effortless' condition the manipulanda are easy to move, whereas in the 'effortful' condition they can be moved only with great difficulty. Since visual cues are excluded the sensory information necessary for making the discrimination in either condition cannot be obtained until the response is actually initiated. But once the response has been initiated the monkey has a strong tendency to complete it, regardless of the discriminanda. In the 'effortless' condition, where it is possible to complete

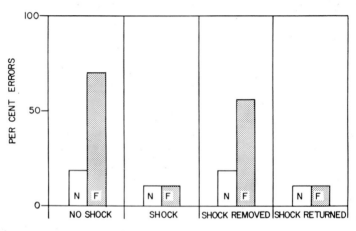

AUDITORY DISCRIMINATION LEARNING and PERFORMANCE

(ROSVOLD, BATTIG, MISHKIN - UNPUBLISHED)

FIG. 5

Effects of frontal lesions on auditory discrimination learning and performance with two different training procedures.

the response with ease, the frontal animals seem to learn the discrimination relatively slowly. In the 'effortful' condition, on the other hand, where completing the response requires considerable strength, frontal animals learn the relevant tactual discrimination as quickly as the controls.[1] Thus, unless frontal monkeys are effectively deterred from completing a response which they have already initiated, they will do so regardless of the discriminanda, and appear to have a tactual deficit when in fact they do not.

A particularly dramatic example of the effect of a non-sensory variable is shown in Fig. 5. As with the visual and tactual discriminations, it may

---

[1] The two graphs in this figure represent the performance of animals from different studies. Therefore, the absolute levels of performance in one study cannot be compared with those in the other. The appropriate comparison is each frontal group with its own control.

be seen that in auditory discrimination, also, the frontal animal is deficient with one training procedure but not with another. The first graph represents the performance level achieved in the last 100 of over 2000 training trials in which responses to the negative stimulus were deterred only by the usual extinction procedure. Up to this point the frontal animal appeared to be completely unable to discriminate the auditory cues. However, as soon as responses to the negative stimulus were severely punished by the introduction of strong electric shocks, this monkey discriminated very well indeed. Within 100 trials it achieved almost perfect discrimination, equalling the performance of the normal. An even more surprising result is illustrated in the last two graphs of the figure. The frontal animal's deficit could be turned on and off, sometimes even within the same testing session, by the simple expedient of removing or reapplying the shock. Such an impairment can hardly be attributed to sensory effects of the lesion.

Let us consider what the nature of the non-sensory deficit might be. The general principle which emerges from the evidence as it has been developed to this point can be stated briefly as follows. The discrimination learning of an animal with a frontal lesion is not impaired when its initial response tendency to the negative stimulus is weak or the deterrent to such a response is particularly strong. Conversely, when a strong tendency to respond to the negative stimulus is coupled with only a weak deterrent, a clear-cut deficit appears. If the principle is correct it provides strong support for the view that damage to the frontal lobes results in a loss of inhibition. This conception of a loss of inhibition following prefrontal damage is a recurrent theme which can be traced at least as far back as Schafer's (1898) *Textbook of Physiology*. Most recently, a sophisticated variation of this hypothesis has been proposed by Konorski and his associates (Brutkowski, Konorski, Ławicka, Stępień and Stępień, 1956).

A particularly clear example of a deficit which might be labelled loss of inhibition is shown in Fig. 6. In this task, a 'go-no go' discrimination, operated monkeys and controls were trained to displace a baited food-cup when they heard one sound, but to refrain from displacing it when they heard another. If an animal made an error by responding to the negative sound, or by failing to respond to the positive one, the same signal was presented again and again until the animal did respond to it correctly. The figure is a plot of the number of extra times the negative stimulus had to be presented minus the number of extra positives, over blocks of 200 trials. Now, the preliminary training on this task develops in the animal a strong tendency to respond on every trial. This is indicated by the fact that even the normal animals initially make more errors by responding when they should not respond, than by not responding when they should. The only deterrent to this strong generalized tendency to respond to the negative cue is the absence of reward. In line with the principle stated earlier the monkeys with frontal lesions exhibited a marked impairment which, in the early part of training at least, may justifiably be labelled a loss of inhibition.

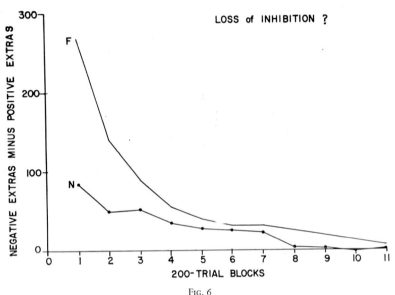

FIG. 6

Effect of frontal lesions on inhibiting responses to the negative stimulus in a 'go-no go' situation.

How can such an impairment be accounted for theoretically? The answer, unfortunately, is that there are numerous possibilities as can be seen in Fig. 7. An inhibitory defect can be postulated at any point in the stimulus-response sequence and it will still provide a reasonable explanation of the frontal animal's deficiency on discrimination tasks. For example, if an inhibitory defect were present at the response and of the chain, the neural model could be a loss of suppression of the cortical motor systems. Specifically, an hypothesis could be developed on the basis of avilable neurophysiological data (Mettler, 1935; Freeman and Krasno, 1940; Dusser de Barenne, Garol and McCulloch, 1942) that frontal cortex, acting through the caudate nucleus, normally exerts a suppressive influence

on motor activity. The frontal animal's impairment in inhibiting conditioned motor responses might then be considered a symptom analogous
to the locomotor hyperactivity 'released' by frontal lobe damage. A
theory somewhat similar to this was, in fact, proposed some time ago by
Stanley and Jaynes (1949).

LOSS OF INHIBITION

Type	Neural Mechanism	Manifestation
Response	Cortical Motor Systems	Locomotor Hyperactivity
Drive	Hypothalamic Drive Systems	Appetitive Hyperactivity
Stimulus	Reticular Activating Systems	Hyper re Activity

FIG. 7

The behavioural manifestations and neural mechanisms associated with three proposed types
of inhibitory defects.

Alternatively, if an inhibitory defect were assigned to the motivational
sphere, the neural mechanism could be a loss of suppression of hypothalamic appetitive systems. By combining the data of Anand and Brobeck
(1951) and Delagdo and Anand (1953) demonstrating hypothalamic
control over food intake with the results of Ward and McCulloch (1947)
demonstrating frontal projections to the hypothalamus, it might be
proposed that frontal cortex normally regulates alimentary inhibition.
Increased appetite, another commonly reported symptom of frontal
damage (Morgan and Stellar, 1950), could then provide the explanation
for the frontal animal's difficulty in inhibiting a conditioned food-getting
response.

Finally, if an inhibitory defect were postulated on the sensory side it
could be ascribed perhaps to a loss of suppression of the diffuse activating
systems. Magoun (1958) has reviewed the evidence indicating that the
brain stem may inhibit as well as facilitate sensory input and the results of
Adey, Segundo and Livingston (1957) suggest that frontal cortex may
exert an important regulating influence on brain stem mechanisms. If
frontal damage caused a loss of suppression of the diffuse sensory input,
this would account first of all for the common observation that the
frontal animal is hyper-reactive to, and easily distracted by extraneous
stimuli (Kennard, Spencer and Fountain, 1941; Malmo, 1942). That it
could also account for the frontal animal's impairment on discrimination

oo

tasks is suggested by the fact, well known in conditioning experiments, that extraneous stimuli tend to disinhibit weakly inhibited responses.

It must of course be emphasized that no attempt has been made here to work out these three hypothetical mechanisms in any rigorous fashion. The point is simply that on the basis of available neurophysiological evidence, together with the abnormal symptoms observed in the frontal animal's general behaviour, a reasonably strong argument can be developed in favour of each of them. It is this very multiplicity of possible mechanisms, however, which is the chief source of weakness in the theory. An uncritical application of the general concept of a loss of inhibition, without specifying the type, can probably be used to explain any complex behavioural effect of frontal lobe damage. On the other hand, when care is taken to specify which type of inhibitory defect is being considered it is found that there is evidence from discrimination learning experiments that is inconsistent with each of them.

Consider first certain predictions which follow from the hypothesis that frontal lesions result in a loss of response inhibition. Suppose that two stimuli A and B are presented at random on separate trials. A signals food on the left, and B signals food on the right. Since both responses are sometimes rewarded, the correct response of going left to A on any particular trail necessitates inhibiting the built-in response tendency to the right. Similarly, going right to B involves inhibiting a strong response-tendency to the left. As noted by Stanley and Jaynes (1949) in the development of their theory, a loss of response inhibition should lead to an impairment on this 'go left-go right' type of descrimination test; yet, in experiments of this kind by Pribram and Mishkin (1955), in vision, and by Battig, Rosvold and Mishkin (unpublished), in audition, no such impairment was found. Now for an opposite example, that is, one in which this particular hypothesis would probably not predict impairment. According to our interpretation, a loss of suppression of the somatic motor systems should produce difficulty in inhibiting well-established locomotor and manipulatory acts. On the other hand, it should not affect the inhibition of such conditioned autonomic reflexes as salivation. However, in experiments by Brutkowski (1957) in which dogs with frontal lesions were trained to differentiate positive from negative conditioned stimuli, a severe impairment in inhibiting salivation to the negative stimulus was observed.

It will be recognized that the preceding illustration, while weakening the hypothesis of a loss of response inhibition, simultaneously strengthens the hypothesis of a loss in the inhibition of appetitive mechanisms. Other evidence, however, raises difficulties for this alternative conception. For

TABLE I

THE EFFECTS OF PREFRONTAL AND PARIETAL LESIONS ON CR

Reinforcement	Type of CR	Conditioned response observed	Prefrontal ablation		Parietal ablation	Authors
			Excitatory CR	Inhibitory CR		
Food	Instrumental	Lifting of the foreleg	Normal (15)*	Disinhibited (15)	Normal (4)	Brutkowski et al. (1956) Brutkowski (1959) Ławicka (1957) Ławicka (unpublished) Chorzyna (unpublished)
Food	Instrumental	Barking	Normal or enhanced (4)	Disinhibited (4)		Ławicka (1957)
Food	Classical	Salivation	Normal or enhanced (6)	Disinhibited (6)	Normal (4)	Brutkowski (1957)
Water	Instrumental	Lifting of the foreleg	Normal (2)	Disinhibited (2)		Zernicki (in preparation)
Electric shock	Classical	Lifting of the hindleg and breathing	Enhanced (3) Normal (1)	Disinhibited (3) Normal (1)		Brutkowski and Auleytner (in preparation) Ławicka (unpublished)
Acid into the mouth	Classical	Salivation and breathing	Enhanced (3)	Disinhibited (3)		Brutkowski and Auleytner (in preparation)
Electric shock	Instrumental (avoidance)	Lifting of the foreleg	Normal (2)	Normal (1) Disinhibited (1)		Zbrozyna (unpublished)

* The numerals indicate the number of dogs used in a given experiment.

example, in a 'go-no go' discrimination in which an animal is rewarded with food for going to one stimulus, and is also rewarded with food for not going to the other stimulus both stimuli should acquire positive reward value. With these conditions of testing, loss of drive inhibition should not affect performance. Yet this technique of symmetrical reward was the one employed in Weiskrantz and Mishkin's (1958) 'go-no go' auditory problem on which frontal animals were so severely impaired. Conversely, the hypothesis of a loss of drive inhibition *should* predict impairment whenever a rewarded stimulus is paired with one that is consistently unrewarded. Thus, in a visual discrimination in which both the positive and negative stimuli are simultaneously present, frontal animals should have greater difficulty than normals in inhibiting responses to the unrewarded cue. Yet, it was the fact that frontal animals were unimpaired on precisely this type of discrimination that first gave rise to the erroneous generalization that frontal damage does not affect performance on any discrimination task.

The final hypothesis to be considered is immune to all the objections that have been raised so far since it does not yield predictions with respect to different cue-response-reward combinations. Predictions that would follow from a loss of stimulus inhibition relate rather to the potentially disruptive effects of extraneous stimuli. Thus, discrimination impairment following frontal damage would be expected to be directly related to the amount of distraction in the testing situation. Unfortunately, the literature on discrimination learning in frontal animals does not provide us with a clear-cut test of this prediction. Nevertheless, there have been gross differences *between* studies in terms of such general testing conditions as noisy *v.* silent apparatus, noisy *v.* sound-shielded testing rooms, the possibility of visual exploration *v.* the exclusion of vision, etc. The presence of certain distracting influences has been shown to have a marked disrupting effect on frontal animals' delayed response performance (Malmo, 1942; Ławicka, 1957). However, as far as can be determined, there is no such relationship between the presence of extraneous stimuli and their impairment on discrimination tasks.

We do not wish to argue that our analysis of the experimental evidence conclusively rules out all possibility of explaining the frontal animals' impairment on discrimination tasks as a loss of some form of inhibition. Perhaps further theorizing along such lines will suggest a mechanism that will overcome the difficulties that have been raised. It should be pointed out, however, that these difficulties may reflect the inadequacy of the general hypothesis of a loss of inhibition from which the various specific hypotheses were derived. On this basis it would seem profitable to begin exploring other possibilities and not confine ourselves to the one class of theoretical concepts.

To summarize the major points of this analysis: A survey of the older literature, reinforced strongly by recent evidence, has shown that with certain conditions of testing frontal lesions produce severe impairment in learning and performance on discrimination tasks in all sensory modalities. An explanation of this deficit in terms of a sensory-perceptual loss was rejected in favour of a non-sensory loss specific to frontal lobe damage. While much of the evidence favours an interpretation of the impairment as a loss of inhibition, a careful examination of three specific types of proposed inhibitory defects shows that none of them satisfactorily accounts for all of the data. In further work directed towards the elucidation of the frontal animals' non-sensory impairment, an important problem will be to determine what relationship, if any, the deficit of the frontal animal on discrimination tasks bears to its deficit on delayed-response tasks, the symptom which has traditionally guided theory and research concerning frontal lobe function.

GROUP DISCUSSION

Disinhibition of inhibitory CRs after prefrontal lesions in dogs

KONORSKI (written comment). Since our laboratory has been directly concerned with the problem of the impairment of inhibitory processes after prefrontal lesions for nearly 10 years, I should like to present very briefly our experimental material dealing with this subject and, with our results as a basis, to comment on some of the statements put forward by Rosvold and Mishkin in their paper.

Our work has been performed on dogs in which we established various types of excitatory and inhibitory CRs; then we removed, to varying extents, the prefrontal areas (or as a control some parts of the parietal areas) and observed the changes in CRs for a long time after these operations. Inhibitory CSs were either stimuli similar to the positive CSs (differentiation) or were compounds composed of a positive CS preceded by another stimulus (so called conditioned inhibition). Inhibitory stimuli were, of course, not reinforced by any UCS.

Prefrontal lesions consisted of amputation of the frontal poles rostral to the presylvian sulcus; in this way gyrus proreus, gyrus subproreus and the anterior part of gyrus orbitalis, as well as subjacent white matter, were removed. Parietal lesions consisted of removal of parts of gyrus entolateralis and suprasplenialis (Fig. 1).

In Table I the results obtained in these experiments are summarized. As seen from this table, after prefrontal lesions positive CRs are either normal or enhanced, while inhibitory CRs are disinhibited. This holds true with respect to both alimentary (food and water) and defensive (electric shock and acid) reflexes. Only in one dog in which the shock reinforcement was weak, and in one dog in which avoidance technique was used (i.e. the stimulus was not applied at all) disinhibition was not observed. In Figs. 2 and 3 the records of some typical experiments are presented.

After parietal ablations no changes occurred in either positive or inhibitory CRs.

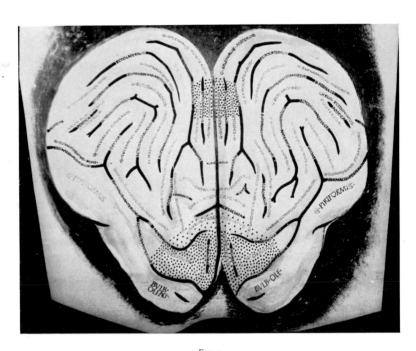

FIG. 1
The extent of prefrontal and parietal (control) lesions in dogs.
The cortex is shown in two dimensions. By dense stippling the usual prefrontal and parietal ablations are shown. Sparse stippling denotes part of the premotor area involved in our extensive prefrontal lesions.
While limited ablations produce disinhibition, the extensive ones produce in addition hyperactivity.

When, after a prefrontal operation, inhibitory CSs are repeatedly applied without reinforcement, inhibitory reflexes are gradually re-established. In some cases restoration occurs after only a few trials, while in others it takes a long time, and may be incomplete. This depends chiefly on the difficulty of the inhibitory task for a given dog and, perhaps, on the extent of its lesion.

The impairment of inhibitory CRs after prefrontal lesions could be ascribed, of course, to the animal's loss of discriminatory ability. But the fact that disinhibition is, as a rule, only partial (which is best seen in salivary reflexes), and especially the

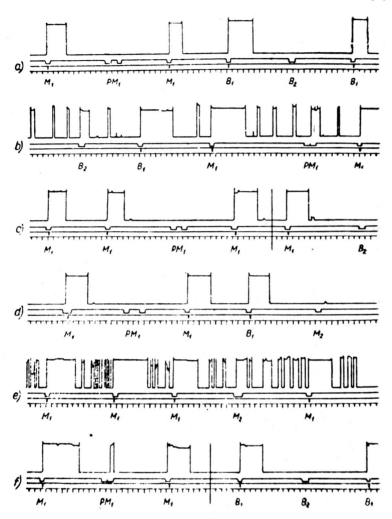

FIG. 2

Kymographic records of parts of some representative experiments in dogs before and after successive operations.

Each record comprises from top to bottom: lifting the right foreleg and putting it on the food-tray; conditioned stimuli; the moment of food presentation; time (5 sec.); symbols of stimuli: M_1, Metronome, B_1, Bell, B_2, differential Bell, PM_1, Propeller + Metronome (inhibitory compound); a, fragment of the last experiment before first frontal ablation; b, fragment of the first experiment after first frontal ablation; c, fragment of an experiment $2\frac{1}{2}$ months after first frontal ablation; d, fragment of an experiment after parietal ablation; e, fragment of an experiment shortly after second frontal ablation; f, fragment of an experiment a month after second frontal ablation (After Brutkowski et al., 1956).

fact that, according to Rosvold and Mishkin, it is not observed when the instrumental reaction to the inhibitory stimulus is punished, speak against this supposition
and support the view that perhaps we have to do here with the impairment of the
inhibitory processes themselves. Therefore, we must consider the question of what
sort of inhibition is affected by prefrontal lesions and in which way it is affected.
Here we must inevitably revert to the classical Pavlovian notions of external and

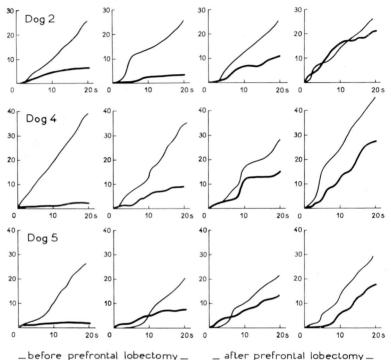

_ before prefrontal lobectomy _　　　_ after prefrontal lobectomy _

Fig. 3

Examples of disinhibition of salivary food conditioned reflexes after prefrontal ablations.
　　Each graph represents the voluminograph of salivation to a positive conditioned stimulus
and to an inhibitory stimulus following it. Note that after prefrontal lobectomy positive
CRs are unchanged, while negative ones are more or less disinhibited (After Brutkowski,
1957).

internal inhibition and to the immense experimental evidence on which these
notions are based. It is quite clear that what is impaired after a prefrontal lesion is
only internal (or conditioned in the wider sense of the word) inhibition, while
external (i.e. antagonistic) inhibition is not affected at all or may even be increased
after this lesion.

　　For our further analysis we shall accept here, as a working hypothesis, a conception put forward some time ago by Konorski (1948), according to which internal
inhibition is based on the formation of inhibitory connections between the central

representations of the CS and UCS, alongside the excitatory connections formed earlier between these two representations. The prefrontal lesion may either destroy these inhibitory connections leaving the excitatory connections unaffected, or else it may, by some unspecific release mechanism (reticular formation?), increase the excitability of unconditioned centres (*both* appetitive and defensive) and in this way give predominance to excitatory over inhibitory impulses. Irrespective of which of these two alternatives (if any) proves to be correct we have here to do exclusively with the phenomenon labelled by Rosvold and Mishkin as loss of drive inhibition: this is obvious for those experiments in which classical CRs were used; as for those experiments in which instrumental reflexes were used it could be shown that disinhibition of instrumental responses faithfully reflected disinhibition of the salivary response, i.e. of the alimentary drive (Brutkowski, 1959).

I cannot agree with Rosvold and Mishkin's argument that the results obtained by Weiskrantz and Mishkin (1958) with a 'go-no go' symmetrical reward schedule to two different sounds are contradictory to the drive disinhibition mechanism. These authors found that after prefrontal lesions a 'no-go' response is disinhibited in spite of the fact that it is rewarded. But we know from the vast experimental evidence of the Pavlov school, as well as from our own experimental data (Konorski and Szwejkowska, 1952), that even the repeated reinforcement of an inhibitory stimulus may not lead to its transformation into a positive stimulus. The stimulus to which the animal was to refrain from responding in order to obtain food was deeply extinguished at the beginning of training, since the animal repeatedly performed the trained movement to it and did not get food; as a result this stimulus probably could not be fully established as a positive CS when, after the instrumental response to it had been inhibited, the animal was reinforced. Had the authors measured salivation, they could have checked whether or not this supposition is correct. According to the view that the prefrontal lesions did produce drive disinhibition of inhibitory alimentary reflexes, the inhibitory stimulus became excitatory, which was reflected in the animal's performing the learned movement to it.

Similarly, it seems to me that the argument of the authors pointing out that simultaneous-discrimination habits should be impaired by drive disinhibition is also not correct. The animal is presented simultaneously with two objects, the reaction to one of them being constantly reinforced. As a result this reaction becomes much stronger than the reaction to the other object since the latter reaction is inhibited both by drive and response inhibition. There is, therefore, no reason why after a prefrontal lesion the first reaction should not predominate.

Yet, we *have* found that after larger prefrontal lesions which include the precruciate areas a new phenomenon ensues which may be defined as 'motor-response disinhibition'. After these lesions the animals not only exhibit locomotor hyperactivity, but also, when put into the experimental situation in which a definite instrumental CR had been established, they perform the trained movement again and again apparently without any relation to the hunger drive (Fig. 2C; Konorski, 1957). It is worth mentioning that this sort of disinhibition is, like the first one, 'conditioned'. In one dog, two different instrumental responses were trained in two different situations; after the more extensive prefrontal lesion this dog manifested hyperactivity of the motor reaction specific to the given situation and not to the other one.

A clear example of locomotor disinhibition after large prefrontal lesions was also found by Shumilina (1949) in Anokhin's laboratory in experiments in which the animal received food at two ends of the stand to two different CSs.

To summarize, we think that, to use convenient expressions introduced by Rosvold and Mishkin, prefrontal lesions may produce either relatively pure drive disinhibition, when the extent of the lesion is limited to the frontal poles, or, in addition, motor-response disinhibition when the lesion encroaches upon the pericruciate area. It remains to be elucidated whether or not it would be possible also to obtain pure motor-response disinhibition (without drive disinhibition) if only the pericruciate area were to be removed.

As to the mechanism of motor-response disinhibition it should also be considered as some release phenomenon, analogous to many forms of hypermotility produced by various subcortical lesions.

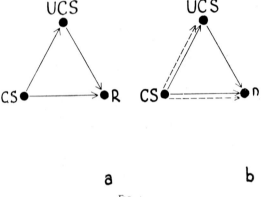

FIG. 4
Schemes of excitatory and inhibitory connections involved in type II conditioned reflex-arcs. a, positive conditioned CR; b, inhibitory CR. Continuous lines, excitatory connections, broken lines, inhibitory connections. Further explanations in text.

According to the vast experimental evidence of our laboratory, the 'reflex-arc' of instrumental CRs should be considered as consisting of two parallel pathways (cf. Wyrwicka, 1952): one pathway runs from the central representation of the CS through the corresponding drive centre to the representation of the instrumental reaction (CS→UCS→R); the second pathway runs directly from the CS 'centre' to the motor 'centre' (CS→R). When an inhibitory CR is established, inhibitory connections are formed between the CS and UCS centres ('drive inhibition') and between the CS and R centres ('motor-response inhibition'), but not between the UCS and R centres, since, to positive CSs, the movement R is performed (Fig. 4). When as a result of prefrontal lesions drive inhibition is impaired, both classical and instrumental inhibitory reflexes are disinhibited, as the pathway CS→UCS is no longer blocked. If motor-response inhibition is impaired the animal will be hyperactive but drive inhibition may be left intact.

As to the third possibility proposed by the authors (loss of stimulus inhibition manifested by hyperreactivity) I would rather doubt whether it exists at all, since we have no conclusive evidence that prefrontal animals are more distracted by extraneous stimuli than are normal animals (cf. the experiments by Butler and Harlow (1956) in which no increased distractability was found, after prefrontal lesions in monkeys). The detrimental effect of extraneous stimuli in prefrontal animals in the delayed-response test is simply due, as we have shown, to the fact that these animals must keep their bodily orientation unchanged during the delay in order to perform the correct response. Since an extraneous stimulus may provoke a change in orientation (just as it does in normal animals), so correct delayed-response performance is impossible for prefrontal animals, while normal animals, not having to maintain their orientation during the delay, are unaffected.

ROSVOLD and MISHKIN (written rebuttal submitted as afterthought). In his discussion of our paper, Konorski has presented evidence which seems to support the view that limited prefrontal lesions produce what we have referred to as a loss of 'drive inhibition'. Let us re-examine the hypothesis in terms of this evidence first.

According to Konorski, the instrumental response to a negative (unrewarded) stimulus is normally inhibited by both drive and response inhibition. For convenience we shall call the sum of their effects the (total) inhibitory tendency. Now if a limited prefrontal lesion impairs drive inhibition, but leaves response inhibition intact, then the total inhibitory tendency should be reduced but not eliminated. Yet, in the experiments on auditory differentiation, the animal's inhibitory response is not simply weakened by the lesion; it is transformed into an excitatory response. Thus it seems to us that the drive disinhibition hypothesis does not account satisfactorily even for data that have been presented to support it. But perhaps this difficulty can be avoided by making some additional assumption, e.g. that normally the total inhibitory tendency depends primarily on drive inhibition, and when this is impaired, sufficient drive excitation is released to overcome the intact, but relatively weaker, response inhibition. In this way, a strong inhibitory response might be transformed by the lesion into, at least, a weak excitatory response. While it is hardly our wish to defend it, let us for the moment accept some such explanation of the impairment in auditory differentiation (in which stimuli are presented successively) and turn next to the experiments on visual discrimination with simultaneously presented stimuli.

In simultaneous discrimination, as opposed to differentiation, impairment after frontal damage has rarely been observed. Konorski suggests a simple explanation: When both positive and negative stimuli are simultaneously present, the strong excitatory response which was conditioned to the positive stimulus before operation will still predominate after operation. This will be true whether the inhibitory tendency to the negative stimulus is now merely reduced, or, according to our added assumption, changed into a weak excitatory tendency. But while this explanation will account for the successful retention of a simultaneous-discrimination habit, we do not believe it will account for successful post-operative learning. When a frontal animal is trained only after operation, an impairment of drive inhibition should retard the development of an inhibitory tendency to the negative stimulus, and thereby delay the appearance of a predominant response to the positive stimulus. In short, discrimination learning should be impaired. Numerous experiments have indicated that, contrary to such a prediction, the frontal animal learns even difficult visual discriminations just as rapidly as its unoperated control.

While, for simultaneous discrimination, Konorski has offered an explanation which we have argued applies to retention but not to learning, he suggests an explanation for the symmetrically rewarded 'go-no go' discrimination which seems to us to apply to learning but not retention. His argument here is as follows. The stimulus to which the animal's response was extinguished (the 'no go' stimulus) also inhibited the animal's alimentary drive, despite the fact that this stimulus was associated with reward whenever the animal did refrain from responding to it. Since inhibition of drive normally aids in establishing an inhibitory instrumental response, a loss of drive inhibition should impair this conditioning process and so produce the reported impairment in discrimination learning. But this does not account for the impairment found in the animals that had learned the task before operation. Early in pre-operative training the 'no go' stimulus may have indeed inhibited the alimentary drive because the animals responded to it regularly, and so were rewarded only rarely. As training progressed, however, the animals tended to respond to the 'no go' stimulus less and less frequently, and as a result were rewarded more and more often. Finally, when the animals learned to inhibit perfectly, the 'no go' stimulus was associated with reward on every occasion. Surely at this stage of the experiment the animals had learned to 'expect' food (or, in conditioning terms, to salivate) at the sound of the 'no go' stimulus. This stimulus should no longer have been inhibiting the drive, in which case a post-operative disinhibition of drive could not have caused the loss in post-operative retention.

Our re-examination of the evidence relates so far only to the hypothesis that *limited* prefrontal lesions produce a loss of drive inhibition. Konorski has suggested, however, that with somewhat more extensive lesions, those invading also the pericruciate area in dogs, a second type of inhibitory defect is produced, viz. loss of response inhibition. But would this combination of disinhibition hypotheses help to explain results which each hypothesis taken singly does not? It seems to us that it would, in fact, make it easier for Konorski to account for his own data demonstrating disinhibition of instrumental (in addition to classical) inhibitory reflexes, and also to account for the impairment on the symmetrically rewarded 'go-no go' discrimination, just discussed. At the same time, however, we believe it would not explain away the *absence* of impairment on simultaneous discriminations, nor on the 'go left-go right' successive discriminations, which we described in our paper.

GRASTYÁN. Some years ago Dr Shuskin published some work about this investigation concerning the influence of extirpation of frontal lobes on the behavioural aspect of conditioned dogs. If I am not mistaken, Dr Shuskin's data from many points of view are in accordance with the data of Dr Rosvold.

ROSVOLD. I don't know these studies. I am very happy to have this reference.

ESTABLE. Do conditioned reflexes increase or decrease the capacity for discrimination? I ask this question because discrimination is used in a very particular sense. If I have ten objects one of which is of iron and a magnet, only the one of iron is attached by the magnet. This is not because there has been any discrimination but simply because it could not be otherwise. In the case of animals with conditioned reflexes, I wonder whether they respond in a specific way to a stimulus which they have discriminated or whether they react because they cannot do otherwise. Does discrimination occur or is it simply a way of reacting?

ANOKHIN. During a period of years, from 1935 to 1949, one of my associates,

Dr Schumilina performed a large number of ablations of the frontal cortex and studied the consequence of that removal under specific experimental conditions. Research on the secretion and motor components of the conditioned reflex was carried out jointly.

This work has led us to consider that it is quite impossible to define the functions of the frontal lobes on the only basis of the 'inhibition' or 'loss of inhibition' concept. Such functions, it appears, are considerably more complex; we have, moreover, gathered evidence that their interpretation is directly determined by the *specific method chosen for the control of the test's results.*

In other words, the decisive factor here is the elaboration of an adequate test method for checking the experimental data. Any correct understanding of results will depend upon that choice.

Our research has also shown the fact that even after extirpation of the frontal lobes normal internal inhibition can develop; this means that this specific cortical function has not been impaired by the operation. However the animal is no longer capable of a higher form of inhibition whereby its brain may store and co-ordinate harmoniously a number of factors of different nature which have simultaneously acted upon its nervous system.

In particular the frontal lobes normally contribute to preventing the enormous amount of stimuli from the environment from releasing a full-scale digestive reflex, even when the stimulating action of the various test conditions is clearly apparent. But, at the moment when the conditioned stimulus starts acting, this hidden integration of the different environmental stimuli becomes effective also and spreads to the peripheral system.

We have also shown that after removal of the frontal lobes, what happens is not an over-all loss of inhibition of any stimuli inhibited up to then, but the release of quite specific stimuli. The stimuli pattern involved specifically requires an alternative motor discrimination between right and left side.

Extensive and valuable literature on the subject has appeared in our country, and I would be glad to provide Dr Rosvold with some of our studies. I shall not fail to send them to him upon returning home.

Rosvold. Dr Anokhin refers to his experiment in which in a situation involving two feeding stands the animals are disinhibited, he interprets it as a loss of afferent inhibition or suppression of stimulus inhibition. Dr Konorski would interpret this as a loss of locomotor or response inhibition. The same experimental material can apparently be interpreted in different ways. Thus, the point of our paper: there are so many varieties of the inhibition notion that it soon becomes impossible to set up a critical experiment.

Myers. Dr Rosvold has been for a long time concerned with the comparative effects of frontal lesion in different species. I wonder what he feels human studies have to contribute to our understanding of the effects of prefrontal damage?

Rosvold. With respect to the comparative approach to this problem we have considerable evidence of progressive changes in effect from dog to man. This makes us wonder whether we are dealing with a unitary phenomenon or not. For example, delayed response performance is invariably impaired in monkeys after prefrontal lesions, but in chimpanzees this is temporary even with radical lesions and has never been demonstrated at all in human. In answer to Dr Myers's question I would say that the principal value of the studies of humans with injured frontal lobes is to emphasize two facts (1) none of our present notions of frontal lobe function has been demonstrated to apply to man in spite of many attempts to do so, and (2) the caution that one should use in generalizing about brain function without reference to all available evidence, including that obtained in man.

HEBB. But let us keep the record clear: the effects of lobotomy are different from those of lobectomy in man.

STUDIES OF HIPPOCAMPAL ELECTRICAL ACTIVITY
DURING APPROACH LEARNING

W. R. ADEY

Attention has been directed, over the past two decades, to the role of the hippocampus and adjacent structures of the temporal lobe in such functions as emotional arousal and memory (Kluver and Bucy, 1939; Bard and Mountcastle, 1948). Human studies have supported the view that interference with anterior and deep temporal structures, including the amygdala and hippocampus, may disrupt both these functions (Scoville and Milner, 1957; Meyer and Yates, 1955; Jasper and Rasmussen, 1958). However, a global view of the functions of these rhinencephalic areas in the process of learning might suggest that they are concerned in the execution of planned behaviour rather than, perhaps, in the specific aspects of memory or emotional functions as such.

The latter point of view provided a frame of reference for the studies reported here. Morphological considerations prompted Elliot Smith (1910) to draw attention to the early differentiation of the hippocampal cortex in the brain of all vertebrates, and to the concurrent development of the fornix as one of the earliest efferent pathways from the cerebrum. The possible role of these structures in aspects of motor performance relating to learned behaviour appears to have attracted little attention from subsequent workers, although Pribram and Mishkin (1955) and Fuller *et al.* (1957) have given elegant accounts of subtle changes in learned motor performance resulting from interference with these deep temporal structures.

The experiments described here were conducted in collaboration with Dr C. W. Dunlop, Dr E. Holmes and Mr C. Hendrix, and in the latter part of the project we were joined by Dr E. Grastyán. We have studied certain aspects of slow-wave discharges in the hippocampal and adjacent deep temporal lobe structures in the cat in the course of approach learning. Our attention has been directed to the possibility of inhomogeneities in the functional activities of different parts of the hippocampal arch, and particularly between the dorsal and ventral parts of the arch. In cross-sections at any one level, the hippocampal arch has been further subdivided into regions CA_1, CA_2, CA_3 and CA_4 by Lorente de Nó (1934). Our implantations have been carefully placed in regions CA_1, CA_3 and CA_4 in both dorsal and ventral parts of the arch, and in the adjacent entorhinal area of the pyriform cortex.

Two essentially opposing hypotheses have been offered in explanation of the major neural fluxes through the hippocampal arch (Fig. 1). These

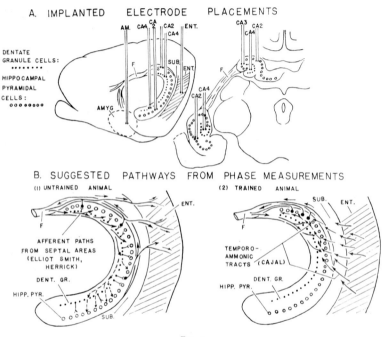

FIG. 1

A. Typical implanted electrode placements in the dorsal and ventral parts of the hippocampal arch (zones CA_2, CA_3, CA_4 dorsally, and CA_2 and CA_4 ventrally), and in the amygdala (AMYG) and entorhinal area (ENT).

B. In the untrained animal, phase measurements with an electronic computer of the slow-wave trains during approach performance are consistent with activity passing from septum to dentate granule cells (DENT. GR), thence to hippocampal pyramidal cells (HIPP. PYR), and across the subiculum (SUB) to the entorhinal area (ENT). This accords with pathways suggested by Elliot Smith and Herrick. The ventral hippocampus shows little correlation of its slow-wave activity with the approach after the first few trials. This arrangement is reversed in the trained animal, with a phase sequence in the slow-wave trains from entorhinal area to hippocampal pyramids, thus following the temporo-ammonic tracts of Cajal to the dendritic trees of the hippocampal pyramids. F, fornix and fimbria.

classical accounts have been based primarily on morphological considerations. Cajal (1909) suggested that activity arising in the entorhinal area traversed the hippocampus by trans-synaptic activation of the pyramidal cell layer, with an efferent flux into the fornix. Contrary hypotheses advanced by Elliot Smith (1910) and Herrick (1933) have proposed an anterior influx from the septum to the dentate granule cells, which in turn relayed to the hippocampal pyramidal cells, with subsequent activation of the entorhinal area. Certainly the results of acute electrophysiological experiments have favoured the latter pathways as a source of the rhythmic slow potentials recorded in the hippocampus during various types of arousal (Green and Arduini, 1954; Green and Adey, 1956; Adey, Merrillees and Sunderland, 1956; Adey, Sunderland and Dunlop, 1957; Adey, Dunlop and Sunderland, 1958). It was to test aspects of these various fluxes through the hippocampus in a training situation that our experiment was designed.

The test situation involved training cats in a T-maze box, with food reward on the basis of a visual cue. Time-lapse photographs were taken in the course of the animal's approach. Our attention was directed particularly to the appearance of certain regular slow-wave trains at 5-6 cycles/sec. in the course of the approach behaviour. All records were obtained with implanted bipolar electrodes 200 μ in diameter and spaced 1.5 mm. between recording tips. Particular attention has been given to the use of appropriate time-constants in the recording amplifiers, to record the slow-wave activity undistorted, and to the elimination of artifacts from the records in freely moving animals (Adey, Dunlop and Hendrix, 1959).

In the naive animal, during its first exposure to the training situation, we found a wide distribution of slow activity extending far into the ventral hippocampus, and exhibiting a wide spectrum from 4-7 cycles/sec. The animal continued to show this activity until one started the training procedure, and the slow activity then rapidly disappeared from the ventral hippocampus in the first few trials (Fig. 2).

After the initial presentations, regular rhythmic slow-wave trains, at 5-6 cycles/sec., appeared with each approach performance. This activity was limited to the dorsal hippocampus, particularly in CA_4, and in the entorhinal area. Bursts of this 5-6 cycles/sec. activity may appear in the entorhinal record on as many as three occasions in the approach performance: once, as the animal approaches first the wrong side of the box; again, as it turns back, and a third time as it finally turns to the right side of the box. In the pre-approach phase, there was often much 4 cycles/sec. activity. In Fig. 3, the animal rapidly proceeded first to the wrong side of the box. After a significant interval, during which the animal stood still, moving its head from side to side, it proceeded to the right side of the box. There was clearly an association of the 5-6 cycles/sec. activity with each of the two phases of motor activity, with very little evidence of rhythmic activity between these two bursts. By contrast, it did not seem correlated with those head movements of the stationary animal which constitute many aspects of an orienting reflex.

Certain aspects of the hippocampal slow-wave activity have been correlated with the orienting reflex of Pavlovian physiology by Grastyán *et al.* (1959). It is not proposed to enter here into a discussion of definitive aspects of this reflex, although it may be observed that Konorski (1948) has defined it as the turning of the head and eyes towards a sudden stimulus, and that such a definition has no connotation of locomotion towards a goal. Our findings in some twenty-one animals have consistently indicated a correlation of bursts at 5-6 cycles/sec. in the dorsal hippocampus

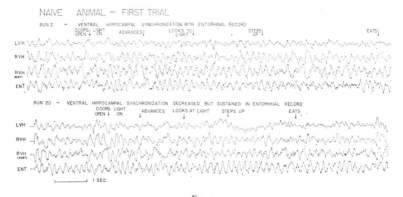

FIG. 2

Records from the left (LVH) and right ventral hippocampus (RVH) and entorhinal area (ENT), showing the rapid disappearance of much of the synchronized slow-wave activity from the ventral hippocampus between the second and twentieth runs of the first trial. At the same time, a sustained 6 cycles/sec. discharge is present at the twentieth trial in the entorhinal record in relation to the approach performance.

and in the entorhinal area with the motor performance, rather than with simple aspects of orientation. It may be further emphasized that this 6 cycles/sec. activity was singularly unadapting in the course of training, persisting unaltered in as many as 1200-1400 trials in immature and adult animals. Throughout training it remained maximal in the dorsal hippocampus and particularly in the entorhinal area.

In studying the distribution of hippocampal slow-waves in the young animal, we have implanted a number of young animals weighing about 1.8 kg. Their head size approached that of the adult, and it was possible to implant and record from them for a period of 2 to 3 months without significant electrode displacement from growth changes. Initially, their behaviour was kittenish, and they were sexually immature. At this time they showed a great deal of 4 cycles/sec. activity in 'resting' records. During the approach performance they showed typical 5-6 cycles/sec. activity in the ventral hippocampus and in the entorhinal area, but there was much less of it in the dorsal hippocampus than in the adult animal. It appeared characteristic of the immature animal that there was a much wider distribution of the 'specific' 5-6 cycles/sec. activity in the approach performance and that it included the ventral hippocampus. In contrast to adult animals, these bursts appeared dissociated in moment of onset in different hippocampal leads, and in duration in different leads.

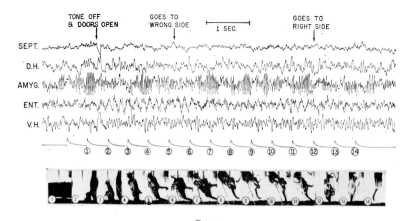

FIG. 3

Simultaneous EEG and time-lapse photographs of animal's approach in T-box. The dividing partition appears at the top of each frame. During the approach to the incorrect side (frames 2-5) there is a burst of 6 cycles/sec. activity in the entorhinal lead (ENT). This disappears as the animal stands, turning head from side to side (frames 6-10) and reappears as the animal changes position to the correct side of the box (frames 11 and 12). The amygdaloid record (AMYG) shows 40/sec. activity typical of the hungry animal, which disappears momentarily on attainment of the food reward.

In such immature animals, trained to a high level of performance over a period of 60-90 days, it was observed that much of the random hippo-campal slow activity disappeared, and that the behaviour became much like an adult cat. Very strikingly, 6 cycles/sec. activity now appeared in the dorsal hippocampus during the approach performance, as seen typi-cally in the adult animal.

With Dr Holmes, we have also trained adult cats in a delayed response situation, in which a 7 second delay preceded approach to a concealed food reward. During the waiting period there was much 4 cycles/sec.

entorhinal activity, and during the actual approach typical bursts of 6 cycles/sec. activity appeared. On extinguishing the response, by removal of the reinforcing food reward, all aspects of 6 cycles/sec. activity disappeared during the period when approach was permitted. Some 4 cycles/sec. activity occurred during the delay period. On retraining, the rapid return of the extinguished response was accompanied by the reappearance of typical 6 cycles/sec. activity in the entorhinal area.

Now it is obvious that the subjective and essentially empirical interpretation of EEG records is open to criticism, and is often quite unconvincing. We have, therefore, endeavoured to overcome some of these subjective aspects of our interpretation by transferring these training records to IBM punchcards. Although a tedious procedure, this permitted the computing of various aspects of the 4 and 6 cycles/sec. wave trains. We have been fortunate in enjoying the use of the IBM-709 electronic computer, installed at the Western Data Processing Center, at the University of California at Los Angeles. The records have been subjected to both auto- and cross-correlation studies. Each hippocampal lead can be auto-correlated; that is, compared with itself, in order to determine aspects of inherent rhythmicity in the slow-wave bursts, and to detect hidden rhythms. In cross-correlation, or comparison of one lead with another, it is possible to determine the phase relations between the slow waves of one hippocampal lead and another.

It will be seen from Fig. 4 that the auto-correlation reveals a high degree of rhythmicity, essentially sinusoidal, in the records from both dorsal hippocampus and the entorhinal area, at approximately 6 cycles/sec.

Cross-correlations of these records have revealed striking and consistent differences in the phase relationships noted in early training when compared with those from the same animal in late training. In early training, the entorhinal lead lags behind, by some 20-30 msec. the 6 cycles/sec. activity in both CA_2 and CA_4 zones of the dorsal hippocampus. This is precisely what would be predicted from acute experiments involving direct septal stimulation. By contrast, cross-correlations in late training show clearly that the initial phase arrangements are now reversed. Now, the entorhinal area consistently leads the discharge in the dorsal hippocampus by as much as 65 msec.

We may, perhaps without undue licence, extrapolate these findings to the morphological systems discussed in Fig. 1. In the untrained animal, the phase distribution in the 6 cycles/sec. bursts, associated with the approach performance, is consistent with the system of pathways proposed by Elliot Smith (1910) and Herrick (1933), and as confirmed in our acute

AUTOCORRELATIONS

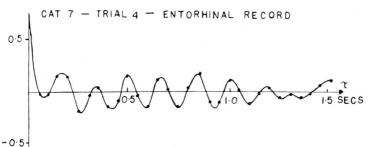

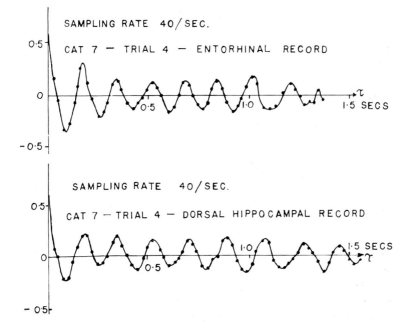

FIG. 4
Auto-correlation functions prepared with an IBM-709 electronic computer, indicating inherently sinusoidal nature of 6 cycles/sec. bursts of hippocampal and entorhinal activity during approach performance.

electrophysiological experiments (Adey, Sunderland and Dunlop, 1957; Adey, Dunlop and Sunderland, 1958). In the trained animal, the phase distribution is totally reversed, taking on an aspect consistent with pathways suggested by Cajal, running from the entorhinal area to the dorsal hippocampus.

The probable significance of these findings is further exemplified by the observations that in animals in late training, awaiting the opportunity to make an approach performance, auto-correlations showed considerable

CROSS-CORRELATIONS — IN EARLY TRAINING
CAT 7 — TRIAL 4 — RUN 14

40 SAMPLINGS/ SEC.   BANDPASS 1-50 C.P.S.

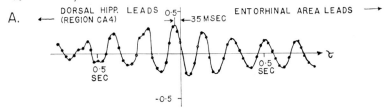

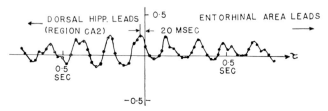

FIG. 5

Cross-correlation functions in early training, prepared with an IBM-709 electronic computer. Here, records from hippocampal zones CA_2 and CA_4 consistently lead those from the entorhinal area by 20-35 msec., thus resembling the effects of septal stimulation in acute experiments (see text).

irregularity in frequency of the hippocampal slow waves, with some strong periodic activity at 3-4 cycles/sec. In cross-correlations, phase angles of this slower 'resting' activity showed considerable variation, but were most consistently those in which the dorsal hippocampus led the entorhinal area. Examination of this 'resting' 3-4 cycles/sec. activity in the trained animal thus showed a strong resemblance to the phase relations of the faster 5-6 cycles/sec. bursts in the approach performance of the untrained animal. It is of some interest that these phase angles can be apparently sharply reversed in relation to the performance of a trained task, and just as quickly resume their 'resting' character. It is a matter for regret that the tedium of preparation of card-punched data has greatly limited the examination of many closely related aspects of these problems.

DISCUSSION

Returning briefly to the general problem of the functions of the hippocampal formation, it may be noted that the hippocampal cortex occupies a dorsomedial position in the hemisphere of all vertebrate brains. In his Arris and Gale lectures to the Royal College of Surgeons in London 50 years ago, Elliot Smith indicated that the discharge from this hippocampal cortex to subcortical structures through the fornix was one of the first great efferent pathways to appear in the evolution of the forebrain. Thus, it would not be surprising if the hippocampus did, in fact, have functions in planned motor performance, rather than, perhaps, in memory or emotional activity. We are further encouraged in this point of view by the recent observation by Hess (1959) that damage to this cortex in birds leads to the permanent loss of imprinting behaviour.

Now it may be asked what significance might attach to such phase shifts in intrahippocampal rhythms in the course of the learning process. Any answer must be entirely speculative, but perhaps not unfruitful, particularly if we accept the need to seek basically different ways of examining neural processes in the course of learning. It may be suggested that the informational coding of some neural signals may be on the basis of certain phase-comparator mechanisms, which would allow an exceedingly subtle and finely graded series of changes to be each differentially integrated in determining the output of either an individual neurone or of the more complex output of a highly organized neural tissue, such as the hippocampus, or cortical structures generally. Aspects of informational coding on the basis of such phase-comparison techniques are well known to communication engineers as, for example, in the transmission of chrominance values in colour television signals, and in phase modulation of telemetry signals.

Can any evidence be adduced to support the existence of a phase-comparator mechanism in the hippocampal systems studied here? No definite answer is possible, but if we turn for a moment to the anatomical organization of the densely packed hippocampal pyramidal cells, it is apparent that they receive afferent fluxes from two main sources, one from the entorhinal cortex via the temporo-ammonic tracts, and the other from septal areas (and, thus, indirectly from the reticular thalamic areas) via the axons of the dentate granule cells. Both these afferent paths come into intimate contact with the laminarly organized, closely grouped apical dendritic trees of the hippocampal pyramidal cells. The patterns of phase relations and the changes observed in these patterns in training, particularly between the entorhinal area and hippocampal areas CA$_2$ and

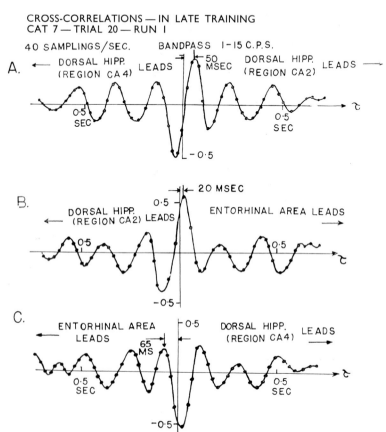

FIG. 6

Cross-correlation functions in late training, from the same animal as in Figs. 4 and 5. By contrast with Fig. 5, the entorhinal area now leads hippocampal region CA$_4$ by as much as 65 msec. and CA$_2$ by 20-25 msec. These findings are consistent with activity following the pathways proposed by Cajal (see text).

CA$_4$, may be interpreted on the basis of such a mechanism. McLardy (1959) has recently proposed an elaborate series of intrahippocampal connections which might also subserve such functions.

If, then, the concept of phase-comparator mechanisms should be found to lie at the basis of the neural process of learning, rather than, perhaps, cybernetic notions of reverberant circuits, or even more convenient neural models in which every brain neurone is connected to every other, we might speculate about the parts of the neurone in which training might produce altered conduction and excitability characteristics, responsible in turn for altered patterns of phase relations. It is probably significant that the regular rhythmic hippocampal slow waves seen here in association with the motor performance are maximally distributed in zone CA_4, a region particularly rich in both dendritic arborizations and fine presynaptic terminals.

There is much evidence that the rhythmic hippocampal slow waves arise in this dendritic layer, and that this activity is not associated with a massive firing of the cells themselves (Green and Machne, 1955). Such waves have been attributed to ephaptic activity between adjacent dendritic trees in the production of the cortical alpha rhythm (Li, McLennan and Jasper, 1952). These findings may indicate the importance of neural integration of considerable complexity occurring in dendritic and presynaptic mechanisms.

It is not improbable that neural integration of this type may occur in the vertebrate central nervous system only in the brain and not in the spinal cord, and that it may be dependent on functional and structural arrangements of dendritic and associated presynaptic structures not seen outside the brain itself. It should be a continuing and salutary reminder to those disposed to extrapolate directly from spinal to cerebral mechanisms in processes of learning that, at the physiological level, singular differences exist between spinal and cerebral synaptic functions on even such a simple basis as the activity of strychnine. This evidence has been reviewed elsewhere (Adey, 1959).

At the behavioural level, it is a matter of concern that the brain of many invertebrates, including arachnids and earthworms, with a complexity far less than that of the human spinal cord (Adey, 1951), can be readily conditioned, whereas conditioning of the human spinal cord has remained at best a most difficult procedure. We might inquire as to whether it is reasonable to interpret all aspects of neuronal excitability solely in terms of the membrane potential and trans-synaptic events impinging on it. It is difficult to avoid the conclusion that such a point of view would reduce the role of intracellular structures to that of air in a balloon. An embracing view of the neurone in the learning process must surely take account, not only of the cell membrane, but also of intra- and extracellular relations, particularly as the so-called 'extracellular' space has been shown in both spinal cord (Wyckoff and Young, 1956) and brain (Green and Maxwell, 1959; Luse, 1959) to be completely occupied by glial tissue through which all ionic and respiratory exchanges must occur. It is in the investigation of such factors as these that the structural or functional changes induced in 'memory traces' may, perhaps, be found to lie. At least, such factors may play a significant role in the genesis of the rhythmic hippocampal slow-wave trains so closely related to the learning process.

ACKNOWLEDGMENTS

The studies described here were assisted by Grants B-1883, B-610 and B-611 from the U.S. Public Health Service.

ROLE OF THE CEREBRAL CORTEX IN THE LEARNING
OF AN INSTRUMENTAL CONDITIONAL RESPONSE

T. Pinto Hamuy

Because of its complex structure and the degree of development it reaches in the more highly evolved species, the cerebral cortex has been thought in the past to be the seat of all learning. At present, however, there is a tendency to accept that cortical function is not necessarily connected with all levels of learning and that as far as learning processes are concerned, cortical and subcortical functions are interdependent.

Pavlov (1942) held that for the learning of a conditioned response (CR) the cerebral cortex is essential. He assumed that the neuronal association between conditioned and unconditioned stimuli developed intracortically.

Pavlov's assumptions have been challenged by others. Thus, in decorticated dogs, Zeliony and Kadykov (1938) observed conditioned responses to visual and auditory stimulation. Girden and his associates (1936) in the same preparation obtained conditioning with thermal, tactile and auditory stimuli.

The results achieved by ablation of specific sensory areas corresponding to the sensory modality of the conditioned stimulus are still more conclusive. Wing (1947) found it possible in dogs deprived of visual cortex to obtain a CR to a luminous stimulus. Marquis and Hilgard (1937) obtained in monkeys with a similar ablation a conditioned palpebral occlusion to light.

The evidence quoted above suggests that the integrity of the cerebral cortex is not essential for the acquisition of certain simple types of CR. We assumed that the more flexible the behaviour, the more important becomes the integrity of the cerebral cortex for its performance. To test this assumption, we decided to study in decorticated rats an instrumental CR (ICR) which, involving an alternative, is an experimental situation of a higher degree of complexity than that employed by Pavlov. We defined the degree of complexity by the number of alternatives of reaction open to the animal.

In our experiments, the animals received an electric shock as unconditioned stimulus (US). The animal could avoid it by escaping to another compartment of the chamber (Fig. 1). In the classical Pavlovian experimental set-up for the establishment of a CR, this stimulus avoidance alternative is not provided.

A learning situation of still higher complexity may be obtained through two successive stages of conditioning, as follows:

1. First stage (electric shock — light): the shock was associated with a luminous stimulus — CS — intended to condition the animal to escape in order to avoid the shock.

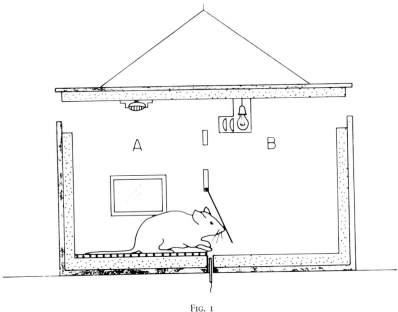

FIG. 1
Test situation.

2. Second stage (light — sound): once the avoidance CR to light was established, the conditioning to sound, by associating it with the light, would be attempted.

Decorticated rats did not learn to react to the light signal, i.e. they failed to acquire an instrumental avoidance conditional response (IACR) to this stimulus (Pinto-Hamuy, Santibañez, Rojas and Hoffmann, 1957) (Fig. 2). The extent of the decortication in these animals averaged 62 per cent of the total cortex (Fig. 3).

The failure of these rats to acquire this CR was contrary to the results obtained by other authors, as mentioned (Girden, Mettler, Finch and Culler, 1936; Zeliony and Kadykov, 1938). We decided to investigate the factors determining the incapacity observed in our rats. This might depend on: (a) the location and size of the lesion; (b) the experimental situation; (c) the animals' lack of pre-operative experience. The first two of these factors (a) and (b) are closely related, since the complexity of the problem can determine the critical level of intact cortex that the learning of a given habit requires.

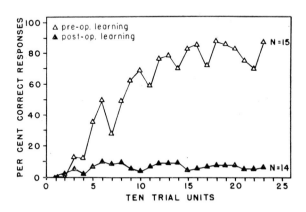

FIG. 2

Learning curves of a visual conditioned response (VCR) corresponding to a group of normal rats (pre-operative learning) and neo-decorticated rats (post-operative learning).

(a) We tried to answer the first point by training two groups of animals on the IACR to light (Pinto-Hamuy, Rojas and Araneda, 1959). One group had an ablation in the rostral half of the cerebral cortex ('anterior group') (Fig. 4); another had an ablation of the caudal half ('posterior group') (Fig. 5).

Each group consisted of thirteen animals; they were operated on and subsequently trained. If the integrity of the visual cortex were essential for this learning, we should expect the performance of the 'posterior group' to be inferior. If, however, quantity was the determining factor, both groups should have a similar level of performance. The curves of the average performance per session for each group are represented in Fig. 6. Here we can compare the performance of both groups with partial lesions with the results obtained in fourteen normal rats as well as in a group of fourteen decorticated animals (the term decorticated is used to mean the group with more extensive lesions (i.e. 62 per cent)). It may be noted that both the 'posterior group' in which the visual area is involved and the

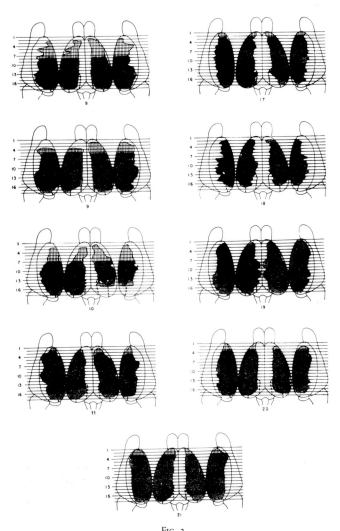

FIG. 3

Diagrams of dorsal and lateral views of the rat brain. Blackened areas indicate complete cortical ablation; striped areas, incomplete cortical ablation. The boundaries corresponding to the cortical projection of the lateral geniculate body are indicated by a dashed line.

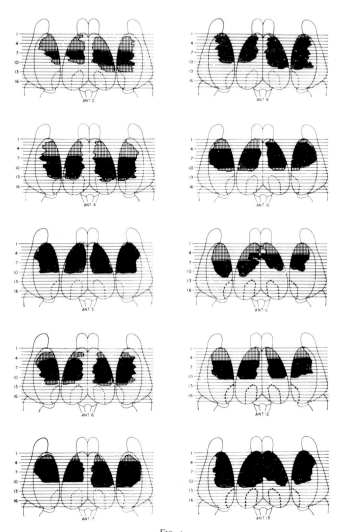

FIG. 4
Cortical lesions corresponding to the rats of the 'anterior group' (see legend
Fig. 3).

group with an anterior lesion show a marked deficit. Differences from the normal group are significant both for the 'posterior' and the 'anterior group' (p < 0.001).

The failure of the 'anterior group' is worth noticing, as until now

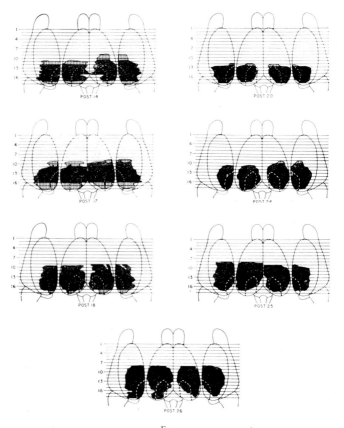

FIG. 5
Cortical lesions corresponding to the rats of the 'posterior group' (see legend Fig. 3).

investigators have explored almost exclusively the effect of lesions in the 'cortical area' of the CS and only rarely the effect of total decortication or of extensive lesions of the non-visual cortex.

The fact that four out of fourteen rats in the 'anterior group' learned the CR might indicate that the average percentage (41 per cent) of ablated cortex was within the range of the critical amount necessary to provoke the failure to learn.

The 'posterior group' with a lower average of ablated cortex presents, however, a clearer deficit than the 'anterior group'. Both groups differ significantly from one another in their performance ($p < 0.05$). These results would indicate that the locus of lesion can also be regarded as a relevant factor. In other words, the involvement of the visual area would determine a greater incapacity than similar lesions in other areas. It should be noted, however, that none of these animals had the visual area totally ablated. The amount of visual cortex removed in the various rats

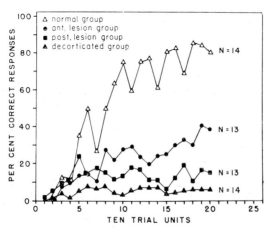

Fig. 6

Learning curves of a VCR corresponding to the following groups of rats: normal, 'anterior', 'posterior' and decorticated.

ranged from a minimum of 60 per cent to a maximum of 92 per cent. On the other hand, the performance of the group combining both lesions was inferior to that of the group with the posterior lesion. It is probable, therefore, that the whole of the cerebral cortex — both the specific as well as the rest of it — plays a role in this type of learning. Summing up, both factors, namely the extent of lesion and its locus, seem to have an influence in this respect.

The fact that some animals of the 'posterior group' with a removal of only 23 or 31 per cent of the total cortex and 70 and 78 per cent respectively of the visual cortex were unable to learn this IACR would suggest that this failure is not exclusively due to the locus or extent of the lesion but to some characteristic of the experimental situation that requires a

QQ

greater integrity of the cortex. In other words, we think that with a similar lesion other types of avoidance CR to a light signal could have been established. The results already mentioned of Wing (1947) and Marquis and Hilgard (1937) would favour this assumption, since they show that it is possible to condition a local motor reaction to a light signal. It is also worth noticing that in these experiments the animal had its own body as a reference for the performance of movements, while in our experiments the movement of the rat involved spatial orientation to reach the exit door from any point of the chamber. Orbach (1959) studied maze learning in peripherally blinded monkeys that had subsequently an ablation of the occipital cortex; he concluded that the visual cortex probably did not have a visual role only but also a function in spatial orientation. It may, therefore, be assumed that cortical integrity may not be essential for the association light–US (shock in our experiments), but that it would affect the integration of a general motor response to a light signal.

Lashley's (1935) experiments with rats eliminate the possibility that the animals did not detect the light signal. It has been shown that although the visual area is essential for the perception of detail vision, its ablation does not alter the formation of habits which require discrimination between degrees of light. In short, the most likely interpretation of our results would be that a facilitating cortical action is necessary to release a general response requiring spacial orientation to a light signal.

For the deficits shown by the anterior group there are two possible reasons: (a) that a cortical lesion of about 41 per cent may determine a serious deterioration of the animal's capacity to acquire an IACR to a light signal, independent of its location; (b) that within the anterior region there may be one or more specific areas the integrity of which is essential for this type of learning. The relevant areas may be: somatic area I and II, motor cortex and orbito-frontal cortex. Ławicka (1956), Ławicka and Konorski (1959), Brutkowski (1959), found that prefrontal lesions determine changes in the behaviour of the animal in a second order conditioned reflex. The first of these authors reports that conditioned inhibition disappears after this ablation. Stępień and Stępień (1959) found a temporal loss of an instrumental CR after ablation of somatic areas. These studies, however, refer to changes observed on post-operative retention. The integrity of the somatic and motor areas may be important for the integration of tactile and proprioceptive cues utilized by the animal to find its way to the door. The motor cortex may be necessary to facilitate this general motor response.

(*b*) To enable us to analyse the experimental situation from the point of view of the factors responsible for the failure of our rats to acquire an avoidance CR, we kept all other elements of the experiment constant, changing only the CS (Saavedra, Garcia, Oberti and Pinto-Hamuy, 1959). For this purpose we used a sound of 2400 c./sec. as CS. A group of fifteen rats with an average of ablated cortex of 62 per cent was trained. The animals managed to learn even though their performance was inferior to that of the normal control group (Fig. 7). They achieved a performance averaging 65 per cent of the CR at the thirtieth session of training.

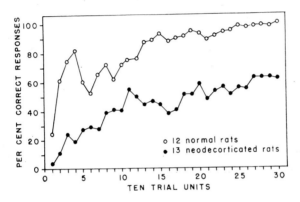

FIG. 7
Learning curves of an auditory conditioned reflex (ACR) corresponding to groups of normal and neodecorticated rats.

The performance appears high if we compare the level reached by this group with the results obtained when trying conditioning by means of a light signal.

We wondered whether this could be related to an easier conditioning with auditory signals. To answer the question we compared the learning of CR of normal rats using luminous and auditory stimuli similar to those employed in the decorticated animals (Saavedra, Garcia, Oberti and Pinto-Humay, 1959). There is a difference which appears in favour of the auditory group, this difference being, however, substantially less marked than in the decorticated animals (Fig. 8). These results agree with those obtained by Chow *et al.* (1957) in cats who established an ACR in 450 trials to light but needed only 150 using a tone. Morrell and Jasper (1956) observed a similar order of difficulty for the conditioning of an alpha flicker response. Girden *et al.* (1936) were able to install in a decorticated dog, CRs to thermal, auditory and tactile stimuli, but were unable to do so with light.

It is possible that the easier establishment of CRs to auditory stimuli in comparison with light signals is related to the fact reported by Bernhaut *et al.* (1953) that auditory stimuli are in general more effective activators of the reticular formation and thus of the cortical projection areas. On the other hand, the assumed facilitatory activity of the cortex would be more essential for the establishment of a visual memory trace on sub-cortical structures.

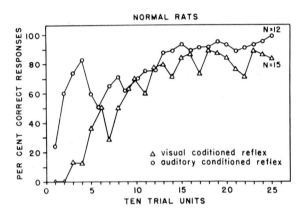

Fig. 8
Learning curves of one ACR and a VCR in two groups of normal rats.

The study of other possible variables depending on the experimental situation are under way.

(*c*) Another point investigated was the influence of preoperative training on the capacity of decorticated rats to acquire a VCR.

Seven animals were trained in this avoidance CR before decortication. Decortication determined a loss of the habit, which could be, however, relearned up to a certain level (Fig. 9). They scored a level of 70 per cent of CR at the twenty-fourth session, which normal rats had already reached at the tenth.

We were also interested in finding out the degree of specificity that this previous experience required: that is, if the training in the pre-operative period should be conducted with the same CS used post-operatively. With this idea in mind, we trained eight animals to respond to an auditory signal (unpublished observations). Once the learning was achieved, they were decorticated and subsequently trained in a CR to a light signal

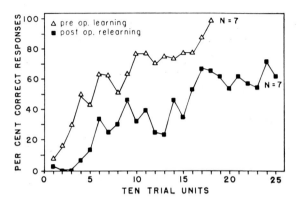

FIG. 9

Pre- and post-operative learning of a VCR in a group of seven rats.

(Fig. 10). In this case, the experience of the general experimental situation was enough to obtain a level markedly superior to that obtained by the decorticated rats without any previous training.

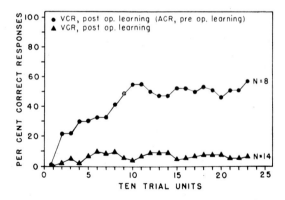

FIG. 10

Learning curves of a VCR in two groups of neodecorticated rats. One with preoperative training in an ACR; the other with no preoperative training.

We believe that our results and those of other authors show that it is difficult to generalize about the function of different structures of the central nervous system in a specific type of learning.

In other words, and in order to draw conclusions concerning the role of the cerebral cortex in the learning of conditioned responses, the following factors must be taken into consideration:

1. The kind of CR that is employed, whether a classical Pavlovian or instrumental response.
2. The nature of the conditioned stimulus.
3. The type of motor response involved in the experimental situation.
4. The previous experience of the animal.
5. The amount of cerebral cortex remaining intact, and
6. The locus of the lesion.

In spite of these limitations, some of our results may be considered conclusive in the sense that: (*a*) the specific cortex of the CS is essential for the acquisition of this visual habit (posterior group); (*b*) a lesion of about 41 per cent (anterior group) placed outside the specific cortex, may also determine a serious deficit. Nevertheless the 'CS specific cortex' would be more important in the sense that, of two lesions of the same size, the one placed in the visual cortex should cause the greater deficit.

Neurologically, the learning of an IACR which implies a general motor response, may be regarded as sharing characteristics with both sensory discrimination learning and serial learning. In our experimental situation, as it also occurs in discrimination learning, the specific cortex is more important than the rest of the cortex; on the other hand, as in maze learning, the participation of other cortical areas is necessary.

Another important possibility is that the integrity of the cerebral cortex is perhaps essential only for the acquisition of a certain habit and not when preoperative training has taken place. We think that the importance of the cortex in the learning of conditioned reflexes has been minimized because research has been mainly concerned, not with acquisition of a habit, but with postoperative retention and relearning. Another source of misinterpretations is the tendency to overlook the fact that conditioned responses obtained in decorticated dogs are deeply modified (Girden *et al.*, 1936). It seems that, in general, deficits are considered as such only when they appear in their maximal expression.

GROUP DISCUSSION

CHOW. I wanted to ask Dr Pinto how she interprets her results in the light of Lashley's old study, and his conclusions on the equipotentiality of the neocortex in the rat.

PINTO-HAMUY. We have come to an intermediate opinion regarding the importance of the cortex in this kind of learning; we consider its function to some extent as a whole, but the specific cortex would also matter. One could suggest that lesions placed outside the specific cortex have to be of a certain extent in order to determine an impairment similar to a smaller lesion placed in the specific cortex.

ROSVOLD. What did the rats do when they did not move?

PINTO-HAMUY. When the shock began they ran to the other compartment. And even that sort of 'unconditioned' response needed a certain learning after ablation of the neocortex.

HEBB. Do I assume that the rats were all reared in small cages? The reason for my asking is a fact which has puzzled us very much; if rats are reared in a small cage, lesions of the anterior part of the brain will have an equal effect with lesions in the posterior part, in complex learning situations. If rats are reared in a large cage with a number of objects, so that they have a naturalistically normal experience during growth, they show a very different picture. The animals with anterior lesions now show little effect. An equal lesion in the posterior part of the cortex (it does not have to be visual cortex) will produce gross defects. Here is another case, when we are talking about the mode of physiological organization of the brain, where we must take into account (as a possible source of variability between experiments) the conditions of rearing and the past history of the animal.

PINTO. I do not think our cages were particularly small; our animals had space to move around. They measured $45 \times 15 \times 28.5$ centimetres.

COVIAN. Have you observed differences with just unilateral neodecortication?

PINTO. We did not study that kind of preparation because we had previous experience with discrimination learning following a unilateral lesion; very obvious changes were not found in this type of learning with unilateral lesion.

SIGNIFICANCE OF THE PHOTIC STIMULUS
ON THE EVOKED RESPONSES IN MAN

E. García-Austt, J. Bogacz and A. Vanzulli

INTRODUCTION

If the retina of a normal man placed in a dark and quiet room is stimulated with flashes of constant intensity and frequency, the subject undergoes a series of psychological phenomena. Of these phenomena the most constant are those pertaining to attention. The attention state follows a defined time pattern. The first flashes, taking the subject by surprise, arouse his attention. Subsequently, through monotonous repetition, the flashes lose significance and he becomes uninterested. If under these conditions the stimulus is discontinued at regular intervals for a constant period of time, a new interest is added, darkness. The stimuli regain significance on being preceded by a period of darkness and once more the subject becomes attentive to them, but he again loses interest on becoming habituated to the regular repetition of the association of darkness and flicker. If on this same attention level a constant tone is added at the end of the period of darkness, the flashes regain significance and the same phenomenon is repeated.

Is there any method of objectifying the neurophysiological processes associated with these modifications in attention? The study of the evoked potentials contribute important elements to the elucidation of this problem. In this connection Hernández-Peón and Donoso (1957), Jouvet and Courjon (1958) worked on subcortical recordings in man. Obviously this method does not allow for a systematic study.

It has been shown that from scalp recordings it has been possible to extract the evoked potentials by the use of different methods, taking into account either the space factor (Grey Walter, 1954; Remond and Ripoche, 1958), or the time factor (Dawson, 1947; Calvet, Cathala, Hirsch and Scherrer, 1956).

In the present investigation, methods of temporal superposition have been used to study in man the influence of the changes in the significance of the photic stimulus on the evoked response.

VISUAL EVOKED RESPONSES

Dawson (1947) was the first author to record through the scalp the evoked responses to electrical stimulation of the peripheral nerves in man. He used the superposition of fifty or more successive sweeps in a single record, leading as is customary the potentials on the Y axis and the sweep synchronized with the stimulus on the X axis. 'In such a record any waves which follow the stimulus by a regular interval will all occur at the same place on the trace; they may thus be detected although they are no larger than the deflection produced by the spontaneous activity of the brain and scalp muscles. As deflections due to these causes are not regularly related to the stimulus, they tend to occur at a different place on each successive sweep and therefore appear only as a thickening of the baseline' (Dawson, 1947). Ciganek (1958 a, b) used this technique for recording the evoked potentials by photic stimuli in man.

Calvet, Cathala, Hirsch and Scherrer (1956), and Calvet, Cathala, Contamin, Hirsch and Scherrer (1956) used another technique of superposition for recording in man the evoked visual, somato-sensorial and auditory responses. They led the cortical potentials on the Z axis thus causing variations in the luminous intensity of the cathode ray. On the X axis the sweep was synchronized with the stimulus, and on the Y axis a high frequency was fed to obtain a wide luminous strip. On a single frame twenty to fifty successive sweeps were superimposed. By this means a strip was obtained whereon the asynchronic waves of the EEG were superposed, giving a grey tone, and the evoked potentials were added together, giving a clear contrast between light and shadow. The strip was analysed after magnification by a photoelectric cell, and a linear record thus obtained.

In this investigation these two techniques were employed to record the evoked visual response in forty-three experiments carried out on normal adults. Dawson's technique (1947) of superposition is simple, reliable, and permits an adequate study of the sequence of the potentials. However, as it is purely a procedure of superposition without adding the potentials, its amplitude was small. When working with the stroboscope at a distance of over 3 m. from the retina the response was not recorded. The technique of superposition and addition of Calvet *et al.* is more complicated, requires a longer procedure and is less safe. A straight baseline cannot always be obtained owing to differences in the luminous intensity of the cathode rays. Potentials are distorted by contrast, by the non-linearity of the photographic process and by the need to use the photo-electric cell with a slot of a given width. On the other hand this method has the advantage of having a greater sensibility, for potentials are added, unlike the other method in which they are superposed only. Their greater sensibility made it possible to record evoked responses with the stroboscope placed at a distance of over 3 m. from the retina.

In all experiments the frequency of the flicker stimulation was of 0.5-5/sec. With both techniques, twenty to fifty sweeps were superimposed. The stroboscope was situated at a distance of 3 m. from the eyes, but in some experiments it was placed nearer to check the effect of the distance.

The visual evoked response was recorded by these procedures in the following regions: occipital (O_2 electrode of 10/20 system), parietal (P_4), central (C_4 and C_6), frontal (F_4) and temporal (T_2 and T_6). C_4, T_2 and O_2 were the positions most often used. No response was recorded in the nose and frequently not in the prefrontal region (Fp_2).

The evoked potential was constituted by a succession of regular monomorphous waves of 4-5 or more hemicycles. The usual sequence of polarity was as follows: surface-negative, positive, negative, positive and negative. The peaks of the three first negative waves developed at 80-120, 180-240, 270-300 msec. and the peaks of the two first positive waves developed at 120-170 and 230-250 msec. In most cases the last waves were of longer duration.

The latency of the first negative wave was 15-40 msec. Sometimes the latency was higher — from 80 to 100 msec. — because the first negative wave was missing. Its absence was noted on various occasions when a common reference electrode was used on the mastoid. On the other hand it was never absent when the nose was used as a reference. The latency of the first negative wave was at its minimum on O_2. On C_4 and T_2 the peak of the first negative wave had a delay of 15-30 msec. with respect to O_2. The duration of the waves was longer on C_4 and T_2 than on O_2.

The amplitude of the response was related to the duration of the waves: the longer the duration, the greater the amplitude. With Dawson's method the values reached were between 30-40 microvolts. The maximum amplitude of the response was obtained on O_2, the minimum on F_4 and in the mastoid, when the nose was the reference electrode.

In general a slight increase in amplitude was observed in all regions with eyes shut, although the superposition was better with the eyes open because the alpha rhythm was then eliminated. All cases were studied in wakefulness. The waking state was controlled by analysing the spontaneous electrical activity recorded by means of an electroencephalograph. On bringing the stroboscope nearer to the retina, and thus increasing the intensity of the stimulus, the amplitude in all the regions was increased.

The evoked response had the same characteristics when it was recorded in the subject after an interval of several days.

Between the evoked responses from the occipital region and those from other regions differences of latency, amplitude, phase and duration were observed. The presence of a single generator located in the depth of the occipital region could explain the differences of amplitude and phase owing to the different distance and orientation of the electrodes. However, the differences in latency and duration of the response cannot be satisfactorily accounted for by the physical propagation of the occipital response, because for the frequencies recorded the reactance of the brain coverings is negligible (Grey Walter, 1950). Furthermore during the continuous or discontinuous flicker stimulation, as will be shown later on, the response of the different regions may vary independently.

It is necessary, therefore, to recognize that other regions of the brain are activated. The magnitude of the delay (15-30 msec.) existing between the occipital potential and the potentials of the other regions, leads to the belief that the latter must course through pathways with more numerous synapses. The small distance between the electrodes eliminates the possibility that this delay may be due solely to axonic conduction.

To sum up, the evoked visual response studied in these experiments is a rhythmic, complex potential, of long latency, of diffuse distribution over the scalp, recorded during wakefulness with the eyes open or shut.

Evoked visual responses have been the subject of numerous studies in animals and in man since Bartley and Bishop (1933) described them for the first time in the cat, by stimulation of the optic nerve. Shape and topographic distribution vary considerably according to the state of attentiveness.

Two components of the evoked response are distinguished regardless of whether the recording is made in the animal in the area of primary projection (Gerard, Marshall and Saul, 1936; Marshall, Talbot and Ades, 1943; Chang, 1950) or in man through the scalp (Ciganek, 1958b): the initial component and the after-discharge. In both cases the after-discharge is similar. It is not known what relation may exist between the initial component recorded in the area of specific projection, primary evoked potential, and the initial component of the response recorded through the scalp. Ciganek (1958b) maintains that some of the waves which constitute the initial component correspond to the primary evoked response.

The distribution of the evoked visual response is not limited to the striate area, but in experimental conditions, in the anaesthetized animal (Gerard, Marshall and Saul, 1936; Marshall, Talbot and Ades, 1943; Clare and Bishop, 1954), in the waking animal (Buser and Borenstein, 1957) as in man (Ciganek, 1958a), it may be recorded at a distance.

The evoked visual response in waking man studied in this investigation corresponds in its characteristics and distribution to that described by Calvet *et al.* (1956) and by Ciganek (1958 a, b). The potential studied by Walter and Grey Walter (1949) is certainly the same one, although described in less detail. On the other hand, other responses recorded in waking man such as the 'waking-on-effect' (Davis, 1939; Davis, Davis Loomis, Harvey and Hobart, 1939) and the 'pointes vertex' (Gastaut, 1953), probably respond to different mechanisms since they have a different distribution.

It may be presumed that this diffuse evoked visual response corresponds in latency, topography and conditions of recording during wakefulness to the 'réponse irradiée' of Buser and Borenstein (1957) recorded in cats.

EFFECT OF CONTINUOUS FLICKER STIMULATION

On application of a continuous flicker frequency the evoked responses underwent progressive changes showing modifications in their amplitude, form, frequency and topographic distribution.

Amplitude. In subjects who had no previous knowledge of the technique and who were unaware of the conditions of the test, the responses to the first flashes were invariably of greater amplitude than to succeeding ones (Figs. 1 and 2). As time passed the amplitude was progressively reduced. This decrease was apparent after 300-500 flashes and was maintained during the whole experiment, which comprised from 2000 to 4000 flashes in 15-20 minutes.

Frequently, after the initial reduction a discrete increase was found in the amplitude without obtaining, however, the initial values recorded at the beginning of the experiment. On some occasions a repeated waxing and waning was observed, but always maintaining a lesser amplitude than the original one.

The reduction of the evoked response in man as a consequence of the repetition of the stimulus is similar to the phenomenon of habituation described in the animal by auditory or photic stimulation (Hernández-Peón, Jouvet and Scherrer, 1957; Jouvet and Hernández-Peón, 1957; Hernández Peón, 1958; Hernández-Peón, Guzman-Flores, Alcaraz and Fernández-Guardiola, 1958; Palestini, Davidovich and Hernández-Peón, 1959).

However, the time course of habituation was considerably faster in man. Whilst the cat requires hours to become habituated to an intermittent photic stimulus, man did this in a few minutes. It should be borne in mind in this respect that in man, as a consequence of the higher development of his nervous system, learning is much faster than in the carnivores. Furthermore, the significance of a flash is much greater to a caged animal on the defensive than to a man who, although he has no previous knowledge of the experiment, knows what a flash is and also knows that he will not have to face anything unpleasant or dangerous during the experiment.

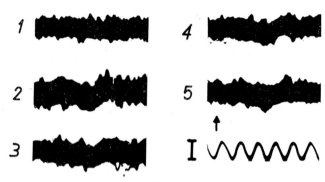

FIG. 1

Changes of the visual evoked response by effect of habituation. Continuous flicker frequency 2/sec. Stroboscope at 3 m. from the retina. Eyes open. Fifty superimposed sweeps. Dawson's technique. Arrow indicates the stimulus. Lead O2-right mastoid (10/20 system). (1) control without stimulation; (2) flashes 1-50, three waves are observed surface-negative-positive-negative; (3) flashes 101-150, the first negative wave tends to disappear and the others are reduced in amplitude; (4) flashes 301-350, the first negative wave has disappeared; (5) flashes 401-450, amplitude even more reduced. Calibrations, 25/sec., 50 microvolts.

To the cat, the flash signifies danger, to man it is simply light. Consequently, it is possible that the latter soon ceases to pay attention to it and becomes habituated.

Persons subjected to the action of a repetitive photic stimulus, on being questioned, stated that after a few hundred flashes their interest decreased on realizing that the stimulus was monotonously repeated.

Some subjects with previous experience showed a lesser amplitude in their response to the first flashes. For example the first 100-150 flashes evoked responses of lesser amplitude than the 150-250 following ones. Subsequently the amplitude was again reduced, the habituation which was to persist throughout the whole experiment becoming apparent. In these subjects the factor of initial surprise was lacking, their attention becoming more concentrated a few minutes after the beginning of the experiment when they were feeling more comfortable.

Form and frequency. During habituation the evoked potential had a tendency to become more complex and to present a greater number of waves (Fig. 2A). The waves multiplied progressively. This change was more noticeable in the first negative wave where a notch appeared which as it became deeper was transformed into a surface negative-positive-negative wave. In some cases all the waves were multiplied, the evoked

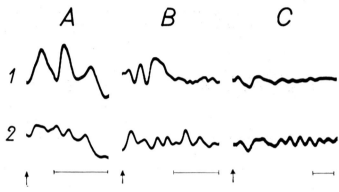

FIG. 2

Changes of the visual evoked response by effect of habituation. Continuous flicker frequency, Stroboscope at 3 m. from the retina. Forty superimposed sweeps. Technique of Calvet and co-workers. Arrows indicate the stimulus. Lead O2-right mastoid. A, B, and C, experiments performed on different subjects. (1) at the beginning of the experiment; (2) when habituation was achieved. A, the initial component before habituation is constituted by three waves and after habituation the amplitude decreases and the waves become more numerous. B, with eyes open, after habituation the amplitude is reduced and a fast after-discharge of 22/sec. develops. C, with eyes closed, after habituation the amplitude does not change and a slow after-discharge of 14/sec. sets in. Calibration, 200 msec.

potential being constituted by a succession of 6 to 8 cycles of low amplitude. Occasionally the progressive reduction of the amplitude finally caused the disappearance of some waves, notably of the first negative wave which generally was of lesser magnitude than the following ones (Fig. 1).

Provided the flicker stimulation was a low frequency (0.5-2/sec.) and that it was prolonged for a lengthy period, there constantly appeared in succession to the evoked response a regular rhythm, present throughout the whole extension of the sweep (which lasted up to 2 seconds (Fig. 2, B and C)). This rhythm was of variable frequencies of two ranges: (1) alpha frequency and (2) 20-45/seconds. The first appeared with closed eyes in all subjects and/or with open eyes in subjects who in these conditions presented an alpha rhythm. Its frequency was the same as that of the spontaneous alpha rhythm. The fast rhythm was present with open eyes in subjects not presenting the alpha rhythm and it had the same frequency as that of the spontaneous rhythm.

The slow after-discharge of alpha frequency is similar to that described by Ciganek (1958b) who, however, noted it as being inconstant. This is explained by the fact that the after-discharge develops only in the course of habituation and this temporal evolution was not taken into account by this author. Hernández-Peón (personal communication) also observed the development of a slow after-discharge in the cat through habituation.

Bremer and Bonnet (1950) studying the response evoked by auditory stimulation in the awake or anaesthetized cat ('encéphale isolé' preparation) described two types of after-discharge: the slow one of 8-12 seconds observed during sleep and the fast one which appeared in wakefulness or under light ether anaesthesia. The after-discharges which appeared by effect of habituation in man are comparable to those described by these authors. Their frequency varied with the background rhythm to the EEG: the subjects showing a moderately synchronized tracing (alpha rhythm) presented a slow discharge. In other activated record presented a rapid after-discharge. In other words, the spontaneous rhythm tends to be synchronous with the photic stimulation as a consequence of being triggered by it.

Topographic distribution. In the course of habituation the evoked responses of O2, C4, T2 and T6 experienced a similar evolution. However, the evoked responses of the central and temporal regions underwent greater reductions in amplitude. In some instances the central and temporal responses disappeared whilst the occipital response persisted (Fig. 3). Since the amplitude of the evoked potential in the central and temporal regions was less than in the occipital region, it might be thought that a reduction in the amplitude of the response would cause the earlier disappearance in those regions where originally the amplitude had been less. Nevertheless a decrease in amplitude and even the disappearance of the central and/or temporal responses was observed without any change appearing in the amplitude of the occipital potential. This fact indicates that during habituation the evoked response undergoes a true reduction in its topographic distribution, and from being diffuse tends to become localized in the occipital region.

The fast or slow after-discharges produced by habituation are recorded preferably in the occipital region. In other regions they were recorded inconstantly.

The lesser variability of the occipital response was more clearly shown

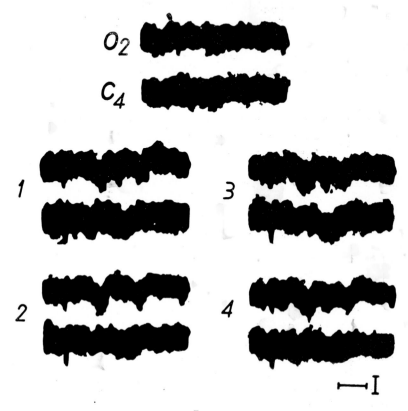

FIG. 3

Changes of the visual evoked response by effect of habituation and attention. Continuous flicker frequency 2/sec. Stroboscope at 1.5 m. from the retina. Eyes open. Forty superimposed sweeps. O2 and C4, controls, leads of the 10/20 system, common reference in the right mastoid. (1) flashes 1-40, same leads, complex responses are observed on O2 and C4; (2) flashes 1081-1120, habituation of the response on C4; on O2, no modifications are observed; (3) flashes 1121-1160, the subject counts number of flashes, the response increases on C4, on O2 no changes (dishabituation by attention); (4) flashes 1161-2000, without counting flashes, response is again reduced on C4 as in (2), on O2 no changes. Calibrations, 100 msec., 100 microvolts.

when the intensity of the flash was increased by bringing the stroboscope near the retina. In some cases with the stroboscope placed at a distance of 1.50 m. or less from the retina, no changes were observed in the amplitude of the occipital potential even when the flicker stimulation was prolonged

RR

for 20 minutes. On the other hand the same subjects showed habituation to this response with the stroboscope at a distance of 3 m. or more. This is not surprising since it is well known that the more intense the stimulation, the harder it is to achieve habituation. Even when, on increasing the intensity of the stimulus no decrease in amplitude was observed during habituation, a slow after-discharge appeared in experiments with closed eyes (Fig. 2, C). It is interesting to emphasize this point since it proves that modifications in the amplitude and form of the response during habituation may take place independently.

Summarizing, the changes in the evoked visual response observed during habituation to a continuous flicker stimulation were as follows: (1) reduction of amplitude, (2) multiplication of the waves, (3) appearance of a fast or slow after-discharge depending on the background rhythm and (4) reduction in diffusion. The changes observed during dishabituation provoked by attention or by modifications in the quality of stimuli, were opposite.

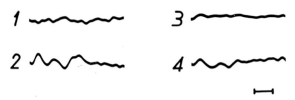

FIG. 4

Changes of the visual evoked response by effect of attention. Continuous flicker frequency 0.5/sec. Stroboscope at 3 m. from the retina. Eyes open. Forty superimposed sweeps. Lead O2-right mastoid 10/20 system. Arrow indicates the stimulus. (1) control without stimulation; (2) flashes 1–40, response formed by three successive oscillations; (3) flashes 41–80, throughout this period an intense tone is associated, the response tends to disappear, the first wave only persisting with a very low amplitude; (4) flashes 81–120, in the same conditions as in (2) without the associated tone, the response reappears. Calibration, 200 msec.

Habituation was a persistent phenomenon. If after habituation had become established the stimulus was suspended for 15–30 minutes, on applying it again the response maintained the same characteristics. In previously trained subjects fewer flashes were needed to establish habituation. Similar results have been obtained in animals by Hernández-Peón, Jouvet and Scherrer (1957).

If during the continuous flicker stimulation, before habituation was established, the attention of the subject was withdrawn from the repetitive stimuli and focused on some other interesting stimulus, the amplitude of the response decreased. This reduction was seen for example when the subject was performing a mental calculation or was made to listen to an intense continuous tone during the flicker stimulation (Fig. 4). Hernández-Peón et al. (1957) reported the same phenomenon in the optic pathways of the cat, Buser and Rougeul (1956) found it in the cerebral cortex, and Jouvet and Courjon (1958) studied it in man by recording from the optic radiations.

Inversely it was possible to provoke a state of dishabituation by increasing the attention directed to the flicker. For example, when the subject counted the flashes (Fig. 3) or simply checked a possible variation in them, the amplitude of the response increased, the after-discharge disappeared the waves became simplified and the response was recorded in other regions as well as in the occipital region. In other words the response regained its pre-habituation characteristics.

When, after habituation, a click or a brief tactile stimulus was associated with each flash, dishabituation was again provoked. If this association was prolonged for a time habituation again set in. On suspending the association and continuing with the pure flicker, dishabituation again took place. That is to say, that habituation was observed whenever the stimulus, either pure or in its associated form, was sufficiently repeated, and dishabituation took place whenever the stimulus was modified by association or disassociation.

EFFECT OF DISCONTINUOUS FLICKER STIMULATION

When, having achieved habituation of the response by continuous flicker stimulation, the stimuli were interrupted for regular and constant periods, after three to seven trials dishabituation was achieved (Fig. 5). The response regained all its initial characteristics. The most remarkable feature was the increase in amplitude.

If a discontinuous flicker stimulation was used initially without previous habituation having been established, an increase in amplitude was again obtained, but this time of lesser magnitude. In either case if stimulation by a discontinuous flicker was continued, after ten to fifteen trials the response became habituated (Figs. 5 and 6). The general evolution of the response was not the same in the different regions explored. Whilst in O2 the increase in amplitude was only discrete and the response was rapidly rehabituated, in C4 and T2 the increase was greater and more persistent.

There were differences in the temporal course of changes in different subjects (Fig. 7).

These modifications of the evoked response caused by discontinuity of

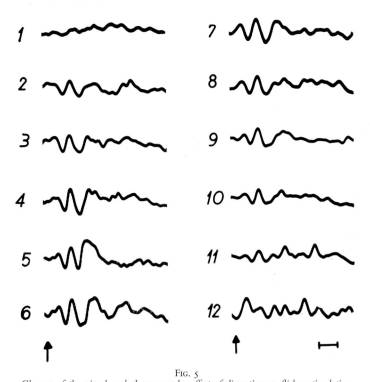

FIG. 5

Changes of the visual evoked response by effect of discontinuous flicker stimulation. Stroboscope at distance of 3 m. from the retina. Eyes open. Forty superimposed sweeps. Flicker frequency 2/sec. during 20 seconds, interrupted during 20 seconds, Lead C4-right mastoid, 10/20 system. Arrows indicate the stimulus. (1) control without stimulation; (2) after habituation to a continuous flicker frequency, after 1200 flashes; (3) first trial after darkness-flicker association, the response is comparable to the previous one; (4-6) 3rd, 4th and 5th trials respectively, the responses increase progressively (dishabituation, time conditioning); (7-10) 7th, 15th, 17th and 19th trials respectively, the response starts to decrease until in (10) it attains amplitude and form comparable to those of (2) (rehabituation); (11 and 12) 21st and 22nd trials respectively, the rehabituation is accentuated and an after-discharge of 20-22/sec. develops. Calibration, 100 msec.

the flicker are an example of electrocortical time conditioning where the period of darkness acts as a conditioned stimulus and the flicker as an unconditioned one.

The interruption of the flicker by regular periods of darkness contributed a new motive of interest to the flashes. Persons subjected to these tests stated that owing to the monotonous repetition of the continuous flicker their attention decreased (habituation). In these circumstances when

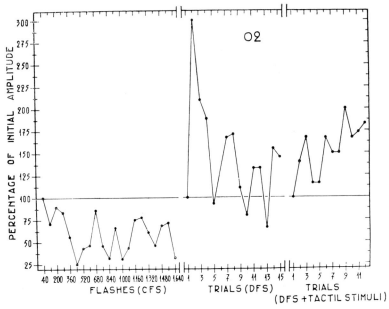

FIG. 6

Changes of the visual evoked response by effect of continuous and discontinuous flicker stimulation and through tactile-flash association. Ordinates, percentage of initial peak to peak amplitude of the evoked response. Abscissas, times, represented by the number of flashes during the continuous flicker stimulation (CFS) at a frequency of 4/sec. and by trials carried out every 10 seconds with discontinuous flicker stimulation (DFS) at the same frequency for 10 seconds. Lead O2-right mastoid. Stroboscope at a distance of 3 m. from the retina. Eyes open. In the first part of the experiment with CFS an irregular reduction of the amplitude is observed. But if under these conditions of habituation a DFS is employed the amplitude increases quickly. However, after a few trials it tends to decrease again. If under these new conditions during the DFS every flash is simultaneously associated with a brief tactile stimulus (tactile-flash association) the response again increases in amplitude until the end of the experiment.

the flicker was suspended for the first time for a few seconds they believed the experiment to have terminated. However, after a few trials associating darkness and flicker they realized that after a certain constant period of darkness the flashes were always resumed and then their attention to the flashes increased. In other words the interruption of the flicker gave new significance to the stimulus. If this darkness-flicker association was prolonged for a time without modifications, they once again lost interest in the stimulus, their attention decreasing accordingly (rehabituation).

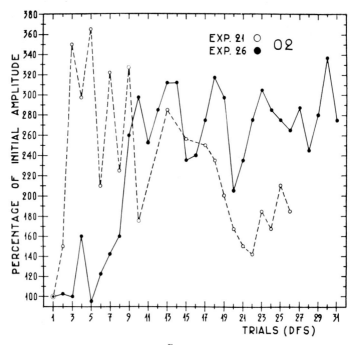

FIG. 7

Changes of the visual evoked response by effect of discontinuous flicker stimulation. Ordinates, percentage of initial peak to peak amplitude of the evoked response. Abscissas, trials carried out every 20 seconds with discontinuous flicker stimulation (DFS) at 2/sec. for 20 seconds. Lead O2-right mastoid. Stroboscope at a distance of 3 m. from the retina. Eyes open. Two experiments carried out in different subjects who had had no previous knowledge of the conditions of the test, are plotted. The temporal course of changes in experiment number 21 (white dots) is faster than the one of experiment 26 (black dots). In experiment 21 the amplitude increases quickly and reaches its highest value in the 5th trial. After the 13th trial it begins to decrease regularly. In experiment 26, the amplitude increases slowly and retains high values until the end of the test at the 31st trial.

INTERACTION BETWEEN THE DISCONTINUOUS FLICKER STIMULATION
AND A TONE

The association of a sound in the period of darkness during the discontinuous flicker also provoked modifications in the response. When after the establishment of habituation to the discontinuous flicker an intense and constant tone was emitted at the end of the period of darkness, for example during the last 10 seconds, the response became dishabituated after three to eight trials (Fig. 8). The increase in amplitude was marked and in some cases surpassed the initial amplitude prevailing before habituation. This phenomenon was always more marked and more rapid than the dis-

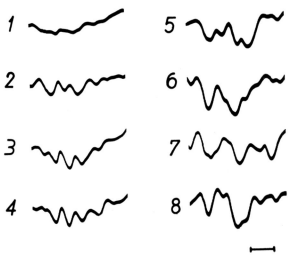

FIG. 8

Changes of the visual evoked response by effect of tone-flicker association. Stroboscope at 3 m. from the retina. Eyes open. Forty superimposed sweeps. Lead C4-right mastoid 10/20 system. Arrows indicate the stimulus. Discontinuous flicker frequency 2/sec. during 20 seconds, interrupted during 20 seconds. (1) control without stimulation; (2) habituation to discontinuous flicker frequency after twelve trials without association with tone. A response of low amplitude and after discharge of 16/sec. is observed. Three to eight successive trials with tone (10 seconds) – flicker (20 seconds) – darkness (10 seconds) association; (3) 1st trial with tone-flicker association, no appreciable changes were noted in respect to previous one; (4) 3rd trial, slight increase in amplitude of response; (5-8) 4th, 7th, 9th, 11th trials respectively, the response continues increasing and is simplified. Calibration, 100 msec.

habituation provoked by the discontinuous flicker stimulation without association of sound.

If the trials with this tone-flicker association were prolonged rehabituation of the response was obtained. This rehabituation was more delayed and inconstant than that in the darkness-flicker association, requiring fifteen to twenty trials to appear.

The presence of the tone at the beginning of the period of darkness, i.e. the flicker-tone association, provoked modifications comparable to the tone-flicker association, but inconstant and less important (Fig. 9). In

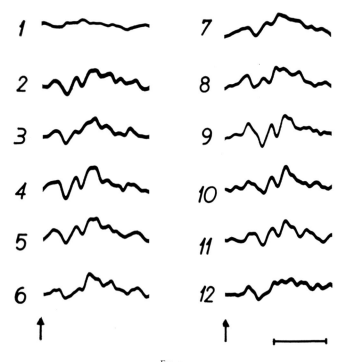

FIG. 9

Changes of the visual evoked response by effect of flicker-tone association. Stroboscope at 3 m. from the retina. Eyes open. Forty superimposed sweeps. Lead O2-right mastoid, 10/20 system. Arrows indicate the stimulus. Discontinuous flicker frequency 2/sec. during 20 seconds, interrupted during 20 seconds. (1) control without stimulation; (2) habituation to discontinuous flicker frequency after ten trials without association with tone; (3–12) successive trials with flicker (20 seconds) — tone (10 seconds) — darkness (10 seconds) association; (3) 1st trial with flicker-tone association, no appreciable modifications with respect to previous trial are noted; (4) 6th trial, the response is considerably increased; (5–7) 7th, 9th and 10th trials respectively, response again decreases; (8–11) 11th, 16th, 21st and 29th trials respectively, an increase takes place and is maintained; (12) 31st trial, decreases again. Calibration, 200 msec.

some experiments the central response underwent remarkable changes whereas the occipital one did not show significant variations (Fig. 10).

The dishabituation obtained by the tone-flicker or flicker-tone associations persisted during various trials when these stimuli were substituted by a discontinuous flicker without tone association. But the subject rapidly became rehabituated if the trials were repeated (extinction). This rehabituation was much more rapid than that caused by persistence of the initial association (tone-flicker).

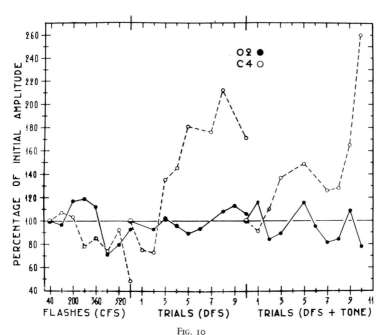

FIG. 10

Changes of the visual evoked response by effect of continuous and discontinuous flicker stimulation and through tone-flicker association. Ordinates, percentage of initial peak to peak amplitude of the evoked response. Abscissas, time, represented by the number of flashes during the continuous flicker stimulation (CFS) at a frequency of 2/sec. and by trials carried out every 20 seconds with discontinuous flicker stimulation (DFS) at the same frequency for 20 seconds. Stroboscope at a distance of 1.5 m. from the retina. Eyes open. Black and white dots, simultaneous records from the occipital and the central regions respectively. During the CFS the response decreases in amplitude chiefly in C4. During the DFS an increase of the amplitude in C4 is observed. In O2 the response does not show significant changes. When a tone is emitted at the end of the periods of darkness (tone-flicker association, DFS+tone), the amplitude of the central responses increases even more. The occipital response undergoes no changes.

In most, the variations in the responses were different in the central, temporal and occipital regions, being more marked and persistent in the first two.

The changes in the evoked visual response by the interaction of tone and flicker constitute another example of the electrocortical conditioning in man. The facilitation of the specific response to an intermittent sound after conditioning by association with a continuous light, was observed in the cat by Jouvet (1956) and Jouvet and Hernández-Peón (1957). The results described in different conditions of stimulation (continuous light, intermittent sound) agree with the statement previously made, that the association of a continuous tone and of an intermittent flight, facilitated the evoked response by light in man, after conditioning. Buser and Rougeul (1956) established that the 'réponse irradiée' increases in amplitude in the course of sensorial conditioning. It has already been stated in this paper that it is probable that this response corresponds to the diffuse response of the scalp record in man.

Dishabituation by conditioning was described in the cat by Hernández-Peón, Jouvet and Scherrer (1957). The auditory response was dishabituated on the acoustic stimulus being given a new significance by association with an electric shock to the forepaw of the animal. Lelord, Fourmant, Calvet and Scherrer (1958) described in man the conditioning of the response evoked by sound (conditioned stimulus) by association with light (unconditioned stimulus). After various trials on successive days a diffuse response was obtained by a sound which before the conditioning evoked no response. This is a phenomenon of delayed appearance, differing, therefore, from the rapid changes of the visual evoked response already described.

When the visual stimulus acted as an unconditioned stimulus in the tone-flicker association the changes in the response were greater than when it took the form of a conditioned stimulus in the flicker-tone association. In other words the changes in the vsiual 'unconditioned' response were greater than in the visual 'conditioned' response. This fact agrees with the view sustained by other authors as Buser and Roger (1957), 'que c'est au niveau de la zone corticale inconditionelle que se concentre l'essentiel des événements caractéristiques de la liaison conditionelle'.

Persons subjected to the tone-flicker interaction stated that after various associations they became aware that the tone was always followed by a series of flashes and consequently when they started listening to it they were already prepared to see the light, thus paying more attention to it. On the other hand, the flicker-tone association had the same effects on attention to sound, the effects on attention to light being variable.

CONCLUDING REMARKS

The amplitude, form and distribution of the scalp visual evoked response in man depend on the significance of the photic stimuli.

When the stimulus is significant and therefore attention is paid to it, the response is relatively simple and widespread. When on the other hand, the stimulus is not significant and no great attention is paid to it, the response is reduced, complex and localized. It is interesting to point out that during the state of attention not only has the evoked potential a greater amplitude but also a much larger area of the brain receives the 'information'.

These changes in the response are closely related to the state of sensorial receptivity of the subject, i.e. the 'attention level' towards the stimulus.

Between these two phenomena, the electrical and the psychological, there may exist: (1) a cause and effect relation, (2) a common cause. Although the first possibility cannot be discarded, it is probable that both are the consequence of processes taking place in the subcortical systems of unspecific projection (Jouvet and Hernández-Peón, 1957; Buser and Roger, 1957; Hernández-Peón, Brust-Carmona, Eckhaus, Lopez-Mendoza and Alcocer-Cuaron, 1958; Gastaut, 1958).

Directing, blocking and switching of the sensorial messages would appear to take place on the level of the reticular formation and/or thalamic reticular system. As a consequence of the analysis and integration taking place in these structures, the cerebral cortex would receive information of correct magnitude and proper distribution for immediate needs. The modifications of the 'level' and 'focus' of attention would be the consequence of this selective activity.

Whatever the explanation is, the electrical changes and the variations of attention run side by side. Therefore, the electrical changes provide an idea and may even go as far as to constitute a measure of the concomitant psychological phenomena. If this should be so, with the equipment available in every neurophysiological laboratory and with a simple and rapid technique it would be possible to obtain an objective appreciation of the time pattern of attention, habituation and other forms of learning in man.

GROUP DISCUSSION

JOUVET. In connection with the significance of the amplitude of the evoked responses in man, I would like to show you some recordings made during stereotaxic surgery on the thalamus. In three patients suffering from intractable pain before the thalamotomy, we recorded from the V.P.L. with a depth electrode somesthetic potentials evoked by mechanical stimulation of the skin (usually the contralateral forearm). When the patients, who were conscious, were paying attention to the stimuli, the evoked responses had a much higher amplitude than when the patients were not (mental calculation, auditory attention ...) In some cases, the evoked responses could disappear almost completely.

NAQUET. I think we must be very careful about the site where the stimulation of the reticular formation is effective. In this respect, I would like to mention some experiments performed by Dumont, Paillas and Hugelin (1959), and by Hugelin, Dumont and Paillas (1959), on the auditory pathways. These authors demonstrated that if an inhibition of evoked response recorded at the level of nucleus cochlearis exists in the animal 'encéphale isolé', this inhibition is not a consequence of a direct action at the level of the first relay, but the result of muscle contraction of the middle ear, induced by this stimulation. Finally, they show that if those auditory muscles are either cut off, or curarized, the response at the level of nucleus cochlearis remains constant in amplitude, but at the level of the auditory cortex it is variable according to the state of synchronization or desynchronization of the cortex. For these authors, this last finding would be due to a purely cortical phenomenon; in our laboratory, with Drs Regis, Fernández-Guardiola and Fischer-Williams: if you put a cat under flaxedil, its pupils change with blood pressure and with the state of synchronization and desynchronization of the cortex – as was shown by Bonvallet, Dell and Hiekel (1954). When the cortex presented some spindles, the pupils narrowed and the response in the optic tract or in corpus geniculatum laterale diminished in amplitude, simultaneously, at the level of the cortex, the response was enhanced and the negative waves became more ample and large and could be followed by a true slow after-discharge, having sometimes the aspect of spindles. When the cortex was desynchronized (activated cortex), the pupils were wide and the response in optic tract or corpus geniculatum laterale increased in amplitude. Simultaneously, on the cortex, the amplitude of the response diminished and its morphology was altered. The positive phase remained unchanged and decreased discreetly in amplitude. The slow negative wave was nearly totally disappearing. After atropine application, pupils being in constant mydriasis had no reaction; there is no relation between their diameter and the state of relative synchronization and desynchronization of the cortex. Evoked potentials are very large at the level of optic tract and corpus geniculatum laterale and do not vary, whatever the cortical electrographic activity. At the level of the cortex, the response followed the same variations as before application of atropine.

These data, as well as the results of Hugelin and co-workers, tend to prove that a control of specific afferences exists after the thalamic relay (as was suggested by King et al., 1956) and may play a more important role than in the first relay.

JOUVET. Investigations in man must be made with careful controls – with atropinized eyes and recording of eye movement because even a slight movement will interfere with the evoked potential at the cortical level.

It is necessary to put some atropine in the eyes and at least record movements of the eyes and eyelids by the electrogram of the blink and by the slow potential of the eyes. This is absolutely necessary because with a flash that is more than twenty centimetres from the eyeballs even a very slight eye movement would give a reduction of the visual evoked potentials.

BERGER. What effect does the frequency of the stimulus have? Regarding habituation, we have made experiments on what we have called fatigue. We exposed the eye to flashes when we thought that attention was continually fixed on the same subject. Depending on the area of the retina which was stimulated, the general fusion frequency decreased significantly during a period of between 20 and

40 minutes of exposure. I would like to know the relation between what you call habituation and fatigue.

GARCÍA-AUSTT. As to Dr Jouvet's remarks I must say that all subjects were given careful instructions beforehand, so that, throughout the experiment, they kept looking at the stroboscope. It is very unlikely that the diameter of the pupil should play an important role as the eyes were fixed on the stroboscope, stimulation was always rhythmic and at constant frequency throughout the experiment. Consequently illumination remained unchanged. The flash intensity was supra-maximal for any given pupillary diameter.

In answer to Dr Berger's questions, we worked with frequencies of 0.5-5/sec. which are very far from the fusion frequency. Between this range we did not find variations in the initial component of the evoked response. However, the after-discharge was not observed at 4-5/sec. Of course, it is not a question of fatigue. It should be mentioned that through association with other stimuli, a response may be habituated or dishabituated and this occurs without any interruption or changes in the flicker frequency.

CONDITIONNEMENT DE DECHARGES HYPER-SYNCHRONES EPILEPTIQUES CHEZ L'HOMME ET L'ANIMAL

R. Naquet

Le mécanisme reflexo-conditionné de certaines épilepsies a été supposé dès la connaissance des travaux de Pavlov. Du point de vue expérimental, Kreindler (1955) conditionne à un stimulus préalablement indifférent (son, odeur ou condition générale de l'expérience) des crises généralisées ou partielles, inconditionnellement provoquées par une injection convulsivante, ou par une stimulation électrique corticale.

Morrell et Naquet (1956) et Morrell (1957) ont étudié l'évolution d'un conditionnement son-lumière (son neutre associé à une stimulation lumineuse intermittente (SLI) chez l'animal (chat et singe), après création de lésions épileptogènes corticales par injection de crème d'alumine. Lorsque la lésion occupait la partie postérieure du gyrus lateralis (chat) ou la région occipitale (singe), le stimulus lumineux inconditionnel faisait apparaître des décharges hypersynchrones généralisées, qui avaient une fréquence indépendante de celle du stimulus inconditionnel et qui pouvaient se poursuivre après sa cessation sous la forme d'une 'post-décharge'. Ces décharges étaient généralisées d'emblée, ou débutaient au niveau du cortex lésé, elles étaient favorisées par l'état de synchronisation du tracé et étaient bloquées par tout stimulus d'éveil.

Au cours des expériences de conditionnement, ils ont constaté que le blocage conditionné (*generalized conditional activation pattern and localized conditional activation pattern*) était plus difficilement obtenu du côté de la lésion, et que les décharges répétitives (*conditional repetitive responses*) apparaissaient de façon plus nette de ce même côté et surtout que la décharge hypersynchrone généralisée (*paroxysmal hypersynchronous response*) pouvait également survenir pendant le stimulus conditionnel ou en l'absence du stimulus inconditionnel.

Naquet et Morrell (1956) chez l'animal normal (chat) comme chez celui porteur d'une lésion occupant le gyrus lateralis ont également noté que l'injection progressive de cardiazol pouvait faciliter l'apparition et le 'conditionnement' de décharges hypersynchrones analogues: en effet, la stimulation lumineuse intermittente provoque sous l'effet du cardiazol des décharges hypersynchrones qui revêtent l'aspect de véritables pointe-ondes généralisés auto-entretenus. Au cours des expériences de conditionnement, si l'on utilise la S.L.I. comme stimulus inconditionnel, ces décharges de pointe-ondes peuvent apparaître pendant le stimulus conditionnel et prendre la place du blocage généralisé ou local qui les précédait. Leur apparition pendant l'application dépend naturellement du niveau d'imprégnation cardiazolique. Pour un niveau trop élevé, la réponse n'est pas différenciable et apparaît pour un stimulus de toute autre nature, et il n'est plus alors question de parler de réponse conditionnée. Qu'il s'agisse de lésions occipitales ou d'injection de cardiazol, les auteurs arrivaient, dès 1956, à la conclusion qu'il y avait une certaine opposition entre les phénomènes de blocage conditionné et l'apparition conditionnelle de ces décharges hypersynchrones, celles-ci n'étant possible que pendant une dépression du 'système d'éveil.'

Chez l'Homme, Gastaut, Regis, Dongier et Roger (1956) publiaient deux observations de malades porteurs d'une épilepsie généralisée de type 'Petit Mal' photosensible caractérisée du point de vue EEGraphique par des décharges de pointe-ondes apparaissant spontanément et favorisées par la S.L.I. Au cours d'expériences reflexo-conditionnées où un stimulus conditionnel était représenté par un bruit continu et un stimulus inconditionnel par une lumière intermittente capable d'engendrer des paroxysmes de pointe-onde, le stimulus conditionnel pouvait faire apparaître des décharges de pointe-ondes généralisées au bout de la 20ème présentation de la lumière, alors que le blocage conditionné était apparu dès les premières.

Plus récemment, Stevens (1959) a rapporté les résultats obtenus au cours d'expériences de conditionnement analogues chez quatre sujets présentant des décharges hypersynchrones de pointe-ondes provoquées par une lumière intermittente: Après 10 à 15 présentations du stimulus conditionnel (son) couplé avec le stimulus inconditionnel (S.L.I.) un stimulus nouveau (son différent) était présenté sans lumière. Chez aucun de ces sujets l'auteur n'a pu mettre en évidence de conditionnement des décharges de pointe-ondes; ces décharges, en revanche, survenaient plus fréquemment pendant le stimulus non renforcé. L'auteur conclut que les réponses à type de pointe-ondes ne pouvaient être conditionnées, mais que la différenciation, l'extinction et les phénomènes de trace, augmentaient leur fréquence: conditions que Pavlov désignait comme favorisant l'inhibition interne ou conditionnée, laquelle permettrait l'apparition des crises.

Dans le Laboratoire de Neurobiologie de Marseille (Professeur Gastaut) une étude similaire était entreprise par Naquet, Infante et Fernandez-

Guardiola. Cette étude est basée sur vingt quatre sujets épileptiques ou non, d'âges variant entre dix et cinquante ans. Tous présentaient en commun des décharges de pointe-ondes généralisées induites par la S.L.I. ayant une fréquence propre, indépendante de celle de la S.L.I. et cessant avec elle ou pouvant se prolonger plus ou moins longtemps après elle (une à plusieurs secondes).[1]

Parmi eux, douze sujets présentaient en outre des décharges de pointe-ondes identiques, au repos ou pendant l'épreuve de l'hyperpnée, indépendantes de la S.L.I. alors que les douze autres n'en présentaient, exclusivement, que pendant la S.L.I. Enfin, quinze sujets présentaient un très important entraînement à la S.L.I., six un discret, et trois pratiquement pas.

Toutes ces expériences ont été réalisées de la façon suivante: le stimulus inconditionnel était représenté par une S.L.I. d'une durée de deux secondes environ utilisée avec une fréquence capable d'induire une décharge de pointe-ondes localisée dans les régions postérieures ou généralisée. Cette stimulation était répétée toutes les vingt secondes, le temps étant donc utilisé comme stimulus conditionnel. La S.L.I. a été présentée au moins 20 fois et parfois jusqu'à 100 fois chez chaque sujet. Les stimulations répétées à intervalles rapprochés étant destinées à favoriser le développement de l'inhibition interne.

RESULTATS

Au cours de ce travail ont été étudiées les modifications de l'activité de fond, celles de la réponse inconditionnelle et celles de la réponse conditionnelle.

(A) Modifications à l'activité de fond.

Chez la plupart des sujets, le rythme alpha se renforce progressivement et s'il existe des fréquences lentes dans le tracé de repos, elles se développent.

Les décharges spontanées de pointe-ondes, si elles sont présentes antérieurement voient leur nombre augmenter, leur durée s'allonger.

Ces modifications qui s'installent progressivement sont parfois brutalement remplacées par une accélération de fréquence des rythmes chez des sujets qui se lassent de l'expérience ou qui sont gênés par des conditions extérieures (inhibition externe).

(B) Les modifications de la réponse au stimulus inconditionnel.

1. L'entraînement à la S.L.I.

L'entraînement est d'autant plus ample que les rythmes de fond du

---

[1] Ces décharges s'accompagnaient soit d'une absence Petit Mal typique, soit d'une myoclonie; elles pouvaient être infracliniques.

sujet sont mieux synchronisés, il tend donc à augmenter d'amplitude et à irradier en dehors de la région postérieure, au cours de l'évolution de l'expérience.

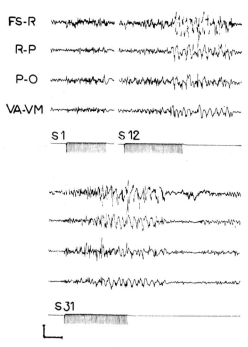

FIG. I

Modifications de la décharge de pointe-ondes induite par le stimulus inconditionnel (stimulation lumineuse intermittente) au cours d'une expérience de conditionnement.

Calibration: amplitude 100 microvolts; vitesse 1 cm. 5 par seconde. Enregistrement bipolaire. FS: frontale supérieure; R: rolandique; P: pariétale; O: occipitale; VA: vertex antérieur; VM: vertex moyen; S: signal.

La première présentation de la lumière (S.1) ne provoque pas de décharge de pointe-ondes. Pour le douzième essai (S.12) la décharge apparaît quelques secondes après la présentation de la lumière. Pour le 31ème assai (S.31) la décharge de pointe-ondes apparaît encore plus tôt.

2. La décharge de pointe-onde généralisée.

La décharge de pointe-onde apparaît plus précocement par rapport au début de l'application du stimulus inconditionnel au fur et à mesure que l'expérience se déroule. Lorsque la décharge de pointe-ondes ne siégeait au début que dans les régions postérieures elle tend à se généraliser. Elle est de plus longue durée, c'est-à-dire que lorsque la décharge est auto-entretenue, elle se continue plus longtemps après la cessation de la S.L.I. (Fig. 1).

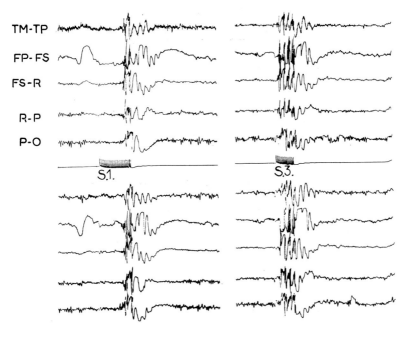

Fig. 2A

Provocation d'une décharge critique focalisée au cours d'une expérience de conditionnement, chez un sujet de 15 ans présentant une épilepsie de type myoclonique.

Calibration: amplitude 100 microvolts; vitesse 1 cm. 5 par seconde. Enregistrement bipolaire. TM: temporale moyenne; TP; temporale postérieure; FP: frontale polaire; FS: frontale supérieure; R: rolandique; P: pariétale; O: occipitale; S: signal. Les 5 premières lignes du tracé correspondent à l'hemisphère droit, et les 5 dernières à l'hémisphère gauche.

La première présentation de la lumière (S.1) provoque une décharge de pointe-ondes généralisée qui apparaît avec un certain retard. La troisième présentation de la lumière (S.3) provoque l'apparition d'une décharge de pointe-ondes généralisée apparaîssant immédiatement après l'application du stimulus lumineux.

Noter que dans les deux cas la décharge de pointe-ondes n'est suivie d'aucun phénomène paroxystique focalisé.

Quoiqu'il n'existe pas de rapport exact, entre la décharge de pointe-ondes et l'état de synchronisation ou de désynchronisation du tracé, il est possible d'affirmer que les pointe-ondes tendent à diminuer lorsque le sujet devient anxieux et gêné et que la fréquence de son tracé s'accélère.

3. L'apparition de crises focalisées.

Dans neuf cas sur vingt quatre, des décharges de pointes rythmiques ont apparu. Dans un cas il s'agissait d'une crise généralisée d'emblée suivant une longue décharge de pointe-ondes également généralisée déclenchée par la trente septième présentation de la lumière. Cette crise électro-

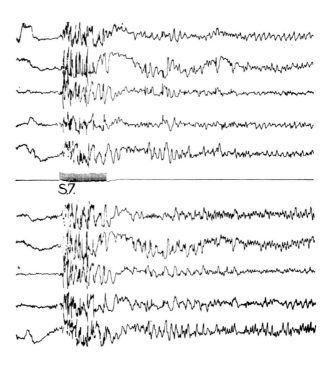

FIG. 2B (suite du 2A)

La septième présentation de la lumière (S.7) provoque une décharge de polypointe-ondes généralisée accompagnée de myoclonies. Elle est suivie après l'arrêt de la S.L.I. d'une décharge de pointes rythmiques rapides occupant la région temporo-occipitale de l'hémisphère gauche.

Pendant ce temps le sujet présente quelques phosphènes et dévie les yeux à droite.

graphique s'accompagnait du point de vue clinique d'une crise Grand Mal typique.

Chez huit sujets, il s'agissait de décharges critiques de pointes rythmiques survenant soit une fois, soit plusieurs fois (jusqu'à huit à dix au cours d'une même séance) soit sur un hémisphère, soit sur les deux, soit tantôt sur l'un, tantôt sur l'autre. Ces décharges étaient focalisées et occupaient en général le carrefour des régions temporale postérieure, pariétale et occipitale (Fig. 2 A et B). Elles pouvaient rester localisées à cette région ou irradier progressivement en avant et se généraliser. Elles pouvaient être parfaitement infracliniques ou s'accompagner de phénomènes visuels (phosphènes ou hémianopsie) même chez les sujets qui n'avaient jamais présenté de crises de cette sorte auparavant. Lorsqu'elles irradiaient en avant, le sujet présentait des hémiclonies suivies ou non d'une crise généralisée. Ces crises apparaissaient rarement dès l'application des premiers stimuli mais plutôt, après plusieurs présentations de la lumière (à partir de la 8ème ou 10ème), lorsque les décharges de pointe-ondes augmentaient d'amplitude, ainsi que l'entraînement à la lumière et que l'ensemble du tracé tendait à se ralentir. Elles ne sont survenues que chez les sujets qui présentaient un très important entraînement à la lumière (neuf sur quinze), jamais chez les autres; elles sont apparues, qu'il existe des pointe-ondes spontanés et provoqués par la lumière, ou seulement provoqués par la lumière.

(C) Les modifications de la réponse au stimulus conditionnel.

1. Pendant les deux secondes qui précédent l'application du stimulus inconditionnel, très rapidement, (entre la 3ème et la 6ème présentation de la lumière) chez tous les sujets, il a été possible de noter une désynchronisation généralisée des tracés (*blocage conditionné généralisé*) (Fig. 3B), avec disparition des ondes lentes et blocage d'une décharge de pointe-ondes, si elle existait spontanément. Ce phénomène plus ou moins durable, varie selon le moment de l'expérience, c'est-à-dire qu'il peut disparaître après deux ou trois combinaisons pour réapparaître après une quinzaine de combinaisons, disparaître à nouveau et réapparaître. Dans six cas sur vingt quatre, une désynchronisation uniquement limitée à la région occipitale (*blocage conditionné localisé*) a pu être affirmée de façon indiscutable (Fig. 3C).

Dans seize cas sur vingt quatre, un renforcement du rythme alpha ou l'apparition d'ondes lentes soit généralisées, soit plutôt localisées à la seule région occipitale a été nettement constaté. En général, ce phénomène apparaît après de nombreuses présentations de la lumière (à partir de quinze environ) lorsque tout phénomène d'activation a disparu, mais il n'existe pas de règle absolue. Par exemple chez un même sujet une désynchronisation généralisée est toujours possible vers la trentième présentation de la lumière, alors qu'une désynchronisation localisée était constatée à la 10ème, et des ondes lentes à la 12ème.

2. Dans aucun cas, il n'a été possible d'enregistrer pendant le stimulus

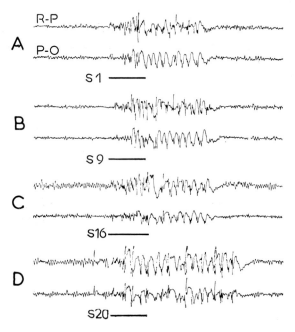

FIG. 3

Modifications des tracés dans l'espace de temps qui précède immédiatement l'application du stimulus inconditionnel, chez un sujet de 20 ans présentant une épilepsie de type 'Petit Mal absence' spontanée et favorisée par la lumière.

Calibration: amplitude 100 microvolts, vitesse 1 cm. 5 par seconde. Enregistrement bipolaire. R: rolandique; P: pariétale; O: occipitale; S: signal. La S.L.I. est représentée par un trait noir continu.

(A) Lors du premier essai (S.1) la S.L.I. provoque une décharge de pointe-ondes généralisée visible sur les deux canaux choisis pour la figure.

(B) Pour le 9ème essai (S.9) un aplatissement généralisé des tracés apparaît avant la présentation de la S.L.I.

(C) Pour le 16ème essai (S.16) l'aplatissement du tracé est simplement localisé à la région la plus postérieure du scalp.
Noter que les rythmes de fond se sont amplifiés dans l'intervalle des stimulations.

(D) Pour le 20ème essai (S.20) apparaît une décharge hypersynchrone juste avant l'application de la S.L.I.
Noter que les rythmes de fond sont toujours plus amples qu'au début de l'expérience et qu'ils se sont ralentis par rapport à ceux notés en C.

conditionnel, l'entraînement de la réponse occipitale (*repetitive response*) induite par le stimulus inconditionnel.

3. Dans sept cas sur vingt quatre sujets utilisés, des décharges de pointe-ondes ont été enregistrées pendant les deux secondes qui précédaient l'application du stimulus inconditionnel (Figs. 4 et 5). Il est à noter, que ces sept sujets présentaient dans leurs tracés de repos des décharges analogues

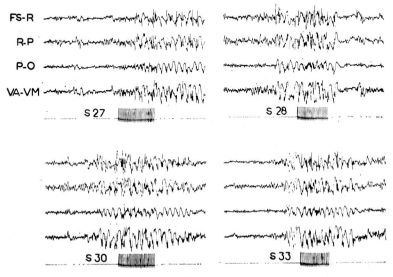

FIG. 4

Apparition de décharges de pointe-ondes généralisées immédiatement avant l'application du stimulus inconditionnel. Continuation de l'expérience notée sur la figure 3.

Calibration: amplitude 100 microvolts, vitesse 1 cm. 5 par seconde. Enregistrement bi-polaire. FS: frontale supérieure; R: rolandique; P: pariétale; O: occipitale; VA: vertex antérieur; VM: vertex moyen; S: signal.

Pour la 27ème présentation de la lumière (S.27) il n'existe pratiquement pas de modifica-tions électrographiques dans les secondes qui précèdent.

Les 28ème-30ème et 33ème présentations de la S.L.I. (S.28, S.30, S.33) sont précédées deux secondes avant d'une décharge de pointe-ondes généralisée.

et qu'elles ne sont jamais apparues chez ceux qui n'en avaient qu'à la S.L.I. Lorsque ces décharges apparaissent, il est possible de les voir se répéter pendant plusieurs stimulations successives, alors qu'elles n'existent pas dans leur intervalle. Elles ne surviennent cependant qu'après de nombreuses présentations de la lumière, en général, à partir de la quin-zième; elles disparaissent lorsque le tracé s'accélère sous l'influence d'une inhibition externe.

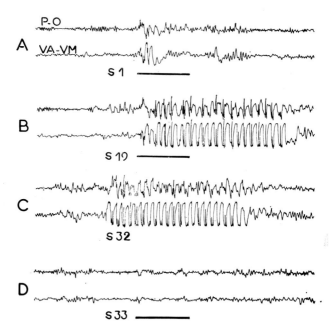

FIG. 5

Apparition d'une décharge de pointe-ondes immédiatement avant l'application du stimulus inconditionnel chez un sujet de 14 ans atteint d'absence de type Petit Mal, survenant spontanément et provoquée par la S.L.I.

Calibration: amplitude 100 microvolts, vitesse 1 cm. 5 par seconde. Enregistrement bipolaire. P: pariétale; O: occipitale; VA: vertex antérieur; VM: vertex moyen; S: signal.

(A) La première présentation de la lumière (S.1) provoque une brève décharge de pointe-ondes prédominant autour du vertex.

(B) La 19ème présentation (S.19) provoque une décharge de pointe-ondes généralisée auto-entretenue, ne cessant pas avec la stimulation lumineuse. Noter qu'elle est immédiatement précédée d'une bouffée d'ondes lentes prédominant dans la région postérieure.

(C) 2 secondes avant la 32ème présentation (S.32) apparaît une décharge de pointe-ondes généralisée analogue à celle rencontrée parfois spontanément, parfois provoquée par la S.L.I. Le stimulus inconditionnel (S.L.I.) n'est pas présenté au sujet.

(D) À la stimulation suivante le tracé est à nouveau rapide, et la 33ème présentation (S.33) ne provoque aucun phénomène paroxystique.

CONCLUSIONS

Ces résultats permettent de tirer les conclusions suivantes:

(*a*) La répétition du stimulus inconditionnel augmente les réponses évoquées par la S.L.I. en même temps qu'elle favorise l'apparition des décharges hypersynchrones paroxystiques à type de pointe-ondes et celle de crises focalisées.

Ces résultats sont dûs très probablement au fait que la technique expérimentale utilisée facilite le développement d'une inhibition interne de répétition ou habituation déjà visible sur les tracés de repos. En effet tout phénomène qui tend à augmenter la synchronisation physiologique des tracés augmente l'amplitude des potentiels évoqués corticaux induits par une stimulation lumineuse intermittente (Naquet et Pruvot, 1956) et favorise l'apparition des décharges de pointe-ondes généralisées alors que toute activation corticale aura tendance à les bloquer, comme cela est admis depuis plusieurs années chez l'Homme et a été démontré expérimentalement chez l'Animal (Naquet, Drossopoulo et Salamon, 1956).

Si les décharges critiques focalisées peuvent apparaître en dehors de toute expérience de conditionnement (Naquet, Fegersten, Bert et Carcassonne-Mottez, 1959), et sont dûes à l'arrivée d'afférences spécifiques dans une aire occipitale hyperexcitable, toute condition qui permettra l'augmentation d'amplitude des potentiels évoqués accroitra les possibilités de déclenchement d'une crise par une S.L.I.

Ces conditions semblent être réunies dans cette série expérimentale chez les sujets qui présentaient spontanément une réponse exagérée à la lumière et chez lesquels le système d'éveil est mis au repos par la répétition rapprochée de la S.L.I. Il est donc nécessaire de faire jouer dans le déclenchement de crises focalisées induites par des afférences visuelles chez l'Homme (véritable "épilepsie de Clementi") un rôle prédominant aux afférences spécifiques, sans négliger cependant l'état des systèmes non spécifiques.

(*b*) Au cours de ces expériences, les phénomènes de blocage généralisé et localisé mis en évidence chez l'animal (Morrell et Jasper, 1956; Morrell, Naquet et Gastaut, 1957), et chez l'Homme (Gastaut et col., 1957) ont été confirmés. Seule la séquence établie par Morrell et Jasper (1956) chez l'animal n'a pas toujours été retrouvée. Il n'a pas été possible de mettre en évidence de conditionnement d'une réponse répétitive, seules des ondes lentes, localisées ou diffuses ont pu être mises en évidence dans l'intervalle qui précède le stimulus inconditionnel. Ceci tendrait à infirmer les travaux de Morrell, Naquet, Gastaut (1957) et à confirmer les travaux de Jouvet,

Benoit et Courjon (1957) chez l'animal, et ceux de Gastaut et col. (1957) ainsi que ceux de Stevens (1959) chez l'Homme.

(c) Toutes les fois qu'une réponse à type de pointe-ondes dépend exclusivement de l'arrivée d'un stimulus lumineux intermittent il n'a jamais été possible de la faire apparaître pendant le stimulus conditionnel.

En revanche, les décharges de pointe-ondes spontanées, c'est-à-dire celles qui existent en dehors d'une stimulation lumineuse intermittente, et ne sont que facilitées par elle, tendent à apparaître pendant le stimulus conditionnel. Mais à l'inverse des phénomènes de blocage qui surviennent très rapidement, ces décharges n'apparaissent qu'après un certain nombre de présentations, lorsque les processus d'inhibition se sont développés; en dehors de l'inhibition interne de répétition déjà signalée, le fait que cette inhibition soit beaucoup plus importante pendant le stimulus conditionnel pose le problème de la création d'une inhibition conditionnée.

Comme ce conditionnement n'apparaît que pour des décharges existant au repos on peut exclure qu'il a été possible de conditionner des décharges de pointe-ondes induites par la S.L.I. mais que l'on a simplement facilité l'apparition de certaines décharges pré-existantes. Le terme d'épilepsie réflexo-conditionnée post-afferentielle ne peut donc s'appliquer aux phénomènes que nous avons obtenus.

Enfin la facilitation des décharges pendant le stimulus conditionné, chez les sujets qui en présentaient spontanément, nous semble également la conséquence d'un phénomène de synchronisation à point de départ cortical localisé (région occipitale) ou sous-corticale (thalamus ou formation réticulée mésencéphalique). Les phénomènes de blocage conditionné empêchent en revanche l'apparition de ces décharges de pointe-ondes, comme tous les phénomènes d'activation précédemment décrits.

Ces faits autorisent donc à parler plutôt (en ce qui conçerne les résultats expérimentaux présentés) de conditionnement d'un état favorisant l'apparition d'une décharge épileptique que de parler de conditionnement de cette même décharge.

SUMMARY

The first chapter is concerned with the analysis of material published in recent years on the use of reflexo-conditioned techniques (tone and light) in the triggering of discharges of an epileptic form in man and animals.

The second chapter is devoted to an analysis of the results obtained recently with these techniques, in the Laboratoire de Neurobiologie of Marseille, on subjects presenting generalized spike-and-wave discharges induced by intermittent photic stimuli (I.P.S.).

(*a*) Repetitive unconditioned stimulation increases the responses evoked by I.P.S. at the same time as it favours the appearance of paroxystic hypersynchronous discharges of spike-and-wave form, as well as focalized seizures in the occipital region.

(*b*) In the course of these experiments, generalized and localized phenomena of blockage have been confirmed. The conditioning of a repetitive response could not be evidenced, localized or diffuse slow waves were found in the intervals preceding the unconditional stimulus.

(*c*) Every time that a spontaneous spike-and-wave discharge depended exclusively on the I.P.S., it was never possible to provoke it during a conditional stimulus. On the contrary, the spontaneous spike-and-wave discharges existing outside the I.P.S. and which are not facilitated by it, tend to appear during the conditional stimulus. But conversely to these phenomena of blockage, which happen very quickly, these discharges appear only after a certain number of presentations.

In the last chapter, the author discusses all these phenomena and particularly the conditioning of the spike-and-wave discharges.

Conclusion: As this conditioning appears only in discharges existing at rest, it is possible to exclude that with these techniques one could condition spike-and-wave discharges induced by I.P.S. One can simply facilitate the appearance of some pre-existing discharges. Therefore, the term 'reflexo-conditional, post-afferential epilepsy' cannot be applied to phenomena as described above, because it seems that it concerns mainly the conditioning of a state which favours the appearance of epileptic discharges, and not the conditioning of this discharge.

GROUP DISCUSSION

MAGOUN. Dr Naquet's presentation emphasizes the role of conditional processes in the prevention and facilitation of cortical seizures. There is a recent paper on this subject by Effren, in which the patient had an uncinate seizure which commenced with an olfactory aura. When a strong odour was presented to the patient each time she felt the aura, further progress of the seizure was blocked. After a sufficient number of such progress, the patient was able to block the progress of an incipient seizure simply by thinking about this strong odour. One might interpret this as a conditioned blockade or inhibition of an incipient seizure. — I wonder whether your being able to manipulate these seizures with conditioning methods might be used therapeutically in selected cases.

NAQUET. My idea was indeed to show a means for preventing the appearance of diffuse or focalized epileptic discharges, or on the contrary to facilitate them. It seems, that, when a conditioning experiment is performed, and that a fit accompanied by generalized spike-and-wave discharges is concerned, the positive phenomena are accompanied by desynchronization of records which prevent the appearance of discharges. When a phenomenon of inhibition appears (induced by habituation or by a conditioning process), a synchronization may favour spike-and-wave discharges.

It is then possible by this technique to prevent or facilitate critical discharges. But as we see, these different states of synchronization and desynchronization of the record are variable and do not depend on the conditioning alone. Therefore, it seems difficult to me to apply, actually, this technique to therapeutics, at least in cases which are not preceded by an aura, and of which the onset is unknown to the patient.

SEGUNDO. Do you think that conditioned facilitation of seizures would act only to a certain extent and within certain limits of discharges 'intensity' as is known to be the case with central brain stem influence upon cortical strychnine spikes? (Arduini and Lairy-Bounes, 1952).

NAQUET. I think so — I demonstrated with Drossopoulos and Salamon (1956) the following phenomenon: after intravenous injection of Metrazol or Megimide in a cat, generalized spike-and-wave discharges are produced. According to the dose of convulsivant injected, it is possible to obtain different effects after electrical stimulation of the reticular formation or sciatic nerve: (a) with feeble doses, the stimulation of the reticular formation is able to stop the generalized discharges, which appear spontaneously or after sensory stimulations; (b) with greater doses, the stimulation threshold necessary to stop them increases, and just before the appearance of generalized seizure, the reticular formation stimulation becomes unable to stop them, and only a mere modification of the shape of the discharge is obtained.

CHOW. How can this conditioning of repetitive discharge be explained on a neuronal basis? We found that in cats with lesions of the anterior part of the thalamus, the conditioned repetitive discharge is very easily established. If you destroy some areas of the cortex and if the lesion is big enough, you cannot establish conditioned repetitive discharge.

NAQUET. It is difficult to reach any conclusion on the significance of the conditioned repetitive discharge. Perhaps we are facilitating the appearance of some rhythms existing before on the cortex. I do not know what the mechanism is, but I agree with you as to the possibility of the cortical origin of these rhythmical phenomena. For example, when repetitive responses appear at the level of the cortex in animals it may mean that the experimenter has used frequencies, ordinarily found at the level of the cortex and that he has obtained conditions which facilitate those frequencies more than others. It is interesting to note that it concerns mostly some slow frequencies similar to focalized true spindles, and able afterwards to become generalized. This fact results from experiments we made with Morrell, after having provoked cortical irritative lesions, as well as from recent experiments on the recruiting response just realized together with Fischer-Williams and Fernandez-Guardiola on anoxia.

MORRELL. This repetitive response is especially apparent when there is evidence of a decrease of reticular discharge to the cortex, i.e. when it is synchronized rather than desynchronized. This represents then a hypersynchronous activity in cortical cells rather than in deeper structures. We have done experiments with unilateral epileptogenic lesions. In those experiments under electro-cortical conditioning we often found repetitive discharges on the side of the lesion and at the same time de-synchronization on the opposite side.

García-Austt. In my experience the possibility of modifying the seizure takes place within a certain range of intensity, judged by the frequency of the spikes and the amplitude. If the spikes are not too frequent, central brain stem excitation may block them, but if the seizure has a certain degree of intensity then you cannot block it by reticular stimulation. I would like to ask whether you tried to develop an inhibitory stimulus and if this stimulus was capable of inhibiting the discharge.

Naquet. In the cat we were able to block the discharge by some negative tone. I did not try it on man.

García-Austt. Another point is that the patient learned to produce seizure discharge, a phenomenon of which he was not conscious. Now, it is hard to conceive learning without a certain degree of consciousness. How would you interpret this contradiction if there is not an intermediate mechanism that could be activated by the flicker?

Naquet. The patients are not unconscious when we use light and during the spike-and-waves discharge. They may have the discharge without any impairment of consciousness. Regarding the development of inhibition, our experiments with lesions in cats and some results we have in man with this type of experiment, may prove that inhibition may start in the cortex rather than in some other subcortical structure.

HEBB. I should like to make two comments on your first group of topics.

The first is that, to the best of my understanding, our agreement on the question of the congenital or the instinctive is very good. There are difficulties of terminology and probably still imperfect communication but so far as I can understand, we have not been saying different things. There is not a head-on conflict.

The second point concerns the distinction that Lashley made in 1938 between reflex and instinct. I think it is most important to recognize that instinctive behaviour is not a complication of reflexes only. Reflexive behaviour depends on specific receptors and effectors, whereas instinctive behaviour is something which is not definable in such terms. It is not itself to be described as a series of reflexes alone.

THORPE. May I say that I entirely agree with what Dr Hebb has just said. I think that this meeting has not revealed any major disagreement about concepts so I don't think much would be gained by attempting a general discussion of innate behaviour now. But there are aspects of innate patterns which are relevant to our present meeting, and one that interests me very much is the origin of patterns of nervous discharge, i.e. the neurophysiological aspect of innate behaviour.

But first I would like to refer again to a general point which I made earlier in this meeting, and that is that the best way to decide whether we are concerned with instinctive patterns of behaviour or with learned ones is to consider the origin of complexity. Where does the complexity of the behaviour come from? If we can see the necessary complexity of the input from the environment then we are provisionally justified in assuming that it has been learned. If there is complexity in the behaviour pattern which is not seen in the immediate, or indeed the whole, previous experience of the individual animal – then we have to assume that this complexity comes from somewhere else, and it can only have come from the inborn organization of the animal. That seems to me to be a valuable method of deciding whether we are talking about something which has been learned, or something that is instinctive.

FESSARD. I also think this an essential distinction but not an easy one to be made in practice. A reflex is an operation in which we can clearly define a stimulus S and a response R, the response thus appearing as a function of the stimulus. But of course, it is also a function of some unknown internal factors which we could call X for instance, and the question of what is a reflex and what is not depends on the importance of X.

Even in the simplest reflex there are determining factors which come from the organism and which are inborn or instinctive. On the other hand, in what we call instinctive response, there are at every instant internal stimuli which have a reflexo-genic power. The distinction between inborn patterns of X factors and actual internal stimuli X is not so easy to make and there are many controversies about this point. I don't mean, however, that we should not make some distinction be-tween reflex and instinct.

ANOKHIN. I agree with Dr Thorpe: the complexity of the inborn nervous structures is the basis for inborn behaviour. We have devoted our research pre-cisely to the mechanisms whereby this complexity emerges. A study of the develop-ing structures of the nervous system of the embryo has shown that they mature and establish between themselves synaptic connections in a highly selective way and fully in conformity with the type of behavioural act which is essential to the newborn of a given species, and at the time when it is necessary.

Thus, for instance, the descending tract of fibres, arising from the tegmentum of the human foetus, when there are not yet any other descending tracts, reaches the 8th cervical segment and establishes there synaptic connections with precisely the motor neurones of the anterior horns, which innervate the deep flexors of the fingers of the hand. In turn, the nerves originating from the cervical cord of the shoulder, innervating the flexors of the fingers, are myelinized earlier than the other nerves of the same level. All these phenomena contribute to the rapid emergence of the grasping reflex in the human foetus which is the first definite behavioural act in the 4th month of its prenatal development. Such heterochrony is even more clearly observed in the growth of structures and in the emergence of functions in birds of different oecologies.

Whereas in the chick hatching out of the egg there is an accelerated differentia-tion of the motor elements of the lumbar region of the spinal chord, in the rook this accelerated differentiation of the neurones affects first the segments of the shoulder cervical region. Thus the accelerated maturation of the nervous structures progresses in exact correspondence with the functions which are the first ones to be essential in relation to the characteristics of the oecology of that animal. This can also be seen, for instance, in the fact that in the organs of Corti of the foetus of the rook there develop precisely those receptor elements which correspond to the cry of the adult bird: 'Kr ... r ... r ... a ... ' (this can be observed through a special acoustic analysis). This accelerated, selective, oecology-conditioned development of the nervous structures, has been named by us *systemo-genesis* since specific functional systems of the organism develop progressively and in a selective way.

It is obvious that all these reactions are truly inborn since, admittedly, the new-born has not yet had time for any learning.

EIBL. ROEDER (1955) pointed out that there is no basic difference between instinc-tive and reflex behaviour as far as the neural elements underlying such behaviour are concerned. Different thresholds of neurones seem to make up the main differ-ence, which is a gradual one. In the stable neurones the excitability remains at a constant resting threshold. It needs a stimulus to bring the excitability to the level of discharge. After discharge the excitability falls to zero, then rises gradually again briefly passing the resting threshold. After this phase of higher irritability it falls back to the normal resting threshold. In the unstable neurones the excitability, and with it the readiness to response, builds up until the threshold of release is reached by itself and a spontaneous discharge can take place. Between these two extremes all gradients can be found. If for example the resting and the response thresholds become approximated one stimulus can lead to a self-perpetuating sequence of discharges, as the curve of excitability will repeatedly reach the releasing threshold. Reflex behaviour always needs an input for discharge and is therefore more strictly under afferent control than the more spontaneous instinctive acts, which can go off in a vacuum. But normally they, too, are released by certain key stimuli.

ANOKHIN. When we speak of inborn behaviour, we should bear in mind that all our considerations can apply only to the very first acts of the newborn, since the first behavioural acts enrich the inborn functional systems by new afferent stimuli from the environment. In practice we never get 'inborn behaviour' in its pure form after 2 or 3 days following the birth of an animal, although the end nucleus of the reaction was included in the embryogenesis on the basis of the heterochronic growth of the nervous structures.

This rule applies to such specific human behaviour as for instance the human mimic reactions. As our research has shown, as early as on the 5th or 6th month of its prenatal life, the human foetus is able to react to external stimuli by quite diverse mimetic reactions.

The emotional quality of these reactions is so well determined that there can be no doubt in the observer's mind: 'this is unpleasant!', 'it hurts!'

FESSARD. I think the use, or for some the abuse, of this expression 'inborn behaviour' is also a question of doctrinal position. Our colleagues from Eastern countries have the view some of us find too extreme that animal behaviour is entirely determined by the stimuli — either external or internal — present at every moment. Most of us prefer making a sharp distinction between what comes from the outside world and what depends upon a set of internal incitations organized according to an inborn, and, so to speak, ever present pattern of dynamic possibilities, to which correspond certain structures within the central nervous system.

ANOKHIN. In connection with the remarks made by Dr Eibl and with the morphological assumptions on inborn behaviour, I should like to stress one physiological feature in the heterochrony and systematic maturation of the nervous structures in embryogenesis. We have been able to note the following rules: the functional system, which from the morphological point of view has been formed earlier than the other system, has a rather low threshold of excitability and therefore acts as the dominant function at that given stage of development. This means that any internal or external stimulus, however small, will indeed first of all stimulate into action the dominant functional system.

In this way the physiological predominance of the functional systems which has matured earlier than others is one of the decisive factors bringing about a high adjustment and adequate timing of inborn behaviour.

TT

Thus, for instance, in the rook at the hatching stage any external stimulus strengthens and speeds up the act of pecking. Whilst in the young bird which has already freed itself from the egg the same stimulus initiates the feeding reaction by the opening of the beak.

In this way the heredity-fixing, heterochrony growth of the nervous structures and the oecological factors of a given animal determine the perfection and accuracy of its inborn behaviour.

THORPE. Obviously an animal is continually dependent on a great many things in the environment (the oxygen supply, for instance), and if this is changed the whole behaviour pattern may go wrong. But I think we can rule out that kind of environmental factor as an adequate 'explanation' for the complexity of instinctive behaviour. I do think, however, that you have touched upon an important point in distinguishing behaviour arising from stimuli from within the nervous system, without being dependent on interoceptors, from behaviour which is dependent on interoceptors. Take behaviour which is emitted at regular intervals (a 24-hour rhythm, for instance). It seems to have been shown that such rhythms can arise in a single cell. A probable instance is provided by the cardiac ganglion of the lobster. This seems to be an important example of behaviour which is dependent neither upon interoceptors nor exteroceptors.

On the other hand, a great many instinctive behaviour patterns are undoubtedly dependent on interoceptors. I think ethologists were to blame at one stage for using the word 'endogenous' very loosely, sometimes meaning 'within the animal' and sometimes 'within the CNS', and that gave rise to much misunderstanding.

A further point: I think the distinction between instinct and reflex referred to is an important one. I think it is perfectly possible to define reflexes in such a way as to include all behaviour. But if we do that we have abandoned a very useful term which is most valuable for denoting the 'partial reflexes' of physiology. If we expand the term 'reflex' to include everything then we tend to speak so loosely that we get involved in much sterile argument about definition.

FESSARD. I think so too, in view of the importance we should give to the notion of 'trigger'. If the trigger is under close control of the environmental factors so that you can make a correspondence between the responses and the variations in the environment, then you can speak of a reflex or of a succession of reflexes. But if the trigger is not under external control and you cannot therefore anticipate what the reaction will be like then we may consider the reaction to be instinctive.

GERARD. X incorporates into itself that part of the experience of the organism which has been fixed, and therefore the reaction of the system is different at each time from what it was before. To some extent, then, any line of division is meaningless: we have a spectrum, not a series of black and white divisions. We would all agree that the inborn, congenital, and reflex mechanism, and I would think a good many of the others also, are set by the original growth — of something — and learning leaves behind a change in the permanent structural substrate, which determines particular responses of that system to given stimuli at any time. From that point of view, it seems useful to consider whether instinct is or is not a reflex. I don't recall the criteria Lashley used, but let me suggest an operational approach to this.

If we find that the behaviour of essentially all normal members of an adequate sample of some species is the same to the same external situation, then we can say that the experience of individuals has been sufficiently uniform to insure a constant response, for all individuals. I have not been specific about this experience for it includes everything that happened from the time the egg was fertilized. Normally, the experience of the 2-cell and the 8-cell and the 32-cell stages of the embryo are enormously constant from one individual to another, so the behaviour that develops is constant, and we can safely call all this, inborn constancy.

On this kind of criterion, is instinct or instinctive behaviour less determined, less reflex, if depending on inborn patterns than is what we call a spinal reflex? If it is as constant, then it might be perfectly valid to think of it as a reflex. My picture is that the emotional patterns elicited from hypothalamic animals, and the like, are just about as stereotyped and universal as the flexor or other reflexes elicited from the spinal cord.

MAGOUN. I was happy to hear Dr Fessard introduce an acknowledgement to philosophy in this discussion and would suggest that we could go back to John Locke who proposed that the mind, as this field was called in the eighteenth century, was a total blank, and that its concept were derived entirely from sensation. But he differentiated the content and responsiveness derived directly from sensation from that derived indirectly from reflection which, I think, is to say that sensation and reflection can be equated with your S and X, since reflection to Locke was the reactivation of previous sensation. In elaborating those arguments, it is of some relevance to consider the attempt to define the problem in philosophical terms at least a century before it began to be studied with physiological techniques.

FESSARD. I am surprised to see that in the course of our debate no mention has been made of 'trial and error' learning.

THORPE. I like to think of 'trial and error' learning as comprising both classical and operant (or instrumental or action) conditioning, whichever term you prefer to use. It is the two together that you almost always see co-operating in the natural learning process of a normal animal. For convenience they are isolated in laboratory experiments but they are hardly ever found isolated in nature. I think 'trial and error learning' is an invaluable term to include the two combined and I have indicated elsewhere (Thorpe, 1956, Table II, page 80) how I think this combination should be understood.

ANOKHIN. I should like to say that when we compare inborn to learned behaviour, we should bear in mind a universal rule of behaviour, which connects both inborn and learned behaviour: the rule of evaluation of the results of an act done with the help of the reverse afferent impulses received by the brain at the end of each act. It is only by this rule that the individual stages and links of instinctive behaviour can be constructed into an orderly chain of acts, leading to the final adjustment effect for a given animal.

The point is simply that for learned behaviour the system of evaluation of the results of an act done (on which I reported at this symposium) — the acceptor of action is established as a result of individual experience. Conversely, in the case of instinctive behaviour, it has been established as a result of a long philogenetic experience and has been fixed by heredity at the time of the birth of the animal.

At the present moment our theory is confirmed by new facts and we believe that it is indeed the most acceptable one to account for the mechanism of the adaptive character of inborn behaviour.

INTRODUCTION OF THE SECOND TOPIC — SPONTANEOUS BEHAVIOUR PATTERNS

THORPE. The physiological origin of patterned nervous discharges is, as I have already indicated, a problem which is fundamental to the study of behaviour. I gave the example of a single cell acting as a pace-maker. I mentioned the possibility of that being so in the cardiac ganglion of the lobster and there are a number of other instances where a single cell seems to be producing a rhythmic discharge which controls an important and complex piece of behaviour. So there, presumably, the whole mechanism for a patterned discharge is contained in a single cell. I would like to ask, then, what you regard as the normal condition for a nerve cell?

Do you think of the 'standard nerve cell' as tending to random discharge when it is not controlled; but subject at times to control by a mechanism which can either completely inhibit it or else can control it so as to produce a temporal pattern of discharge? That seems to me to be the really fundamental aspect of this problem. But in addition to that I should be extremely interested to hear the views of the various members of this symposium on the extent to which intracranial receptors (and other internal receptors) govern the discharge of nerve cells. In a slab of isolated cortex must the lack of discharge be regarded as the normal state or as a special case of inhibition? There are many other similar problems but I hope I have said enough to indicate to you the kind of thing that strikes me as so particularly important. I hope I have made myself clear, if not I can perhaps add a word or two in the discussion later.

MORRELL. I would like to raise two questions with respect to the subject of spontaneous behaviour patterns. I think one of the most striking examples of built-in behaviour patterns is that disclosed by the work of Olds in the self-stimulation experiments. In those studies it would appear that it is the precise anatomical localization of the stimulating electrode which determines whether the stimulated point will be rewarding or 'punishing'. One wonders whether these same anatomical sites have the same positive or negative significance in the newborn animal as they do in the adult. It might be interesting to see whether life experience plays some role in determining whether given anatomical regions become positively or negatively rewarding. My second question has to do with an observation that has been made repeatedly for many years in psychological studies of learning. Most of us have observed that learning curves do not really flatten out after the initial phase of acquisition but actually continue to demonstrate a considerable amount of oscillation. In our experience this is true of habituation as well as of positive learning. One wonders whether at least some portion of this oscillation is not attributable to inborn excitability cycles which might determine the degree of responsiveness possible at any given moment in time. Biological rhythms of this sort may have a wide variation in frequency ranging from months or days (circadian rhythms) to cycles of very much shorter duration. Both Dr Hernández-Peón and I have been impressed with such oscillatory systems in our studies of habituation.

HEBB. It seems to me that the meaning of the self-stimulation data is exactly opposed to that of spontaneous behaviour. The seeking for stimulation in these experiments is initiated by stimulation itself, as the learning process goes on. The nervous system acts in such a way as to produce an equivalent of external stimulation: the action being by way of behaviour, by bar pressing.

OLDS. I am not sure that I would come to exactly the same conclusion as Dr Hebb. I think particularly relevant here is the case where we were reinforcing unit discharges rather than reinforcing the overt response. In either case, though, let me point out, that the response had to be omitted first, in order to be reinforced. We really have in a sense two problems here of the spontaneous or the innate, first that the original response has to be in the repertory and has to occur by chance or 'reflex' before it can be reinforced; second that in the structure of our organism there has to be a hypothalamic mechanism or a system of hypothalamic mechanisms which, when stimulated, will either cause the previous behaviour to be repeated or, in one way or another, cause the animal to come back for more. That is to say two things have to be here prior to learning: one is the spontaneous response and the second is the hypothalamic reinforcement mechanism whatever we postulate it to be.

One of the other points that I would like to put on record: The hypothalamic reinforcement system appears to be an innately differentiated mechanism; i.e. anatomically divided into functional groups. As an example I would cite the precise anatomical determination of self-stimulation rates. We are sure, in the rat, that by far the greater part of the variance in self-stimulation rate is accounted for by the placement of the electrodes.

Let me now go on with the concept of reinforcement here. The behaviour occurs spontaneously and there excitation in the hypothalamus occurs; at this point something has to happen to the previous behaviour, or shall we say to the structure in the organisms which somehow produces that behaviour or elicits that behaviour — it must somehow become stronger, more frequent or what have you. I am greatly tempted, and perhaps it is solely a matter of preference from these recent studies on the reinforcement of single-unit discharges, and from the apparent phenomenon that we sometimes elicit the unit discharge, say by the pressure of introduction of the wire, and then reinforce it, to hope, I will not say to suppose, only to guess that the unit itself, the spontaneous unit discharge, is something which can be reinforced. That is, that there is a spontaneous discharge pattern which has a certain probabilistic rate and that this can be augmented by stimulating the hypothalamus after the response has occurred in a fashion that you would not get if you stimulated the hypothalamus at some different time.

ANOKHIN. In connection with the problem of the so-called 'spontaneous behaviour', I should like to draw the attention to those forms of behaviour which depend on the presence of nervous cells with a specialized metabolism. At the present time it can be agreed that certain cells of the hypothalamus and of the midbrain have a metabolic process which from the chemical point of view is quite accurate and specific. Indeed, the slightest departure from this specific metabolism leads to the release of a 'trigger' and to the outburst of nervous impulses which are already spreading within the limits of given functional systems. It will suffice to mention the cells of the respiratory centre or the receptor formations of the sinocarotid region, which fire as a result of a slight increase of CO_2 in the blood.

Even more surprising is that nervous mechanism which is 'tuned' to the level of the osmotic pressure of the blood.

As it has been shown, one finds in the hypothalamus nervous cells which by all their construction are adjusted to perceive the slightest changes in the osmotic pressure of the blood. Special vesicles, representing part of these nervous cells, react to the variations of the osmotic pressure of the blood by diminishing or expanding their volume; these variations in volume bring about an emergence and dissemination of nervous impulses. We know that these impulses often belong to one or two cells and can have a rather widespread influence leading for instance to a feeling of thirst and to setting in action important mechanisms of the body, which lead to quenching this thirst. These cells, which are rather few in number, act as 'servo-mechanisms' in the true sense of the word, transmitting small energetic variations in the effort of the whole organism with all its muscular power.

Numerous behavioural acts are constructed according to this pattern, i.e. by setting in action nervous elements having a rather specialized metabolism. Unfortunately we, as neurophysiologists, do not pay sufficient attention to this chemical specialization in the metabolic process of individual nervous cells, whereas many forms of the so-called 'spontaneous behaviour' are connected to this characteristic of the neuro-humoral transmitting mechanisms.

HEBB. I will speak directly to the point of self-stimulation. I think we have a tendency to assume that self-stimulation is the same as excitation. I noticed that the two words are used synonymously very often. And this is relevant to the third point, as a matter of fact, in asking about the spontaneous discharge, and whether the cell is inhibited or excited in many of these conditions of learning. You will remember perhaps that in reply to an earlier question Dr Olds said that he thought that self-stimulation, at least in learning, must be a jamming of the normal activities. Now I would think that at the present time we are not certain what action on nerve units our system of self-stimulation has. One thing is to define the stimulation from the point of view of behaviour because it results in a behaviour, but I think it is important for us to realize that this behaviour might be the result of jamming one mechanism and releasing another. And it is very clear to us, and we can give several examples in which stimulation sometimes elicits that kind of behaviour, sometimes it prevents this kind of behaviour. And I think we can frequently get off the track by assuming immediately that self-stimulation, or any other sort of stimulation, is necessarily excitation. It might be excitation in behavioural terms but in neural terms it might be inhibition or jamming.

OLDS. We are surprised how often cortical units that we try to reinforce appear to be inhibited by stimulation of the very hypothalamic areas which cause self-stimulation. We are sure from proximal recording in the hypothalamus that hypothalamic units, have, of course, their firing rate augmented. That is, we can elicit proximal hypothalamic units, which is not surprising, nevertheless we are probably disrupting patterns. My own conception of the disruption experiments is precisely that while the stimulation of these hypothalamic mechanisms to excessive discharge causes repetition of the preceding behaviour and I think leads to organization of positive reinforcement mechanisms, at the same time it causes disruption of the spontaneous patterns which are there, and I think thereby confusion ensues whenever acuity in a learning situation is required. This is of course theoretical.

MYERS: I should like to respond to Dr Morrell's earlier comments regarding oscillation in learned behaviour. Dr Morrell described a kind of instability or variation in the level of sustained performance in some of his animals. We have found both stability and lack of stability in our own learning experiments with cats and I think we can specify to a certain extent the situations in which each may occur. When a learned response seems 'easy' for an animal – and 'easy' may be defined either in terms of total number of trials required to learn or in terms of the objective degree of difference between two patterns to be discriminated – then remarkable stability of performance usually obtains. This stability manifests itself not only in constant high level performance from day to day but also, as Dr Konorski has described, in high level performance on resetting after long, practice-free intervals of up to a year or more. Instability of performance occurs, on the other hand, when the difficulty of the response approaches the limit of the animal's capacity to attend to the differences in the stimuli. Brain-operated animals may exhibit instability in performance on 'easy' discriminations implying that an 'easy' discrimination may become 'difficult' for them.

CHOW. The most fundamental problem is the first point that Dr Thorpe made. This problem of self-stimulation, learning and behavioural oscillation is to me an irrelevancy. The most fundamental point is how a single nerve cell in its environment which is probably relatively stable gets this oscillation. At the cellular or molecular level you must think of a mechanism to account for it. A build-up and discharge and so on. I do not know enough about it to suggest an explanation but I think this is really the problem.

HERNÁNDEZ-PEÓN. In reply to Dr Thorpe's question as to whether or not sensory receptors govern the discharge of nerve cells in the central nervous system I would like to point out that in the adult brain there is a considerable amount of tonic inhibition acting upon the spontaneous activity of nerve cells in the central nervous system. In this respect, recent experiments of Soderberg and Arden showed that in rabbits a lesion of the optic tract enhanced the electrical activity of the lateral geniculate body. Brain stem lesions also increased this activity. These results indicate that there is certain degree of ascending inhibition coming from the retina and tonic inhibition from the brain stem, both acting upon the lateral geniculate body.

GERARD. The major advance in neurophysiology in this century was the recognition that we did not have, either in nerve or neurone or whole nervous system, an inert passive instrument waiting for something to arouse it. There is continuing activity. This ultimately reduces to processes at the molecular level — which is metabolism — and it is well recognized in physical chemistry that regular rhythmic changes result only from continuous processes. Comparably, only a constant wind produces a regularly flapping flag. I think the really basic questions are at this level. There is a constant active metabolism and from this rhythms develop. It is perhaps only secondary, although of the greatest interest, as to whether these rhythms are primarily within a single cell — self-stimulated if you want to put it that way — whether there are microcircuits, or whether there are macrocircuits. As a matter of fact, the rhythms we found long ago in the olfactory bulb were recently shown by a couple of my students to depend in part at least on microcircuits between mitral and granule cells — in the olfactory cortex.

The patterns of behaviour must always involve patterns of structure and patterns of time. Certain cells are connected with certain other cells by definite paths; and these connections are either inborn or formed as a result of learning. And there are also patterns in time, which may be continuous activities or may vary with the physiological properties of the responding units — double firing, summation, etc. So that I would say we cannot now give an explicit answer but we can indicate the factors that enter into the answer.

THORPE. The answers which have been given have carried us much further towards an explanation. I have learnt much from them. I think that consideration of the actual physical or biochemical mechanism inside a cell which can be giving rise to rhythmic behaviour is of extreme interest and I wish we had time to discuss it much further. Perhaps, however, it is rather too much off the main line of interest at the moment. But I am very grateful to the members of the symposium for the comments they have made. To close the discussion with one final suggestion it seems to me that the sort of rhythmic mechanism which appears to be acting within a single cell might also be the kind of mechanism which is acting between cells — to inhibit or control or establish a rhythm.

KONORSKI. To open the discussion on this topic I would like to emphasize the radical change in our views, concerning the location of plastic changes, which took place in the last decade or two. At the end of the nineteenth and in the first half of the present century the view was held that the ability to form new inter-neural connections is a characteristic of only higher parts of the nervous system, and in higher animals chiefly, or even exclusively, of the cerebral cortex. The lower parts of the nervous system were supposed to be endowed with inborn connections only, i.e. connections developed during ontogeny independently of the animal's experience. The chief protagonist of this view was Pavlov, who maintained that the functional specificity of the cerebral cortex lies in the formation of acquired connections; i.e. that the cerebral cortex may be considered as an organ of conditioning. According to Pavlov, the decorticate animal retains the whole repertory of inborn, or unconditioned reflexes (including instincts) but is not able to form conditioned connections on their basis.

However attractive this view, it proved with the lapse of time more and more inadequate. On one hand it was shown that many innate activities (unconditioned reflexes) depend on the cerebral cortex. To give some examples: according to the well-known studies of Bard and Brooks placing and hopping reflexes depend on the sensory-motor cortex, maternal behaviour, as shown by Beach, depends on the medial parts of the cerebral cortex, and so on. A great body of evidence showing the role of the cerebral cortex in the course of unconditioned reflexes was recently given by Dr Asratyan.

On the other hand we have now a rapidly increasing amount of evidence to show that lower parts of the nervous axis are also apt either to form new inter-neural connections, or to ameliorate the existing ones, according to new 'experiences' (i.e. combinations of stimuli). Much evidence of that kind was presented at the present symposium by Dr Eccles and Dr Hernández-Peón.

Therefore, it seems that the time is ripe to abandon the old view and to accept a new one, according to which the difference between the lower and the higher parts of the nervous system is not that the first of them control inborn activities and the second acquired activities, but that the higher the centres, the greater is the complexity of activities controlled by them. And so those forms of plastic changes which correspond to the level of functional complexity proper to the spinal cord can occur at the spinal level, as shown in Dr Hernández-Peón's experiments on habituation to somatic stimulations or in Dr Eccles's experiments on the increase of spinal reflexes by use. Some simple forms of conditioning and even differentiations can be established in decorticate animals according to the structural complexity of the centres involved. But those learning processes, as well as unconditioned reflexes, which require for their occurrence a complex analysis of external stimuli, such as patterned vision or sound patterns, are mediated by particular areas of the cerebral cortex. The examples of such learning processes were given at this symposium in the papers of Dr Myers, Dr Chow and my own.

GALAMBOS. I would like to extend Dr Konorski's remarks on brain 'levels' where the neuronal events responsible for behavioural acts are oganized. We tend to conceive these levels as 'higher' and 'lower' cortical and subcortical. What goes on in the cortex is supposed to be both different from and superimposed upon what transpires lower down; a kind of neuronal packing order exists, with cerebral cortex on top. Several workers have recently been stressing a contrary view which this symposium has not yet considered. According to it the neuronal organization responsible for certain behavioural responses is essentially longitudinal, running from front to back in the brain. The vomiting act, for instance, can be aroused by shocks to localized areas of palaeocortex, hypothalamus and medulla, and while performance differs somewhat depending on which site is stimulated, the same result, evacuation of the stomach, is achieved by all three. In some manner, therefore, the neural organizations responsible for the response are equal at several different 'levels'. No clear pecking order is discernible. Whatever the 'higher' level imposes upon the 'lower' one is unimportant compared to the fact that all are involved in producing the act.

The idea of searching for the plastic changes of learning in the longitudinal as well as in the highest transverse (i.e. cerebral cortical) dimension of the brain is, as Dr Konorski points out, an important new direction in which research efforts are tending. It can in fact be argued from the accumulating evidence for widespread involvement of cortical and subcortical structures during learning that an understanding of the succession of events transpiring in cells organized in the rostro-caudal dimension of the brain is actually what holds the key to the neural basis of learning. Cerebral cortex probably participates merely as a link in the chain of events. Since animals without cerebral cortex obviously create the plastic brain changes required for learning we must conclude that what cortex does so supremely well can be accomplished by non-cortical brain tissue also. Despite the reasons for denying an exclusive or unique role to the cortex in learning no reasonable objection whatever can be raised against the stand that knowledge of the cortical changes that do occur in learning would be valuable to have. That plastic events occur only there and that these are the most 'important' ones to study if we wish to comprehend the processes at work are, however, two ideas open to much question.

ANOKHIN. I am very much interested in the role played in the process of learning by the different structures of the brain, the cortex and the subcortical formations. At the present time one can hardly maintain that the process of learning is the exclusive prerogative of any one nervous structure, the cortex or subcortex.

The principle of the dynamic activation of nervous activity has shown that all these component parts of the brain functioning at a given moment are jointly involved in this dynamic activation.

The main thing, however, is that each of these parts brings its own specific contribution to the process of learning, i.e. to the activity of the whole brain. This is why experiments made by extirpating different sections of the brain give contradictory results, which we cannot understand so far.

One can only safely affirm that the function of the cortex of the brain is to carry out the analysis and synthesis of the complicated and always diverse information entering through extero-receptors and intero-receptors. It should be remembered that this information enters through the sensory organs almost always in a complicated form — to use the language of cybernetics: in 'codified' form.

The deciphering of this code, the distribution of its components to different structures, the comparison of this information with the previous experience of the nervous system and, lastly, as a result of all this, the most important process of afferent synthesis which I discussed in my report — such are the different processes which may take place in the cortex, preceding any learning, i.e. preceding the creation of the elementary conditioned reflex.

We know now, however, that none of these processes of the cortex can take place without the constantly activating action of the reticular formation of the brain stem and of the hypothalamus. This very fact emphasizes that the whole brain is an organic unit when it carries out a behavioural act, however elementary this act may be.

ASRATYAN. It seems to me that what I want to say is connected to a great extent with a problem discussed.

First of all I should like to say something in connection with the problem of the role of brain cortex in nervous activity. Recently we have tried out some investigations in which we studied different inborn reflexes and different neural and humoral regulations of the functions of the organism in chronic experiments, before and after extirpation of the brain cortex in the animals. In most cases we extirpated the entire cortex of the brain. But in cases when we studied the reflexes of paired organs (such as salivary glands, extremities, etc.) only cortex of one hemisphere was removed. In the latter experiments the undamaged side served as a control for the damaged one. All inborn reflexes, i.e. unconditioned, motor and vegetative, were changed to a great extent both in their quality and stability. Many properties of these reflexes, once changed remained so. We consider it as a proof that cortex takes part in the accomplishment of inborn nervous activity, not only in complicated activity but also in simple reflexes. It should be noted that decortication brings also changes in the humoral regulations of the functions of the organism. We had about forty decorticate dogs and several rabbits, the same result was obtained in all of them.

Further I would like to say a few words on the influence of constant environmental factors on the higher nervous activity. There is sufficient factual and theoretical material for the hypothesis that this influence may be represented as a tonic conditioned reflex. Reflexes of this type are elaborated in response to such constantly acting factors as the time of experimentation, the experimenter, the room and place of experiments, some details in the physical arrangement of the apparatus, etc. It is well known that there are two types of inborn reflex activity: tonic and phasic. We have concrete facts which allow us to divide conditioned reflex activity also into tonic conditioned reflexes and phasic conditioned reflexes. Such tonic conditioned reflexes play a very great role in higher nervous activity because they constitute a background for the phasic conditioned reflex activity and provide for it a functionally steady basis. In other words, I imagine the relations between these two types of conditioned reflexes similar to those well-known relations which exist between tonic and phasic unconditioned reflexes and which were so excellently investigated by Sherrington, Magnus and others.

HERNÁNDEZ-PEÓN. I agree completely with the view expressed by Dr Konorski who points out very clearly that all the levels of the central nervous system participate in learning and, of course, each level participates in different types of learning. I should like also to add to this general discussion that in the absence, however, of certain parts of the brain some other part may take over the function of the absent part. This phenomenon has been known for a long time and has been called 'neural equivalence'. Therefore, in designing experiments for testing the function of a given part of the brain we must consider separately the immediate and the late effects of the lesion.

SEGUNDO. The hypothesis can be advanced that a degree of freedom exists which enables different individuals or even the same individual under different circumstances to learn one specific task utilizing different regions or systems in the brain. No direct proof of this is as yet available but such a possibility would agree with the following observations. (i) Interference (by destruction or excitation) with a given neural structure may affect learned behaviour in different or even contradictory manners. At the level of the caudate nucleus for instance, lesions abolished a conditioned response in certain preparations but did not affect it in others (Galeano, Roig, Segundo and Sommer-Smith, in preparation) and stimulation effects were conflicting (Olds, this volume). This could indicate that, in different preparations, the same structure participated differently in production of the same reaction. (ii) In many instances, cerebral mutilation has provoked loss of a learned ability that was re-established by subsequent training. Participation of the destroyed structure obviously was necessary initially but, since re-learning was possible, the same necessary role must have been assumed by a different nucleus.

THORPE. I agree with what Dr Segundo has just said. It seems that an animal can learn the same thing simultaneously in two or more different structures in the central nervous system. In this connection, the case of the animals reared under imperfect conditions and so not of normal health, is of special interest. Sometimes such animals cannot perform certain activities normally regarded as 'instinctive' without practice or experience, but can nevertheless learn them very rapidly. It may be that the process which results in the completion of the innate behaviour pattern by learning takes place in the same locus, but I think it is very likely that it takes place in a different locus and that would perhaps be a similar instance to that Dr Segundo had in mind: the same pattern being acquired by two different nervous structures.

MYERS. An oft-mentioned argument should perhaps be added here to supplement Dr Segundo's and Dr Thorpe's discussion. Behavioural test situations given the same name may yet differ in details to the extent that divergent results are obtained with animals having presumably identical brain lesions. Dr Rosvold has already given us an interesting example of such a situation in which the amount of energy an animal must exert in responding may determine whether or not a deficit is seen. Other important variables are the degree of definition of figure from ground; whether stimuli are presented simultaneously or successively; the nature and amount of punishment given for incorrect response and the like. In a word investigators working with learning in relation to brain lesions must be acutely aware of the behavioural variables in their experiments and must exercise themselves excessively to maintain consistency in these details throughout an experimental series, and, finally must give good enough account of these variables that others may determine precisely what had been done.

FOURTH TOPIC: NATURE OF THE CHANGE

ECCLES. As an investigator of the properties of nerve cells and neural pathways in the central nervous system, I have been particularly interested in the various theoretical accounts of the neural changes that are responsible for conditioned reflexes. There have been many attempts to explain learning and conditioning by the growth and development of synapses, as for example by Tanzi in 1893; by Cajal in 1911, and by Hebb in 1949; but no model has been presented that conforms with known neurophysiological properties of neurones, and at the same time accounts for the simplest phenomena of learning, i.e. conditioned reflexes of the Pavlovian type. Some years ago in my book *The Neurophysiological Basis of Mind*, I discussed critically two types of these postulated changes and presented in outline a new hypothesis that at least had the merit of being based on properties of the nervous system that had been experimentally demonstrated. So far as I know this hypothesis has aroused very little interest either from psychologists or from investigators of conditioned reflexes, so I welcome this opportunity to present it to you in the hope that there will be some critical discussion.

Fig. 1A shows diagrammatically an explanation of conditioning that has been developed by Konorski and Gastaut. The conditioned and unconditioned stimuli (CS and US) activate respectively the emitting centre (EC) and the receiving centre (RC). They postulated that the potential connections between these two centres (dotted lines) are transformed into 'actual excitatory connections' when excitation in the first centre coincides in time with a rise in excitation in the second centre. This change in connections between the centres was envisaged as being due to a growth and multiplication of synaptic connections, but unfortunately there is no experimental evidence that activation of a nerve centre (RC) could cause the development of connections onto it from an adjacent activated centre (EC) or even an increased efficacy of connections already in existence. An alternative postulate is illustrated in Fig. 1B, which shows simply that the CS and US lines are assumed to converge on the same neurones, activation by the US in close temporal contiguity with CS excitation being assumed to cause a general increase in excitability of the neurones, which consequently can eventually be excited to discharge by the CS alone, whereas initially CS was ineffective. Again there is no experimental evidence

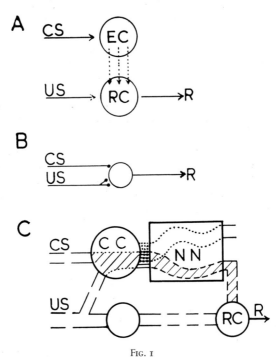

FIG. 1

Diagrams illustrating attempts to explain conditioned reflexes by plastic changes in synaptic connections. Full description in the text. CS and US show input into central nervous system of conditioned and unconditioned stimuli respectively. In A the arrows indicate nervous pathways, while B is a redrawing of a highly simplified model in which Shimbel shows converging synaptic connections of the CS and US lines. In C nervous pathways are drawn as broad bands along which conduction occurs as described in the text, particularly in the neuronal network, NN. The interruptions in the bands indicate synaptic relays. Nerve centres containing large populations of neurones are indicated by circles, while the neuronal network, NN, would be an extremely complex neuronal system; for example, an area or areas of the cerebral cortex (Eccles, 1953, reproduced by permission of the publishers).

for this non-specific increase in neuronal excitability. Increased activation of neurones changes only the synapses actually activated, i.e. it appears to be pre-synaptic or synaptic not post-synaptic. Moreover, it gives rise to a serious problem in attempting to extract from such a system an adequate degree of specificity when the lowering of threshold is non-specific for all synapses on a neurone. This is the problem of redundant conditioning, as it is appropriately called by Shimbel.

The hypothesis that I proposed in 1952 was built upon properties of neuronal networks that derived from the convergence of synaptic excitatory action on neurones and also upon the postulate that synaptic use resulted in an enduring trace of increased efficacy. At that time there was little direct evidence for this latter postulate, but very convincing experimental evidence has now been obtained in my laboratory, and presented earlier in this symposium. The essential features of the hypothesis are displayed in this diagram (Fig. 1C), but it is important to realize that the actual neural events occur in the neuronal networks of the diagram which are shown as black boxes but are of unimaginable complexity. Hence it is important to make brief reference to the properties that these networks are believed to have.

In order to generate the discharge of an impulse from a neurone it is usually necessary that there be convergence onto it of several excitatory nerve impulses within a few milliseconds. Thus effective neuronal action does not occur for a serial one to one arrangement of neurones. Rather the propagation in a neuronal network resembles an advancing front of traffic with many cells activated in parallel at each synaptic linkage in the chain. With such an arrangement it can be shown that two completely different inputs into a neuronal network can involve many neurones in common and yet emerge as completely different outputs, i.e. the same neurones can participate in countless specific patterns of activity. A further feature is that closed loops of activated neurones are possible in which impulses circulate again and again over approximately the same neuronal pathway being thus responsible for the reverberatory activity that has often been postulated.

In the diagram (Fig. 1C) there is firstly the unconditioned reflex pathway US-RC-R just as in A, but this pathway is assumed also to branch so that it converges on to the same complex centre of neurones as does the conditioned stimulus, CS. In this convergence centre (CC) it is postulated that two changes are brought about: there is synaptic facilitation so that many more neurones and neuronal pathways are excited to discharge impulses than would be by either CS or US alone; and there is increased efficacy of synaptic knobs on account of the excess use, those specially activated as a consequence of the summation of CS and US being particularly important. As a consequence of these two factors there will be a specific pattern of activation of CC as shown diagrammatically by the hatched pathway and this will be further elaborated in the neuronal network NN that leads to the efferent pathway, RC to R. Since the spatio-temporal pattern of neuronal activation in CC is dependent in part on US, it would be expected that, as shown in the diagram, it would in part achieve efferent expression in the same RC as occurs for the unconditioned reflex evoked by US. It is evident that, if the discharges of impulses into NN are set up by CS and US in close temporal sequence and with an adequate number of repetitions, the increase in synaptic efficacy in the hatched zone both in the convergence centre (CC) and in the neuronal network

(NN) will cause impulses from CS alone to be effective in evoking a pattern of impulses in NN that leads to the response R, i.e. a conditioned reflex has been established. Of course the distinction between CC and NN in the diagram is arbitrary. It is done merely to separate the predominantly afferent function of CC and the more integrative and efferent function of NN, where we can think of the eventual response as being synthesized. There is no more time for elaboration of the postulate so that it can be made to account for many of the phenomena of conditioning. Possibly this will be possible when attempting to answer criticisms.

GERARD. Before we consider Dr Eccles's model let me put before you the one by Beurle to which I have referred several times. The two are basically alike: Beurle's is worked out in rather more detail. (For a fuller exposition, and the physiological evidence bearing on the model, see my summary chapter in the *Handbook of Neurophysiology*). Beurle assumes a population of neurones, randomly placed in a layer (such as the cortex) and randomly connected with each other, except for a progressive falling off of connections with distance of separation. Each neurone receives impulses from many and passes on impulses to many. Several incoming impulses are needed to fire a cell: thresholds at specific synapses tend to fall slowly with repeated activation: and thresholds may be temporarily and reversibly raised or lowered by the action of inhibitory or facilitatory elements.

A wave of activity, entering such a cell mass, does not engage all cells in its path; but it does tend to engage a progressively large fraction until all cells are active, or a smaller fraction until the wave dies out, unless there is regulation by a negative feedback loop. With this, a wave of constant intensity can travel through the mass, the fraction of cells engaged in any volume depending on the past history of the system and on the current action of positive and negative feedback systems. Moreover, two or more individually characteristic waves may pass through the same neurone mass, each engaging its own special group of neurones. Two such waves might, therefore, travel simultaneously through the neurone pool, cross one another, reflect upon each other or from some other discontinuity in the mass, and facilitate one another at the trajectory of crossing wave fronts.

Indeed, because of the more than linear building up of excitation with the number of active neurones, the locus of intercepting waves can serve as a source of new waves, reflecting back through the cell mass along the route of either of the incoming waves. With sufficient threshold lowering by repeated activity, the characteristic waves can originate at such loci even without specific incoming stimulation. Here is the beginning of a neural mechanism for memory association, recall and even imagination. If recurrent connections carried messages back from the output of the mass to the input region, internal testing of alternate behaviours, rather than external testing, becomes possible, and the model accounts for reason based on imagination and memory, and is able to choose the 'good' response for its first act.

All the assumptions here are based on legitimate neurophysiological knowledge; even the existence of a feedback loop (through the diffuse neural system of reticular formation and related structures) which facilitates responses to 'important' inputs and which favours and fixes 'good' outputs.

In contrast to most models that have been offered, which are either empirically descriptive of observed neural behaviour or are mathematically rigorous but little related to real nervous systems, this model is based on neurophysiologically valid assumptions and leads to mathematically rigorous consequences, some not easily anticipated, which are congruent with many facts of the complex behaviour of mammals and man.

DOTY. All these schemes ignore the most difficult and probably the most important element of the problem: the temporal order. Instead, their main reliance is placed upon the convergence of excitations from multiple sources upon a common network. This is a safe and reasonable assumption since such convergence is well known for many regions of the nervous system (e.g. mesencephalic reticular formation, Amassian and DeVito, 1954; amygdala, Machne and Segundo, 1956; basal ganglia, Segundo and Machne, 1956; somatosensory cortex, Ricci, Doane and Jasper, 1957). Dr Buser has just given us another excellent example for the cortical level. Victor Wilson's demonstration (1955) that post-tetanic potentiation in one multisynaptic spinal cord system is available through non-tetanized afferents assures us these convergent networks exist at a functional level. Yet real as they are, these effects give no adequate basis for explaining the formation of conditioned reflexes. The temporal order of these effects is exactly the opposite of those in conditioning. In all multi-synaptic convergence systems it is the antecedent excitation which alters the response to a subsequent event. In forming conditioned reflexes on the other hand, the antecedent excitation (the CS) has essentially no effect upon the response to the subsequent stimulation (the US); rather it is the effect produced by the antecedent excitation which becomes altered. One might call this the 'temporal paradox' of conditioning.

It is true that Dr Asratyan has just shown us that a linkage exists in a conditioned reflex situation whereby the subsequent stimulation can elicit the effects of the antecedent, a 'backward' linkage in terms usually employed for conditioned reflexes. Perhaps the foregoing 'convergence theories' explain this phenomenon. These effects, however, are feeble and normally overwhelmed completely by the appearance of the conditioned reflex. Dr Asratyan showed equally well the prime importance of the temporal factor in forming conditioned reflexes, indeed, a previously formed CR was lost when the CS and US were given simultaneously. Dr Giurgea and I have also added here to an extensive literature on the temporal aspects of conditioning. Randomized or reversed temporal relations in the pairing of cortical stimulations did not produce conditioned reflexes, whereas the same stimuli present in the usual order did so. Appropriate temporal ordering is absolutely essential to conditioning. Thus one can speculate about converging and 'growing' pathways indefinitely, and with a certain shadow of truth; but until the reason for this 'paradoxical' temporal relation is clear, we will not understand the processes of conditioning or learning.

UU

ANOKHIN. I should like to add something to the remarks made by Dr Konorski.

It is true that Pavlov believed that the role of the cortex of the brain is a decisive one in the creation of a conditioned reflex. However, his views were not absolutely categorical on this point. He recognized clearly that under certain circumstances the conditioning may be carried out by the subcortical system also.

In normal conditions, however, when the animal has a normal cortex, conditioning is always carried out under the decisive influence of the cortex.

In fact, even in those cases when one can note electrophysiologically a conditioned reaction in the subcortical system also, this reaction is not initiated there, but has been formed in the very preliminary stage of the orientating-experimental reaction under the direct control of the cortex.

SEGUNDO. I feel that the essence of theories put forward by Dr Eccles and Dr Gerard is that the passage of a wave leaves the pathway more permeable. I would like to ask whether these schemes would be adaptable to habituation, a process which apparently involves the closure of permeable pathways? And if so, how?

FESSARD. I would like to add some comments in line with what has been said on the use of models for the understanding of learning mechanisms. I think that recourse to models — either mathematical or physical — is useful, given the fact that the multitude of elements and extreme complexity of their interconnections leave no hope that we can ever know every detail of a neuronal field and its functional properties. Models help to schematize the main dynamic features of a field but may also be misleading. This is the case, I believe, of models which exhibit a complicated and diversified circuitry as in a radio set: such 'machines' may imitate the different modalities of conditioning, they may 'learn' but they are of little help to give us a better understanding of how the CNS actually works during learning operations. This is why probabilistic theories applied to more or less diffuse neuronal networks are to be preferred. In this respect, the mathematical model by Beurle, as recalled by Dr Gerard, is certainly a remarkable and highly suggestive one.

I also think that some useful qualitative and unsophisticated evidence must be ascertained before any mathematical treatment is attempted, when one considers the most familiar connectivity patterns, especially those exhibited by the widely distributed network-like structures This is quite apparent when we consider the illuminating diagram Dr Eccles has just presented to us. I made use of similar notions in a report with Dr Gastaut (Symposium on 'Conditionnement et Apprentissage, Strasbourg, 1956; Presses Univ. France, 1958, p. 216) where we had first gathered all the experimental evidence then available which appeared to show the important role played by subcortical polyneuronic nuclei — namely, mesencephalic reticular formation and so-called 'diffuse thalamic system' — in the formation of new conditioned reflexes. This justifies our belief that some speculation should be made on the general properties of neuronal networks. By their very nature they are sites of election for convergences and interactions of heterosensory signals. Our schema differs from the one of Eccles only in that he makes a difference between a convergence centre (CC) and a neuronal network (NN) whereas we think that convergences and associative interactions can take place within the same neuronal assemblies as those present in the brain stem and non-specific diencephalic nuclei.

In my opinion, the weakness of all models so far proposed is that they usually neglect the states of autogenic repetitive firing which are so common in the nerve cells of cerebral structures in waking animals. This I tried to point out in my paper. Utilization of this general property would probably lead to a better understanding of the formation of new associative links as giving their functional role to the plastic effects which are the consequence of repetitive bombardments. In that respect, I do not believe that closed-loop circulations of impulses can be the only, not even the main cause of prolonged firings. Whatever the case, it is difficult to believe that the process of reverberation, when it operates through multiple, intricate, micro-loops and zig-zag recurrent pathways as are present in neuronal networks, can have another net result than that of deteriorating the informative content of sensory messages, in one word of increasing 'noise' in the communication of signals within the brain. Shall we assume that learning mechanisms might depend on such a process?

Another essential mechanism to which sufficient credit has not been given in models is that of *inhibition*.

In answer to Dr Segundo's remark, one can say that it would not be difficult to introduce inhibitory functions into the models just alluded to. Habituation, extinction, differentiation, inasmuch as they involve inhibitory actions could thus receive a good symbolic representation. May I mention in addition that plastic changes like post-tetanic potentiation apply to inhibitory synapses as well as to excitatory ones.

Finally, I must confess that I have also been puzzled by the question raised by Dr Doty and which he calls the 'temporal paradox of conditioning'.

Could it not be that the conditional message being weak and ineffectual meanders through neuronal networks, thereby losing time, so that finally it reaches the associative synaptic fields at the moment when they receive the unconditional signal?

HEBB. The difficulty with these schemes is that they are quite unrealistic, because they depend on a gross selection of data. There are so many facts of behaviour, so much psychological research that they do not comprehend, that they cannot be taken seriously — at least until they show how they are going to handle some of the main facts which have accumulated in the criticism of exactly such theories as these. Here is a hastily compiled list of the sort of thing they need to take into account:

There is the whole effect of early experience, as modifying the adult capacity to associate stimulus with response. I don't need to go into the question of whether Riesen's chimpanzees reared in darkness were able to see, organically; the chimpanzee reared in unpatterned light was equally incapable in his visual learning.

There is the factor of attention. I may remind you again of Lashley's experiment in which there was a failure of learning to discriminate patterns in 200 trials —

three times as many as would be needed in other circumstances — because, prior to that experience, he had arranged things so as to direct the animal's attention to the *size* of the diagrams only; the necessary sensory stimulation occurred, but the central factor of attending was absent. Attention is fundamental; where does it fit in such theories as the ones we are discussing now?

There are the phenomena of visual transfer and patterning. These theories talk as though the stimulus input from one object went to one part of the brain, from another to another part: a spatial separation is assumed for different stimulus objects. But inevitably there is overlap of excitations and the differentiation between objects is a matter of patterning, not the gross locus of stimulation or central conduction.

When theories can deal with that kind of problem they will be getting closer to the realities of behaviour. There are the problems of time relations in serial order, and the fact that most learning is not a one-shot output with a single input; characteristically it is serialized, each reaction producing further stimulation, with further reaction, and so on. As Lashley showed in his Hixon symposium paper, the time properties of conduction, and reaction time, are such as to prevent us from treating serialized behaviour as simply a series of conditioned reflexes; there is an intra-cerebral serialization as well. This aspect of the problem is directly related to the question of ideation, as demonstrated experimentally by Broadbent's holding phenomenon.

These conditioned-reflex theories assume a one-way, through transmission in CNS, with the exception that as I understand Dr Gerard, Beurle's theory postulates a reverberatory process going on until a 'satisfactory outlet' is achieved, at which point it would stop. What stops it, in physiological terms? The whole question of reinforcement is raised here, and this is a difficult question indeed. There is the fact, for example, that frequent repetition of a response may decrease, instead of increase, the probability that that response will be made again (and this without overt punishment of any kind). The phenomena of memory and forgetting and the facts to which I referred briefly in earlier discussion (i.e. the conditions in which visual learning is or is not retained), all these and other factual data have to be taken account of. When there is so much selection, in the phenomena on which a theory of learning is based, it cannot be taken seriously.

ECCLES. I am very grateful for these criticisms, because they give me a chance to show that the hypothesis is much more adaptable than would appear at first sight. The full potentialities of the hypothesis are not revealed by the simplified account I gave. For example, the neuronal networks CC and NN would be very widely dispersed over the cortex and involve millions of neurones, as would necessarily be the case if convergence is to occur between different sensory modalities and to be so highly specific, as for example occurs with conditioning for an ellipse and not for a circle. Multiple representation of the neuronal networks is also not excluded, hence conditioned reflexes could survive extensive cerebral lesions and ablations. In fact the hypothesis will encompass any sensory experience that can be analysed by the central nervous system. Presumably such analysis has to be attributed to the operation of spatio-temporal patterns of neuronal activity.

I agree that the phenomena of attention and of the orienting reflex are of great importance in a fully developed theory of conditioning. I would suggest that cortical inhibition is somehow involved in suppressing much of the developing neural activity that would otherwise arise from the sensory input and that is being rejected. Already there are many instances of inhibition operating on the earliest synaptic relays on sensory pathways. The orienting reflex can be regarded as operating to increase the level of excitability in the convergence centre, which consequently functions more effectively and intensely.

Related considerations help to answer Dr Doty's criticism. The temporal sequence for effective conditioning can be accounted for by postulating that CS has to develop its specific spatio-temporal pattern of activity in CC, possibly of reverberatory character, before the application of the dominant US. It is helped to do this by the background excitation added by the orienting reflex. But for this temporal sequence, the US would dominate the neuronal activity of CC and NN to the exclusion of CS, and as a consequence there would not be the development of the specific patterns of increased synaptic efficacy that arise by the conjoint CS and US input. I think Dr Lashley in the Hixon Symposium greatly underestimated the time that could be occupied in developing specific patterns of neuronal activity in the unimaginably complicated networks of the cerebral cortex. The events involved are of a different order of complexity compared to physiological reflex phenomena.

I haven't yet answered all of the specific criticisms, but perhaps I have indicated the way in which necessary development of the hypothesis can occur. We would all agree that conditioning must be explained in terms of neural changes and that immensely complex neural pathways are concerned. The hypothesis that I have proposed merely attempts to show how the physiological properties that have been experimentally demonstrated for the synapse can account for conditioning, given the complexity of pathways that forms the basis of all our thinking about higher nervous activities.

ANOKHIN. I should like to remark that there are two fundamentally distinct phenomena, which are usually confused when discussing the problem of the formation of conditioned-reflex connections.

The first phenomenon is the property of the nervous tissue to retain a succession of any stimuli provided they be above threshold. This is a characteristic of the nervous matter, it occurs irrespective of which stimulus follows which, whatever their order and even irrespective of whether or not these stimuli contribute something significant to the life of the organism, in the wide biological sense.

The second phenomenon is the genuine conditioned reflex, i.e. a constant succession of stimuli ending by some purposeful adjusting effect for the organism, i.e. a succession of stimuli consolidated by a final emotional effect, the unconditioned stimulus.

An example of the phenomenon of the first type may be the well-known EEG 'conditioned reflex', when using in a constant succession the 'sound-light' stimuli.

An example of the second type can be the generalized desynchronization of the electric activity of the cortex which is linked to a stimulation of all the vegetative organs and which occurs in the case of a biological reinforcement, i.e. which ends by an emotional discharge.

Taking all this into account, one should, in my view, first consider by which mechanisms emotional discharges do contribute to the selective consolidation of fully determined synaptic connections, corresponding to the succession precisely of those stimuli which led to this emotional discharge.

I believe that the solution to the problem of the conditioned reflex requires first of all the characteristics of the biological condition for the closing of the circuit itself and only this aspect will enable us to succeed.

Without it any synaptic combination of hypotheses for explaining the conditioned reflex cannot lead us to a solution of this difficult problem.

GERARD. Dr Eccles has taken up the several points raised, and my answers are much the same as his. Certainly time sequences are involved in behaviour, but it does not really work backward in conditioning, and the modifications in neurones and synapses are quite explicitly able to account for conditioned responses.

Turning from Dr Doty's question to Dr Segundo's, the issue is now a reversal in reinforcement rather than in time. Habituation could be easily understood in two ways, facilitation of inhibitory pathways with a feedback action, or effective channelization of impulses into appropriate outputs, with the corresponding diminution of irradiation to non-effective units. This parallels the recent evidence regarding learning; widespread cortical activity occurs while a correct response is being learned, this mostly disappears as highly channelized activity develops with a learned response, but reappears when the problem is changed or an error is made in the response.

Dr Hebb's many points, far from posing difficulties for the model, are among the very things that it effectively does explain. The Broadbent phenomenon and model fit excellently with that of Beurle; the Lashley experiment fits with the feedback mechanisms indicated and so for the other specific points raised. As I see it, the neurophysiological mechanisms now available for interpreting behaviour can account, in principle, for everything except the basic value hierarchy of the individual, which things matter to it; and this I suspect is largely the residue of earlier experience, with its reinforcements and punishments. I can only refer Dr Hebb to the chapter already mentioned for a fuller discussion of these problems.

BIBLIOGRAPHY

The following references have been carefully checked at source with the exception of a few items, mainly the Proceedings of local Congresses and Symposia, which it has not been possible to see.

ADEY, W. R. (1951) The nervous system of the earthworm Megascolex. *J. comp. Neurol.*, **94**, 57-93.

ADEY, W. R. (1958) Organization of the rhinencephalon. In *Henry Ford Hosp. Int. Symp.: Reticular Formation of the Brain*, pp. 621-644, Boston, Little, Brown and Co.

ADEY, W. R. (1959) Inhibition in the nervous system and gamma-aminobutyric acid. In *Int. Symp., City of Hope Medical Center*, Duarte, California. In the Press.

ADEY, W. R., DUNLOP, C. W. and HENDRIX, C. (1959) Spatial distribution and phase relationships of hippocampal slow wave activity in the course of approach learning. In the Press.

ADEY, W. R., DUNLOP, C. W. and SUNDERLAND, S. (1958) A survey of rhinencephalic interconnections with the brain stem. *J. comp. Neurol.*, **110**, 173-203.

ADEY, W. R., MERRILLEES, N. C. R. and SUNDERLAND, S. (1956) The entorhinal area; behavioural, evoked potential, and histological studies of its interrelationships with brainstem regions. *Brain*, **79**, 414-38.

ADEY, W. R., SEGUNDO, J. P. and LIVINGSTON, R. B. (1957) The corticifugal influences on intrinsic brain stem conduction in cat and monkey. *J. Neurophysiol.*, **20**, 1-16.

ADEY, W. R., SUNDERLAND, S. and DUNLOP, C. W. (1957) The entorhinal area; electrophysiological studies of its interrelations with the rhinencephalic structures and the brainstem. *Elechoenceph clin. Neurophysiol.*, **9**, 309-24.

ADRIAN, E. D. (1941) Afferent discharges to the cerebral cortex from peripheral sense organs. *J. Physiol. (Lond.)*, **100**, 159-191.

ADRIAN, E. D. and MORUZZI, G. (1939) Impulses in the pyramidal tract. *J. Physiol. (Lond.)*, **97**, 153-199.

AJURRIAGUERRA, J. and HECAEN, H. (1960) *Le Cortex Cérébral*. Paris, Masson.

AKELAITIS, A. J. E. (1941) Studies on the corpus callosum. VIII. The effects of partial and complete section of the corpus callosum on psychopatic epileptics. *Amer. J. Psychiat.*, **98**, 409-414.

AKERT, K. and ANDY, O. J. (1953) Experimental studies on the Ammon's formation in cats and monkeys. *Trans. Amer. Neurol. Ass.*, **78**, 194-195.

ALBE-FESSARD, D. and SZABO, TH. (1954) Étude microphysiologique du neurone intermédiaire d'une chaîne réflexe disynaptique. *C.R. Soc. Biol., Paris*, **148**, 281-284.

ALLEN, W. F. (1940) Effect of ablating the frontal lobes, hippocampi, and occipito-parietotemporal (excepting pyriform areas) lobes on positive and negative olfactory conditioned reflexes. *Amer. J. Physiol.*, **128**, 754-771.

AMASSIAN, V. E. and WALLER, H. J. (1958) Spatiotemporal Patterns of Activity in Individual Reticular Neurons. In *Henry Ford Hospital Int. Symp. Reticular Formation of the Brain*. pp. 69-110, Boston, Little, Brown and Co.

ANAND, B. K. and BROBECK, J. R. (1951) Localization of a 'feeding center' in the hypothalamus of the rat. *Proc. Soc. exp. Biol. Med.*, **77**, 323-324.

ANDERSON, E., BATES, R. W., HAWTHORNE, E., HAYMAKER, W., KNOWLTON, K., RIOCH, D.McK., SPENCE, W. T. and WILSON, H. (1957) The effects of midbrain and spinal cord transection on endocrine and metabolic functions with postulation of a midbrain hypothalamico-pituitary activating system. *Recent Progr. Hormone Res.*, **13**, 21-59.

ANDREW, W. (1955) Amitotic division in senile tissues as a probable means of self-preservation of cells. *J. Geront.*, **10**, 1-12.

ANGELERGUES, R. and HECAEN, H. (1958) La douleur au cours des lésions des hémisphères cérébraux. *J. Psychol. norm. path.*, **55**, 42-69, 184-203.

ANOKHIN, P. K. (1932) Active secretory motor method for the study of the dynamics of the higher nervous activity. *Med. J. Gorki*.

ANOKHIN, P. K. (1933) The study of the dynamics of the higher nervous activity. *Sechenov J. Physiol.*, N.5.

ANOKHIN, P. K. (1935) The problem of the centre and periphery in modern physiology of the higher nervous activity. In *Problems of Higher Nervous Activity*, pp. 9-70, Gorki.

ANOKHIN, P. K. (1949) Keypoints in the study of the higher nervous activity. In *Problems of Higher Nervous Activity*. Moscow.

ANOKHIN, P. K. (1955) Peculiarities of the afferent apparatus of the conditioned reflex and their significance for psychology. *J. Probl. Psychol.*, N.6, 16-38.

ANOKHIN, P. K. (1956) Sur la nature physiologique des composantes végétatives de la réaction conditionnelle. *Ž. vyss̆. nerv. Dejat Pavlova*, **6**, 32-43.

ANOKHIN, P. K. (1957) Role of the Reticular Formation in various forms of higher nervous activity. *Sechenov J. Physiol.*, **43**, 987-998.

ANOKHIN, P. K. (1957) The physiological substratum of signal reactions. *Ž. Vyss̆. Nerv. Dejat. Pavlova*, **7**, 30-48.

ANOKHIN, P. K. (1958) *Electroencephalographic Analysis of the Conditioned Reflex* (English Text by author). Moscow: State Publishing House for Medical Literature, 75 pp.

ANOKHIN, P. K. (1958) The role of orienting exploratory response in the elaboration of the conditioned reflex. *Orienting Reflex and Exploratory Behaviour*. Moscow, pp. 9-20.

ANOKHIN, P. K. (1958) *Internal Inhibition*. Moscow.

ANOKHIN, P. K. and IVANOV, A. (1936) Experimentelle Veränderungen der phylogenetischen Verbindungen im Gebiet des Nervos vagus. *Pflüg. Arch. Ges. Physiol.*, **237**, 536-557.

ANREP, G. V. (1923) The mediation of conditioned reflexes. *Proc. Roy. Soc. Lond.*, B, **94**, 404-426.

APELBAUM, J., SILVA, E. N. and FRICK, O. (1959) Frequency discrimination and 'arousal' reaction. 18, XXI International Congress of Physiological Sciences. Buenos Aires, 9-15, August 1959. Abstracts of communications.

APPELBERG, B., KITCHELL, R. L. and LANDGREN, S. (1959) Reticular influence upon thalamic and cortical potentials evoked by stimulation of the cat's tongue. *Acta physiol. scand.*, **45**, 48-71.

ARDUINI, A. and ARDUINI, M. G. (1954) Effect of drugs and metabolic alterations on brain stem arousal mechanism. *J. Pharmacol. (Kyoto)*, **110**, 76-85.

ARDUINI, A. and MORUZZI, G. (1953) Olfactory arousal reactions in the 'cerveau isolé' cat. *Electroenceph. clin. Neurophysiol.*, **5**, 243-250.

ARIENS KAPPERS, C. U. (1917) Further contributions on neurobiotaxis IX. An attempt to compare the phenomena of neurobiotaxis with other phenomena of taxis and tropism. The dynamic polarization of the neurone. *J. comparative Neurol.*, **27**, 261-298.

ARTEMYEV, V. V. and BOZLANOVA, N. I. (1952) Electrical reaction of the auditory area of the cortex of the cerebral hemisphere during the formation of a conditioned defence reflex. *Tr. Inst. Fiziol. (Mosk.)*, I, 228-236.

ARVANITAKI, A. (1942) Effects evoked in an axon by the activity of a contiguous one. *J. Neurophysiol.*, **5**, 89-108.

ASCHER, P. and BUSER, P. (1958) Modalités de mise en jeu de la voie pyramidale chez le chat anesthésié au chloralose. *J. Physiol.*, *Paris*, **50**, 129-132.

ASCHER, P. and JASSIK-GERSCHENFELD, D. (1960) Modalités d'obtention de décharges périphériques par stimulation corticale chez le chat. *J. Physiol.*, *Paris*, **52**, 7-8.

ASHBY, W. R. (1952) *Design for a Brain*. New York, John Wiley and Sons.

ASRATYAN, E. A. (1952) Contribution to the Physiology of Temporary Connections. *Proc. XV Conf. Higher Nervous Activity*, p. 68.

ASRATYAN, E. A. (1955) New Data on Unconditioned and Conditioned Reflexes. *Ž. Vyss̆. Nerv. Dejat. Pavlova*, **5**, 48.

ASRATYAN, E. A. (1955) Nouveaux éléments sur les réflexes inconditionnels et conditionnels. *Ž. vyss̆. Nerv. Dejat. Pavlova*, **5**, 480-492.

ASRATYAN, E. A. (1957) New Data on Switching in Conditioned-Reflex Activity. (Reprint of a communication delivered at the XV International Psychological Congress in Brussels.)

ASRATYAN, E. A. (1960) Some aspects of the elaboration of conditioned connections and formation of their properties. This volume, pp. 95-113.

BALAKHIN, B. (1935) Experimental dissociation of the integral response of animals to conditioned stimuli. *Reports on the Problems of centre and periphery for the physiology of Higher Nervous Activity*. Moscow, pp. 379-413.

BARD, P. and MACHT, M. B. (1958) The behaviour of chronically decerebrate cats. In *Ciba Foundation Symposium on the Neurological Basis of Behaviour*. London, J. A. Churchill, pp. 55-71.

BARD, P. and MOUNTCASTLE, V. B. (1948) Some forebrain mechanisms involved in the expression of rage with special reference to suppression of angry behavior. *Res. Publ. Ass. nerv. ment. Dis.*, **27**, 362-398.

BARD, P. and RIOCH, D. McK. (1937) A study of four cats deprived of neocortex and additional portions of the forebrain. *Bull. Johns Hopk. Hosp.*, **60**, 73-125.

BARLOW, J. A. (1956) Secondary motivation through classical conditioning: a reconsideration of the nature of backward conditioning. *Psychol. Rev.*, **63**, 406-408.

BARRON, D. and MATTHEWS, B. H. C. (1935) Intermittent conduction in the spinal cord. *J. Physiol. (Lond.)*, **85**, 73-103.

BARTELMEZ, G. W. (1915) Mauthner's cell and the nucleus motorius tegmenti. *J. comp. Neurol.*, **25**, 87-116.

BARTELMEZ, G. W. and HOERR, N. L. (1933) The vestibular club endings in Ameiurus. Further evidence on the morphology of the synapse. *J. comp. Neurol.*, **57**, 401-428.

BARTLEY, S. H. and BISHOP, G. H. (1933) The cortical response to stimulation of the optic nerve in the rabbit. *Amer. J. Physiol.*, **103**, 159-172.

BARTLEY, S. H. and HEINBECKER, P. (1938) The response of the sensorimotor cortex to stimulation of a peripheral nerve. *Amer. J. Physiol.*, **121**, 21-31.

BATINI, C., MORUZZI, G., PALESTINI, M., ROSSI, G. F. and ZANCHETTI, A. (1958) Persistent patterns of wakefulness in the pretrigeminal midpontine preparation. *Science*, **128**, 30-32.

BATINI, C., MORUZZI, G., PALESTINI, M., ROSSI, G. F. and ZANCHETTI, A. (1959a) Effects of complete pontine transections on the sleep-wakefulness rhythm: the midpontine pretrigeminal preparation. *Arch. ital. Biol.*, **97**, 1-12.

BATINI, C., MAGNI, F., PALESTINI, M., ROSSI, G. F. and ZANCHETTI, A. (1959b) Neural mechanisms underlying the enduring EEG and behavioral activation in the midpontine pretrigeminal cat. *Arch. ital. Biol.*, **97**, 13-25.

BATINI, C., PALESTINI, M., ROSSI, G. F. and ZANCHETTI, A. (1959) E.E.G. activation patterns in the midpontine pretrigeminal cat following sensory deafferentation. *Arch. ital. Biol.*, **97**, 26-32.

BATTIG, K., ROSVOLD, H. E. and MISHKIN, M. Non-sensory effects of prefrontal and caudate lesions in monkeys on visual and auditory discrimination. (In preparation.)

BAUER, K. F. (1953) *Organisation des Nervengewebes und Neurencytiumtheorie*. Berlin, Urban und Schwarzenberg.

BEACH, F. A. and JAYNES, J. (1954) Effects of early experience upon the behavior of animals. *Psychol. Bull.*, **51**, 239-263.

BECK, E. C., DOTY, R. W. and KOOI, K. A. (1958) Electrocortical reactions associated with conditioned flexion reflexes. *Electroenceph. clin. Neurophysiol.*, **10**, 279-289.

BEKHTEREV, V. M. (1887) *Physiology of the Motor Area of the Brain Cortex*. Kharkov (in Russian).

BEKHTEREV, V. M. (1927) *Fundamentals of Human Reflexology*. Moscow (in Russian).

BERITOV, I. S. (1924) On the fundamental nervous processes in the cortex of the cerebral hemispheres. I. The principal stages of the development of the individual reflex: its generalization and differentiation. *Brain*, **47**, 109-148.

BERITOV, I. S. (1932) *Individually Acquired Activity of the Central Nervous System*. Tbilisi.

BERITOV, I. S. (1956) Morphological and physiological foundations of temporary connections in the cerebral cortex. *Coll. Papers Physiol. Inst. Acad. Sci. Georgian S.S.R.*, **10**, 3.

BERLYNE, D. E. (1950) Novelty and curiosity as determinants of exploratory behaviour. *Brit. J. Psychol.*, **41**, 68-80.

BERNHAUT, M., GELLHORN, E. and RASMUSSEN, A. T. (1953) Experimental contributions to problem of consciousness. *J. Neurophysiol.*, **16**, 21-35.

BERNSTEIN, A. L. (1934) Temporal factors in the formation of conditioned eyelid reaction in human subjects. *J. gen. Psychol.*, **10**, 173.

BEURLE, R. L. (1956) Properties of a mass of cells capable of regenerating pulses. *Phil. Trans.*, **240**, 55-94.

BIANCHI, L. (1922) *The Mechanisms of the Brain and the Function of the Frontal Lobes*. Trans. by J. H. MacDonald. New York, Wm. Wood and Co.

BICKFORD, R. G., MULDER, D. W., DODGE, H. W., JR., SVIEN, H. J. and ROME, H. P. (1958) Changes in memory function produced by electrical stimulation of the temporal lobe in man. In *The Brain and Human Behavior*. Association for Research in Nervous and Mental Diseases, Publication 36. Baltimore, Williams and Wilkins, pp. 227-243.

BIELSCHOVSKY, M. (1935) Allgemeine Histologie und Histopathologie des Nervensystems. In *Handbuch der Neurologie*. Bumke und Foerster, Berlin, Julius Springer, I, pp. 35-226.

BISHOP, G. H. (1933) Cyclic changes in excitability of the optic pathway of the rabbit. *Amer. J. Physiol.*, **103**, 213-224.

BLUM, R. A. (1952) Effects of subtotal lesions of frontal granular cortex on delayed reactions in monkeys. *Arch. Neurol. Psychiat. Chicago*, **67**, 375-386.

BLUM, J. S., CHOW, K. L. and PRIBRAM, K. H. (1950) A behavioral analysis of the organization of the parieto-temporo-occipital cortex. *J. comp. Neurol.*, **93**, 53-100.

BODIAN, D. (1937) The structure of the vertebrate synapse. A study of the axon endings on Mauthner's cell and neighboring centers in the goldfish. *J. comp. Neurol.*, **68**, 117-145.

BODIAN, D. (1942) Cytological aspects of synaptic function. *Physiol. Rev.*, **22**, 146-169.

BOEKE, J. (1949) The sympathetic endformation, its synaptology, the interstitial cells, the periterminal network, and its bearing on the neurone theory. Discussion and critique. *Acta anat (Basel)*, **8**, 18-61.

VON BONIN, G. and BAILEY, P. (1947) *The Neocortex of Macaca Mulatta*. Urbana, Univ. Illinois Press.

BONVALLET, M., DELL, P. and HIEBEL, G. (1954) Tonus sympathique et activité électrique corticale. *Electroenceph. clin. Neurol.*, **6**, 119-144.

BORLONE, M., DITTBORN, J. and PALESTINI, M. (1959) E.E.G. correlations within an operational definition of hypnosis. *Neurocirugía*, **12**, 67-68.

BRADY, J. V. and HUNT, H. F. (1955) An experimental approach to the analysis of emotional behavior. *J. Psychol.*, **40**, 313-324.

BRATTGÅRD, S. O. (1952) The importance of adequate stimulation for the chemical composition of retinal ganglion cells during early post-natal development. *Acta radiol. (Stockh.)*, **96.**

BRATTGÅRD, S. O. and HYDÉN, H. (1952) Mass, lipids, pentose nucleoproteins and proteins determined in nerve cells by X-ray microradiography. *Acta Radiol. (Stockh.)*, **94.**

BREGADZE, A. H. (1956) Elaboration of Temporary Connections to Indifferent Stimuli. Collection of articles: *Problems of Modern Physiology of the Nervous-Muscular System*, p. 279 (in Russian).

BREMER, F. (1935) Cerveau 'isolé' et physiologie du sommeil. *C.R. Soc. Biol. (Paris)*, **118**, 1235-1241.

BREMER, F. (1941) Le tétanos strychnique et le mécanisme de la synchronisation neuronique. *Arch. int. Physiol.*, **51**, 211-260.

BREMER, F. (1943) Étude oscillographique des réponses sensorielles de l'aire acoustique corticale chez le chat. *Arch. Int. Physiol.*, **53**, 53-103.

BREMER, F. (1949) Considérations sur l'origine et la nature des 'ondes' cérébrales. *Electroenceph. clin. Neurophysiol.*, **1**, 177-193.

BREMER, F. (1953) *Some Problems in Neurophysiology*. University of London, The Athlone Press.

BREMER, F. (1954) The neurophysiological problem of sleep. *Brain Mechanisms and Consciousness*. J. F. Delafresnaye, Editor. Symposium organized by C.I.O.M.S. Oxford, Blackwell Scientific Publications, pp. 137-162.

BREMER, F. and BONNET, V. (1950) Interprétation des réactions rythmiques prolongées des aires sensorielles de l'écorce cérébrale. *Electroenceph. clin. Neurophysiol.*, **2**, 389-400.

BREMER, F. and STOUPEL, N. (1959) Facilitation et inhibition des potentiels évoqués corticaux dans l'éveil cérébral. *Arch. int. Physiol.*, **67**, 240-275.

BROADBENT, D. E. (1956) Successive responses to simultaneous stimuli. *Quart. J. exp. Psychol.*, **8**, 145-152.

BRODAL, A. and ROSSI, G. F. (1955) Ascending fibers in brain stem reticular formation of cat. *Arch. Neurol. Psychiat. (Chicago)*, **74**, 68-87.

BRODMANN, K. (1912) Neue Ergebnisse über die vergleichende histologische Lokalisation der Grosshirnrinde mit besonderer Berücksichtigung des Stirnhirns. *Anat. Anz.*, **41**, Ergänzungsheft, 157-216.

BROGDEN, W. J. and GANTT, W. H. (1942) Intraneural conditioning. Cerebellar conditioned reflexes. *Arch. Neurol. Psychiat. (Chicago)*, **48**, 437-455.

BROMILEY, R. B. (1948) Conditioned responses in a dog after removal of neocortex. *J. comp. Physiol. Psychol.*, **41**, 102-110.

BROOKHART, J. M. and ZANCHETTI, A. (1956) The relation between electro-cortical waves and responsiveness of the cortico-spinal system. *Electroenceph. clin. Neurophysiol.*, **8**, 427-444.

BROOKS, V. B. (1956) An intracellular study of the action of repetitive nerve volleys and of botulinum toxin on miniature end-plate potentials. *J. Physiol.*, **134**, 264-277.

BRUSH, E. S. and MISHKIN, M. (1959) The relationship of object preference to learning-set performance in brain-operated monkeys. Paper presented at Eastern Psychological Association Meetings.

BRUTKOWSKI, S. (1957) The effect of prefrontal lobectomies on salivary conditioned reflexes in dogs. *Acta Biol. exp. Versovie*, **17**, 327-337.

BRUTKOWSKI, S. (1959) Comparison of classical and instrumental alimentary conditioned reflexes following bilateral prefrontal lobectomies in dogs. *Acta Biol. exp. Varsovie*, **19**. In the Press.

BRUTKOWSKI, S. and AULEYTNER, B. The effect of prefrontal ablations on the defensive conditioned reflexes in dogs. In preparation.

BRUTKOWSKI, S., KONORSKI, J., ŁAWICKA, W., STEPIEŃ, I. and STEPIEŃ, L. (1955) The effects of the removal of prefrontal areas of the cerebral hemispheres on the conditioned motor reflexes in dogs. *Soc. Sci. Lodz.*, **3**, 7-60.

BRUTKOWSKI, S., KONORSKI, J., ŁAWICKA, W., STEPIEŃ, I. and STEPIEŃ, L. (1956) The effect of the removal of frontal poles of the cerebral cortex on motor conditioned reflexes. *Acta Biol. exp. Varsovie*, **17**, 167-188.

BRYDEN, M. P. (1958) The role of eye movements in perception. Unpublished Master's thesis, McGill University.

BUCHWALD, N. A. and ERVIN, F. R. (1957) Evoked potentials and behavior. A study of responses to subcortical stimulation in the awake, unrestrained animal. *Electroenceph. clin. Neurophysiol.*, **9**, 477-496.

BURNS, B. D. (1950) Some properties of the cat's isolated cerebral cortex. *J. Physiol., Lond.*, **111**, 50-68.

BURNS, B. D. (1958) *The Mammalian Cerebral Cortex*. London, Arnold.

BUSER, P. and ALBE-FESSARD, D. (1957) Explorations intracellulaires au niveau du cortex sensorimoteur du chat. *Colloques internationaux du Centre National de la Recherche Scientifique*. No. 67, Paris, p. 333-352.

BUSER, P. and ASCHER, P. (1960) Miss en jeu réflexe du système pyramidal chez le chat. *Arch. ital. Biol.*, **98**, 123-164.

BUSER, P. and BORENSTEIN, P. (1957a) Réponses corticales 'secondaires' a la stimulation sensorielle chez le chat curarisé non anesthésié. *Electroenceph. clin. Neurophysiol.*, **6**, 89-108.

BUSER, P. and BORENSTEIN, P. (1957b) Suppression élective des réponses 'associatives' par stimulation réticulaire chez le chat sous anesthésie profonde au chloralose. *J. Physiol. (Paris)*, **49**, 86-89.

BUSER, P. and BORENSTEIN, P. (1959) Réponses somesthésiques, visuelles et auditives, recueillies au niveau du cortex 'associatif' suprasylvien chez le chat curarisé non anesthésié. *Electroenceph. clin. Neurophysiol.*, **11**, 285-304.

BUSER, P., JOUVET, M. and HERNÁNDEZ-PEÓN, R. (1958) Modifications, au cours du conditionnement chez le chat, du cycle d'excitabilité au niveau de la réticulée mésencéphalique. *Acta Neurol. lat.-amer.*, **4**, 268-278.

BUSER, P. and IMBERT, M. (1959) Données sur l'organisation des projections afférentes au niveau du cortex moteur du chat. *An. Fac. Med., Montevideo*, **44**, 220-229.

BUSER, P. and ROGER, A. (1957) Interprétation du conditionnement sur la base des données électroencéphalographiques. Premier Congrès International des Sciences Neurologiques Bruxelles. *Acta Medica Belgica*, 417-444.

BUSER, P. and ROUGEUL, A. (1956) Réponses sensorielles corticales chez le chat en préparation chronique — Leurs modifications lors de l'établissement de liaisons temporaires. *Rev. Neurol.*, **95**, 501-503.

BUTLER, R. A. and HARLOW, H. F. (1956) The effects of auditory distraction on the performance of monkeys. *J. gen. Psychol.*, **54,** 15-20.

BYKOV, K. (1924-25) Versuche an Hunden mit Durchschneiden des Corpus callosum. *Zbl. ges. Neurol. Psychiat.*, **39,** 199.

CALVET, J., CATHALA, H. P., CONTAMIN, F., HIRSCH, J. and SCHERRER, J. (1956) Potentiels évoqués corticaux chez l'homme. Étude analytique. *Rev. neurol.*, **95,** 445-454.

CALVET, J., CATHALA, H. P., HIRSCH, J. and SCHERRER, J. (1956) La réponse corticale visuelle de l'homme étudiée par une méthode d'intégration. *C.P. Soc. Biol. (Paris)*, **150,** 1348-1351.

DEL CASTILLO, J. and KATZ, B. (1955) Local activity at a depolarized nerve-muscle junction. *J. Physiol.*, **128,** 396-411.

DEL CASTILLO, J. and KATZ, B. (1957) A study of curare action with an electrical micro-method. *Proc. roy. Soc. B*, **146,** 339-356.

CHANG, H. T. (1950) The repetitive discharges of cortico-thalamic reverberating circuit. *J. Neurophysiol.*, **13,** 235-257.

CHANG, H. T. (1951) Dendritic potential of cortical neurons produced by direct electrical stimulation of the cerebral cortex. *J. Neurophysiol.*, **14,** 1-21.

CHILD, C. M. (1921) The Origin and Development of the Nervous System. Chicago.

CHORAZYNA, H. (1959) Investigations of recent memory of acoustic stimuli in normal dogs. *Bull. Acad. pol. Sci.*, **7,** 119-121.

CHORAZYNA, H. and STEPIEŃ, L. Unpublished data.

CHOW, K. L. (1950) A retrograde degeneration study of the cortical projection field of the pulvinar in the monkey. *J. comp. Neurol.*, **93,** 313-340.

CHOW, K. L. (1951) Effects of partial extirpations of the posterior association cortex on visually mediated behavior in monkeys. *Compve. Psychol. Monogr.*, **20,** 187-217.

CHOW, K. L. (1952) Further studies on selective ablation of associative cortex in relation to visually mediated behavior. *J. comp. physiol. Psychol.*, **45,** 109-118.

CHOW, K. L. (1954a) Lack of behavioral effects following destruction of some thalamic association nuclei in monkeys. *A.M.A. Arch. Neurol. Psychiat.*, **71,** 762-771.

CHOW, K. L. (1954b) Effects of temporal neocortical ablation on visual discrimination learning sets in monkeys. *J. comp. physiol. Psychol.*, **47,** 194-198.

CHOW, K. L., DEMENT, W. C. and JOHN, E. R. (1957) Conditioned electrocorticographic potentials and behavioral avoidance response in cat. *J. Neurophysiol.*, **20,** 482-493.

CHOW, K. L. and HUTT, P. J. (1953) The 'association cortex' of *Macaca mulatta*: a review of recent contributions to its anatomy and functions. *Brain*, **76,** 625-677.

CHOW, K. L. and ORBACH, J. (1957) Performance of visual discriminations presented tachistoscopically in monkeys with temporal neocortical ablations. *J. comp. Physiol. Psychol.*, **50,** 636-640.

CHOW, K. L. and SURVIS, J. (1958) Retention of overlearned visual habit after temporal cortical ablation in monkey. *A.M.A. Arch. Neurol. Psychiat.*, **79,** 640-646.

CIGANEK, L. (1958a) Potentiels corticaux chez l'homme évoqués par les stimuli photiques. *Rev. neurol.*, **99,** 194-196.

CIGANEK, L. (1958b) Postdécharge rythmique corticale chez l'homme, évoquée par les stimuli photiques. *Rev. neurol.*, **99,** 196-198.

CLARE, M. H. and BISHOP, G. H. (1954) Responses from an association area secondarily activated from optic cortex. *J. Neurophysiol.*, **17,** 271-277.

CLARE, M. H. and BISHOP, G. H. (1955) Properties of dendrites; apical dendrites of the cat cortex. *Electroenceph. clin. Neurophysiol.*, **7,** 85-98.

CLARK, W. E., LE GROS (1941) Observations on the association fibre system of the visual cortex and central representation of the retina. *J. Anat. (Lond.)*, **75,** 225-235.

CLARK, S. L. and WARD, J. W. (1945) Electroencephalogram of different cortical regions of normal and anaesthetized cats. *J. Neurophysiol.*, **8,** 99-112.

COGHILL, G. E. (1929) Anatomy and the Problems of Behaviour. New York, Macmillan.

COHEN, S., LEVI-MONTALCINI, R. and HAMBURGER, V. (1954) A nerve growth-stimulating factor isolated from sarcomas 37 and 180. *Proc. nat. Acad. Sci. (Wash.)*, **40,** 1014-1018.

COLLE, J. and MASSION, J. (1958) Effet de la stimulation du cortex moteur sur l'activité électrique des nerfs phréniques et médians. *Arch. int. Physiol.*, **66,** 496-514.

CORDEAU, J. P. and MANCIA, M. (1959) E.E.G. synchronizing mechanism originating in the lower brain stem. *Electroenceph. clin. Neurophysiol.*, **11,** 382. Soc. Proc.

CORDEAU, J. P. and MANCIA, M. (1958) Effect of unilateral chronic lesions of the midbrain on the electrocortical activity of the cat. *Arch. ital. Biol.*, **96**, 374-399.

COWAN, E. A. (1923) Experiment testing ability of the cat to make delayed response and to maintain a given response toward a varying stimulus. *J. comp. Psychol.*, **3**, 1-9.

CULLER, E. A. and METTLER, F. A. (1934) Conditioned behaviour in a decorticate dog. *J. comp. Psychol.*, **18**, 291-303.

CURTIS, D. R. and ECCLES, J. C. (1960) Synaptic action during and after repetitive stimulation *J. Physiol. (Lond.)* **150**, 374-398.

DARWIN, C. (1839) *Narrative of the Surveying Voyages of His Majesty's Ships, Adventure and Beagle, between the years 1826-1836.* Vol. III, London.

DARWIN, C. (1859) *On the Origin of Species by means of Natural Selection.* London.

DARWIN, C. (1871) *The Descent of Man, and Selection in Relation to Sex.* London.

DARWIN, C. (1872) *The Expression of the Emotions in Man and Animals.* London.

DARWIN, C. (1887) *Life and Letters of Charles Darwin.* Ed. Francis Darwin. 3 vols. New York and London, Appleton.

DARWIN, C. (1958) *The Autobiography of Charles Darwin* (1809-1882). Ed. Nora Barlow. London, Collins.

DAVIS, H., DAVIS, P. A., LOOMIS, A. L., HARVEY, E. N. and HOBART, G. (1939) Electrical reactions of the human brain to auditory stimulation during sleep. *J. Neurophysiol.*, **2**, 500-514.

DAVIS, P. A. (1939) Effects of acoustic stimuli on the waking human brain. *J. Neurophysiol.*, **2**, 494-499.

DAWSON, G. D. (1947) Cerebral responses to electrical stimulation of peripheral nerve in man. *J. Neurol., Neurosurg. Psychiat.*, **10**, 137-140.

DE CASTRO, F. (1942) Modelación de un arco reflejo en el simpático, uniéndolo con la raíz aferente central del vago. Nueva ideas sobre la sinapsis. *Trab. Inst. Cajal. Invest. Biol.*, **34**, 217-301.

DE CASTRO, F. (1951) Aspects anatomiques de la transmission synaptique ganglionnaire chez les mammifères. *Arch. Int. Physiol.*, **59**, 479-513.

DELGADO, J. M. R. (1959) Prolonged stimulation of brain in awake monkeys. *J. Neurophysiol.*, **22**, 458-475.

DELGADO, J. M. R. and ANAND, B. K. (1953) Increase in food intake induced by electrical stimulation of the lateral hypothalamus. *Amer. J. Physiol.*, **172**, 162-168.

DELL, P. (1957) Personal demonstration.

DEMENT, W. (1958) The occurrence of low voltage, fast, electroencephalogram patterns during behavioral sleep in the cat. *Electroenceph. clin. Neurophysiol.*, **10**, 291-296.

DEMENT, W. and KLEITMAN, N. (1957) Cyclic variations in EEG during sleep and their relation to eye movements, body motility, and dreaming. *Electroenceph. clin. Neurophysiol.*, **9**, 673-690.

DEMPSEY, E. W. and MORISON, R. S. (1943) The electrical activity of a thalamocortical relay system. *Amer. J. Physiol.*, **138**, 283-296.

DEMPSEY, E. W., MORISON, R. S. and MORISON, B. R. (1941) Some afferent diencephalic pathways related to cortical potentials in the cat. *Amer. J. Physiol.*, **131**, 718-731.

DE ROBERTIS, E. (1955) Submicroscopic organization of some synaptic regions. *Acta neurol. lat.-amer.*, **1**, 3-15.

DE ROBERTIS, E. (1958) Submicroscopic morphology and function of the synapse. *Exp. Cell Res.*, **5**, 347-369.

DE ROBERTIS, E. D. P. and FRANCHI, C. M. (1956) Electron microscope observations on synaptic vesicles in synapses of the retinal rods and cones. *J. biophys. biochem. Cytol.*, **2**, 307-318.

DESMEDT, J. E. and LA GRUTTA, G. (1957) The effect of selective inhibition of pseudocholinesterase on spontaneous and evoked activity of the cat's cerebral cortex. *J. Physiol.*, **136**, 20-40.

DETWILER, S. R. (1936) *Neuroembryology; an Experimental Study.* New York, Macmillan.

DI GIORGIO, A. M. (1943) Ricerche sulla persistenza dei fenomeni cerebellari nell 'animale spinale. *Arch. Fisiol.*, **43**, 47-63.

DOBROVOLSKII, W. M. (1911) On alimentary trace reflexes. Russian Dissertation.

DODGE, R. (1923) Habituation to rotation. *J. exp. Psychol.*, **6**, 1-36.

DOTY, R. W. (1959) Conditioned reflexes formed and evoked by brain stimulation. In *Electrical Stimulation of the Brain*. D. E. Sheer, Editor. Houston, University of Texas Press. In the Press.

DOTY, R. W., BECK, E. C. and KOOI, K. A. (1959) Effect of brain-stem lesions on conditioned responses of cats. *Exp. Neurol.*, **1**, 360-385.

DOTY, R. W. and RUTLEDGE, L. T. (1959) 'Generalization' between cortically and peripherally applied stimuli eliciting conditioned reflexes. *J. Neurophysiol.*, **22**, 428-435.

DOTY, R. W., RUTLEDGE, L. T., JR. and LARSEN, R. M. (1956) Conditioned reflexes established to electrical stimulation of cat cerebral cortex. *J. Neurophysiol.*, **19**, 401-415.

DOWNER, J. L. DEC. (1958) Role of corpus callosum in transfer of training in *Macaca mulatta*. *Fed. Proc.*, **17**, 37.

DUMONT, S. and DELL, P. (1958) Facilitations spécifiques et non-spécifiques des réponses visuelles corticales. *J. Physiol. (Paris)*, **50**, 261-264.

DUNCAN, C. P. (1948) The retroactive effect of electroshock on learning in rats. *J. comp. physiol. Psychol.*, **42**, 32-44.

DUSSER DE BARENNE, J. G., GAROL, H. W. and McCULLOCH, W. S. (1942) Physiological neuronography of the cortico-striatal connections. *Res. Publ. Assoc. nerv. ment. Dis.*, **21**, 246-266.

EBNER, F. F. and MYERS, R. E. (1960) Inter- and Intra-hemispheric transmission of tactile gnosis in normal and corpus callosum-sectioned monkeys. *Fed. Proc.*, **19**, 292.

ECCLES, J. C. (1951) Interpretation of action potentials evoked in the cerebral cortex. *Electroenceph. clin. Neurophysiol.*, **3**, 449-464.

ECCLES, J. C. (1953) *The Neurophysiological Basis of Mind.* London, Oxford University Press.

ECCLES, J. C. (1957) The physiology of nerve cells. London, Oxford University Press.

ECCLES, J. C. and KRNJEVIC, K. (1959a) Potential changes recorded inside primary afferent fibres within the spinal cord. *J. Physiol. (Lond.)*, **149**, 250-273.

ECCLES, J. C. and KRNJEVIC, K. (1959b) Presynaptic changes associated with post-tetanic potentiation in the spinal cord. *J. Physiol. (Lond.)*, **149**, 274-287.

ECCLES, J. C., KRNJEVIĆ, K. and MILEDI, R. (1959) Delayed effects of peripheral severance of afferent nerve fibres on the efficacy of their central synapses. *J. Physiol. (Lond.)*, **145**, 204-220.

ECCLES, J. C. and McINTYRE, A. K. (1953) The effects of disuse and of activity on mammalian spinal reflexes. *J. Physiol. (Lond.)*, **121**, 492-516.

ECCLES, R. M. and WESTERMAN, R. A. (1959) Enhanced synaptic function due to excess use. *Nature (Lond.)*, **184**, 460-461.

ECHLIN, F. A., ARNETT, V. and ZOLL, J. (1952) Paroxysmal high voltage discharges from isolated and partially isolated human and animal cerebral cortex. *Electroenceph. clin. Neurophysiol.*, **4**, 147-164.

ECTORS, L. (1936) Étude de l'activité électrique du cortex cérébral chez le lapin non narcotisé ni curarisé. *Arch. int. Physiol.*, **43**, 267-298.

EDDS, M. V., JR. (1950) Hypertrophy of nerve fibers to functionally overloaded muscles. *J. com. Neurol.*, **93**, 259-275.

EIBL-EIBESFELDT, I. (1955a) Angeborenes und Erworbenes im Nestbauverhalten der Wander-ratte. *Naturwiss. ensthaften.*, **42**, 633-634.

EIBL-EIBESFELDT, I. (1955b) Zur Biologie des Iltis (Putorius putorius L.). *Verh. dtsch. zool. Ges. Zool. Anz.*, **19**, 304-314.

EIBL-EIBESFELDT, I. (1956a) Angeborenes und Erworbenes in der Technik des Beutetötens (Versuche am Iltis, *Putorius putorius* L.) *Z. Säugetierkunde*, **21**, 135-137.

EIBL-EIBESFELDT, I. (1956b) Über die ontogenetische Entwicklung der Technik des Nüsseöff-nens vom Eichhörnchen (*Sciurus vulgaris* L.). *Z. Säugetierkunde*, **21**, 132-134.

EIBL-EIBESFELDT, I. (1956c) Putorius putorius L.: Beutefang I. (Töten von Wanderratten). Enstitut f.d. wiss. Film Encyclopaedia cinematographia. E 106, Göttingen.

EIBL-EIBESFELDT, I. (1957) Rattus norvegicus BERK. Nestbau erfahrener und unerfahrener Tiere. Institut f.d. Wiss. Film, Encyclopaedia cinematographia E. Göttingen.

EIBL-EIBESFELDT, I. (1958) Das Verhalten der Nagetiere. *Handbuch der Zoologie*, **10** (13), 1-88. Berlin, Walter de Gruyter.

EIBL-EIBESFELDT, I. and KRAMER, S. (1958) Ethology, the comparative study of animal behavior. *Quart. Rev. Biol.* **33**, 181-211.

EIDELBERG, E. (1959) Personal communication. In the Press.

EIDELBERG, E., KONIGSMARK, B. and FRENCH, J. D. (1959) Electrocortical manifestations of epilepsy in the monkey. *Electroenceph. clin. Neurophysiol.*, **11**, 121-128.

ELDRED, E., GRANIT, R. and MERTON, P. A. (1953) Supraspinal control of the muscle spindles and its significance. *J. Physiol. (Lond.)*, **122**, 498-523.

ELLIOT SMITH, G. (1910) Some problems relating to the evolution of the brain. The Arris and Gale Lectures. *Lancet*, **1**, 1, 147, 221.

ENDRÖCZI, E., BATA, G. and MARTIN, J. (1958) Untersuchungen über die Sekretion von Nebennierenrindenhormonen. *Endokrinologie*, **35**, 280-290.

ENDRÖCZI, E. and LISSÁK, K. (1960) The role of the mesencephalon, diencephalon and orchicortex in the activation and inhibition of the pituitary-adrenocortical system. *Acta Physiol. hung.*, **17**, 39-55.

ENDRÖCZI, E., LISSÁK, K., BOHUS, B. and KOVÁCS, S. (1959) *Acta Physiol. hung.*, **16**, 17.

ENDRÖCZI, E., LISSÁK, K. and TELEGDY, G. (1958) Influence of sexual and adrenocortical hormones on the maternal aggressivity. *Acta Physiol. hung.*, **14**, 353.

ENDRÖCZI, E., TELEGDY, G. and LISSÁK, K. (1957) *Acta Physiol. hung.*, **11**, 393.

ERICKSON, T. C. (1940) Spread of the epileptic discharge. An experimental study of the afterdischarge induced by electrical stimulation of the cerebral cortex. *Arch. Neurol. Psychiat. (Chicago)*, **43**, 429-452.

ESTABLE, C. (1923) Notes sur la structure comparative de l'écorce cérébelleuse, et dérivées physiologiques possibles. *Trab. Lab. Invest. Biol. Univ. Mad.*, **19**, 169-256.

ESTABLE, C. (1957) Espectro sináptico, constantes sinápticas y revisión del concepto de sinapsis. *Asociación Latino Americana de Ciencias Fisiológicas. Primera Reunión Científica, Punta del Este, Uruguay*, **74.**

ESTABLE, C., FRANCHI, C. M. and TRUJILLO-CENOZ, O. Unpublished observations.

ESTABLE, C., REISSIG, M. and DE ROBERTIS, E. (1954) Microscopic and submicroscopic structure of the synapsis in the ventral ganglion of the acoustic nerve. *Exp. Cell Res.*, **6**, 255-262.

ETTLINGER, G. and WEGENER, J. (1958) Somaesthetic alternation, discrimination and orientation after frontal and parietal lesions in monkeys. *Quart. J. exper. Psychol.*, **10**, 177-186.

EULER, C. VON, MAGOUN, H. W. and RICCI, G. (1956) Characteristics of evoked potentials in the auditory cortex. Communication XXe Cong. int. Physiol., Bruxelles, pp. 932-933.

FATT, P. (1954) Biophysics of junctional transmission. *Physiol. Rev.*, **34**, 674-710.

FELDBERG, W., MALCOLM, J. L. and DARIAN SMITH, I. (1957) Effect of tubocurarine on the electrical activity of the cat's brain under chloralose. *J. Physiol. (Lond.)*, **138**, 178-201.

FENG, T. P., LIU, Y. and SHEN, E. (1956) Pathways mediating irradiation of auditory and visual impulses to the sensorimotor cortex. XXe Cong. int. Physiol., Bruxelles, p. 997.

FEOKRITOVA, Y. P. (1912) [Time as conditioned stimulus of salivary glands] (Russian). Dissertation.

FERRIER, D. (1875) The Croonian Lecture. Experiments on the brain of monkeys (second series). *Phil. Trans.*, **165**, 433-488.

FESSARD, A. (1954) Mechanisms of nervous integration and conscious experience. In *Brain Mechanisms and consciousness.* Oxford, Blackwell, pp. 200-236.

FESSARD, A. (1960a) Le conditionnement considéré à l'échelle du Neurone. In the Moscow Colloquium on Electroencephalography of Higher Nervous Activity (Moscow, Oct. 1958). *Electroenceph. J. clin. Neurophysiol.*, **13**, 157-184.

FESSARD, A. (1960b) The rôle of neuronal networks in sensory communications within the Brain. *Symposium on Sensory Communications*, Boston, July 1959. In the Press.

FESSARD, A. and GASTAUT, H. (1958) Corrélations neurophysiologiques de la formation des réflexes conditionnés. In *Le Conditionnement et l'Apprentissage, Symposium de Strasbourg*, 1956. Presses Universitaires, France, Paris, p. 216.

FESSARD, A. and SZABO, TH. (1953) Sur l'organisation anatomofonctionnelle des lobes électriques de la Torpille. *J. Physiol. (Paris)*, **45**, 114-117.

FESSARD, A. and SZABO, TH. (1959) Possibilité d'un transfert de la facilitation post-tétanique dans une chaîne disynaptique. *J. Physiol. (Paris)*, **51**, 465-466.

FESSARD, A. and TAUC, L. (1958) Effet de répétition sur l'amplitude des potentiels postsynaptiques d'un soma neuronique. *J. Physiol. (Paris)*, **50**, 277-281.

Fessard, A. and Tauc, L. (1960) Variations prolongées du rythme de neurones autoactifs provoquées par la stimulation synaptique. *J. Physiol. (Paris)*, **52,** 101.

Fiodorov, V. K. (1952) Basic Principles of Mutual Influences Between Different Motor Reactions. *Sechenov J. Physiol.*, **37,** vol. XXXVII, No. 5, p. 559. In Russian.

Finan, J. L. (1942) Delayed response with pre-delay reinforcement in monkeys after the removal of the frontal lobes. *Amer. J. Psychol.*, **55,** 202-214.

Forbes, A. and Morison, B. R. (1939) Cortical response to sensory stimulation under deep barbiturate narcosis. *J. Neurophysiol.*, **2,** 112-128.

Forbes, A. and Sherrington, C. S. (1914) Acoustic reflexes in the decerebrate cat. *Amer. J. Physiol.*, **35,** 367-376.

Freeman, G. L. and Krasno, L. (1940) Inhibitory functions of the corpus striatum. *Arch. Neurol. Psychiat. (Chicago)*, **44,** 323-327.

French, J. D., Amerongen, F. K. von and Magoun, H. W. (1952) An activating system in brain stem of monkey. *Arch. Neurol. Psychiat, (Chicago)*, **68,** 577-590.

French, J. D., Gernandt, B. E. and Livingston, R. B. (1956) Regional differences in seizure susceptibility in monkey cortex. *A.M.A. Arch. Neurol. Psychiat.*, **75,** 260-274.

French, J. D., Hernández-Peón, R. and Livingston, R. B. (1955) Projections from cortex to cephalic brain stem (reticular formation) in monkey. *J. Neurophysiol.*, **18,** 74-95.

French, J. D. and Magoun, H. W. (1952) Effects of chronic lesions in central cephalic brain stem of monkeys. *Arch. Neurol. Psychiat. (Chicago)*, **68,** 591-604.

French, J. D., Verzeano, M. and Magoun, H. W. (1953a) An extralemniscal sensory system in the brain. *Arch. Neurol. Psychiat. (Chicago)*, **69,** 505-518.

French, J. D., Verzeano, M. and Magoun, H. W. (1953b) A neural basis of the anesthetic state. *A.M.A. Arch. Neurol. Psychiat.*, **69,** 519-529.

Freud, S. (1933) *New Introductory Lectures on Psycho-analysis.* New York, Norton.

Freud, S. (1947) *The Ego and the ID.* London, Hogarth Press.

Freud, S. (1953) *On Aphasia.* New York, Internat. Univ. Press.

Frued, S. (1954) *The Origins of Psycho-analysis.* New York, Basic Books.

Fuller, J. L., Rosvold, H. E. and Pribram, K. H. (1957) The effect on affective and cognitive behavior in the dog of lesions of the pyriformamygdala-hippocampal complex. *J. comp. physiol. Psychol.*, **50,** 89-96.

Furshpan, E. J. and Potter, D. D. (1959) Transmission at the giant motor synapses of the crayfish. *J. Physiol. (Lond.)*, **145,** 289-325.

Gagel, O. (1953) Kritik der Neuronenlehre. In *Handbuch der inneren Medizin* (Bergmann and Staehelin), 4th ed., Vol. 5, pt. 2, 487-491, Berlin, Springer.

Galambos, R. (1959) Electrical correlates of conditioned learning. *The Central Nervous System and Behavior.* M. A. B. Brazier, Editor. Transactions of the first conference. New York, Josiah Macy, Jr. Foundation, p. 450.

Galambos, R. and Sheatz, G. An EEG study of classical conditioning. Manuscript in preparation.

Galambos, R., Sheatz, G. and Vernier, V. G. (1956) Electrophysiological correlates of a conditioned response in cats. *Science*, **123,** 376-377.

Galeano, C., Roig, J. A., Segundo, J. P. and Sommer-Smith, J. A. (1959) Alternate application of tone and subcutaneous stimulus in cat. I. Effect of tone cessation. *XXI International Congress of Physiological Sciences, Buenos Aires. 9-15 August 1959. Abstracts of Communications*, 101.

Gant, H. (1942) Cardiac conditioned reflexes to painful stimuli. *Fed. Proc.*, Vol. I, No. I, Part II, p. 28.

Garol, H. W. (1942) The 'motor' cortex of the cat. *J. Neuropath. exp. Neurol.*, **1,** 139-145.

Gastaut, H. (1958) Some aspects of the neurophysiological basis of conditioned reflexes and behaviour. In *Ciba Foundation Symposium on the Neurological Basis of Behaviour.* London, J. & A. Churchill.

Gastaut, H. (1958) The Role of the Reticular Formation in Establishing Conditioned Reactions. *Reticular Formation of the Brain.* Boston, pp. 561-590.

Gastaut, H. and Hunter, J. (1950) An experimental study of the mechanism of photic activation in idiopathic epilepsy. *Electroencheph. clin. Neurophysiol.*, **2,** 263-287.

Gastaut, H. and Fischer-Williams, M. (1959) *The physiopathology of epileptic seizures.* Chapter XIV. Handbook of Physiology, Section 1: Neurophysiology, Vol. 1, Ed. John Field. American Physiological Society, Washington, D.C.

GASTAUT, H., JUS, C., MORRELL, F., STORM VAN LEUWEN, W., DONGIER, S., NAQUET, R., REGIS, H., ROGER, A., BEKKERING, D., KAMP, A. and WERRE, J. (1957) 'Étude topographique des réactions électroencéphalographiques conditionnées chez l'Homme.' *Electroenceph. clin. Neurophysiol.*, **9**, 1-34.

GASTAUT, H., RÉGIS, H., DONGIER, S. and ROGER, A. (1956) Conditionnement électroencéphalographique des décharges épileptiques et notion d'épilepsie réflexo-conditionnée. *Rev. Neurol.*, **94**, 829-835.

GASTAUT, H. and ROUGET, A. (1958) Neurophysiological basis of the higher nervous activity. Report. Internat. Coll. on EEG of the Conditioned Reflex. Moscow.

GASTAUT, H., NAQUET, R. and VIGOUROUX, R. (1953) Un cas d'épilepsie amygdalienne expérimentale chez le chat. *Electroenceph. clin. Neurophysiol.*, **5**, 291-294.

GASTAUT, Y. (1953) Les pointes négatives évoquées sur le vertex. Leur signification psychophysiologique et pathologique. *Rev. neurol.*, **89**, 382-399.

GAUTHIER, C., PARMA, M. and ZANCHETTI, A. (1956) Effect of electrocortical arousal upon development and configuration of specific evoked potentials. *Electroenceph. clin. Neurophysiol.*, **8**, 237-243.

GAVLICEK, V. (1958) Electroencephalographic characteristics of conditioned defensive dominant state. *Sechenov J. Physiol.*, **49**, 4.

GEIGER, R. S. (1957) *In vitro* studies on the growth properties of brain cortex cells of adult individuals. *Ultrastructure and Cellular Chemistry of Neural Tissue.* H. Waelsch, Editor. New York, Paul B. Hoeber, pp. 83-99.

GERARD, R. W. (1949) Physiology and Psychiatry. *Amer. J. Psychiat.*, **106**, 161-173.

GERARD, R. W. (1951) The physiology of pain: abnormal neuron states in causalgia and related phenomena. *Anesthesiology*, **12**, 1-13.

GERARD, R. W. (1953) What is memory? *Sci. Amer.*, **189**, 118-125.

GERARD, R. W. (1955) Biological roots of psychiatry. *Science*, **122**, 225-230.

GERARD, R. W. (1960a) Neurophysiology, an integration. *Handbook of Physiology*. John Field, Horace Magoun and Victor Hall, Editors. Washington, D.C., The American Physiological Society. In the Press.

GERARD, R. W. (1960b) Becoming: the residue of change. In *Darwin Centenary Volume.* S. Tax, Editor. Chicago, University of Chicago Press. In the Press.

GERARD, R. W., MARSHALL, W. H. and SAUL, L. J. (1936) Electrical activity of the cat's brain. *Arch. Neurol. Psychiat. (Chicago)*, **36**, 675-738.

GERSUNI, G. V., KOJEVNIKOV, V. A., MARUSEWA, A. M., AVAKIAN, R. V., RODIONOWA, E. A., ALTMAN, J. A. and SOROKO, V. I. (1958) Reactivity modifications and electrical responses of the auditory system in different states of the higher nervous activity. Moscow Colloquium on EEG and Behavior. *Electroenceph. clin. Neurophysiol.* In the Press.

GIRDEN, E., METTLER, F. A., FINCH, C. and CULLER, E. (1936) Conditioned responses in decorticate dog to acoustic, thermal and tactile stimulation. *J. Comp. Psychol.*, **21**, 367-385.

GIURGEA, C. (1953a) *Elaborarea Reflexului Conditionat prin Excitarea Directa a Scoartei Cerebrale.* Bucharest, Editura Academiei Rep. Pop. Romane, 154 pp.

GIURGEA, C. (1953b) Dinamica elaborarii conexiunii temporare, prin excitarea directa a scoartei cerebrale. *Studii Cercetari Fiziologie si Neurologie.*, **4**, 41-73.

GIURGEA, C. and RAICIULESCU, N. (1957) Noi date asupra reflexului conditionat prin excitarea directa a cortexului cerebral. *Rev. Fiziol.*, **4**, 218-225.

GIURGEA, C., RAICIULESCU, N. and MARCOVICI, G. (1957) Reflex conditionat interemisferic prin excitarea directa corticala dupa sectionarea corpului calos, Studiu anatomo-histologic. *Rev. Fiziol.*, **4**, 408-414.

GIURGEA, C. and RAICIULESCU, N. (1959) Étude électroencéphalographique du reflexe conditionnel a l'excitation electrique corticale directe. *Proc. First int. Cong. Neurol. Sci.*, **3**, van Bogaert, L. and Radermecker, J. (Ed.). London, Pergamon.

GLICKMAN, S. E. (1958) Deficits in avoidance learning produced by stimulation of the ascending reticular formation. *Canad. J. Psychol.*, **12**, 97-102.

GOLDBERG, J. M., DIAMOND, I. T. and NEFF, W. D. (1957) Auditory discrimination after ablation of temporal and insular cortex in cat. *Fed. Proc.*, **16**, 47.

GOLTZ, F. (1884) Ueber Localisationen der Functionen des Grosshirnes. *Verhdtsch. Kongr. inn. Med.*, **3**, 261-275.

GOLTZ, F. (1892) Der Hund ohne Grosshirn. *Pflüg. Arch. ges. Physiol.*, **51**, 570-614.

XX

GOMULICKI, B. R. (1953) The development and present status of the trace theory of memory. Cambridge University Press, Cambridge.

GORSKA, T. and JANKOWSKA, E. (1959) Instrumental conditioned reflexes of the deafferentated limb in cats and rats. *Bull. Acad. pol. Sci.*, **7**, 161-164.

GRANIT, R. (1955*a*) *Receptors and sensory perception.* New Haven: Yale University Press.

GRANIT, R. (1955*b*) Centrifugal and antidromic effects on ganglion cells of retina. *J. Neurophysiol.*, **18**, 388-411.

GRANIT, R. (1956) Reflex rebound by post-tetanic potentiation, temporal summation, spasticity. *J. Physiol. (Lond.)*, **131**, 32-51.

GRASTYÁN, E., LISSÁK, K. and KÉKESI, F. (1956) Facilitation and inhibition of conditioned alimentary and defensive reflexes by stimulation of the hypothalamus and reticular formation. *Acta Physiol. hung.*, **9**, 133-150.

GRASTYÁN, E., LISSÁK, K., KÉKESI, F., SZABÓ, I. and VEREBY, GY. (1956) Beiträge zur Physiologie des Hippocampus. *Physiol. bohemoslov.*, **7**, 9-18.

GRASTYÁN, E., LISSÁK, K., MADARÁSZ, I. and DONHOFFER, H. (1959) Hippocampal electrical activity during the development of conditioned reflexes. *Electroenceph. clin. Neurophysiol.*, **11**, 409-430.

GREEN, J. D. (1958) The Rhinencephalon: Aspects of Its Relation to Behavior and the Reticular Activating System. *Reticular Formation of the Brain.* Boston-Toronto, pp. 607-620.

GREEN, J. D. and ADEY, W. R. (1956) Electrophysiological studies of hippocampal connections and excitability. *Electroenceph. clin. Neurophysiol.*, **8**, 245-262.

GREEN, J. D. and ARDUINI, A. (1954) Hippocampal electrical activity in arousal. *J. Neurophysiol.*, **17**, 533-557.

GREEN, J. D. and MACHNE, X. (1955) Unit activity of rabbit hippocampus. *Amer. J. Physiol.*, **181**, 219-224.

GREEN, J. D. and MAXWELL, D. (1959) Electron microscopy of hippocampus and other central nervous structures. *Anat. Rec.*, **133**, 449.

GREEN, J. D. and NAQUET, R. (1957) Étude de la propagation et à distance des démarches épileptiques. *IV Congrès International d'Electroencéphalographie et de Neurophysiologie.* Bruxelles: Editions 'Acta Medica Belgica', pp. 225-249.

GRETHER, W. F. (1938) Pseudo-conditioning without paired stimulation encountered in attempted backward conditioning. *J. Comp. Psychol.*, **25**, 91-96.

GREY WALTER, W. (1950) Technique Interpretation. *Electroencephalography.* D. Hill and G. Parr, Editors. New York, MacMillan Co., pp. 63-91.

GREY WALTER, W. (1954) Theoretical properties of diffuse projection systems in relation to behaviour and consciousness. *Brain mechanisms and consciousness.* J. F. Delafresnaye, Editor. Charles C Thomas, Springfield, Illinois, pp. 345-369.

GRIFFITH, C. R. (1920) An experimental study of dizziness. *J. exp. Psychol.*, **3**, 89-125.

GRIFFITH, C. R. (1924) A note on the persistence of 'practice effect' in rotation experiments. *J. comp. Psychol.*, **4**, 137-149.

GROHMANN, J. (1939) Modifikation oder Funktionsreifung. *Z. Tierpsychol.*, **2**, 132-144.

GROSSMAN, F. S. (1909) [Materials concerning physiology of salivary trace conditioned reflexes] (Russian). Dissertation.

GUTMANN, E. and SANDERS, F. K. (1943) Recovery of fibre numbers and diameters in the regeneration of peripheral nerves. *J. Physiol. (Lond.)*, **101**, 489-518.

GUZMÁN, F. C., ALCARÁZ, V. M. and FERNÁNDEZ, G. A. (1957) Potenciales evocados en la corteza visual durante el proceso de condicionamiento. *Bol. Inst. Estud. med. biol.*, **15**, 73-85.

HAAS, A. M. L., LOMBROSO, C. and MERLIS, J. K. (1953) Participation of the cortex in experimental reflex myoclonus. *Electroencph. clin. Neurophysiol.*, **5**, 177-186.

HAGBARTH, K. E. and FEX, J. (1959) Centrifugal influences on single unit activity in spinal sensory paths. *J. Neurophysiol.*, **22**, 321-338.

HAGBARTH, K. E. and KERR, D. I. B. (1954) Central influences on spinal afferent conduction. *J. Neurophysiol.*, **17**, 295-307.

HAGBARTH, K. E. and KUGELBERG, E. (1958) Plasticity of the human abdominal skin reflex. *Brain*, **81**, 305-318.

HAMBERGER, C. A. (1949) Cytochemical investigations on N. vestibularis. *Acta oto-laryng. (Stockh.)*, Supp. **78**, 55-62.

HAMBERGER, C. A. and HYDÉN, H. (1949a) Production of nucleoproteins in the vestibular ganglion. *Acta oto-laryng. (Stockh.)*, Supp. **75**, 53-81.

HAMBERGER, C. A. and HYDÉN, H. (1949b) Transneuronal chemical changes in Deiters' nucleus. *Acta oto-laryng. (Stockh.)*, **75**, 82-113.

HAMMER, G. (1958) On quantitative cytochemical changes in spiral ganglion cells after acoustic trauma. *Acta oto-laryng. (Stockh.)*, **140**, 137-144.

HARLOW, H. F. (1949) The formation of learning sets. *Psychol. Rev.*, **56**, 51-65.

HARLOW, H. F. and DAGNON, J. (1943) Problem solution by monkeys following bilateral removal of the prefrontal areas: I. The discrimination and discrimination-reversal problems. *J. exp. Psychol.*, **32**, 351-356.

HARLOW, H. F., DAVIS, R. T., SETTLAGE, P. H. and MEYER, D. R. (1952) Analysis of frontal and posterior association syndromes in brain-damaged monkeys. *J. comp. physiol. Psychol.*, **45**, 419-429.

HEARST, E., BEER, B., SHEATZ, G. C. and GALAMBOS, R. (1960) Some electrophysiological correlates of conditioning in the monkey. *Electroenceph. clin. Neurophysiol.*, **12**, 137-152.

HEBB, D. O. (1953) Heredity and environment in mammalian behaviour. *Brit. J. anim. Behav.*, **1**, 43-47.

HEBB, D. O. (1949) *The Organization of Behavior*. New York, Wiley.

HEBB, D. O. (1958) *A Textbook of Psychology*. Philadelphia, Saunders.

HELD, H. (1897) Beiträge zur Structur der Nervenzellen und ihrer Fortsätze. *Arch. Anat. Physiol. Anat. M. Abt.*, Suppl. Bd., 273-312.

HEINROTH, O. (1911) Beiträge zur Biologie, namentlich Ethologie und Psychologie der Anatiden. *Verh. 5. int. Orn. Kongr.*, Berlin, pp. 589-702.

HEISSLER, N. (1958) Quelques travaux des Psychologues soviétiques sur la réaction d'orientation. *Année Psychol.*, **58**, 407-426.

HENRY, C. E. (1950) Observations on alternating burst-suppression activity of deafferented cortex. *Electroenceph. clin. Neurophysiol.*, **2**, 232.

HERNÁNDEZ-PEÓN, R. (1955) Central mechanisms controlling conduction along central sensory pathways. *Acta Neurol. lat.-amer.*, **1**, 256-264.

HERNÁNDEZ-PEÓN, R. (1957) Discussion on Interpretation of conditioning on the basis of Electroencefalographic Data. IV. *International Congress of Electroencephalography and Clinical Neurophysiology*. Acta Med. Belgica (Bruxelles), pp. 450-455.

HERNÁNDEZ-PEÓN, R. (1958) Habituation in the visual pathway. *Acta Neurol. lat.-amer.*, **4**, 121.

HERNÁNDEZ-PEÓN, R. (1959) Neurophysiological correlates of habituation and other manifestations of plastic inhibition (internal inhibition). *Colloquium on Electroencephalographic Study of Higher Nervous Activity. Academy of Sciences of the U.S.S.R. Moscow. Electroenceph. clin. Nuerophysiol.* (Suppl.). In the Press.

HERNÁNDEZ-PEÓN, R., ALCOCER-CUARON, C., LAVIN, A. and SANTIBAÑEZ, G. (1959) Centrifugal suppression of induced activity in the olfactory bulb during distraction and olfactory habituation. (To be published.)

HERNÁNDEZ-PEÓN, R., BRUST-CARMONA, H., ECKHAUS, E., LÓPEZ-MENDOZA, E. and ALCOCER-CUARÓN, C. (1958) Effects of cortical and subcortical lesions on salivary conditioned response. *Acta Neurol. lat.-amer.*, **4**, 111-120.

HERNÁNDEZ-PEÓN, R., DAVIDOVICH, A. and MIRANDA, H. Habituation to tactile stimuli in the spinal trigeminal sensory nucleus. (To be published.)

HERNÁNDEZ-PEÓN, R. and DONOSO, M. (1957) Influence of attention and suggestion upon subcortical evoked electric activity in the human brain. Vol. III. van Bogaert and Radermecker J. Ed. First international congress of neurological sciences. Bruxelles, pp. 385-396.

HERNÁNDEZ-PEÓN, R., GUZMÁN-FLORES, C., ALCARAZ, M. and FERNÁNDEZ-GUARDIOLA, A. (1956) Photic potentials in the visual pathway during 'attention' and photic 'habituation'. *Fed. Proc.*, **15**, 91-92.

HERNÁNDEZ-PEÓN, R., GUZMÁN-FLORES, C., ALCARAZ, M. and FERNÁNDEZ-GUARDIOLA, A. (1957) Sensory transmission in visual pathway during 'attention' in unanesthetized cats. *Acta neurol. lat.-amer.*, **3**, 1-8.

HERNÁNDEZ-PEÓN, R., GUZMÁN-FLORES, C., ALCARAZ, M. and FERNÁNDEZ-GUARDIOLA, A. (1958) Habituation in the visual pathway. *Acta neurol. lat.-amer.*, **4**, 121-129.

HERNÁNDEZ-PEÓN, R. and HAGBARTH, K. E. (1955) Interaction between afferent and cortically induced reticular responses. *J. Neurophysiol.*, **18**, 44-55.

HERNÁNDEZ-PEÓN, R., JOUVET, M. and SCHERRER, H. (1957) Auditory potentials at cochlear nucleus during acoustic habituation. *Acta neurol. lat.-amer.*, **3**, 144-156.

HERNÁNDEZ-PEÓN, R. and SCHERRER, H. (1955) Inhibitory influence of brain stem reticular formation upon synaptic transmission in trigeminal nucleus. *Fed. Proc.*, **14**, 71.

HERNÁNDEZ-PEÓN, R. and SCHERRER, H. (1955) 'Habituation' to acoustic stimuli in cochlear nucleus. *Fed. Proc.*, **14**, 71.

HERNÁNDEZ-PEÓN, R., SCHERRER, H. and JOUVET, M. (1956) Modification of electric activity in cochlear nucleus during 'attention' in unanesthetized cats. *Science*, **123**, 331-332.

HERNÁNDEZ-PEÓN, R., SCHERRER, H. and VELASCO, M. (1956) Central influences on afferent conduction in the somatic and visual pathways. *Acta neurol. lat.-amer.*, **2**, 8-22.

HERON, W. (1957) Perception as a function of retinal locus and attention. *Amer. J. Psychol.*, **70**, 38-48.

HERRICK, C. J. (1933) The functions of the olfactory parts of the cerebral cortex. *Proc. Nat. Acad. Sci. (Wash.)*, **19**, 7-14.

HERRICK, C. JUDSON (1956) *The Evolution of Human Nature*. Austin: Univ. of Texas Press.

HESS, E. H. (1955) An experimental analysis of imprinting: A form of learning. *Progr. Rep. U.S. Publ. Hlth. Serv.*, M-776.

HESS, R., JR., KOELLA, W. P. and AKERT, K. (1953) Cortical and subcortical recordings in natural and artificially induced sleep in cats. *Electroenceph. clin. Neurophysiol.*, **5**, 75-90.

HESS, W. R. (1948) Das Zwischenhirn. B. Schwabe, Basel.

HESS, W. R. and BRÜGGER, M. (1943) Das subkortikale Zentrum der affektiven Abwehrreaktion. *Helv. physiol. Pharmacol. Acta*, **1**, 33-52.

HILGARD, E. R. and BIEL, W. C. (1937) Reflex Sensitization and Conditioning of Eyelid Responses at Intervals Near Simultaneity. *J. gen. Psychol.*, **16**, 223.

HILGARD, E. R. and MARQUIS, D. G. (1940) *Conditioning and Learning*. New York: D. Appleton Century Company.

HILL, D. K. (1950) The volume change resulting from stimulation of a giant nerve fibre. *J. Physiol. (Lond.)*, **111**, 304-327.

HINDE, R. A. (1958) The nest-building behaviour of domesticated canaries. *Proc. zool. Soc., Lond.*, **131**, 1-48.

HINDE, R. A., THORPE, W. H. and VINCE, M. A. (1956) The following response of young Coots and Moorhens. *Behaviour*, **9**, 214-242.

HOLST, E. VON (1932) Untersuchungen über die Funktionen des Zentralnervensystems beim Regenwurm. *Zool. J.*, **51**, 547-588.

HOLST, E. VON (1933) Weitere Versuche zum nervösen Mechanismus der Bewegung beim Regenwurm. *Zool. Jb.*, **53**, 67-100.

HOLST, E. VON (1935) Über den Prozess der zentralnervösen Koordination. *Pflüg. Arch. ges. Physiol.*, **236**, 149-158.

HOLST, E. VON (1936) Versuche zur Theorie der relativen Koordination. *Pflüg. Arch. ges. Physiol.*, **237**, 93-121.

HOLST, E. VON and ST. PAUL, U. VON (1958) Das Mischen von Trieben (Instinktbewegungen) durch mehrfache Stammhirnreizung beim Huhn. *Naturwissenschaften.*, **45**, 579.

HOUSEHOLDER, A. S. and LANDAHL, H. D. (1945) *Mathematical Biophysics of the Central Nervous System*. Bloomington, Indiana: Principia Press.

HUBBARD, J. (1959) Unpublished observations.

HUBEL, D. H. (1957) Tungsten microelectrode for recording from single units. *Science*, **125**, 549-550.

HUGELIN, A. and BONVALLET, M. (1957a) Tonus cortical et contrôle de la facilitation motrice d'origine réticulaire. *J. Physiol. (Paris)*, **49**, 1171-1200.

HUGELIN, A. and V BONBALLET, M. (1957b) Étude expérimentale des interrelations réticulo-corticales — Proposition d'une théorie de l'asservissement réticulaire à un système diffus cortical. *J. Physiol. (Paris)*, **49**, 1201-1223.

HUGHES, J. R. (1958) Post-tetanic Potentiation. *Physiol. Rev.*, **38**, 91-113.

HUMPHREY, G. (1933) *The nature of learning in its relation to the living system*. London: Kegan Paul, Trench.

HUNT, C. C. (1951) The reflex activity of mammalian small-nerve fibres. *J. Physiol. (Lond.)*, **115**, 456-469.

HUNT, C. C. and KUFFLER, S. W. (1951) Stretch receptor discharges during muscle contraction. *J. Physiol. (Lond.)*, **113**, 298-315.

HUNTER, W. S. (1913) The delayed reaction in animals and children. *Behav. Monogr.*, **2**, No. 1.

HYDÉN, H. (1943) Protein metabolism in the nerve cell during growth and function. *Acta physiol. scand.*, **6**, Supp. 17.

HYDÉN, H. (1950) Spectroscopic studies on nerve cells in development, growth and function. In *Genetic Neurology* 177, University of Chicago Press.

HYDÉN, H. (1953) Determination of mass of nerve-cell components. *J. Embryol. exp. Morph.*, **1**, 315-317.

INGRAM, W. R. (1958) Modification of learning by lesions and stimulation in the diencephalon and related structures. In *Reticular Formation of the Brain*. H. H. Jasper, L. D. Proctor, R. S. Knighton, W. C. Noshay, R. T. Costello, Editors. Boston, Little, Brown and Co., p. 535.

IWAMA, K. and JASPER, H. H. (1957) The action of gamma aminobutyric acid upon cortical electrical activity in the cat. *J. Physiol. (Lond.)*, **138**, 365-380.

JACKSON, J. H. (1958) *Selected Writings of John Hughlings Jackson*. Two volumes. Basic Books, New York.

JACOBSEN, C. F. (1935) Functions of frontal association areas in primates. *Arch. Neurol. Psychait. (Chicago)*, **33**, 558-568.

JACOBSEN, C. F. and HASLERUD, G. M. (1936) Studies of cerebral function in Primates. *Comp. Psychol. Monogr.*, **13**, No. 63.

JANKOWSKA, E. (1959) Instrumental scratch reflex of the deafferentated limb in cats and rats. *Acta. Biol. exp. Varsovie*, **19**, 233-247.

JASPER, H. H. (1949) Diffuse projection systems: the integrative action of the thalamic reticular system. *Electroenceph. clin. Neurophysiol.*, **1**, 405-419.

JASPER, H. H. (1958) Recent Advances in Our Understanding of Ascending Activities of the Reticular System. In *Reticular Formation of the Brain*. Boston, pp. 319-332.

JASPER, H. H. and AJMONE-MARSAN, C. (1952) Thalamocortical integrating mechanisms. *Res. Publ. Assoc. nerv. ment. Dis.*, **30**, 493-512.

JASPER, H. H. and GRUIKSHANK, R. M. (1937) Electroencephalography II, Visual stimulation and the after image as affecting the occipital alpha rhythm. *J. gen. Physiol.*, **17**, 29-48.

JASPER, H. H. and MONNIER, A. M. (1938) Transmission of excitation between excised non-myelinated nerves. An artificial synapse. *J. cell. comp. Physiol.*, **11**, 259-277.

JASPER, H. H., NAQUET, R. and KING, E. E. (1955) Thalamocortical recruiting responses in sensory receiving areas in the cat. *Electroenceph. clin. Neurophysiol.*, **7**, 99-114.

JASPER, H. H. and RASMUSSEN, T. (1958) Studies of clinical and electrical responses to deep temporal stimulation in man with some considerations of functional anatomy. *Res. Pub. Ass. nerv. ment. Dis.*, **36**, 316-334.

JASPER, H. H., RICCI, G. F. and DOANE, B. (1958) Patterns of cortical neuronal discharge during conditioned responses in monkeys. *Neurological basis of behaviour*. G. E. W. Wolstenholme and C. M. O'Connor, Editors. Ciba Foundation Symposium. London, Churchill, p. 277.

JAYNES, J. (1957) Imprinting: The Interaction of Learned and Innate Behaviour. II. The Critical Period. *J. Comp. Physiol. Psychol.*, **50**, 6-10.

JOHN, E. R. and KILIAM, K. F. (1959) Electrophysiological correlates of avoidance conditioning in the cat. *J. Pharmacol. exp. Ther.*, **125**, 252-274.

JOHNSON, H. C. and WALKER, A. E. (1952) Response of experimental epileptic foci to intravenous and topical Metrazol. *Electroenceph. clin. Neurophysiol.*, **4**, 131-139.

JONES, E. (1953-57) *The Life and Work of Sigmund Freud*. 3 vols. New York, Basic Books.

JOUVET, M. (1956a) Analyse électroencéphalographique de quelques aspects du conditionnement chez le chat. *Acta neurol. lat.-amer.*, **2**, 107-115.

JOUVET, M. (1956b) Aspects neurophysiologiques de quelques mécanismes du comportement. *J. Psychol. norm. path.*, **53**, 141-162.

JOUVET, M. (1956c) Les liaisons temporaires. Thèse de Médecine, Lyon.

JOUVET, M. (1957) Étude neurophysiologique chez l'homme de quelques mécanismes sous-corticaux de l'attention. *Psychol. franç.*, **2**, 250-256.

JOUVET, M., BENOIT, O. and COURJON, J. (1956a) The influence of experimental epilepsy produced by cortical stimulation upon responses of the specific and unspecific systems to auditory signals. *Electroenceph. clin. Neurophysiol.*, **8**, 732.

JOUVET, M., BENOIT, O. and COURJON, J. (1956b) Aspects EEG de la formation de liaisons temporaires dans le cerveau. Communication XXe Congrès International de Physiologie, *Bruxelles*, 475-476.

JOUVET, M., BENOIT, O. and COURJON, J. (1956c) The influence of expérimental epilepsy produced by cortical stimulation upon responses of the specific and unspecific systems to auditory signals. *Electroenceph. clin. Neurophysiol.*, **8**, 732.

JOUVET, M., BENOIT, O. and COURJON, J. (1956) Étude EEG des processus de liaison lumière-son chez le chat. *Rev. Neurol.*, **94**, 871-872.

JOUVET, M. and COURJON, J. (1957) Discussion du rapport sur l'EEG du conditionnement chez l'animal. Ier Congrès International des Sciences Neurologiques, Bruxelles. *Acta Medica Belgica*, 334-338.

JOUVET, M. and COURJON, J. (1958) Variations des réponses visuelles sous-corticales au cours de l'attention chez l'homme. *Rev. Neurol.*, **99**, 177-178.

JOUVET, M. and COURJON, J. (1957) Discussion du rapport sur l'EEG du conditionnement chez l'animal. Premier Congrès International des Sciences Neurologiques, Bruxelles. *Acta Medica Belgica*, 334-338.

JOUVET, M. and DESMEDT, J. E. (1956) Contrôle central des messages acoustiques afférents. *C.R. Acad. Sci. (Paris)*, **243**, 1916-1917.

JOUVET, M. and HERNÁNDEZ-PEÓN, R. (1955) Mécanismes Neurophysiologiques concernant l'habituation, l'attention et le conditionnement. *Electroenceph. clin. Neurophysiol.*, **6**, 39-49.

JOUVET, M. and MICHEL, F. (1958) Recherches sur l'activité électrique cérébrale au cours du sommeil. *C.R. Soc. Biol. (Paris)*, **152**, 1167-1170.

JOUVET, M. and MICHEL, F. (1959) Aspects électroencéphalographiques de l'habituation de la réaction d'éveil. *J. Physiol. (Paris)*, **51**, 489-490.

JOUVET, M., MICHEL, F. and COURJON, J. (1959a) L'activité électrique du rhinencéphale au course du sommeil chez le chat. *C.R. Soc. Biol. (Paris)*, **153**, 101-105.

JOUVET, M., MICHEL, F. and COURJON, J. (1959b) Aspects électroencéphalographiques de deux mécanismes inhibiteurs télencéphalique et rhombencéphalique entrant en jeu au cours du sommeil. *J. Physiol. (Paris)*, **51**, 490-492.

JOUVET, M., MICHEL, F. and COURJON, J. (1959c) Sur la mise en jeu de deux mécanismes à expression EEG différente au cours du sommeil physiologique chez le chat. *C.R. Acad. Sci.*, **248**, 3043-3045.

JUNG, R. (1953) Allgemeine Neurophysiologie. In *Handbuch der inneren Medizin* (Bergmann and Staehelin), 4th ed., Vol. **5**, pt. 1, 1-181, Berlin, Springer.

JUNG, R. (1958) Coordination of specific and nonspecific afferent impulses at single neurons of the visual cortex. In *Henry Ford Hosp. Int. Symp.: Reticular Formation of the Brain.* Boston, Little, Brown and Co., pp. 423-434.

KALISCHER, O. (1912) Über die Bedeutung der Dressurmethode für die Erforschung des Nervensystems. *Neurol. Zbl.*, **31**, 1316-1317.

KALISCHER, O. (1914) Über neuere Ergebnisse der Dressurmethode bei Hunden und Affen. *Ber. Physiol. Ges.*, 6.

KARAZINA, S. (1958) The significance of stimulus novelty and differentiation in desynchronization of cortical electrical activity. *Orienting Reflex and Exploratory Behaviour*, pp. 60-68.

KARMANOVA, I. G. (1955) Concerning Temporary Connections Between Indifferent Stimuli in Pigeons. Collection of articles. In *Problems of Comparative Physiology and Pathology of the Higher Nervous Activity*, p. 168. (In Russian.)

KASYANOV, V. M. (1950) The participation of the respiratory component in the conditioned motor response. *Bull. exp. Biol. Med.*, **2**, 88-94.

KATZ, B. (1958) Microphysiology of the neuro-muscular junction. A physiological 'quantum of action' at the myoneural junction. *Bull. Johns Hopk. Hosp.*, **102**, 275-295.

KENNARD, M. A., SPENCER, S. and FOUNTAIN, G., JR. (1941) Hyperactivity in monkeys following lesions of the frontal lobes. *J. Neurophysiol.*, **4**, 512-524.

KIMURA, DOREEN (1959) The effect of letter position on recognition. *Canad. J. Psychol.*, **13**, 1-10.

KINDER, E. F. (1927) A study of nest-building activity of the Albino Rat. *J. exp. Zool.*, **47**, 117-161.

KING, W. T. (1927) Observations on the rôle of the cerebral cortex in the control of the postural reflex. *Amer. J. Physiol.*, **80**, 311-326.

KLOPFER, P. (1959) The development of sound preferences in ducks. *Wilson Bull.* In the Press.

KLÜVER, H. and BUCY, P. C. (1939) Preliminary analysis of functions of the temporal lobes in monkeys. *Arch. Neurol. Psychiat. (Chicago)*, **42**, 979-1000.

KOBAYASHI, Y., OSHIMA, K. and TASAKI, I. (1952) Analysis of afferent and efferent systems in the muscle nerve of the toad and cat. *J. Physiol. (Lond.)*, **117**, 152-171.

KOGAN, A. B. (1958a) Expression of the processes of the higher nervous activity in electrical potentials of the cerebral cortex of unrestrained animals. Internat. Colloquium on the EEG of the conditioned reflex. Moscow.

KOGAN, A. B. (1958b) The manifestation of the higher nervous activity in the electrical potentials of the brain cortex during free behaviour of the animal. Moscow Colloquium on EEG and Behavior. *Electroenceph. clin. Neurophysiol.* In the Press.

KOLLER, G. (1955) Hormonale und psychische Steuerung beim Nestbau weisser Mäuse. *Verh. dtsch. zool. Ges. Zool. Anz.*, **19**, 123-132.

KONIGSMARK, B. W., ABDULLAH, A. F. and FRENCH, J. D. (1958) Cortical spread of after-discharge in monkey. *Electroencephal. clin. Neurophysiol.*, **10**, 687-696.

KONORSKI, J. (1948) *Conditioned reflexes and neuron organization*. University Press, London, pp. 78-79.

KONORSKI, J. (1950) The mechanisms of learning. *Symp. Soc. Exp. Biol.*, **4**, 409-431.

KONORSKI, J. (1956) On the influence of the frontal lobes of the cerebral hemispheres higher nervous activity in dogs. In *Problems of the modern physiology of the nervous and muscle system*. Tbilisi — Academy of Sciences Georgian SSR.

KONORSKI, J. (1957) On animals' hyperactivity after ablations of prefrontal lobes of cerebral hemispheres. *Problems of the physiology of central nervous system (Russian)* Academy of Sciences, Moscow.

KONORSKI, J. (1959) A new method of physiological investigation of recent memory in animals. *Bull. Acad. pol. Sci.*, **7**, 115-117.

KONORSKI, J. and ŁAWICKA, W. (1959) The physiological mechanism of delayed reactions. I. The analysis and classification of the delayed reactions. *Acta Biol. exp. Varsovie*, **19**. In the Press.

KONORSKI, J. and SZWEJKOWSKA, G. (1952) Chronic extinction and restoration of conditioned reflexes. IV. The dependence of the course of extinction and restoration of conditioned reflexes on the 'history' of the conditioned stimulus. (The principle of the primacy of first training.) *Acta Biol. exp. Varsovie*, **16**, 7, 95-113.

KONORSKI, J., STEPIEŃ, L., BRUTKOWSKI, S., ŁAWICKA, W. and STEPIEŃ, I. (1952) The effect of the removal of interprojective fields of the cerebral cortex on the higher nervous activity of animals. *Bull. Soc. Sci. Lett., Lodz*, **3**, 1-5.

KONORSKY, J. and MILLER, S. (1936) Conditioned Reflexes of the Motor Analyser. Collected Papers of the Physiological Laboratories of I. P. Pavlov, vol. VI, No. 1, p. 119. In Russian.

KOPELOFF, L. M., BARRERA, S. E. and KOPELOFF, N. (1942) Recurrent convulsive seizures in animals produced by immunologic and chemical means. *Amer. J. Psychiat.*, **98**, 881-902.

KOPELOFF, L. M., CHUSID, J. G. and KOPELOFF, N. (1954) Chronic experimental epilepsy in Macaca mulatta. *Neurology*, **4**, 218-227.

KOPELOFF, L. M., CHUSID, J. G. and KOPELOFF, N. (1955) Epilepsy in Macaca mulatta after cortical or intracerebral alumina. *AMA Arch. Neurol. Psychiat.*, **74**, 523-526.

KORIARIN, M. F. (1958) Postural excitation in the conditioned defensive motor reflex in the dog. *Sechenov J. Physiol.*, **44**, 359-369.

KREINDLER, A. (1955) *Epilepsia. Editura Academiei Republicii Populare Romine*. Bucarest, pp. 367, 482 and 485.

KREPS, E. M. (1933) On the possibility of the formation of a conditioned reflex in case of precedence of an unconditioned stimulus to an indifferent one. *Coll. Papers Physiol. Lab. I. P. Pavlov*, **5**, 5-20. (In Russian.)

KRISTIANSEN, K. and COURTOIS, G. (1949) Rhythmic electrical activity from isolated cerebral cortex. *Electroenceph. clin. Neurophysiology*, **1**, 265-272.

KUFFLER, S. W., HUNT, C. C. and QUILLIAM, J. P. (1951) Function of medullated small-nerve fibers in mammalian ventral roots; efferent muscle spindle innervation. *J. Neurophysiol.*, **14**, 29-54.

KUO, Z. Y. (1930) The genesis of the cat's responses to the rat. *J. comp. Psychol.*, **11**, 1-35.

KUO, Z. Y. (1932) Ontogeny of embryonic behavior in Aves, I. *J. exp. Zool.*, **61**, 395-430.

KUPALOV, P. S. (1948) Non-accomplished Reactions as Conditioned Alimentary Agents. Proceedings of the Joint Session dedicated to the 10th anniversary of Pavlov's death, p. 67. In Russian.

KUPALOV, P. S. (1956) Some Problems of Physiology of higher nervous activity. *XXth int. Congress of Physiology*, **1**, 345-346. (Brussels.)

KUPALOV, P. S. and LUKOV, B. N. (1933) [The effect of short application of conditioned stimulus.] (Russian.) *Arch. Sci. Biol., Moscow*, **33**, 665.

LANCE, J. W. and MANNING, R. L. (1954) Origin of the pyramidal tract in the cat. *J. Physiol. (Lond.)*, **124**, 385-399.

LANDIS, C. and HUNT, W. A. (1939) *The Startle pattern*. New York, Farrar et Rinehart.

LANGWORTHY, O. R. (1928) The area frontalis of the cerebral cortex of the cat, its minute structure and physiological evidence of its control of the postural reflex. *Bull. Johns Hopk. Hosp.*, **42**, 20-60.

LAPTEV, I. I. (1941) The EEG method for the study of the conditioned reflex. *First Moscow Physiol., Biochem., Pharmacol. Congr.* Moscow, 135.

LAPTEV, I. I. (1949) The environment as a complex conditioned stimulus. *Problems of Higher Nervous Activity*, Moscow, pp. 540-558.

LAPTEV, I. I. (1949) The EEG method for the study of conditioned reflex activity of the dog. *Problems of Higher Nervous Activity*. Moscow, p. 147.

LARSSON, L. E. (1956) The relation between the startle reaction and the non-specific EEG response to sudden stimuli with a discussion on the mechanism of arousal. *Electroenceph, clin. Neurophysiol.*, **8**, 631-644.

LASHLEY, K. S. (1929a) *Brain Mechanisms and Intelligence*. Chicago, Univ. of Chicago Press.

LASHLEY, K. S. (1929b) Nervous mechanisms in learning. In *The Foundations of Experimental Psychology*. C. Murchison, Editor. Worcester, Mass., Clark University Press, pp. 524-563.

LASHLEY, K. S. (1935) The mechanism of vision. XII. Nervous structures concerned in the acquisition and retention of habits based on reactions to light. *Comp. Psychol. Monogr.*, **11**, No. 52, 43-79.

LASHLEY, K. S. (1951) The problem of serial order in behavior. *Cerebral Mechanisms in Behavior*. L. A. Jeffress, Editor. New York, Wiley, pp. 112-136.

LASHLEY, K. S. (1958) Cerebral organization and behavior. *Res. Publ. Assoc. Res. nerv. ment. Dis.*, **36**, 1-14.

LAUGHTON, N. B. (1928) Studies on the occurrence of extensor rigidity in mammals as a result of cortical injury. *Amer. J. Physiol.*, **85**, 78-90.

LAVÍN, A., ALCOCER-CUARÓN, C. and HERNÁNDEZ-PEÓN, R. (1959) Centrifugal Arousal in the Olfactory Bulb. *Science*, **129**, 332-333.

ŁAWICKA, W. (1957) The effect of the prefrontal lobectomy on the vocal conditioned reflexes in dogs. *Acta Biol. exp. Varsovie*, **17**, 317-325.

ŁAWICKA, W. (1957) Physiological analysis of the disturbances of the delayed responses in dogs after prefrontal ablation. *Bull. Acad. pol. Sci.*, **5**, 107-110.

ŁAWICKA, W. (1959) The physiological mechanism of delayed reactions, II. Delayed reactions in dogs and cats to directional stimuli. *Acta Biol. exp. Varsovie*, **19**. In the Press.

ŁAWICKA, W. and KONORSKI, J. (1959) The physiological mechanism of delayed reactions. V. The effects of prefrontal ablations on delayed reactions in dogs. *Acta Biol. exp. Varsovie*, **19**. In the Press.

LAYCOCK, T. (1860) *Mind and Brain*. 2 vols. New York, Appleton.

LEBEDINSKAÏA, S. I. and ROSENTHAL, J. S. (1935) Reactions of a dog after removal of the cerebral hemispheres. *Brain*, **58**, 412-419.

LEHRMAN, D. S. (1953) A critique of Konrad Lorenz's theory of instinctive behavior. *Quart. Rev. Biol.*, **28**, 337-363.

LEHRMAN, D. S. (1956) On the organization of maternal behavior and the problem of instinct. In *L'Instinct dans le Comportement des Animaux et de l'Homme*. P. P. Grassé, editor. Paris, Masson & Cie, pp. 475-520.

LEKSELL, L. (1945) The action potential and excitatory effects of the small ventral root fibres to skeletal muscle. *Acta physiol. scand.*, **10**, Suppl. 31, 1-84.

LELORD, G., FOURMENT, A., CALVET, J. and SCHERRER, J. (1958) Le conditionnement de la réponse évoquée électrocorticale chez l'homme. *C.R. Soc. Biol., Paris*, **152**, 1680-83.

LESSE, H. (1957) Electrographic recordings of Amygdaloid activity during a conditioned response. *Fed. Proc.*, **16**, 79.

LEUKEL, F. (1957) A comparison of the effects of ECS and anesthesia on acquisition of the maze habit. *J. comp. physiol. Psychol.*, **50**, 300-306.

LEVINE, J. (1945) Studies in the interrelations of central nervous structures in binocular vision: II. The conditions under which interocular transfer of discriminative habits takes place in the pigeon. *J. genet. Psychol.*, **67**, 131-142.

LEYHAUSEN, P. (1956) Verhaltensstudien an Katzen. *Z. Tierpsychol.*, **2**, 1-120.

LI, C. L., CULLEN, C. and JASPER, H. H. (1956a) Laminar microelectrode studies of specific somatosensory cortical potentials. *J. Neurophysiol.*, **91**, 111-130.

LI, C. L., CULLEN, C. and JASPER, H. H. (1956b) Laminar microelectrode analysis of cortical unspecific recruiting responses and spontaneous rhythms. *J. Neurophysiol.*, **19**, 131-143.

LI, C. L., MCLENNAN, H. and JASPER, H. H. (1952) Brain waves and unit discharge in cerebral cortex. *Science*, **116**, 656-657.

LIBET, B. and GERARD, R. W. (1939) Control of the potential rhythm of the isolated frog brain. *J. Neurophysiol.*, **2**, 153-169.

LIBET, B. and GERARD, R. W. (1941) Steady potential fields and neurone activity. *J. Neurophysiol.*, **4**, 438-455.

LIDDELL, E. G. T. and PHILLIPS, C. G. (1944) Pyramidal section in the cat. *Brain*, **67**, 1-9.

LIFSCHITZ, W., PALESTINI, M. and ARMENGOL, V. (1959) Habituation in lemniscal and extralemniscal systems. Communication to the 21st International Congress of Physiological Sciences. Buenos Aires.

LILEY, A. W. (1956) The quantal components of the mammalian end-plate potential. *J. Physiol. (Lond.)*, **133**, 571-587.

LILLY, J. C. (1958) Correlations between neurophysiological activity in the cortex and short-term behavior in the monkey. In Harlow, H. F., and Woolsey, C. N., Editors. *Biological and Chemical Bases of Behavior*. Madison, Univ. of Wisc. Press, p. 83-100.

LINDBLOM, U. F. and OTTOSSON, J. O. (1953) Effects of spinal sections on the spinal cord potentials elicited by stimulation of low threshold cutaneous fibres. *Acta physiol. scand.*, **106**, 191-208.

LINDSLEY, D. (1958) The Reticular System and Perceptual Discrimination. In *Reticular Formation of the Brain*. Boston-Toronto, pp. 513-534.

LINDSLEY, D. (1959) Vision and Visual Perception. Lecture read in Sechenov Institute of Physiology.

LINDSLEY, D. B., SCHREINER, L. H., KNOWLES, W. B. and MAGOUN, H. W. (1950) Behavioral and E.E.G. changes following chronic brain stem lesions in the cat. *Electroenceph. clin. Neurophysiol.*, **2**, 483-498.

LISSÁK, K., ENDRÖCZI, E., BOHUS, B. and KOVÁCS, S. (1958) Steroid-Hormon Symposion. Budapest, pp. 8-9.

LISSÁK, K. and ENDRÖCZI, E. (1959) *Die Neuroendokrine Steuerung der Adaptationstätigkeit*. Akadémiai Kiadö, Budapest.

LISSÁK, K., ENDRÖCZI, E. and MEGGYESY (1957) Somatisches Verhalten und Nebennierenrindentätigkeit. *Pflüg. Archiv. ges. Physiol.*, **265**, 117, 124.

LISSÁK, K. and GRASTYÁN, E. (1957) The significance of activating systems and the hippocampus in the conditioned reflex. *Proc. 1st Internat. Congress of Neurological Science*. Brussels, pp. 445-449.

LISSÁK, K., GRASTYÁN, E., CSANAKY, A., KÉKESI, F. and VEREBY, GY. (1957) A Study of hippocampal junction in the waking and sleeping animal with chromically implanted electrodes. *Acta physiol. pharmacol. neerl.*, **6**, 451-459.

LISSÁK, K., MEGGYESI, P., TÉNYI, I. and ZÖRÉNYI, I. (1958) Einfluss des adrenocorticotropen Hormons auf die höhere Nerventätigkeit. [Influence of the adrenocorticotropic hormone on higher nervous activity.] *Acta Physiol. hung.*, **14**, 361-365.

LIVANOV, M. N. (1938) Analysis of bioelectrical oscillations of the cerebral cortex of mammals. *Trans. Brain Inst.*, 3-4, 487-535.

LIVANOV, M. N. (1958) Concerning the establishment of temporary connections, Results of electrophysiological investigations. Moscow Colloquium on EEG and Behavior. *Electroenceph. clin. Neurophysiol*. In the Press.

LIVINGSTON, R. B. (1958) Central Control of Afferent Activity. In *Reticular Formation of the Brain*. Boston-Toronto, pp. 177-185.

LLOYD, D. P. C. (1949-50) Post-tetanic potentiation of response in monosynaptic reflex pathways of the spinal cord. *J. gen. Physiol.*, **33**, 147-170.

LORENTE DE NÓ, R. (1934) Studies on the structure of the cerebral cortex II. *J. Psychol. Neurol. (Lpz.)*, **46**, 113-177.

LORENTE DE NÓ, R. (1938) Synaptic stimulation of motoneurons as a local process. *J. Neurophysiol.*, **1**, 195-206.

LORENTE DE NÓ, R. (1943) Cerebral cortex: architecture, intracortical connections, motor projections. *Physiology of the Nervous System.* J. F. Fulton. 2nd ed. New York, Oxford University Press.

LORENZ, K. (1937) Über die Bildung des Instinktbegriffes. *Naturwiss. enschaften*, **25**, 289-300, 307-318, 324-331.

LORENZ, K. (1941) Vergleichende Bewegungsstudien an Anatiden. *J. Orn. Lpz.*, **89**, 194-293.

LORENZ, K. (1943) Die angeborenen Formen möglicher Erfahrung. *Z. Tierpsychol.*, **5**, 535-409.

LORENZ, K. (1950) The comparative method in studying innate behaviour patterns. *Symposia Soc. Exp. Biol.*, **4**, 221-268.

LORENZ, K. (1958) The Deprivation Experiment, its limitations and its value as a means to separate learned and unlearned elements of behavior. Lecture held at the Dawning Hospital, Univ. of Chicago, Oct. (Manuscript.)

LOUCKS, R. B. (1935) The experimental delimitation of neural structures essential for learning. II. The conditioning of salivary and striped muscle responses to faradization of the sigmoid gyri. *J. Psychol.*, **1**, 5-44.

LUSE, S. A. (1959) Electron microscopic observations of the central nervous system. In *Inhibition in the nervous system and gamma-aminobutyric acid.* An International Symposium. In the Press.

LYAN-CHI-AN (1958) Interaction of the Cortical Points of Combined Stimuli. *Trans. 2nd Moscow Inst.*, **12**, 129.

MCALLISTER, W. G. (1932) A further study of the delayed reaction in the albino rat. *Comp. Psychol. Monogr.*, **8**, 1-103.

MCCONNELL, J. V., JACOBSEN, R. and MAYNARD, D. M. (1959) Apparent retention of a conditioned reflex following total regeneration in the planarian. *Amer. Psychologist*, **14**, 410 (abstract).

MCCOUCH, G. P., AUSTIN, G. M., LIU, C. N. and LIU, C. Y. (1958) Sprouting as a cause of spasticity. *J. Neurophysiol.*, **21**, 205-216.

MCINTYRE, A. K. (1953) Synaptic function and learning. *XIX International Physiological Congress*, 107-114.

MCKIBBEN, P. S. (1929) Experiments on the motor cortex of the cat. *Anat. Rec.*, **42**, 57.

MCLARDY, T. (1959) Hippocampal formation of brain as detector-coder of temporal patterns of information. *Perspect. Biol. Med.*, **2**, 443-452.

MACLEAN, P. D. (1949) Psychosomatic disease and the 'visceral brain'; recent development bearing on Papez theory of emotion. *Psychosomat. Med.*, **11**, 338-353.

MADISON, N. J. (1959) *The Central Nervous System and Behavior.* First Macy Conference. Madison Printing Co., pp. 287-291, 375-385.

MAGNI, F., MORUZZI, G., ROSSI, G. F. and ZANCHETTI, A. (1959) EEG arousal following inactivation of the lower brain stem by selective injection of barbiturate into the vertebral circulation. *Arch. ital. Biol.*, **97**, 33-46.

MAGOUN, H. W. (1950) Caudal and cephalic influences of the brain stem reticular formation. *Physiol. Rev.*, **30**, 459-474.

MAGOUN, H. W. (1954) The ascending reticular system and wakefulness. In *Brain mechanisms and consciousness.* Oxford, Blackwell, pp. 1-20.

MAGOUN, H. W. (1958a) *The Waking Brain.* Springfield, Charles C Thomas.

MAGOUN, H. W. (1958b) Non-specific brain mechanisms. In Harlow, H. F. and Woolsey, C. N., Editors. *Biological and Chemical Bases of Behavior.* Madison, Univ. of Wisc. Press, pp. 25-36.

MAGOUN, H. W. and RANSON, S. W. (1938) Behaviour of cats following bilateral removal of rostral portion of the cerebral hemispheres. *J. Neurophysiol.*, **1**, 39-44.

MAHUT, H. (1957) Effects of subcortical electrical stimulation on learning in the rat. *Amer. Psychologist*, **12**, 466.

MAKAROV, J. A. (1960) Changes in the secretory and respiratory components of the conditioned reflex during interaction of defensive and food dominants. *Ž. vyš. nérv. Dějat. Pavlova.* In the Press.

MALMO, R. B. (1942) Interference factors in delayed response in monkeys after removal of frontal lobes. *J. Neurophysiol.*, **5**, 295-308.

MAIER, N. R. F. and SCHNEIRLA, T. C. (1935) *Principles of Animal Behavior*. New York, McGraw-Hill.

MANCIA, M. (1959) Personal communication.

MARQUIS, D. G. and HILGARD, E. R. (1937) Conditioned responses to light in monkeys after removal of the occipital lobe. *Brain*, **60**, 1-12.

MARSALLON, A. (1959) Contribution à l'étude EEG de l'extinction de la réaction d'orientation. *Thèse de Médecine*, Lyon, Bosc. Ed.

MARSHALL, C. (1936) The functions of the pyramidal tracts. *Quart. Rev. Biol.*, **2**, 35-56.

MARSHALL, W. H. (1959) Spreading cortical depression of Leao. *Physiol. Rev.*, **39**, 239-279.

MARSHALL, W. H., TALBOT, S. A. and ADES, H. W. (1943) Cortical response of the anesthetized cat to gross photic and electrical afferent stimulation. *J. Neurophysiol.*, **6**, 1-15.

MASON, J. W. (1958) Restraining chair for the experimental study of primates. *J. appl. Physiol.*, **12**, 130-133.

MASON, J. W. (1958) The Central Nervous System Regulation of ACTH Secretion. In *Reticular Formation of the Brain*. Intern. Sympos. sponsored by Henry Ford Hospital, Detroit, Mich. Little, Brown and Company, Boston, pp. 645-662.

MASSERMAN, J. H. (1943) *Behavior and Neurosis*. Chicago, Univ. of Chicago Press, 269 pp.

MATTHEWS, B. H. C. (1933) Nerve endings in mammalian muscle. *J. Physiol. (Lond.)*, **78**, 1-53.

MELZACK, R. and HAUGEN, F. P. (1957) Responses evoked at the cortex by tooth stimulation. *Amer. J. Physiol.*, **190**, 570-574.

METTLER, F. A. (1935a) Corticifugal fiber connections of the cortex of *Macaca mullatta*. The frontal region. *J. comp. Neurol.*, **61**, 509-542.

METTLER, F. A. (1935b) Corticifugal fiber connections of the cortex of *Macaca mulatta*. The parietal region. *J. comp. Neurol.*, **62**, 263-291.

MEYER, D. R. (1958) Some Psychological determinants of sparing and loss following damage to the brain. *Biological and Biochemical Bases of Behavior*. H. F. Harlow and C. N. Woolsey, Editors. Madison, University of Wisconsin Press, pp. 173-192.

MEYER, V. and YATES, A. J. (1955) Intellectual changes following temporal lobectomy for psychomotor epilepsy. *J. Neurol. Neurosurg. Psychiat.*, **18**, 44-52.

MEYER, D. R., HARLOW, H. F. and SETTLAGE, P. H. (1951) A survey of delayed response performance by normal and brain-damaged monkeys. *J. comp. physiol. Psychol.*, **44**, 17-25.

MILLER, G. A. (1956) The magical number seven, plus or minus two: some limits on our capacity for processing information. *Psychol. Rev.*, **63**, 81-97.

MILNER, B. and PENFIELD, W. (1955) The effect of hippocampal lesions on recent memory. *Trans. Amer. neurol. Ass.*, **80**, 42-48.

MILNER, P. M. (1957) The cell assembly: Mark II. *Psychol. Rev.*, **64**, 242-252.

MILNER, P. M. (1959) Learning in neural systems. Interdisciplinary conference on self-organizing systems, Chicago (to be published).

MIRSKY, A., MILLER, R. and STEIN, M. (1953) Relation of adrenocortical activity and adaptive behavior. *Psychosomat. Med.*, **15**, 574-588.

MISHKIN, M. and HALL, M. (1955) Discrimination along a size continuum following ablation of the inferior temporal convexity in monkeys. *J. comp. physiol. Psychol.*, **48**, 97-101.

MISHKIN, M. and PRIBRAM, K. H. (1954) Visual discrimination performance following partial ablations of the temporal lobe: I. Ventral *vs*. lateral. *J. comp. Physiol. Psychol.*, **47**, 14-20.

MISHKIN, M. and PRIBRAM, K. H. (1956) Analysis of the effects of frontal lesions in monkeys: II. Variations of delayed response. *J. comp. physiol. Psychol.*, **49**, 36-40.

MONAKOW, C. VON and MOURGUE, R. (1928) *Introduction biologique à l'étude de la neurologie et de la psychopathologie*. Alcan, Paris, 416 pp.

MORGAN, C. T. and STELLAR, E. (1950) *Physiological Psychology*. New York, McGraw-Hill.

MORISON, R. S. and DEMPSEY, E. W. (1941-42) A study of thalamo-cortical relations. *Amer. J. Physiol.*, **135**, 281-292.

MORISON, R. S. and DEMPSEY, E. W. (1943) Mechanism of thalamocortical augmentation and repetition. *Amer. J. Physiol.*, **138**, 297-308.

MORISON, R. S., DEMPSEY, E. W. and MORISON, B. R. (1940) On the propagation of certain cortical potentials. *Amer. J. Physiol.*, **131**, 744-751.

MORRELL, F. (1957) An anatomical and physiological analysis of electrocortical conditioning. *Proc. 1st Internat. Congress of Neurological Science*, Brussels, pp. 377-391.

MORRELL, F. (1958) Some electrical events involved in the formation of temporary connections. In *Reticular formation of the brain*, Henry Ford Hosp. Int. Symp. Boston, pp. 545-560.

MORRELL, F. (1959) Electroencephalographic studies of conditioned learning. *The Central Nervous System and Behavior*. M. A. B. Brazier, Editor. Transactions of the first conference. New York, Josiah Macy, Jr. Foundation, pp. 450.

MORRELL, F. (1959) Experimental focal epilepsy in animals. *AMA Arch. Neurol.*, 1, 141-147.

MORRELL, F. (1960) Microelectrode and steady potential studies suggesting a dendritic locus of closure. In The Moscow Colloquium on Electroencephalography of Higher Nervous Activity (Moscow, October 1958). *Electroenceph. J. clin. Neurophysiol.*, 13, 65-79.

MORRELL, F. and FLORENZ, A. (1958) Modification of the freezing technique for producing experimental epileptogenic lesions. *Electroenceph. clin. Neurophysiol.*, 10, 187.

MORRELL, F. and JASPER, H. H. (1955) Conditioning of cortical electrical activity in the monkey. *Electroenceph. clin. Neurophysiol.*, 7, 461.

MORRELL, F. and JASPER, H. H. (1956) Electrographic studies of the formation of temporary connections in the brain. *Electroenceph. clin. Neurophysiol.*, 8, 201-215.

MORRELL, F. and NAQUET, R. (1956) Conditionnement de décharges hypersynchrones généralisées chez des chats porteurs de lésions épileptogènes. *Rev. Neurol.*, 94, 828.

MORRELL, F. and TORRES, F. (1958) On the nature of epileptic interference. *Electroenceph. clin. Neurophysiol.*, 10, 764.

MORRELL, F., NAQUET, R. and GASTAUT, H. (1957) Evolution of some electrical signs of conditioning. Part I. Normal Cat and Rabbit. *J. Neurophysiol.*, 20, 574-587.

MORRELL, F., ROBERTS, L. and JASPER, H. H. (1956) Effect of focal epileptogenic lesions and their oblation upon unconditioned electrical responses of the brain of the monkey. *Electroenceph. clin. Neurophysiol.*, 8, 217-236.

MORUZZI, G. (1956) Spontaneous and evoked electrical activity in the brain stem reticular formation. *XX Internat. Physiol. Congress*. Brussels, pp. 269-286.

MORUZZI, G. (1958) Tonic Activity of the Ascending Reticular System. Report at Internat. Coll. on the EEG of the Conditioned Reflex. Moscow.

MORUZZI, G. (1959a) Personal communication.

MORUZZI, G. (1959b) The role of the ascending reticular system in sensory integration. *Colloquium on sensory integration*. Paris 1958. To be published.

MORUZZI, G. and MAGOUN, H. W. (1949) Brain stem reticular formation and activation of the EEG. *Electroenceph. clin. Neurophysiol.*, 1, 455-473.

MULLAN, S. and PENFIELD, W. (1959) Illusions of comparative interpretation and emotion. *A.M.A. Arch. Neurol. Psychiat.*, 81, 269-284.

MUNN, N. L. (1950) *Handbook of Psychological Research on the Rat*. Cambridge, Mass., Riverside Press.

MUSKENS, L. J. J. (1926) *Epilepsie vergleichende Pathogenese, Erscheinungen, Behandlung*. Berlin, Springer.

MYERS, R. E. (1955) Interocular transfer of pattern discrimination in cats following section of crossed optic fibers. *J. comp. physiol. Psychol.*, 48, 470-473.

MYERS, R. E. (1956) Function of corpus callosum in interocular transfer. *Brain*, 79, 358-363.

MYERS, R. E. (1959a) Localization of function in the corpus callosum: visual gnostic transfer. *A.M.A. Archives of Neurol. Psychiat.*, 1, 74-77.

MYERS, R. E. (1959b) Interhemispheric communication through corpus callosum: Limitations under conditions of conflict. *J. comp. physiol. Psychol.*, 52, 6-9.

MYERS, R. E. (1960) Failure of interocular transfer in corpus callosum-sectioned chimpanzees. *Anat. Rec.*

MYERS, R. E. and SPERRY, R. W. (1958) Interhemispheric communication through the corpus callosum: Mnemonic carry-over between the hemispheres. *A.M.A. Arch. Neurol. Psychiat.*, 80, 298-303.

NAQUET, R. and MORRELL, F. (1956) Conditionnement des décharges hypersynchrones de type myoclonique induites par injection de cardiazol chez le Chat. *Rev. Neurol.*, 94, 826-828.

NAQUET, R. and PRUVOT, PH. (1956) Essai d'interprétation de quelques variations des réponses EEG induites par la stimulation lumineuse intermittente chez l'Homme. *C.R. Soc. Biol. (Paris)*, 150, 1232-1233.

NAQUET, R., DROSSOPOULO, G. and SALAMON, G. (1956) Étude expérimentale des effets de certains convulsivants: leur relation avec l'excitabilité du système réticulaire. *Rev. Neurol.*, 95, No. 6, 484-490.

NAQUET, R., FEGERSTEN, L., BERT, J. and CARCASSONNE-MOTEZ, B. (1959) Les décharges électrographiques critiques focalisées induites par la stimulation lumineuse intermittente (S.L.I.) dans la régions postérieure du scalp. *Electroenceph. clin. Neurophysiol.*, **11**, 393.

NARBUTOVICH, I. O. and PODKOPAYEV, N. A. (1936) The Conditioned Reflex as an Association. Coll. Papers Physiol. Lab. I. P. Pavlov, **6**, 5. (In Russian.)

NARIKASHVILI, S. P. (1957) Primary response reaction and the 'spontaneous' electrical activity of the cerebral cortex. *Sechenov J. Physiol.*, **43**, 598-606.

NAUTA, W. J. H. and KUYPERS, H. G. J. M. (1958) Some ascending pathways in the brain stem reticular formation. In *Reticular formation of the brain*. Boston, Little, Brown and Co., pp. 3-30.

NEFF, W. D. and IRVING, T. D. (1958) The neural basis of auditory discrimination. In *Biological and Biochemical Bases of Behavior*. Harry F. Harlow and Clinton N. Woolsey, Editors. Madison: The University of Wisconsin Press, pp. 101-126.

NIKOLAEVA, N. I. (1957) Summation of stimuli in the cerebral cortex. *Sechenov J. Physiol.*, **43**, 27-34.

NIMS, L. F., MARSHALL, C. and NIELSEN, A. (1940-41) Effect of local freezing on the electrical activity of the cerebral cortex. *Yale J. Biol. Med.*, **13**, 477-484.

NISSEN, H. W., RIESEN, A. H. and NOWLIS, V. (1938) Delayed response and discrimination learning by chimpanzees. *J. comp. Psychol.*, **26**, 361-386.

OLDS, J. (1956) Runway and maze behaviour controlled by basomedial forebrain stimulation in the rat. *J. comp. physiol. Psychol.*, **49**, 507-512.

OLDS, J. (1958) Self-stimulation of the brain. *Science*, **127**, 315-324.

OLDS, J. and TRAVIS, R. Relations of isopropylmeprobamate to chlorpromazine, meprobamate, pentobarbital in self-stimulation tests. J. G. Miller, Editor. Detroit, Wayne State Univ. Press. In the Press.

OLMSTED, J. M. D. and LOGAN, H. P. (1925) Lesions in the cerebral cortex and extension rigidity in cats. *Amer. J. Physiol.*, **72**, 570-582.

ORBACH, J. (1959) 'Functions' of striate cortex and the problem of mass action. *Psychol. Bull.*, **56**, 271-292.

ORBACH, J. and FANTZ, R. L. (1958) Differential effects of temporal neo-cortical resections on overtrained and non-overtrained visual habits in monkeys. *J. comp. physiol. Psychol.*, **51**, 126-129.

ORESHUK, F. A. (1950) Contribution to the Comparative Physiology of Associative Connections. *Sechenov J. Physiol.*, **36**, No. 4.

OSWALDO-CRUZ, E. and TSOULADZÉ, S. (1957) Activité évoquée par stimulation de nerfs d'origine musculaire ou cutanée dans le gyrus sigmoïde antérieur du chat. *J. Physiol. (Paris)*, **49**, 327-329.

OTIS, L. S. and CERF, J. A. (1958) The effects of heat narcosis on the retention of a conditioned avoidance response. *Amer. Psychologist*, **13**, 419. (Abstract.)

PIMENOV, P. P. (1907) [A particular group of conditioned reflexes.] (Russian.) Dissertation.

PIMENOV, P. P. (1908) A Special Group of Conditioned Reflexes. Dissertation. St. Petersburg. Russian.

PINTO HAMUY, T., BROMILEY, R. B. and WOOLSEY, C. N. (1956) Somatic afferent areas I and II of dog's cerebral cortex. *J. Neurophysiol.*, **19**, 485-499.

PINTO HAMUY, T., ROJAS, A. and ARANEDA, S. (1959) Mass action of the cerebral cortex in the learning of an instrumental conditioned response. XXI International Congress of Physiological Science. Abstracts of Communication, 212.

PINTO HAMUY, T., SANTIBAÑEZ, G., ROJAS, A. and HOFFMANN, A. (1957) Reflejos condicionados en ratas con lesiones parciales y totales de la corteza cerebral. Primera Reunión Científica Latino-americana de Ciencias Fisiológicas. Montevideo, p. 140.

PISAREV, D. (1958) Selected Philosophical, Social and Political Essays. Tr. R. Dixon. Moscow, Foreign Languages Publishing House.

PLATONOV, G. (1955) Kliment Arkadyevich Timiryazev. Moscow, Foreign Languages Publishing House.

POLEZHAEV, E. F. (1953) Correlation between excitation and inhibition in the course of alteration of the motor conditioned reflexes. *Conf. Ryasan med. Inst.*, 24.

POLYANZEV, V. A. (1959) Correlations between EEG impulsive and tonic components. V. Conference of Young Scientists. Moscow, p. 59.

POPE, A., MORRIS, A. A., JASPER, H. H., ELLIOTT, K. A. C. and PENFIELD, W. (1947) Histo-chemical and action potential studies on epileptogenic areas of cerebral cortex in man and the monkey. *Proc. Ass. Res. Nerv. Ment. Dis.*, **26**, 218-233.

POPOV, N. F. (1911) Recherches en physiologie du cerveau sur les animaux (Russian). Moscow, 1911 (Reed, 1953).

PORTER, P. B. and STONE, C. P. (1947) Electroconvulsive shock in rats under ether anesthesia. *J. comp. physiol. Psychol.*, **40**, 441-456.

PORTER, R. (1955) Antidromic conduction of volleys in pyramidal tract. *J. Neurophysiol.*, **18**, 138-150.

POUILLON, J. (1956) *Les temps modernes*, 126-168.

PRIBRAM, H. B. and BARRY, J. (1956) Further behavioral analysis of parieto-temporo-preoccipital cortex. *J. Neurophysiol.*, **19**, 99-106.

PRIBRAM, K. H. and MISHKIN, M. (1955) Simultaneous and successive visual discrimination by monkeys with inferotemporal lesions. *J. comp. physiol. Psychol.*, **48**, 198-202.

PRIBRAM, K. H., MISHKIN, M., ROSVOLD, H. E. and KAPLAN, S. J. (1952) Effects on delayed-response performance of lesions of dorsolateral and ventromedial frontal cortex of baboons. *J. comp. physiol. Psychol.*, **45**, 565-575.

PROSSER, C. L. and HUNTER, W. S. (1936) The extinction of startle responses and spinal reflexes in the white rat. *Amer. J. Physiol.*, **117**, 609-618.

PURPURA, D. P. and GRUNDFEST, H. (1956) Nature of dendritic potentials and synaptic mechanisms in cerebral cortex of cat. *J. Neurophysiol.*, **19**, 573-595.

PURPURA, D. P., HOUSEPIAN, E. M. and GRUNDFEST, H. (1958) Analysis of caudate-cortical connections in neuraxially intact and telencéphale isolé cats. *Arch. ital. Biol.*, **96**, 145-167.

PAKOVICH, B. I. (1956) Concerning the Impossibility of Forming Motor-defensive Condi-tioned Reflexes when the Indifferent and Unconditioned Stimuli Act in Strict Simul-taneity. *Papers of the U.S.S.R. Academy of Sciences*, **111**, 205. (In Russian.)

PAKOVICH, B. I. (1958) Concerning the Minimal Time of Precedence of Acoustic Stimuli to a Painful Stimulus Necessary for the Formation of Motor-Defensive Conditioned Reflexes in Dogs. *Papers of the U.S.S.R. Academy of Sciences*, **116**, 335. (In Russian.)

PALADE, G. E. (1954) Electron microscope observations of interneuronal of neuromuscular synapses. *Anat Rec.*, **118**, 335-336.

PALAY, S. L. (1954) Electron microscope study of the cytoplasm of neurones. *Anat Rec.*, **118**, 336-337.

PALAY, S. L. (1956) Structure and function in the neuron. *Progress in neurobiology. I. Neuro-chemistry.* S. R. Korey and J. I. Nurnberger, Editors, pp. 64-82.

PALAY, S. L. (1956) Synapses in the central nervous system. *J. biophys. biochem. Cytol.*, **2**, Suppl. 193-202.

PALAY, S. L. (1958) An electron microscopical study of Neuroglia. *Biology of Neuroglia.* Compiled and edited by W. F. Windle. Springfield, Illinois, Charles C. Thomas Publ., pp. 24-38.

PALESTINI, M., DAVIDOVICH, A. and HERNÁNDEZ-PEÓN, R. (1959) Functional significance of centrifugal influences upon the retina. *Acta Neurol. lat.-amer.*, **5**, 113-131.

PALESTINI, M., LIFSCHITZ, W. and ARMENGOL, V. (1959) Ascending inhibitory influence of the lower brain stem reticular formation. Communication to the 21st International Congress of Physiological Sciences. Buenos Aires.

PANTIN, C. F. A. (1950) Behaviour patterns in lower invertebrates. In *Symposia of the Society for Experimental Biology, No. IV, Physiological Mechanisms in Animal Behaviour.* Cambridge: Cambridge Univ. Press, pp. 175-195.

PAPEZ, J. W. (1958) The Visceral Brain, Its Components and Connections. In *Reticular Formation of the Brain.* Boston-Toronto, pp. 591-605.

PARMA, M. and ZANCHETTI, A. (1956) Ascending reticular influences upon thalamically evoked pyramidal discharges. *Amer. J. Physiol.*, **185**, 614-616.

PASIK, P., PASIK, T., BATTERSBY, W. S. and BENDER, M. B. (1958) Visual and tactual dis-criminations by Macaques with serial temporal and parietal lesions. *J. comp. physiol. Psychol.*, **51**, 427-436.

PAVLOV, I. P. The dynamic stereotype of the higher levels of the brain Report. X Internat. Physiological Congress, Copenhagen. Pavlov, vol. III, pp. 496-499.

PAVLOV, I. P. (1928) *Lectures on Conditioned Reflexes.* Vol. I. Tr. and Ed. W. H. Gantt. New York, Internat. Press.

PAVLOV, I. P. (1941) *Lectures on conditioned reflexes.* New York, International Publishers, 2 vols. (Reprint.)

PAVLOV, I. P. (1929) *Leçons sur le Travail des Hémisphères Cerebraux.* Paris, Amédée Legrand.

PAVLOV, I. P. (1942) *Los reflejos condicionados.* Mexico, D. F. Edición Pavlov.

PAVLOV, I. P. (1949) *Problems in physiology of the hemispheres of the brain.* Pavlov, vol. III. Moscow-Leningrad, pp. 378-390.

PAVLOV, I. P. (1954) *Œuvres Choisies.* Paris, Librairie du Globe.

PAVLOV, I. P. (1955) *Selected Works.* Ed. K. S. Koshtoyants. Moscow, Foreign Languages Publishing House, p. 654.

PAVLOVA, V. I. (1914) [On trace conditioned reflexes.] (Russian.) *Transactions of the Society of Russian Physicians.* January.

PAVLOVA, V. I. (1933) Can a Conditioned Reflex Be Formed if an Unconditioned Stimulus Precedes an Indifferent One? Vol. V, pp. 21-32. In Russian.

PENFIELD, W. (1958) Centrencephalic integrating system. *Brain,* **81,** 231-234.

PENFIELD, W. (1959) The interpretive cortex. *Science,* **129,** 1719-1725.

PENFIELD, W. G. and JASPER, H. H. (1954) *Epilepsy and the Functional Anatomy of the Human Brain,* Boston, Little, Brown, and Co. p. 896.

PETROVA, M. K. (1933) Dependence of the Size of the Conditioned Reflex on the Quantity of the Reinforcing Substance in Castrated Dogs of Different Types of Nervous System. Collected Papers of the Physiological Laboratories of I. P. Pavlov, vol. V, p. 49. In Russian.

PETROVA, M. K. (1941) Contributions to the Knowledge of the Physiological Mechanism of Voluntary Movements. Collected Papers of the Physiological Laboratories of I. P. Pavlov, vol. X, p. 41. In Russian.

PETROVA, M. K. (1914c) Contribution to the Theory of Irradiation of Excitation and of the Inhibitory Processes. Dissertation. St. Petersburg. In Russian.

POLYÁK S. L. (1941) *The Retina,* Chicago, University of Chicago Press, **7,** p. 596.

RABE, A. and GERARD, R. W. (1959) The influence of drugs on memory fixation time. *Amer. Psychologist,* **14,** 423. (Abstract.)

RAICIULESCU, N. and GIURGEA, C. (1957) Reflex conditionat interemisferic prin excitarea electrica directa a scoartei cerebrale dupa sectionarea corpului calos. *Rev. Fiziol.,* **4,** 336-339.

RAICIULESCU, N., GIURGEA, C. and SAVESCU, C. (1956) Reflex conditionat la excitarea directa a cortexului cerebral dupa distrugerea ganglionului lui Gasser. *Rev. Fiziol.,* **3,** 304-308.

RAMON Y CAJAL, S. (1891) Significación fisiológica de las expansiones protoplasmaticas y nerviosas de las células de la sustancia gris. *Rev. Cienc. méd. Barcelona,* 1-15.

RAMON Y CAJAL, S. (1893) Nuevo concepto de la histología de los centros nerviosos. *Rev. Cienc. méd. Barcelona,* **18,** 1-68.

RAMON Y CAJAL, S. (1911) Histologie du Système Nerveux de l'Homme et des Vertébrés. Vol. II. Paris, Maloine.

RAMON Y CAJAL, S. (1935) Die Neuronenlehre, 887-994 in Handbuch der Neurologie. Herausgegeben von O. Bumke und O. Foerster. *Erster Bank, Berlin, Verlag von Julius Springer.*

RANSMEIER, R. E. (1954) The effects of convulsion, hypoxia, hypothermia and anaesthesia on retention in the hamster. Unpublished doctoral dissertation. University of Chicago.

RANSMEIER, R. E. and GERARD, R. W. (1954) Effects of temperature, convulsion and metabolic factors on rodent memory and EEG. *Amer. J. Physiol.,* **179,** 663-664. (Abstract.)

RASHEVSKY, N. (1938) *Mathematical Biophysics.* Chicago, University of Chicago Press, p. 340.

RÉMOND, A. and RIPOCHE, A. (1958) Technique topographique: sur un compteur d'intégration, exemples d'utilisation. *Rev. Neurol.,* **99,** 179-186.

RHEINBERGER, M. B. and JASPER, H. H. (1937) Electrical activity of the cerebral cortex in the unanesthetized cat. *Amer. J. Physiol.,* **119,** 186-196.

RICHET, C. (1882) *Physiologie des muscles et des nerfs.* Paris, Germer-Baillière.

RICCI, G., DOANE, B. and JASPER, H. H. (1957a) Microelectrode studies of conditioning: technique and preliminary results. *Excerpta Med.,* **4,** 401-415.

RICCI, G., DOANE, B. and JASPER, H. H. (1957b) Microelectrode studies of conditioning: technique and preliminary results. Premier congrès international des Sciences neurologiques. Brussels, *Acta Medica Belgica,* pp. 401-415.

RIESS, B. F. (1954) The effect of altered environment and of age on the mother-young relationships among animals. *Ann. N.Y. Acad. Sci.,* **57,** 606-610.

RIMBAUD, L., PASSOUANT, P. and CADILHAC, J. (1955) Participation de l'hippocampe à la régulation des états de veille et de sommeil. *Rev. Neurol.*, **93**, 303-308.

RIOCH, D. McK. (1954) Psychopathological and neuropathological aspects of consciousness. In *Brain mechanisms and consciousness*. Oxford, Blackwell, pp. 470-478.

RIOPELLE, A. J., ALPER, R. G., STRONG, P. N. and ADES, H. W. (1953) Multiple discrimination and patterned string performance of normal and temporal-lobectomized monkeys. *J. comp. physiol. Psychol.*, **46**, 145-149.

ROBERTS, W. W. (1958) Both rewarding and punishing effects from stimulation of posterior hypothalamus of cat with same electrode at same intensity. *J. comp. physiol. Psychol.*, **51**, 400-407.

DE ROBERTIS, E. D. P. and BENNETT, H. S. (1955) Some features of the submicroscopic morphology of synapses in frog and earthworm. *J. biophys. biochem. Cytol.*, **1**, 47-58.

ROBERTSON, J. D. (1956) The ultrastructure of a reptilian myoneural junction. *J. Biophys. Biochem. Cytol.*, **2**, 381-394.

ROEDER, K. D. (1955) Spontaneous activity and behavior. *Sci. Monogr. Wash.*, **80**, 362-370.

ROGER, A. (1954) Doctoral Dissertation, Universite d'Aix-Marseille, Marseille, France.

ROGER, A., ROSSI, G. F. and ZIRONDOLI, A. (1956) Le rôle des afférences des nerfs craniens dans le maintien de l'état vigile de la préparation 'encéphale isolé'. *Electroenceph. clin. Neurophysiol.*, **8**, 1-13.

ROIG, J. A., SEGUNDO, J. P., SOMMER-SMITH, J. A. and GALEANO, C. Study of evoked somatic sensory cortical potentials in free unanaesthetized cats. (To be published.)

ROKOTOVA, N. A. (1952) Formation of Temporary Connections in the Cerebral Cortex of Dogs under the Action of Several Indifferent Stimuli. *Ž. vyš. Nerv. Dějat. Pavlova*, **2**, 753.

ROSE, J. E. and WOOLSEY, C. N. (1958) Cortical connections and functional organization of the thalamic auditory system of the cat. In *Biological and Chemical Bases of Behavior*. H. F. Harlow and C. N. Woolsey, Editors. Madison, Univ. Wisc. Press, pp. 127-150.

ROSENBLUETH, A. and CANNON, W. B. (1942) Cortical responses to electric stimulation. *Amer. J. Physiol.*, **135**, 690-741.

ROSENTAHL, I. S. (1936) An Elementary Motor Conditioned-Alimentary Reflex in Normal Animals. *Sechenov J. Physiol.*, **21**, No. 2, 183. Russian.

ROSSÍ, G. F. and BRODAL, A. (1956) Corticofugal fibers to the brain-stem reticular formation. An experimental study in the cat. *J. Anat. (Lond.)*, **90**, 42-62.

ROSVOLD, H. E. (1959) Physiological psychology. *Ann. Rev. Psychol.*, **10**, 415-454.

ROUGEUL, A. (1958) Observations électrographiques au cours du conditionnement instrumental alimentaire chez le chat. *J. Physiol. (Paris)*, **50**, 494-496.

ROSSÍ, G. F. and ZANCHETTI, A. (1957) The brain stem reticular formation. Anatomy and Physiology. *Arch. ital. Biol.*, **95**, 199-435.

RUSINOV, V. S. and RABINOVICH, M. Y. (1958) Electroencephalographic researches in the laboratories and clinics of the Soviet Union. *Electroenceph. clin. Neurophysiol.*, **8**, 1-36.

ROUSINOV, V. S. and SMIRNOV, G. D. (1957) Quelques données sur l'étude EEG de l'activité nerveuse supérieure. *Electroenceph. clin. Neurophysiol. supplementum.*, **6**, 9-23.

ROWLAND, V. (1957) Differential electroencephalographic response to conditioned auditory stimuli in arousal from sleep. *Electroenceph. clin. Neurophysiol.*, **9**, 585-594.

ROYTBACK, A. I. (1956) Dendrity i proces tormozhenya. *Gagrskiye Besedy*, Vol. 2, 165. Georgian Acad. Sci.

ROYTBACK, A. I. (1958) Concerning the mechanism of extinction of orientation and conditioned reflexes. *Physiol. bohemoslov.*, **7**, 125-134.

RUSSELL, W. R. (1959) *Brain, Memory, Learning*. Oxford, Clarendon Press.

SAAVEDRA, M. A., GARCIA, E. R., OBERTI, C. and PINTO HAMUY, T. (1952) Acquisition of an auditory avoidance conditioned reflex in normal and neodecorticated rats. XXI International Congress of Physiological Science. Abstracts of Communication, 239-240

SAMUELS, I. (1959) Reticular mechanisms and behavior. *Psychol. Bull.*, **56**, 1-25.

SANDERS, F. K. and WHITTERIDGE, D. (1946) Conduction velocity and myelin thickness in regenerating nerve fibres. *J. Physiol. (Lond.)*, **105**, 152-174.

SAVICH, A. A. (1913) Further Contributions to the Question of the Mutual Influence of Alimentary Reflexes. Dissertation. St. Petersburg. In Russian.

SCHÄFER, E. A. (1898-1900) *Textbook of Physiology*. London, Longmans, Green and Co., 2 vols.

SCHALTENBRAND, G. and COBB, S. (1930) Clinical and anatomical studies on two cats without cortex. *Brain*, **53**, 449-488.
SCHEIBEL, M. E. and SCHEIBEL, A. B. (1958) Structural substrates for integrative patterns in the brain stem reticular core. In *Reticular Formation of the Brain*. Boston, Little, Brown, & Co. pp. 31-55.
SCHLOSBERG, H. (1928) A study of the Conditioned Patellar Reflex. *J. exp. Psychol.*, **11**, 468-494.
SCHNEIRLA, T. C. (1956) Interrelationships of the 'Innate' and the 'Acquired' in instinctive behavior. In *L'Instinct dans le Comportement des Animaux et de l'Homme*. P. P. Grassé, ed. Paris, Masson & Cie, pp. 387-452.
SCOVILLE, W. B. and MILNER, B. (1957) Loss of recent memory after bilateral hippocampal lesions. *J. Neurol. Neurosurg. Psychiat.*, **20**, 11-21.
SECHENOV, I. M. (1935) *Selected Works*. Ed. A. A. Subkov. Moscow-Leningrad.
SEGUNDO, J. P., ARANA, R., MIGLIARO, E., VILLAR, J. E., GARCIA GUELFI, A. and GARCIA AUSTT, E. (1955) Respiratory responses from fornix and wall of third ventricle in man. *J. Neurophysiol.*, **18**, 96-101.
SEGUNDO, J. P., ROIG, J. A. and SOMMER-SMITH, J. A. (1959) Conditioning of reticular formation stimulation effects. *Electroenceph. clin. Neurophysiol.*, **11**, 471-484.
SEGUNDO, J. P., SOMMER-SMITH, J. A., GALEANO, C. and ROIG, J. A. (1959) Potentials evoked by absolute stimuli in the course of conditioning. *XXI International Congress of Physiological Sciences, Buenos Aires*. 9-15 August 1959. *Abstracts of Communications*, 248.
SEMMES, J. and CHOW, K. L. (1955) Motor effects of lesions of precentral gyrus and of lesions sparing this area in monkey. *Arch. Neurol. Psychiat. (Chicago)*, **73**, 546-556.
SERGEYEV, B. F. Formation of Conditioned Connections Between 'Indifferent' Stimuli in Intact Animals. Transactions of the Lesgaft Institute, vol. 28. In Russian.
SERGIO, G. and LONGO, V. G. (1959) Action of drugs on the EEG of rabbits after removal 2. vols.
of the neocortex. *Electroenceph. clin. Neurophysiol.*, **11**, 382.
SHARPLESS, S. (1954) *Role of the Reticular Formation in Habituation*. Thèse pour le doctorat en philosophie. McGill University, Montréal.
SHARPLESS, S. and JASPER, H. H. (1956) Habituation of the arousal reaction. *Brain*, **79**, 655-680.
SHEERER, M. and REIFF, R. (1959) *Memory and Hypnotic Age Regression*. New York, International Universities Press.
SHELL, W. F. and RIOPELLE, A. J. (1958) Progressive discrimination learning in platyrrhine monkeys. *J. comp. physiol. Psychol.*, **51**, 467-470.
SHIDLOVSKI, V. A. (1959) Electromanometric Investigations of Peculiarities of Cardiac Vessel Component of Conditioned and Unconditioned Responses. IX All Union Physiological, Biochemical, Pharmachological Congress, p.
SHUMILINA, A. I. (1945) On the duplex nature of motor excitation in the central Nervous System. *Sechenov. J. Physiol.*, **31**, 5-6, 272.
SHUMILINA, A. I. (1949) The conditioned defensive response of deafferented limb. *The Problems of Higher Nervous Activity*. Moscow, pp. 174-185.
SHUMILINA, A. I. (1949) Functional significance of frontal areas of the cerebral cortex in the conditioned-reflex activity of dog. *The Problems of Higher Nervous Activity*. Moscow (Russian), pp. 561-627.
SHUMILINA, A. I. and ANOKHIN, P. K. (1939) New data on the mechanism of the conditioned reflex. Vth Conference on physiological problems. Moscow-Leningrad.
SIEGEL, P. S., McGINNIES, E. M. and BOX, J. C. (1949) The runway performance of rats subjected to electroconvulsive shock following nembutal anesthesia. *J. comp. physiol. Psychol.*, **42**, 417-421.
SJÖSTRAND, F. S. (1956) Synaptic structures of the Retina of the mammalian eye. In *Proceedings International Conference Electron Microscopy, London 1954. The Royal Microscopical Society, London*.
SKIPIN, G. V. (1947) *Concerning the Mechanism of Formation of Conditioned Alimentary Reflexes*. Moscow. (In Russian.)
SLOAN, N. and JASPER, H. (1950) The identity of spreading depression and 'suppression'. *Electroenceph. clin. Neurophysiol.*, **2**, 59-78.
SNYAKIN, P. G. (1959) On reflex responses of receptors. *Vestn. Akad. med. Nauk*, **4**, 44-51.
SOKOLOV, E. N. (1953) Le reflexe d'orientation et le problème de la réception. *Dok Lady na Sovechtanii po voprossam psykhologii*, 212-216.

SOLTYSIK, S. Unpublished data.

SOMMER-SMITH, J. A., GALEANO, C., ROIG, J. A. and SEGUNDO, J. P. (1959) Alternate application of tone and subcutaneous stimulus in cat. II. Effect of tone initiation. *XXI International Congress of Physiological Sciences, Buenos Aires.* 9-15 August 1959. Abstracts of Communications, 259.

SPALDING, D. A. (1873) Instinct with original observations on young animals. Macmillans Mag., **27,** 282-293, reprinted 1954, Brit. J. anim. Behav., **2,** 2-11.

SPENCER, H. (1899) *The Principles of Psychology.* 3 vols. Fourth edition. London.

SPENCER, H. (1904) *An Autobiography.* 2 vols. London.

SPERANSKY, A. D. (1935) *A basis for the theory of medicine.* Moscow, Inra Co-operative Publishing Society, 452 pp.

SPERRY, R. W. (1947) Cerebral regulation of motor coordination in monkeys following multiple transection of sensorimotor cortex. J. Neurophysiol., **10,** 275-294.

SPERRY, R. W. (1955) On the neural basis of the conditioned response. Brit. J. Anim. Behav., **3,** 41-44.

SPERRY, R. W. (1957) High-order integrative functions in surgically isolated somatic cortex in cat. Anat. Rec., **127,** 371.

SPERRY, R. W. (1958) Physiological plasticity and brain circuit theory. *Biological and Biochemical Bases of Behavior.* H. F. Harlow and C. N. Woolsey, Editors. Madison, University of Wisconsin Press, pp. 401-424.

SPERRY, R. W. (1959) Preservation of high-order function in isolated somatic cortex in callosum-sectioned cat. J. Neurophysiol., **22,** 78-87.

SPERRY, R. W., MINER, N. and MYERS, R. E. (1955) Visual pattern perception following subpial slicing and tantalum wire implantations in the visual cortex. J. comp. physiol. Psychol., **48,** 50-58.

SPERRY, R. W., STAMM, J. S. and MINER, N. (1956) Relearning tests for interocular transfer following division of optic chiasma and corpus callosum in cats. J. comp. physiol. Psychol., **49,** 529-533.

STAMM, J. S. and SPERRY, R. W. (1957) Function of corpus callosum in Contralateral transfer of somesthetic discrimination in cats. J. comp. physiol. Psychol., **50,** 138-143.

STANLEY, W. C. and JAYNES, J. (1949) The function of the frontal cortex. Psychol. Rev., **56,** 18-32.

STARZL, T. E., TAYLOR, C. W. and MAGOUN, H. W. (1951a) Collateral afferent excitation of reticular formation of brain stem. J. Neurophysiol., **14,** 479-496.

STARZL, T. E., TAYLOR, C. W. and MAGOUN, H. W. (1951b) Ascending conduction in reticular activating system, with special reference to the diencephalon. J. Neurophysiol., **14,** 461-477.

STARZL, T. E., TAYLOR, C. W. and MAGOUN, H. W. (1951c) Collateral afferent excitation of reticular formation of brain stem. J. Neurophysiol., **14,** 479-496.

STEIN, L. and HEARST, E. (1958) Inhibitory effect of positively reinforcing brain stimulation on learning. Amer. Psychologist, **13,** 408.

STEINIGER, F. (1950) Beitrage zur Soziologie und sonstigen Biologie der Wanderratte. Z. Tierpsychol., **7,** 356-379.

STEPIEŃ, I. and STEPIEŃ, L. (1958) The effects of ablations of the sensori-motor cortex on instrumental (type II) conditioned reflexes. I. The lesions of sensory cortex in dogs. Bull. Acad. pol. Sci., **6,** 309-312.

STEPIEŃ, I. and STEPIEŃ, L. (1959) The effect of sensory cortex ablations on instrumental (type II) conditioned reflexes in dogs. Acta. Biol. exp., Varsovie, **19,** 257-272.

STEPIEŃ, I., STEPIEŃ, L. and KONORSKI, J. (1960) The effects of bilateral lesions on the motor cortex on type II conditioned reflexes in dogs. Acta Biol. exp. Varsovie, **20,**

STEPIEŃ, I., STEPIEŃ, L. and KONORSKI, J. The effects of ablations of premotor cortex on the instrumental conditioned reflexes. In preparation.

STEPIEŃ, L., CORDEAU, A. and RASMUSSEN, A. Personal communication.

STEPIEŃ, L. and CORDEAU, A. Personal communication.

STEVENS, J. (1959) Personal communication.

STOEHR, PH., JR. (1957) Mikroskopische Anatomie des vegetativen Nerven systems in von Mollendorf Handbuch der mikroskopischen Anatomie des Menschen. *Springer Verlag,* Berlin, Goettingen, Heidelberg, Vierter Band.

STRAUSS, H. (1929) Das Zusammenschrecken: Experimenten-kinematographische Studie zur Physiologie und Pathophysiologie der Reaktionbewegungen. *J. Psychol. Neurol.*, **39**, 111-231.

STROM, G. (1951) Physiological significance of post-tetanic potentiation of the spinal mono-synaptic reflex. *Acta Physiol. scand.*, **24**, 61-83.

STRUCHKOV, M. I. (1958) Food as a Conditioned Stimulus in the Elaboration of a Conditioned Motor and Vasomotor Reflex. Proceedings of the 18th Conference on Problems of Higher Nervous Activity. Theses of communications and essays. No. 7, p. 146. In Russian.

SWEET, W. H., TALLAND, G. A. and ERVIN, F. R. (1959) Loss of recent memory following section of the fornix. *Amer. Neurol. Assoc.*, Eighty-Fourth Meeting Program, pp. 21-22. (Abstract.)

SZABO, Th. (1954) Un relais dans le système des connexions du lobe électrique de la Torpille. *Arch. Anat. micr. Morph. exp.*, **43**, 187-201.

SZENTÁGOTHAI, J. and RAJKOVITS, K. (1955) Die Rückwirkung der spezifishen Funktion auf die Struktur der Nervenelemente. *Acta morph. Acad. Sci. hung.*, **5**, 253-274.

TANZI, E. (1893) I fatti e la induzione nell' odierne istologia del sistema nervoso. *Riv. sper. Freniat.*, **19**, 419-472.

TEN CATE, J. (1934) Können die bedingten Reaktionen sich auch ausserhalb der Grosshirn-rinde bilden? *Arch. néerl. Physiol.*, **19**, 469-481.

TEN CATE, J. (1938) Bedingte Reflexe bei Hunden nach beiderseitiger Extirpation der regio occipitalis der Grosshirnrinde *Arch. néerl. Physiol.*, **23**, 219-253.

THAL, N. (1956) Premedication for electroshock treatment. *Dis. nerv. Syst.*, **17**, 52-57.

THOMPSON, R. (1957) The comparative effects of ECS and anoxia on memory. *J. comp. physiol. Psychol.*, **50**, 397-400.

THOMPSON, R. (1958) The effect of intracranial stimulation on memory in cats. *J. comp. physiol. Psychol.*, **51**, 421-426.

THOMPSON, R. and DEAN, W. (1955) A further study on the retroactive effect of ECS. *J. Comp. physiol. psychol.*, **48**, 488-491.

THOMPSON, R. and MCCONNELL, J. (1955) Classical conditioning in the planarian. *Dugesia dorotocephala*. *J. comp. physiol. Psychol.*, **48**, 65-68.

THORPE, W. H. (1944) Some problems of animal learning. *Proc. Linnean Soc. Lond.*, 70-83.

THORPE, W. H. (1950) The concepts of learning and their relation to those of instinct. *Symp. Soc. Exp. Biol.*, **4**, 387-408.

THORPE, W. H. (1950) The concepts of learning and their relation to those of instinct. *Physiological Mechanisms in animal behaviour.* Cambridge University Press.

THORPE, W. H. (1955) Comments on 'The Bird Fancyer's Delight', together with notes on imitation in the sub-song of the Chaffinch. *Ibis*, **97**, 247-251.

THORPE, W. H. (1956) Learning and Instinct in Animals. London, Methuen, viii+493 pp.

THORPE, W. H. (1958) The learning of song patterns by birds. *Ibis*, **100**, 535-570.

THORPE, W. H. and PILCHER, P. M. (1958) The nature and characteristics of sub-song. *Brit. Birds*, **51**, 509-514.

TINBERGEN, N. (1948) Social releasers and the method required for their study. *Wilson Bull.* **60**, 6-51.

TINBERGEN, N. (1951) *The Study of Instinct.* London, Oxford University Press.

TINKLEPAUGH, O. L. (1928) An experimental study of representative factors in monkeys. *J. comp. Psychol.*, **8**, 197-236.

TOBIAS, J. M. (1952) Some optically detectable consequences of activity in nerve. *Cold Spring Harbor Symposium on Quantitative Biology*, **17**, 15-25.

TOENNIES, J. F. (1949) Die Erregungssteuerung im Zentralnervensystem. *Arch. Psychiat. Nervenkr.*, **182**, 478-535.

TORRES, F., ZIEGLER, DEWEY, K. and WISSOF, H. S. (1958) Spontaneous and induced activity of the isolated cerebral cortex in cats. *Electroenceph. clin. Neurophysiol.*, **10**, 190-191.

TOWER, S. S. (1935) The dissociation of cortical excitation from cortical inhibition by pyramid section, and the syndrome of that lesion in the cat. *Brain*, **58**, 238-255.

TROFIMOV, L. G., LYUBIMOV, N. N. and NAUMOVA, T. S. (1958) Cortical-subcortical relation-ship in the conditioning of defence and food reflexes in dogs. Moscow Colloquium on EEG and Behavior. *Electroenceph. clin. Neurophysiol.* In the Press.

VARGA, M. E. (1953) Contribution to the Question of Two-Way Conditioned-Reflex Connections. *Papers of the U.S.S.R. Academy of Sciences*, vol. 89, No. 2, p. 365. In Russian.

VARGA, M. E. (1958) Concerning the Physiological Significance of the Precedence of a Signalling Stimulus in Conditioned-Reflex Activity, vol. VIII, No. 5, p. 710. In Russian.

VARGA, M. E. and PRESSMAN, Y. M. (1958) Some Peculiarities of Conditioned-Reflex Connections Arising from the Combination of So-called Indifferent Stimuli. Collection of articles: 'Orienting Reflex and Orienting Investigatory Activity'. Moscow. In Russian.

VILLEGAS, A. Personal communication.

VINCE, M. A. (1956-59 and in press) 'String pulling' in birds. (1) Individual differences in wild adult Great Tits. (2) Differences related to age in Greenfinches, Chaffinches and Canaries. (3) Developmental changes in responsiveness in the Great Tit. *Brit. J. anim. Behav.*, **4,** 111-116; *Anim. Behav.*, **6,** 53-59; *Behaviour* (In the Press).

VINOGRADOV, N. V. (1933) The formation of New Connections in Inhibited Areas of the Cerebral Cortex. Collected Papers of the Physiological Laboratories of I. P. Pavlov, vol. V, pp. 33-48. In Russian.

VON EULER, C., MAGOUN, H. W. and RICCI, G. (1956) Characteristics of evoked potentials in the auditory cortex. Communication XX° Congrès International de Physiologie, Bruxelles, p. 932.

VORONIN, L. G. (1952) Analysis and Synthesis of Complex Stimulations in Higher Animals. Moscow. Russian.

VORONIN, L. G. and SOKOLOV, E. N. (1958) Cortical mechanisms of the orienting reflex and its relation to the conditioned reflex. Moscow Colloquium on EEG and Behavior. *Electroenceph. clin. Neurophysiol.* In the Press.

WADDINGTON, C. H. (1957) *The Strategy of the Genes.* New York, Macmillan.

WADDINGTON, C. H. (1960) In *Evolution after Darwin.* Evolutionary Adaptation. S. Tax, Editor. Chicago, University of Chicago Press, pp. 381-402.

WADE, M. (1947) The effect of sedatives upon delayed response in monkeys following removal of the prefrontal lobes. *J. Neurophysiol.*, **10,** 57-61.

WALL, P. D. (1958) Excitability changes in afferent fibre terminations and their relation to slow potentials. *J. Physiol. (Lond.)*, **142,** 1-21.

WALTER, V. J. and GREY, WALTER, W. (1949) The central effects of rhythmic sensory stimulation. *Electroenceph. clin. Neurophysiol.*, **1,** 57-86.

WALTON, A. C. (1915) The influence of diverting stimuli during delayed reaction in dogs. *J. Anim. Behav.*, **5,** 259-291.

WARD, A. A. and McCULLOCH, W. S. (1947) The projection of the frontal lobe on the hypothalamus. *J. Neurophysiol.*, **10,** 309-314.

WAYNER, M. J., JR. and REIMANIS, G. (1959) Combined effects of reserpine and electro-convulsive shock on learning and retention in the hooded rat. *J. comp. physiol. Psycho!.*, **52,** 46-49.

WEIDMANN, U. (1956) Some Experiments on the Following and the Flocking Reactions of Mallard Ducklings. *J. Anim. Behav.*, **4,** 78-79.

WEIDMANN, U. (1958) Verhaltenstudien in der Stockente (*Anas platyrhynchos* L.) II. Versuche zur Auslösung und Pragung der Nachfolge-und Anschlussreaktionen. *Z. Tierpsychol.*, **15,** 277-300.

WEISKRANTZ, L. and MISHKIN, M. (1958) Effects of temporal and frontal cortical lesions on auditory discrimination in monkeys. *Brain*, **81,** 406-414.

WEISS, P. (1955) Nervous system (neurogenesis). *Analysis of Development.* B. H. Willier, P. A. Weiss and V. Hamburger, Editors. Philadelphia, W. B. Saunders, pp. 346-401.

WERTHEIMER, M. and LEVENTHAL, C. M. (1958) 'Permanent' satiation phenomena with kinesthetic figural after effects. *J. exp. Psychol.*, **55,** 255-257.

WHITLOCK, D. G. and NAUTA, W. J. H. (1956) Subcortical projections from the temporal neocortex in Macaca mulatta. *J. comp. Neurol.*, **106,** 183-212.

WHITMAN, C. O. (1899) *Animal behaviour.* Biol. Lect. mar. biol. Lab., Woods Hole, 285-338.

WIENER, N. (1949) *Cybernetics or control and communication in the animal and the machine.* Paris, Hermann.

WILSON, M. (1957) Effects of circumscribed cortical lesions upon somesthetic and visual discrimination in monkeys. *J. comp. physiol. Psychol.*, **50,** 630-635.

WILSON, V. J. (1955) Post-tetanic potentiation of polysynaptic reflexes of the spinal cord. *J. gen. Physiol.*, **39,** 197-206.

WILSON, W. A., JR. and MISHKIN, M. (1959) Comparison of the effects of inferotemporal and lateral occipital lesions on visually guided behavior in monkeys. *J. Comp. physiol. Psychol.*, **52**, 10-17.

WING, K. G. (1946) The role of the optic cortex of the dog in the retention of learned responses to light conditioning with light and shock. *Amer. J. Psychol.*, **59**, 583-612.

WING, K. G. (1947) The role of the optic cortex of the dog in the retention of learned responses to light: conditioning with light and food. *Amer. J. Psychol.*, **60**, 30-67.

WING, K. G. and SMITH, K. U. (1942) The role of the optic cortex of the dog in the determination of the functional properties of conditioned reactions to light. *J. exp. Psychol.*, **31**, 478-496.

WOLFLE, H. M. (1937) Time Factors in Conditioning Finger Withdrawal. *J. gen. Psychol.*, **4**, 372.

WOODBURY, D. M. (1952) Effect of adrenocortical steroids and adrenocorticotrophic hormone on electroshock seizure threshold. *J. Pharmacol.*, **105**, 27-36.

WOODBURY, D. M. (1954) Effect of hormones on brain excitability and electrolytes. *Rec. Progr. Hormone Res.*, **10**, 65-107.

WOODBURY, D. M., EMMETT, J. W., HINCKLEY, C. V., JACKSON, N. R., BATEMAN, J. D., GOODMAN, J. H. and SAYERS, G. (1951) Antagonism of adrenocortical extract and cortisone to desoxycorticosterone: brain excitability in adrenalectomised rats. *Proc. Soc. exp. Biol.*, **76**, 65-68.

WOODBURY, D. M., TIMIRAS, S. P. and VERNADAKIS, A. (1957) *Hormones, Brain-Function and Behaviour.* New York, Academic Press Inc. Publ.

WOOLSEY, C. N. (1958) Organization of somatic sensory and motor areas of the cerebral cortex. In *Biological and Biochemical Bases of Behavior.* H. F. Harlow and C. N. Woolsey, Editors. Madison, Univ. Wisc. Press, p. 63-81.

WOOLSEY, C. N. and CHANG, H. T. (1948) Activation of the cerebral cortex by antidromic volleys in the pyramidal tract. *Res. Publ. Ass. nerv. ment. Dis.*, **27**, 146-161.

WYCKOFF, R. W. G. and YOUNG, J. Z. (1956) The motoneuron surface. *Proc. roy. Soc., B*, **144**, 440-450.

WYRWICKA, W. (1952) Studies on motor conditioned reflexes. 5. On the mechanism of the motor conditioned reaction. *Acta Biol. Exp. Varsovie*, **16**, 10, 131-137.

YARBOROUGH, J. U. (1917) Delayed reaction with sound and light in cats. *J. Anim. Behav.*, **7**, 87-110.

YASHII, N. (1956) Methodological principles of electroencephalographic investigation on conditioned behavior. *Folia. Psychiat. Neurol. Jap.*, **9**, 341-365.

YERKES, R. M. and YERKES, D. N. (1928) Concerning memory in the chimpanzee. *J. comp. Psychol.*, **8**, 237-271.

YERKES, R. M. (1912) The intelligence of earthworms. *J. Anim. Behav.*, **2**, 332-352.

YOSHII, N., MATSUMOTO, J. and HORI, Y. (1957) Electroencephalographic study on conditioned reflex in animals. Proc. 1st Internat. Congress of Neurological Sciences, Brussels.

YOSHII, N. (1957) Princepes méthodologiques de l'investigation électroencéphalographique du comportement conditionné. Methodological principles of electroencephalographic investigation on conditioned behaviour. *Electroenceph. clin. Neurophysiol.*, Supplementum, **6**, 75-88.

YOSHII, N., PRUVOT, P. and GASTAUT, H. (1957) Electrographic activity of the mesencephalic reticular formation during conditioning in the cat. *Electroenceph. clin. Neurophysiol.*, **9**, 595-608,

YOUNG, J. Z. (1938) In *Evolution.* Essays presented to E. S. Goodrich, G. R. de Beer, Editor. Oxford, pp. 179-205.

YOUNG, J. Z. (1951) Growth and plasticity in the nervous system. *Proc. roy. Soc., B*, **139**, 18-37.

ZANGWILL, O. L. and THORPE, W. H. *Problems of Animal Behaviour.* Cambridge University Press. In the Press.

ZBROZYNA, A. W. (1958) On the conditioned reflex of the cessation of the act of eating. I. Establishment of the conditioned cessation reflex. *Acta Biol. exp. Varsovie*, **18**, 137-162.

ZELIONY, G. P. (1928) Observations Upon a Decorticated Dog. Proceedings of the 3rd U.S.S.R. Congress of Physiologists, p. 237. In Russian.

ZELIONY, G. P. (1929) Contribution to the Methods of Investigating Motor Conditioned Reflexes. *J. Biol. Méd. exp. Moscow*, vol. XII, No. 31, p. 74. In Russian.

ZELIONY, G. P. Cited by Pavlov, I. P., 1941.

ZELIONY, G. P. and KADYKOV, B. I. (1938) Contribution to the study of conditioned reflexes in the dog after cortical extirpation. *Med. exp. Kharkov.*, **3**, 31-34. *Psychol. Abstr.*, **12**, No. 5829.

ZERNICKI, B. The effect of prefrontal lobectomy on the water instrumental conditioned reflexes in dogs. In preparation.

ZIPPELIUS, H. M. and SCHLEIDT, W. (1956) Ultraschall-Laute bei Mäusen. *Naturwissenschaften*, **43**, 502.

ZUBEK, J. P. (1952) Studies in somesthesis. II. Role of somatic areas I and II in roughness discrimination in cat. *J. Neurophysiol.*, **15**, 401-408.

ZUCKERMANN, E. (1959) Effect of cortical and reticular stimulation on conditioned reflex activity. *J. Neurophysiol.*, **22**, 633-643.

INDEX

INDEX

Acceptor apparatus of reflex action, 203
Adaptability, 22
Afferent influences on reflex action, 191
  synthesis of conditioned reflex, 197, 198,
    202
Alimentary conditioning, 403, 404
  instrumental, 527-54
Amygdala, effect of stimulation, 300
  influence on fixation, 28
Angiogliocytes, 310
Animorgs, 21
Anoxia, effect of fixation of experience, 29
Aphasia, 13
Approach learning, hippocampal electrical
  activity during, 577-88
Arousal reaction, habituation, 456, 473
Auditory discrimination during learning,
  effects of frontal lesions, 557, 560

Barbiturates, effect on learning, 29, 32
Behaviour, 21
  effects of tones reinforced by cessation of
    painful stimuli, 265-91
  electrical correlates, 243
  instinctive, 641
  neurohumoral factors in control, 293-308
  patterns, innate, 66
    unlearned, interactions with learning in
      mammals, 53-73
  primitive, 3
  reflex, 641
  spontaneous, 646
Birds, imprinting in, 78-81
  learning in, 75-93
  vocalization, 81-90
Brain change in learning, 233, 235
  electrical stimulation, conditioned reflexes
    established by, 133-51
    effect on learning, 157, 172
    single-unit response, 172
  function, evolutionary concepts, 1-20
  functional regression, 5, 13
  gnostic intercommunication between cere-
    bral hemispheres, 485
  lesions, effect on memory, 122
  phylogenetic development, 2
Bulbo-pontine reticular formation, functions, 413-31

Cerebellum, electrical stimulation, 133
Cerebral cortex, evoked potentials, changes
  by previous reticular stimulation,
  433-44
    response to previous reticular stimula-
      tion, 433-44

role in learning of instrumental conditioning response, 589-600
sensorimotor, effect of ablation on
  learning, 527-54
Concentration lack, 38
Conditional response, instrumental, role of
  cerebral cortex in learning of, 589-600
Conditioned reaction effector apparatus,
  formation, 211
Conditioning, alimentary, 403, 404
  instrumental, 527-54
  functional role of subcortical structures,
    402-12
Connections, conditioned, elaboration and
  formation of their properties, 95-113
Corpus callosum and visual gnosis, 481-505

Darwin and concepts of brain function, 1-20
Deprivation and learning in mammals, 55, 65
Dentate gyrus, single-unit response to
  electrical stimulation, 175
Digit tests of memory, 41, 46
Discrimination learning and performance,
  non-sensory effects of frontal lesions,
  555-76

Earthworm, learning in, 38
Effector apparatus of reflex action, 211
Ego, 14
Electroencephalogram, effects of learning on,
  236, 237
  effects of tones reinforced by cessation of
    painful stimuli, 265-91
  in study of conditioned reflex, 190
Endocrine factors in control of animal behaviour, 293-308
Environment, influence on conditioned
  reflex connections, 304
Epileptic discharges, reflex conditioning,
  625-39
Excitation, electrical, conditioned reflexes
  established by, 133-51
Experience, fixation of, 21-35
  effects of drugs, 29

Fimbria, single-unit response to electrical
  stimulation, 175, 183
Fixation of experience, 21-35
Flexor response, conditioned, 404, 405
Flicker stimulation, continuous, significance
  on evoked responses, 607
  discontinuous, significance on evoked
    responses, 613
Forgetting, 28